Pipeline Pigging and Integrity Technology

FOURTH EDITION

Pipeline Pigging and Integrity Technology

FOURTH EDITION

John Tiratsoo, Editor

Pipeline Pigging and Integrity Technology
Fourth Edition

Published by
Tiratsoo Technical
(*a division of Great Southern Press*)
PO Box 21, Beaconsfield, HP9 1NS, UK
and
Clarion Technical Publishers
3401 Louisiana, Suite 255, Houston, TX 77002, USA

ISBN 978-0-9575310-0-0 (UK)
ISBN 978-0-9717945-8-0 (USA)

Library of Congress Control no.: 2012956267

Set in 10/12pt Goudy Old Style

Printed by KnowledgePoint, Earley, Reading, RG6 4UT, UK

Table of Contents

Note: the Table includes the substantive section headings from each section. Authors' contemporary affiliations are shown at the introduction of each paper: due to the passage of time, some of these have inevitably changed. The date given after each title is the date of the original presentation or publication.

Section 1: Cleaning and black powder

Black powder migration in gas pipelines and associated problems (2008) 1
Dr John Smart and Robert Winters
Black powder movement in gas pipelines 2
Gas velocity to move solids in a pipeline 2
Black powder deposits in pipelines 3
How clean is a pipeline? 4
Intelligent pig inspection 6
Other problems with black powder 6
Monitoring black powder 7
Pipeline pigging and cleaning 8

Development and operational experience of a new pigging technology for effective black powder removal (2012) 11
Dr Hubert Lindner
Cleaning experience 12
Development of a new cleaning tool for black powder 12
Evaluation of run data and tool performance 14

Enhancing pipeline efficiency through chemical cleaning (2008) 19
Daniel Falabella and Dulce Gomez
San Martin pipeline steady-state model 20
Chemical-mechanical cleaning 21
Analysis of the solvent to be used 24

Chemical gel cleaning prior to MFL ILI of a natural gas transmission pipeline: a case study (2011) 31
Brett Wakeham, Jeff Fleming, and Michael Cismaru
2010 MFL re-inspection 31
Historical information 32
Preparation for gel cleaning 35
Project execution 38
Evaluation of success 40

Chemical-assisted pipeline pigging cleaning operations (2011) 43
Jonathan Wylde
Chemicals used to clean transportation pipelines 44
Laboratory development and testing 45
Case histories 48

Section 2: Corrosion and defect assessment

Development of a predictive model for pipeline external corrosion rates (2007) 57
Dr Julia Race, Sarah J Dawson, Leanne Stanley, and Dr Shahani Kariyawasam
Determination of corrosion growth rates 59
Development of corrosion-scoring model 66

Calibration of corrosion-scoring model ... 70
Further planned model developments ... 73
Establishment of reassessment intervals ... 74
Operator assessment of ILI defects (2007) ... 79
Kevin W Ferguson
Basic ground rules ... 80
Methodology ... 82
Discussion of results ... 84
Software-based, vendor-backed results ... 87
ILI performance verification and assessment (2007) ... 89
Guy Desjadins, Randy Nickle, and Mike Read
ILI accuracy ... 90
Benefits of accurate ILI data ... 91
ILI accuracy assessment and the effect of the number of excavations ... 93
Optimum number of excavated anomalies ... 96
Practical considerations ... 97
Development and application of local corrosion growth rates for pipeline integrity assessments (2012) ... 101
Pamela J Moreno, Neil A Bates, David A R Shanks, William V Harper, David J Stucki, Clifford J Maier, and Dr Thomas A Bubenik
Statistically-active corrosion methodology ... 102
Comparison using raw ILI data ... 103
Determining corrosion-growth rates ... 108
Application of corrosion science ... 110
Examples of applications and tailored solutions ... 110

Section 3: EMAT

ILI with high-resolution EMAT technology: crack detection and coating disbondment (2008) ... 115
Hamad Al-Qahtani, Thomas Beuker, and Dr Joerg Damaschke
Field testing ... 116
Inspection technology ... 117
Data evaluation ... 119
Crack detection ... 121
Coating disbondment detection ... 121
Validation of the latest generation EMAT ILI technology for SCC management (2011) ... 123
Jim E Marr, Elvis San Juan Riverol, Gabriela Rosca, Jeff Sutherland, and Andy Mann
TransCanada SCC overview ... 123
EMAT and TransCanada history ... 124
PII EMAT tool specification ... 125
Excavation and correlation programme results ... 126
Programme lessons and developments ... 131
Evaluation of EMAT tool performance by monitoring industry experience (2012) ... 137
Ming Gao, Samarth Tandon, and Ravi Krishnamurthy
Current EMAT technologies and claimed capabilities ... 138
Methods for tool-performance assessment ... 144

Tool performance evaluation ... 147
Evaluation of EMAT performance against hydrotesting ... 155
Combining EMAT ILI multiple data sets for crack detection in natural gas pipelines to reduce validation costs (2012) ... 161
Jim E Marr, Richard Kania, Gabriela Rosca, Rahim Ruda, Elvis San Juan Riverol, Stefan Klein, Nikola Jansing, Thomas Beuker, N Daryl Ronsky, and Ralf Weber
Data integration and analysis ... 163
Results of the validation ... 164

Section 4: Failure assessment

A methodology for the prediction of pipeline failure frequency due to external interference (2009) ... 169
C Lyons, Dr Jane Haswell, Dr Phil Hopkins, R Ellis, and N Jackson
The role of UKOPA ... 170
Prediction of the probability and frequencey of failure due to external interference ... 172
Prediction of probability failure due to external interference ... 173
Failure-frequency predictions and comparisons ... 176
FFREQ predictions and use ... 182
Annexe A - overview of dent-gouge failure model ... 185
Annexe B - predictive methodology ... 188
Evaluating damage to on- and offshore pipelines using data acquired using ILI (2009) ... 191
Dr Chris Alexander
Background ... 191
Analysis of dents ... 199
Discussion ... 203
Effects of inline inspection sizing uncertainties on the accuracy of the largest features and corrosion rate statistics (2011) ... 207
Dr Luc Huyse and Albert van Roodselaar
Sizing-uncertainty models ... 208
Effect on ILI reported sizes ... 210
Effect on maximum feature size ... 212
Effect of sizing error on order statistics ... 216
Impact of sizing error on corrosion-rate statistics ... 217
Impact of sizing error on marginal corrosion-rate distributions ... 221

Section 5: Integrity management

Integrity management of a pipeline crossing the Andes (2008) ... 225
Andres Mendizabal and Fabian Sanchez
OCP pipeline description ... 227
Pipeline integrity-management plan and risk analysis ... 234
Legal issues in pipeline integrity programmes (2009) ... 235
Chris Paul
Bases of exposure ... 237
Continuum of exposure ... 238
IM in the United States ... 240

Measuring exposure ... 243
Legal issues ... 243
What can go wrong? ... 244
Solutions ... 245
Contracting for IM services ... 246

How well do you know your pipeline? (2010) ... 249
Paul Birkinshaw
The piggability study ... 250
Getting hold of the pipeline data ... 251
Assessment of available pipeline data ... 252

Advanced assessment of pipeline integrity using ILI data (2010) ... 255
Dr Ted Anderson
Level 3 crack assessment as an alternative to hydrostatic testing ... 256
Rapid assessment of metal loss with compression-wave UT ILI data ... 260
Level 3 dent assessment ... 262

Measuring the effectiveness of the US IMP programme (2011) ... 265
Terry Boss, David Johnson, Bernie Selig, and John Zurcher
Reportable-incident data ... 266
Reportable-leak data ... 267
Reportable integrity-management data ... 268
Integrity measures: comparison of INGAA and PHMSA data ... 270

Integrity management of offshore pipelines using risk-based inspection planning (2011) ... 275
Jens Erik Thygesen
What is AIS? ... 276
How will such a system improve pipeline-integrity management? ... 279
The use of AIS ... 280

A review of crack-detection ILI case studies (2011) ... 281
Neil A Bates, David Lee, and Clifford J Maier
Analysis method ... 281
Case studies ... 286

Optimizing magnetic-flux leakage inspection sizing model performance using high-resolution non-destructive examination data (2012) ... 299
Scott Miller and Stuart Clouston
Sizing model generation and performance ... 300
Managing and utilizing high-resolution corrosion-verification data ... 302
Case study ... 304

Predicting future pipeline integrity in landslides using ILI mapping data (2012) ... 309
Aaron Lockey and Andy Young
Strain-based assessment ... 310
Modelling approach ... 311
Calculation example ... 312
Evaluation of methodology ... 312
Benefits to a pipeline operator ... 314

Section 6: New technology

A case study of the crack sizing performance of the GE ultrasonic phased-array tool on the Centennial pipeline (2010) ... 317
T Hrncir, S Turner, S J Polaski, Patrick Vieth, D Allen, I Lachtchouk, Petra Senf, and Geoff Foreman
Ultrasound crack-detection refresher ... 319
Phased-array refresher ... 319
GE's ultrasound phased-array inspection tool ... 320
Recent innovations in pipeline seam-weld integrity assessment (2012) ... 329
Dr Ted Anderson
Can a 'conservative' approach be unsafe? ... 330
Failure model for cracks ... 332
Quantifying toughness for pipeline steels ... 334
Real-time pressure cycle fatigue analysis ... 334
Improving ILI benchmarking through new technology (2012) ... 337
Michael Krywko, Shamus McDonnell, Douglas Spencer, and Mark Gluskin
Improving ILI benchmarking ... 341
22-Hz sensors ... 344
Geophone ... 346
Acoustic frequency analysis and Doppler shift ... 348
Remote tracking ... 348
Case studies ... 349

Section 7: Operations

Commissioning the world's longest LPG pipeline and retrieval of stuck pigs: a case study (2008) ... 359
Partha Jana
Commissioning of the JLPL ... 360
Section 7: scenario and problem identification ... 364
Analysis of commissioning pigging activities ... 364
Contingency plan ... 365
Retrieval activities and execution ... 367
Factors affecting the design and selection of pigging tools for multi-diameter pipelines (2009) ... 371
Karl Dawson
The process of pig selection ... 372
Step-by-step design guide ... 372
Pipeline data are critical ... 375
Case study ... 377
Design and construction of 42-in liquids'-pipeline batch-pig facilities (2009) ... 381
Robert W Kratsch
Batch pig system design basis ... 382
Batch pig launcher and receiver system design ... 383
Batch pig facility design and layout ... 386
Design of operational sequencing and automation ... 390

Batch pig facility construction ... 393
Facility commissioning ... 394
Ethanol transportation: status of research and integrity management (2009) ... 397
Dr John Beavers, Patrick Vieth, and Dr Narasi Sridhar
Environmental factors affecting SCC in FGE ... 400
Metallurgical factors affecting ethanol SCC ... 402
Mitigation of ethanol SCC ... 402
The fundamentals of pigging systems and the importance of trap assessments (2010) ... 405
Christian J Cloyde
Launchers and launcher systems ... 408
Receivers and receiver systems ... 410
Pig trap design considerations ... 413
Pig-trap/pigging-system assessments ... 415
Multi-diameter bi-directional pigging for pipeline precommissioning (2010) ... 419
Magne Andreas Vik, Alf Age Kristiansen, Simon Sykes, Steve Hutcheson, and Dr Aidan O'Donoghue
Pig selection ... 421
Pig design ... 422
Seal design ... 424
Testing ... 425
Offshore operation ... 428
Capabilities of MFL inspection in Duplex steel pipelines (2010) ... 431
Hendrik Aue, Werner Thale, Age E Pedersen, and Samuel Moe
Duplex material ... 432
Duplex sample analysis ... 433
FEM calculation ... 434
Pull test investigation ... 436
Augmenting ILI tools to assess external coatings (2010) ... 441
Dr J Bruce Nestleroth and Jason K Van Velsor
Sensor design ... 447
Pull test results ... 447

Section 8: Administrative and regulatory issues

Integrity first: voluntary performance reporting in a goal-oriented regulatory environment (2009) ... 451
Ziad A Saad, Kim J McCaig, and Brenda Kenny
The public context of pipeline development in Canada ... 452
The need for industry-driven solutions ... 453
Linking goals and performance ... 454
Expected results ... 458
Dealing with uncertainty in pipeline integrity and rehabilitation (2009) ... 461
Rafael G Mora, Dr Alan Murray, Joe Paviglianiti, Sara Abdollahi
Uncertainty ... 462
Introducing errors ... 462
Case study ... 464

Detection uncertainty ... 471
Identification uncertainty ... 472

Section 9: Stress-corrosion cracking

Re-assessment intervals for managing stress-corrosion cracking in pipelines (2007) ... 475
Dr Raymond R Fessler and Steve C Rapp
Hydrostatic re-rest model ... 476
Re-assessment intervals for ILI ... 484
Re-inspection intervals for SCC DA ... 485

Self-excited eddy currents for the detection of SCC (2009) ... 487
Richard Kania and Grant A Coleman
SEEC technology ... 488
Magnetic modelling ... 489
Physical SEEC system ... 490
SEEC sensor system ... 491
SEEC data ... 492
Initial field results ... 494

A new joint-industry project addressing the integrity management of SCC in gas transmission pipelines (2012) ... 497
Dr A David Batte, Dr Raymond R Fessler, Jim E Marr, and Steve C Rapp
Update of service experience ... 499
Review of integrity-management practices and experience ... 500
Hydrostatic testing ... 502
Excavations and SCC direct assessment ... 502
Crack-detection ILI ... 502
Developments in the application of data from crack-detection (EMAT) ILI ... 503
The way ahead for integrity management: continuous improvement ... 506

Main subject index ... 511

List of contributors

Sara Abdollahi 461
Dr Chris Alexander 191
D Allen 317
Dr Ted Anderson 255, 329
Hamad Al-Qahtani 115
Hendrik Aue 431
Neil A Bates 101, 281
Dr A David Batte 497
Thomas Beuker 115, 161
Dr John Beavers 397
Paul Birkinshaw 249
Terry Boss 265
Dr Thomas A Bubenik 101
Michael Cismaru 31
Stuart Clouston 299
Christian J Cloyde 405
Grant A Coleman 487
Dr Joerg Damaschke 115
Sarah J Dawson 57
Karl Dawson 371
Guy Desjadins 89
R Ellis 169
Daniel Falabella 19
Kevin W Ferguson 79
Dr Raymond R Fessler 475, 497
Jeff Fleming 31
Geoff Foreman 317
Ming Gao 137
Mark Gluskin 337
Dulce Gomez 19
William V Harper 101
Dr Jane Haswell 169
Dr Phil Hopkins 169
T Hrncir 317
Steve Hutcheson 419
Dr Luc Huyse 207
N Jackson 169
Partha Jana 359
Nikola Jansing 161
David Johnson 265
Richard Kania 161, 487
Dr Shahani Kariyawasam 57
Brenda Kenny 451
Stefan Klein 161
Robert W Kratsch 381
Ravi Krishnamurthy 137
Alf Age Kristiansen 419
Michael Krywko 337

I Lachtchouk 317
Dr Hubert Lindner 11
Aaron Lockey 309
C Lyons 169
Clifford J Maier 101, 281
Andy Mann 123
Jim E Marr 123, 161, 497
Kim J McCaig 451
Shamus McDonnell 337
Andres Mendizabal 225
Scott Miller 299
Samuel Moe 431
Rafael GMora 461
Pamela J Moreno 101
Dr Alan Murray 461
Dr J Bruce Nestleroth 441
Randy Nickle 89
Dr Aidan O'Donoghue 419
Chris Paul 235
Joe Paviglianiti 461
Age E Pedersen 431
S J Polaski 317
Dr Julia Race 57
Steve C Rapp 475, 497
Mike Read 89
Elvis San Juan Riverol 123, 161
N Daryl Ronsky 161
Gabriela Rosca 123, 161
Rahim Ruda 161
Ziad A Saad 451
Fabian Sanchez 225
Bernie Selig 265
Petra Senf 317
Dr John Smart 2
David A R Shanks 101
Douglas Spencer 337
Dr Narasi Sridhar 397
Leanne Stanley 57
David J Stucki 101
Jeff Sutherland 123
Simon Sykes 419
Samarth Tandon 137
Werner Thale 431
Jens Erik Thygesen 275
S Turner 317
Albert van Roodselaar 207
Jason K Van Velsor 441
Patrick Vieth 317, 387
Magne Andreas Vik 419
Brett Wakeham 31
Ralf Weber 161

Robert Winters 2
Jonathan Wylde 43
Andy Young 309
John Zurcher 265

❖ ❖ ❖

Preface

IT IS HARD to remember that when the first edition of this book was published, in 1988, the internet had not kicked-off, email was almost unheard-of, and txt msgs were a concept of which no-one had dreamt. In the world of pigging (almost considered an 'art' in those days, not the 'science' which it has become), the issues of high resolution vs low resolution were being wrestled with in the early developments of the inspection industry, and the difficulties provided by unpiggable pipelines were only just beginning to be acknowledged.

The intervening 25 years have, of course, seen massive advances in communications, as well as in this industry. But, surprisingly, some matters remain sources of concern, and some problems have got no closer to solutions than they were in the days of typewriters. The inspection industry is not in the latter category: superb high-technology solutions have been developed, using some of the most advanced and reliable technology, paralleling the aerospace industry, and feature assessments down to millimetric sizes are almost the norm. Inspection data interpretation has also developed to the stage where it's no longer a black art: survey results can be examined and analysed on a client's own PC or laptop, the thought of which was almost unheard of only a decade ago. But still some basic questions remain unanswered, probably the most basic of all being 'how clean is my pipeline?', and 'how best to design a pig launcher and receiver?'.

The pigging industry has developed a tremendous range of techniques and technologies, and it's probably fair to say that there are few pipelines that cannot be cleaned and inspected, although the success of such operations will sometimes depend on the available budget. There is, however, a fantastic global resource of expertise, equipment, and experience in the pigging and inspection industry, and its successful application is testified to by the rarity of pipeline failures and the safety with which millions of litres and cubic metres of hazardous materials are daily transported around the world without effect on the communities through (or under) which the pipelines pass.

This book, as with previous editions, provides an overview of some of the latest thinking and achievements in the area of pigging technology and integrity management. Its content is 41 papers from the series of conferences entitled *Pipeline pigging and integrity management* (now known as PPIM) that the publishers have organized in Houston and elsewhere between 2007 and 2012, chosen to represent a wide range of issues concerning the pipeline industry and maintenance of its integrity. I am most grateful to the authors of these papers, as well as to the others on our conference programmes, all of whom have been willing to share their thoughts and experiences, answer questions, and stimulate discussion.

As many readers will be aware, technology has not only moved on in great leaps in the pipeline and communications' industries, but also in publishing. This means that – more than ever – any errors in this book are solely the responsibility of the editor, and absolutely not that of the contributors. I hope very much that any that there are do not detract from the important issues being described.

Some readers will also know that I have been enormously privileged to be part of a superb group developing the 'pigging conferences', the chief members of which have been my good friends BJ Lowe and Gerri Ayers. Clarion's Traci Branstetter has been – and continues to be – an astonishing and dedicated administrator for our events, and other more recent additions to the group include Lyndsie Mewett (now Lyndsie Clark) and my colleagues from Australia, and Liz Foster in our UK office. While it is my enormous privilege to have my name on the front (and rear!) cover, this is only possible as a result of the valued friendships and unselfish support these good people have provided.

In closing, I must acknowledge my thanks to two others from the industry. The first is Cees Bal, who gave us the original idea in 1982 to organize a conference on pigging, following his ground-breaking event in The Netherlands the previous year ('Pigging: an art...or a science?'). The second is someone who did more than anyone else to set the foundations for the way the industry has developed over recent decades: Jim Cordell. Sadly now no longer with us, Jim was a great friend and tremendous contributor. He was the founding father of the Pigging Products & Services Association, and guided its development for many years; he was a great speaker and trainer, and if the industry ever had an orator, Jim was it. He was also a generous supporter of the events mentioned above, and loved little better than having an excuse to talk – with irrepressible humour and great knowledge – about the astonishing and fascinating subject of pipeline pigging.

John Tiratsoo
January, 2013

Nam et ipsa scientia potestas est.

For knowledge itself is power.

Meditationes Sacrae (1597) 'Of Heresies'
Francis Bacon (1st Baron Verulam and Viscount St Albans) 1561-1626
English lawyer, courtier, philosopher, and essayist

Section 1: Cleaning and black powder

Black powder migration in gas pipelines and associated problems

by Dr John S Smart[1] and Robert Winters[2]

1 John Smart Consulting Engineers, Houston, TX, USA
2 Champion Technologies, Lafayette, LA, USA

BLACK POWDER, a mix of iron sulphides, oxides, and other material can represent a serious threat to the integrity of gas pipelines by plugging pipelines, eroding compressor components, plugging instrumentation and pipeline drips, preventing valid in-line inspection by in-line inspection (ILI) tools, and causing damage to customer equipment. The velocity to cause movement of dry black powder in gas pipelines can be calculated, and is in the range of 12 ft/sec for 24-in pipelines. Once black powder starts to move, it will continue to move until the flow rate is reduced or the gas is compressed. Examples of black powder problems in the field are presented, and rules of thumb discussed about cleanliness in gas pipelines. Black powder can be partially controlled by using corrosion inhibitors, by using slug catchers or cyclones, or cleaning the line by pigging.

BLACK POWDER is the least understood but most prominent contamination problem in gas pipelines [1], and is a problem that is increasingly being recognized. Black powder is the name given to the mixture of iron oxides and sulphides found in gas pipelines, and can also include salt, sand, clay, mineral scales such as calcium carbonates and gypsum, strontium and barium sulphates, NORM (naturally occurring radioactive material), and metal powder. The sources of black powder include millscale, corrosion products, salts and scales from gas wells and wet gas gathering systems, and atmospheric rusting [1]. The variability of black powder is illustrated by reports of the powder being completely iron sulphide [1] to completely iron oxide [2]. Figure 1 shows an electron photomicrograph of magnetite black powder. Red rust (rouge) can be present both from atmospheric oxidation of pipe not properly stored nor cleaned, or from air oxidation of pyrophoric iron sulphide. Dry iron sulphide powder will spontaneously ignite if exposed to air,

Fig. 1. SEM photomicrographs of black powder. Particles range from about 100 microns and smaller. SEM Photomicrographs courtesy of Edgar Zapata, Anderson & Associates, Inc., Houston, TX.

and represents a safety, storage and disposal problem. This paper will illustrate that the problem of black powder is as much one of powder movement as one of the presence of black powder.

Black powder movement in gas pipelines

Wicks [3] has developed a theory to predict the movement of dry black powder in pipelines based on drag by fluid velocity. The velocity required to pick up and move black powder solids depends on gas density and viscosity, particle size and density, and pipe inside diameter. The theory is based on lifting particles out of a bed of particles to form a single powder particle that then can be moved by gas flow. The analysis has been presented by Smart for movement of solids in liquid and natural gas pipelines [4, 5]. Once freed, powder will continue moving in a pipeline as long as the velocity is high enough. The nature of particle motion depends strongly on gravity, but also on particle shape and the roughness of the surface over which the particles move.

- Rounded particles roll, especially if the surface is smooth.
- Long thin particles slide if the surface is smooth or may tumble if it is rough.
- Rough or irregularly shaped particles move in a succession of bounces called 'saltation flow'.
- Flake-like particles can move like leaves in the wind if they can be lifted by viscous forces or pushed by pigging.

Black powder can consist of many compounds, and Fig.5 shows the gas velocity to move various compounds in a 24-in pipeline at 1000 psi and 60°F. The velocity is slightly different for each compound, and in the balance of this paper, the velocity for magnetite (millscale) will be used, being slightly higher than iron carbonate and iron sulphide.

Gas velocity to move solids in a pipeline

The velocity to move 1-micron diameter black powder (magnetite) in a 24-in gas pipeline at various pressures, as calculated by Wicks' model, is shown in Fig.6. For a 1000-psi pipeline with 1-micron diameter magnetite particles, the velocity is 12 ft/sec for dry powder, and perhaps an additional

Fig.2. Salt in a gas pipeline with encapsulated black powder, likely the result of a producer unloading a well into the line leaving salt deposits.

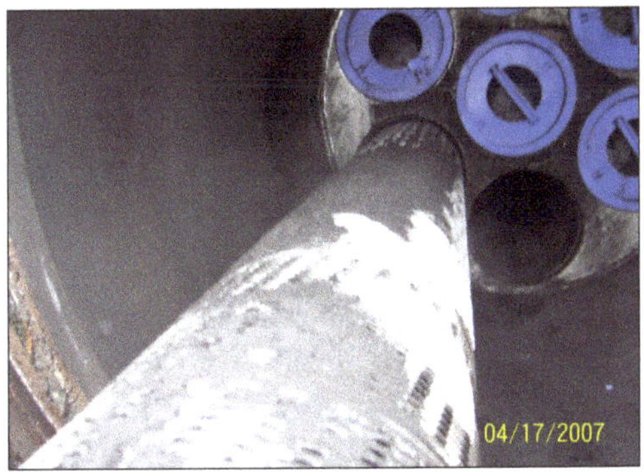

Fig.3. Black powder plugging gas filters.

10% to move solids uphill. Lower pressures require higher velocity to move solids. Figure 7 shows, however, that the flow rate to move black powder is lower at lower pressure. Since the flow rate required to sweep solids decreases as the pressure decreases, once a solid particle begins to move, it will continue moving until either gas is withdrawn from the pipe to lower the flow rate or the gas reaches a compressor or wide spot in the line. If the gas velocity is not high enough to move solids, they will accumulate in the pipeline until the bed height of solids has reduced the cross-sectional area for flow enough to raise the gas velocity to the solids sweep velocity

Tsochatzidis [2] and others have reported that black powder fractures and becomes very fine as it moves in a pipeline. Finer particle size reduces the sweep velocity, but the effect is not significant until the particle size is less than about 0.1 microns, as shown in Fig.8. Thus fines may be swept through a pipeline even if larger particles of black powder are not moving, and this represents a particularly difficult filtering problem requiring sub-micron filters.

Black powder deposits in pipelines

At velocities less than the sweep velocity, beds of particles will accumulate in the pipeline. Operators have reported that some pipelines develop black powder deposits of significant height, such as perhaps half full, which increases the gas velocity to the point where movement occurs and increases pressure drop through the pipeline [6-8]. Wicks' theory also can be used to predict the bed height for powder based on the remaining cross-sectional area for flow. Movement of black powder lying in beds wetted by compressor oil or glycol, or powder treated with corrosion

Fig.4. Rouge, finely divided hematite or red rust, is found in a new pipeline left exposed to air. Rouge is a polishing compound and is highly abrasive in pipelines. Rouge will not form in natural gas pipelines due to the low oxygen content of natural gas. Large particle sized hematite is coloured black and can be differentiated from millscale because it is not magnetic.

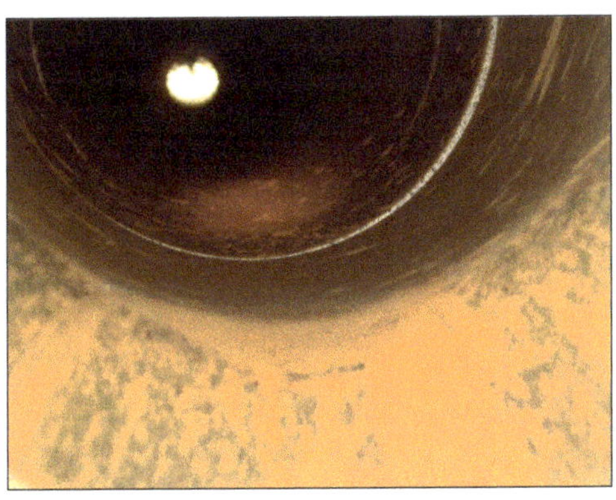

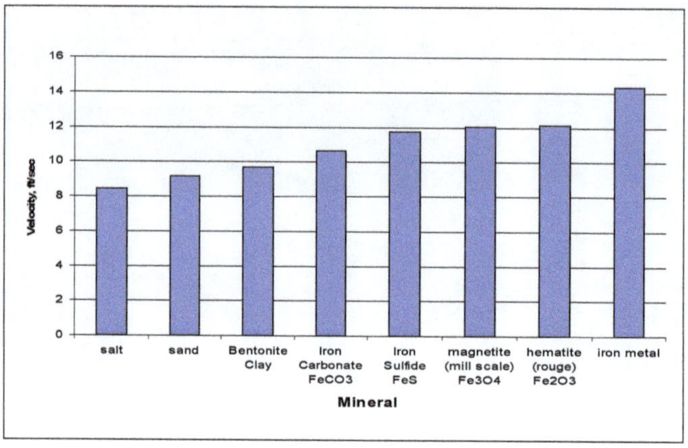

Fig.5. Velocity to move 1-micron black powder constituents in a 24-in pipeline at 1000 psi and 60°F.

inhibitor, will require higher velocity to move, as these particles are 'stuck' in the beds and require higher velocity to lift them out. This will lead to higher bed height and even greater pressure drop and efficiency loss. An additional velocity increment of up to 10% is required to move solids up-hill, likely causing deeper beds in up-hill sloping sections of the line in a manner similar to water accumulation in wet pipelines. If a pipeline is operating at less than the solids'-sweep velocity, black powder deposits will accumulate if solids are in the line. For the 24-in pipeline used as the example in Figs 6-8, at 1000 psi the sweep velocity is 12 ft/sec. If the velocity is reduced to 8.7 ft/sec, the bed height can be up to 5.75in, and at 4.4 ft/sec, the pipe can be up to half full of solids. Deposits of this type obviously can have severe consequences in pipeline operations, including high pressure drop, very difficult pigging, and prevent inspection pigs from operating. A 24-in line half full of solids has a pressure drop 3.45 times that of a clean pipe.

If a pipeline is operated at a velocity below the sweep velocity, black powder can accumulate in the line. If the flow rate is then raised or the line pigged to loosen the powder, high concentrations of black powder can travel down the line, plugging filters, damaging compressors, and potentially damaging customer equipment.

How clean is a pipeline?

The question of what is a clean pipeline is an interesting one, with as many different answers as people in the discussion. Engineers and operators have advised that they consider a pipeline clean when:

- the friction factor is less than a certain value
- solids are not evident in the receiving pig trap ahead of a pig
- there is less than 2 lbs powder/MMSCF gas
- pipeline filters do not have to be cleaned very often
- an intelligent pig inspection can be made obtaining valid data in the line
- a bare foam pig run through the line arrives 'clean', that is it has less than 0.5in penetration of dirt into the foam
- pipeline flow efficiency is improved and compressor fuel usage decreased.

There are no industry standards for black powder in pipelines. Some companies have an operating definition of 'commercially-pure' for gas delivery [1], while some commercial codes specify that the product be harmless to the customers' equipment. Pipeline black powder problems may have been aggravated when the US FERC Order 636 (The Restructuring Rule) was passed. FERC Order 636

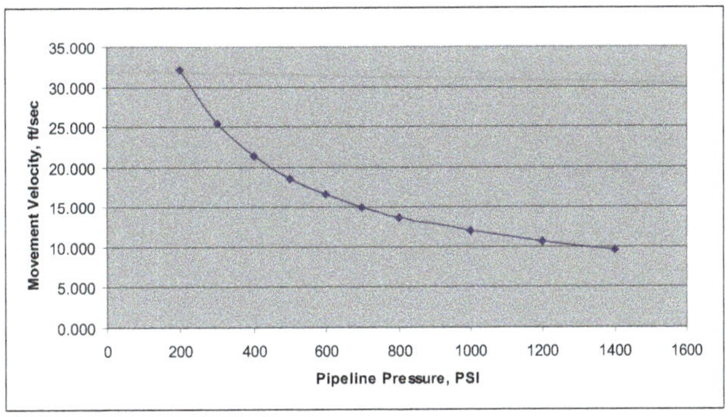

Fig.6. Velocity to move 1-micron black powder as a function of pipeline pressure in a 24-in natural gas pipeline containing 0.63 specific gravity natural gas at 60°F.

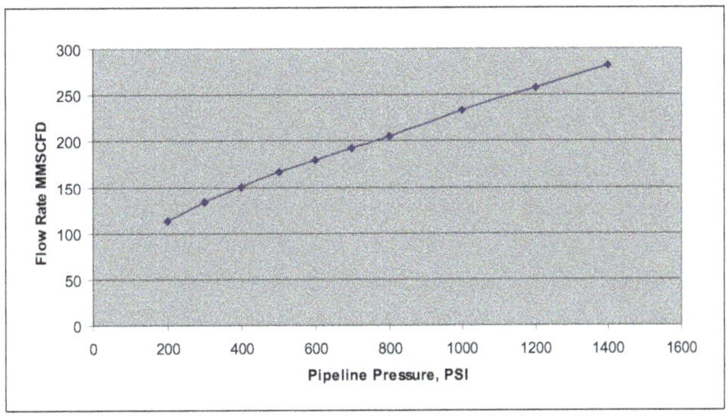

Fig.7. Flow rate (MMSCFD) to move 1-micron black powder vs pressure in a 24-in pipeline for 0.63 specific gravity natural gas at 1200 psi and 60°F.

Fig.8. Solids' sweep velocity vs black powder particle size for a 24-in pipeline containing natural gas. The velocity to sweep black powder begins to fall at about 1 micron according to Wicks' model, and is reduced to about half at 0.01 micron. As black powder fractures, it will move at a lower velocity, and may become much more difficult to remove with filters.

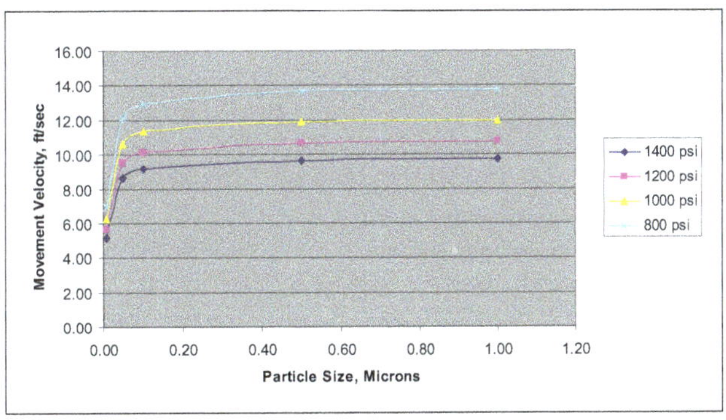

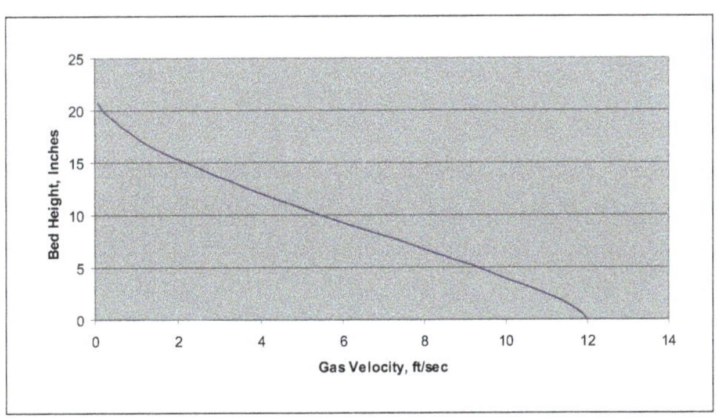

Fig.9. Bed height for 1-micron magnetite in a 24-in natural gas pipeline at 1000 psi and 60°F. The pipeline would be half full of black powder at a velocity of 4.4 ft/sec.

Fig. 10. Gas-fired peak shaving turbine generator in an electrical generating plant in which the refractory ceramic coating on the blades was fluxed by black powder from the natural gas pipeline, resulting in failure of blades and temporary loss of the equipment.

unbundled the pipeline industry, and the gas pipeline market essentially became a fully competitive market. Unbundling led to gas being received from not only the historical producers but also from many production sources which may not have had adequate quality controls. Gas was also freely exchanged among pipeline companies adding to the spread of black powder problems in US pipelines.

The problem of black powder is more than just one of product purity, however, as solids can affect metering runs by building-up in front of orifice plates, plugging instrument tubing, filling corrosion pits to make measurement by ILI inaccurate, rendering controls inoperable, damaging compressors and valves, and damaging customer equipment.

Intelligent pig inspection

Solids present in the pipe can have a detrimental effect on acquiring accurate intelligent pig information. Black powder accumulations can fill gouged and pitted areas on internal pipe surfaces causing intelligent pig sensors to travel further away from the pipe wall, thus masking pipeline anomalies and wall loss areas. Prior to smart pigging, dry and wet (chemically aided) pigging to clean the line of black powder accumulations is highly recommended. Oil and gas pipeline cleaning chemistries have been developed that have superior water wetting, absorption, and cleaning dispersion characteristics to dissolve oil, glycol, and paraffin matrices that can hold black powder particles to pipe walls. After being dispersed, the particles can be pigged out of the pipeline.

Other problems with black powder

Black powder found in gas pipelines affects the integrity of infrastructure as well as posing other industry problems. As submicron particles, migration of the black powder can cause product quality problems, as well as excessive wear and erosion on – for example – compressor pistons and valves, pipeline pigs, internal pipe walls, internal girth welds, tube turns, valve seats, orifice plates, vessel baffle plates, filter elements, and turbine blades. Accumulated solids can plug small orifices affecting equipment that measures gas and are used to safely operate pipeline facilities. As the particles settle out of the gas stream, accumulating and filling-in surface pits and other internal pipe wall anomalies, they often prevent accurate smart pig logging of internal surfaces and evidence of wall loss. Concurrently, settling of deposits in water-wet pipeline sag bends promotes the occurrence of dissimilar metal corrosion and can harbour corrosive bacteria. Frequent pigging and chemical treatments with biocides and corrosion inhibitors can control internal corrosion caused by solids' deposition.

Plugging of pipeline drips, causing internal corrosion

Black powder travelling in a pipeline will fill in any dead space it can reach. Foremost among these are drip pots intended to collect compressor oils and glycol downstream of gas plants and compressors. Once filled, water can be trapped in the drip pots leading to internal corrosion from the galvanic cells set up between the black powder particles and the pipe steel. Further, these sites serve as a haven for bacteria, leading to possible MIC in pipelines that are nominally dry.

Damage to customers' equipment

Black powder can also damage customers' equipment if delivered into the customers' plant. Figure 10 shows two views of a turbine blade from a peak-shaving turbine generator fired by natural gas. The plant had two trains, and apparently ran successfully when only one train was in service. When the second train was put into service, black powder caused the damage seen in this figure by fluxing the refractory ceramic coating on the blades of both turbine generators. The plant had a gas filter in place. Velocity in the gas pipeline when both generators were in service was 29.7 ft/sec, while the velocity to move black powder was 17.5 ft/sec. Thus, when only one generator was in service, black powder would not move, but when both were, it did.

Monitoring black powder

The dynamics of flow in natural gas pipelines has been investigated by researchers and operating companies for years. Add black powder to the equation, and a lot of the sound judgments on design and operation can be thrown out of the window. Therefore, testing for the presence of solid deposits in the gas stream is a must. Monitoring for black powder in piping can consist of: origin/source determinations, field facility spot checks, analysing gas, water and solids composition, field testing for FeS with HCl, knowing where the water is (sag bends and accumulating areas), bacteria testing, piping/vessel clean outs, gas filter inspections, and failure analyses.

Once the investigator discovers the presence of the black powder, then tracing the migration back to the source is recommended to ascertain if it is bacteria-, or chemistry-borne. Based on this determination, chemical treatments and other mitigation measures can be administered to control future migrations.

Sand meters

Sand meters are used in oil and gas production piping to detect sand production. Two types are used, one which measures erosion caused by the sand and the other listening for the 'pings' made by sand particles hitting the wall or probe. *Clamp-On* sand probes are acoustic, and can be mounted on the outside of the pipe. These could also be used to detect black powder movement in pipelines.

Laser isokinetic sampling probes

Laser isokinetic sampling probes (LISP) [9] are instruments that can measure particle flow in gas using a laser, in particle sizes from 0.3 to 50 microns and at particle densities up to 107 particles

Fig. 11. Black powder being discharged from a gas pipeline during cleaning of a pig trap following pigging [2].

per cubic cm for submicron sizes, and up to 10 g/m^3 for particles greater than 1 micron. The instrument is in use for the measurement of efficiency in filtration and scrubbers.

Pipeline pigging and cleaning

The type of pig used to clean a line depends on the nature of the material in the pipeline. Migrating black powder deposits in a pipeline can be controlled using 'dry' and 'wet' pigging practices. The type of pigging used by the pipeline industry depends on the beneficial end results desired.

Dry pigging

Dry pigging involves routine running of scraper pigs to remove accumulated solids, semi-solids, liquids, black powder, and other loose deposits. Pigs used in black-powder-laden pipelines should be bi-directional scraper pigs with two or more stout rubber or polyurethane sealing discs in the front and back of the pig. Pig locators or 'pingers' can be attached to the pig to locate it in the event that it becomes stuck and has to be retrieved. Heavier durable pigs have better scraping action, and thus better ability to loosen and bring the solids out of the pipeline. After conventional pigs have been used to get the major portion of the solids out of the line, the remaining dust can be captured using magnetic cleaning pigs with powerful magnets located in close proximity to the pipe wall. Dry pigging should be used to dislodge solids so that corrosion inhibitors and biocides can be more effective in controlling internal pipeline corrosion.

Wet pigging

Wet pigging applies various chemistries (acids, solvents, surfactants, anti-foulants, gels, corrosion inhibitors, biocides, etc.) between an aggressive scraper front pig and a sealing pig in the rear.

Pre-cleaning recommendations for a pipeline start with a laboratory analysis of samples taken from the inside of the pipeline. Compositional analysis defines the type of matrix binding contaminant black powder particles to the pipeline. The analysis allows chemists to determine the exact cleaning agents and the optimum concentrations necessary to breakdown the deposits. This process helps to ensure a successful, thorough cleaning of the pipeline.

Each pipeline to be cleaned has its own characteristics that need to be studied: quality of product, pipeline design, geography, flow regimes, corrosion history, operations and maintenance, are large factors in estimating the condition of the pipeline. In newer pipelines, simple pig cleaning and liquid flushes may suffice. Most older pipelines have a greater degree of deposit build-up requiring very sophisticated cleaning technology.

Chemical treatments should be based on laboratory analysis and testing of specific products to dissolve the pipeline's contamination matrix. Organic acids and partitioning micro-emulsions consisting of advanced blends of wetting agents, dispersing surfactants, and co-solvents are effective in dissolving black powder deposits on pipe walls, suspending the debris to prevent re-deposition, and allowing free flushing out of the pipeline.

Calculated chemical treatment volumes (100+ gallons/diameter-inch) should be administered using aggressive pigging practices. Chemical volumes after pig runs should still retain sufficient activity. Pigs should not run dry of chemical before the entire pipeline segment to be cleaned has been chemically-wetted.

It is recommended to batch 50 to 100 gallons of chemical ahead of the first pig for lubricity and a smooth run in a dual pig train. Effective pig batching is usually run on-stream and at constant product stream velocities of 5-15 mph or 2-7 m/sec to prevent surging. The carrier liquid (diesel, condensate, clean oil, water, methanol, etc.) and the batched chemical have to be compatible.

Time to clean pipelines (in days) varies with flow, geography, design, liquids/solids holdup volumes, and other uncontrollable conditions.

Disposal of pipeline contents is the responsibility of the operating company. Disposal costs on pipeline cleaning projects can run upward of an additional 30% to 40% based on regulatory edicts. In the US, wet pig cleaning costs per mile for a relatively dirty pipeline (60 miles of 30-in) may range from $5,000 to $10,000 per mile with disposal costs included.

Tsochatzidis and Maroulis [2] have reported that they used a cyclone separator to remove voluminous black powder deposits received in their natural gas pipeline in Greece. The cyclone separates the powder, which can then be hauled away by the truck-load.

References

1. R.Baldwin, 1998. Technical assessment: black powder in the gas industry – sources, characteristics, and treatment. Gas Machinery Research Council Report TA 97-4, May. Report available at www.gmrc.org/technology-reports.html Report 97-4
2. N.A.Tsochatzidis and K.E.Maroulis, 2007. Methods help remove black powder from gas pipelines. *Oil and Gas Journal*, March.
3. M.Wicks, 1971. Transport of solids at low concentration in horizontal pipelines. *In*: Advances in solid-liquid flow in pipelines and its applications. *Ed*: I.Zandi, Pergammon Press, New York, pp101-124.
4. J. Smart, 2007. Determining the velocity required to keep solids moving in pipelines. 19th Pipeline Pigging and Integrity Management Conference, Houston, TX, February. Published in *The Journal of Pipeline Engineering*, **6**, 1.

5. J.Smart, 2007. Movement of black powder in gas pipelines. *Pipeline and Gas Journal*, November.
6. R.Winters, 2002. The black powder problem in gas pipelines – an industry overview. 14th Annual Pipeline Pigging, Integrity Assessment, and Repair Conference, Houston, TX, January.
7. R.Baldwin, 2006. What is black powder? An overview. Presented at the Black Powder Forum, 17 Feb., Houston.
8. A.Black and D.Glasscock, 2006. Dealing with black powder: an operator's perspective. Presented at the Black Powder Forum, 17 Feb., Houston. Discussion at Black Powder Forum, 17 Feb., Houston.
9. Laser Isokinetic Sampling Probes, http://terrauniversal.com/products/ measuring/portablepart

Development and operational experience of a new pigging technology for effective black powder removal

by Dr Hubert Lindner

Rosen Engineering GmbH, Lingen, Germany

OVER THE last decade, the occurrence of black powder has attracted increased attention in the natural gas industry worldwide. Pipeline operators now regularly deal with the existence, formation and consequences of black powder in their systems. Black powder not only has adverse effects on pipeline systems by creating a gradual drop in pressure and by clogging installations and instruments, but also on the product quality itself. In addition, it also interferes with pigging activities by potentially increasing the friction and wear on polyurethane discs or cups, in particular, and by hampering precise measurements with inspection tools due to sensor lift-off.

Both its adverse effects on the condition of pipeline systems themselves and its interference with effective in-line activities call for effective methods to remove black powder. This paper describes the development and operational experience of a new type of mechanical cleaning tool to remove black powder from pipelines in order to prepare them for in-line inspection. It also explains the flushing technology's mode of operation and presents results from various runs conducted. The results reveal that the new technology is able to remove remarkable volumes of black powder from a pipeline (for example, 7 m^3 dust in one 48-in run). Based on the on-board data acquisition system, the behaviour analysed leads to an improved understanding of the interaction between the tool, pipeline, and powder accumulation.

BLACK POWDER can be found in both dry and wet gas lines and in conjunction with any other contaminants found in gas pipelines such as water, liquid hydrocarbons, and sand. Black powder is a general term used for a wide range of different compounds, notably iron oxides, iron sulphide, iron carbonate, and millscale created by different chemical reactions. It can also include other components such as sand and other minerals. Under dry conditions, it can take the form of very fine dust, (typically between 1 and 100 microns) or solid sediment, whereas under wet conditions it usually appears as a tar-like substance [1]. Depending on the nature of its composition, black powder can have a wide variety of effects. Most notably, it can significantly increase the wear rate of the sealing and guiding elements of pipeline pigs (typically made from polyurethane or rubber), although some types of black powder only have a slight effect on plastics. In some wet environments, black powder predominantly interacts with the metal rather than plastic components of the tools.

Based on the new developed cleaning technology for removing black powder from pipelines, Rosen has built tools in different sizes. With these tools various runs were performed and experiences regarding the reliability and performance were gained. The results were collected and evaluated in the company's Technology and Research Centre (RTRC). Based on the measured data and on-site information (such as pictures and accumulated dust), the tools' mode of functioning was analysed and compared to their predicted behaviour. The large number of available run results, which in many instances were based on entire series of runs for one segment, led to a better understanding of the technology on the one hand and the definition of adaptive tool modifications and corrective actions on the other.

Fig. 1. Cleaning tool after a run through black powder.

Cleaning experience

Conventional cleaning methods involving standard cleaning tools showed both low efficiency and heavy wear on the polyurethane of the cleaning equipment used. Even Rosen's cleaning tools, otherwise well proven for their high wear resistance in long gas pipelines, showed heavy wear in relatively short pipelines containing dry black powder (Fig.1). Under these particular conditions, even an increased volume of polyurethane on the cleaning tools did not remarkably improve their wear resistance. The combination of heavy wear and low cleaning efficiency means that a large number of cleaning runs are required, thereby causing both heavy operating efforts and high spare part costs. Experience has shown that although the use of magnetic-inspection tools provides better cleaning efficiency, it is still marked by heavy wear on the tool components. This causes high maintenance and spare part replacement for a tool which was originally built for pipeline inspection rather than cleaning.

Due to the ongoing challenge of contamination, other methods have been developed. These include, for example, cleaning procedures such as batch washing or gel pigging. While these procedures are more effective than standard cleaning, they are very laborious and expensive: they necessitate analysis of the line, the powder, and the specific composition of chemicals as well as the use of batching trains. Moreover, the problem of high wear is not only virtually the same as in standard cleaning tools, but the inserted fluids can cause additional problems. For example, the carrier liquid water may react with the powder either mechanically or chemically, and new contaminants with different characteristics could be formed. Finally, all inserted fluids and chemicals must be removed from the pipeline completely by means of a complex procedure.

Development of a new cleaning tool for black powder

Faced with the challenge of removing black powder in preparation for intelligent pipeline inspections, Rosen has developed a new cleaning system which is particularly efficient in dry gas lines. Combining the advantages of regular cleaning tools with those of magnetic-inspection tools, the new approach also incorporates a specifically developed by-pass system. Carried by support wheels which are sloped so as to create continuous rotation for the purpose of preventing uneven wear of wall-touching or weight-bearing components, the tool is equipped with polyurethane

Fig.2. Rosen's 48-in black powder cleaning tool before launching.

guide and sealing discs or cups. To improve cleaning capability, it is also equipped with spring-supported magnetic brushes. All these mechanical components can be adapted to suit any pipeline configuration, thereby optimizing cleaning efficiency under a wide range of different conditions.

The central feature of the new technology is a calculated by-pass flow running through the centre of the tool. The negative pressure created as a result of the acceleration of the medium permits the use of suction tubes, located in the space between the discs behind the brushes in the run direction. The evacuated medium flows into the by-pass nozzle from where it is transported, together with the central by-pass flow, to the downstream area of the tool. In order to generate a defined suction flow, the evacuated volume has to be continuously replaced, and is done so through a specially designed inlet channel. Due to the special flow guidance of the tool, a flow vortex is created in the brush / suction area. The specific dynamic of the tool's suction flow means that an optimized quantity of powder particles can be sucked off the pipeline wall. Moreover, the by-pass flow through the middle of the tool transports additional powder particles. Finally, the combined flow through the tool creates a flushing effect in the downstream area and supports particle transportation.

As these explanations show, the new technology, which is the result of more than 20 years of pipeline cleaning and inspection experience, is based on several different components, all of which make a specific contribution to the cleaning process as a whole. The overall characteristics and performance of such complex interlinked processes must be calculated using computational fluid dynamics. Thus the brush / magnet system not only ensures surface cleaning but also the required differential pressure. Furthermore, the actual pressure and flow in the line has to be taken into account to optimize cleaning performance on the one hand and to prevent run problems due to excessive by-pass on the other.

A particular challenge in this context is the passage of full-bore tees. On account of the flow around the front disc package, the by-pass value has to be calculated to allow for this situation. It is imperative therefore that all pipeline and run conditions are taken into account to ensure optimal preparation of these particular cleaning tools.

To monitor overall performance and function, each tool is equipped with a pipeline-data logger (PDL) data-acquisition system. The data logger measures temperature, absolute and differential pressure, and acceleration in three orthogonal directions with one data triple per second (minimum, maximum, average).

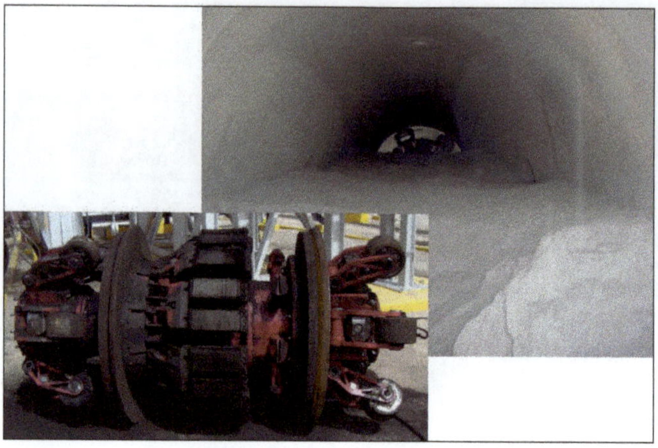

Fig.3. Receiver filled with black powder and cleaning tool after more than 170km in this pipeline.

Field experience

On the basis of the specifically developed technology, Rosen has built 42-in, 48-in, and 56-in tools and performed numerous cleaning runs with each tool. Figure 2 shows the 48-in black powder cleaning tool just before launching in a 170-km natural gas pipeline which was known to be affected by the common challenge of heavy black powder contamination. Figure 3 indicates the dust-filled receiver after conducting one of the most effective runs. In the background, the front of the cleaning tool can be seen: it brought out 4800 li of black powder into the receiver alone, and the amount of dust blown through the offtake during the run can only be estimated.

Perhaps even more impressive than its cleaning capacity was the tool's condition after the run: it was so good that it could be launched again without the need to replace any parts. Even the discs only showed minor signs of wear – and all this after a run in more than 170km of dry black powder.

Despite the tool's successful application, however, some runs failed to remove any significant volume of black powder. In consequence, it was necessary to analyse the measured PDL data as well as the condition of the tools to find the reasons for the differences and take corrective measures if possible. The details of these evaluations and measures are described below.

Evaluation of run data and tool performance

As mentioned above, a pipeline-data logger was used to measure line pressure, temperature, acceleration and, most importantly since it permits monitoring general tool function and progress, the differential pressure across the tool. The data given below explain in more detail how the differential pressure created by the friction of the tool's brushes along the wall generates by-pass flow through the tool and hence suction flow from the cup-bounded cleaning volume.

Figure 4 (top graph: Run 1) shows time-based measurement of the differential pressure at the tool and suction area during a very effective cleaning run (see Fig.3). The diagrams indicate the minimum (blue), average (green), and maximum (red) values of data samples collected during the run. The tool's differential pressure begins with a constant average value of about 0.3 bar for the first 12 hours (except the launcher area) and is thus within the designed range for this project. A remarkable increase in differential pressure (DP) up to 1.5 bar on average then occurs. Having reached the peak value, the pressure decreases again slightly without falling below 0.7 bar. This pressure trace clearly demonstrates the fundamental principle of this method: the more the

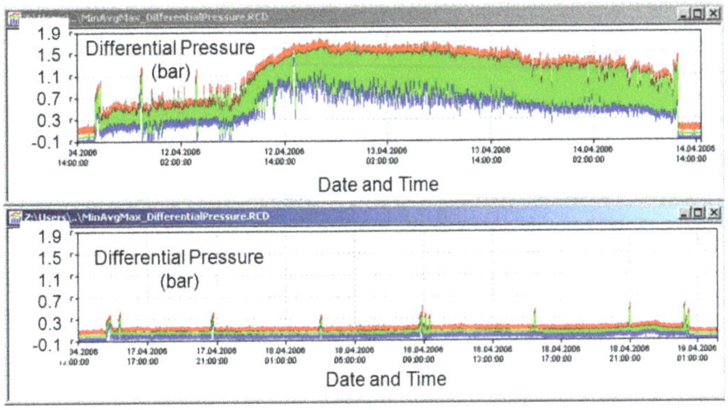

Fig.4. Tool differential pressure for Run 1 and 2 through a 170-km 48-in segment.

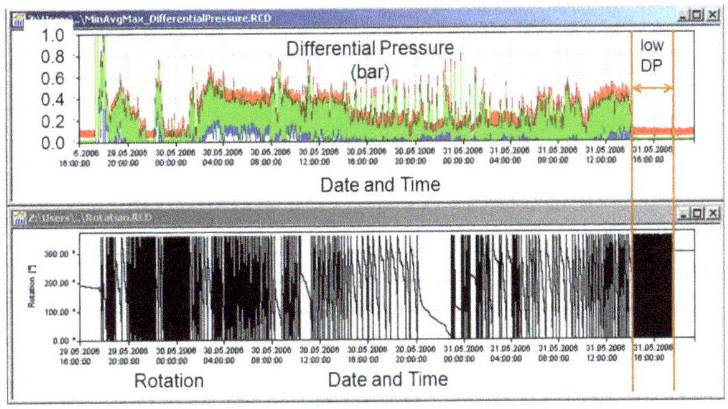

Fig.5. Run 1, performed in a 48-in pipeline, produced 0.25m^3 of black powder. Top: tool differential pressure; bottom: tool rotation.

pipeline is contaminated and / or the more debris is accumulated in front of and around the tool, the higher the DP and hence the better the tool's cleaning efficiency.

These results could not be repeated consistently, however. Subsequent runs showed irregular pressure profiles and consequently varying cleaning results. The differences between Runs 1 and 2 in the same segment of a 48-in line as shown in Fig.5 are especially striking: while the top graph shows the above-discussed pressure trace along the tool, the second run performed six days later produced completely different tool behaviour, and the differential pressure remained below 0.1 bar for the entire line. These measurements were supported by the visible cleaning results: whereas Run 1 yielded at least 4.8 m^3 of black dust collected in the receiver, hardly any debris was gathered during Run 2.

Since higher differentials were only measured in the periodical heavy wall sections, the low average differential pressure of about 0.05 bar of Run 2 could only be explained by non-touching brush systems. An examination of the yokes subsequently confirmed this assumption. Dust had accumulated in the yoke support system thus preventing full stroke of the yokes. Based on this finding, the tool's design was slightly modified and spring system maintenance increased.

Detailed analysis of the tool performance

Despite these measures, tool behaviour continued to be inconsistent. Although more detailed analyses were conducted based on a series of runs through a particular 48-in segment, the tool performance varied to a great extent and ranged from the recovery of 7m^3 of black powder from the receiver in Run 4 to hardly anything in the previous runs. The following figures provide a selection of some meaningful pressure recordings for different performance levels in this line: the data are presented in a combination of two diagrams, one representing the differential pressure along the tool and the other the tool's rotation. Experience showed that because of the slanted

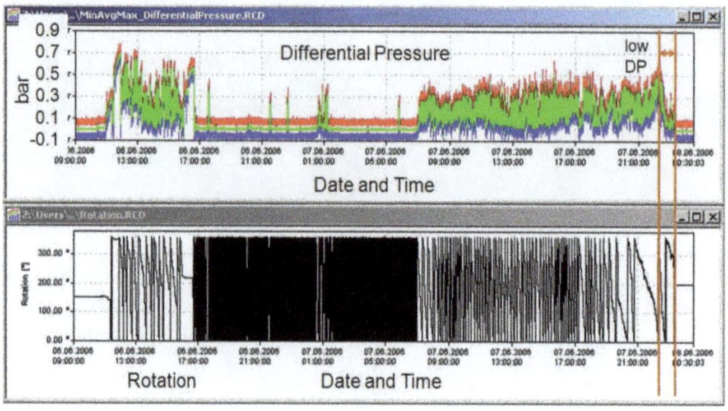

Fig.6. Run 3 resulted in 0.6m^3 of black powder. Top: tool differential pressure; bottom: tool rotation.

support wheels, the tool's rotation can be used as an indicator for tool velocity, with fast rotation rates indicating high tool speed, and vice versa.

Run 1 indicates a good pressure record for most of the operation (Fig.5, top). The average differential pressure (DP – green line) is between 0.2 and 0.4 bar for most time, although two stretches of low pressure were measured in the first quarter of the run. At a superficial glance, it seems that the tool generated differential pressure throughout the operation. But comparing its differential pressure to its rotation rate, it becomes clear that the DP dropped three hours before the rotation stopped (indicating the end of the run). At the same time, the rotation rate increased remarkably (Fig.5, vertical lines). From this, it can be assumed that cleaning performance during these last hours was negligible; this inference was confirmed by the fact the tool brought out only a small amount of dust (0.25 m^3).

The next run (No 2) showed very similar behaviour to the first one, with a jagged pressure pattern for most of the run but at a lower DP. But at about three hours before receiving, the DP again dropped to almost zero, coinciding with reduced tool rotation. This once again suggests that the tool's cleaning performance did not last to the end of the line. Before the next run intensive maintenance on the tool mechanics was executed.

Cleaning run No 3 (Fig.6) produced different tool behaviour compared to the first two runs. It started with relatively high differential pressure, then degraded to the familiar zero patterns for about 15 hrs before reverting to the described working / friction pattern for the next 16 hrs. Again the pressure dropped at the end, but this time only for 13mins (between vertical lines). The amount of dust collected was slightly higher than that of the previous runs but still low.

The tool rotation record for Run 4 (Fig.7) showed a relatively constant distribution over the runtime compared to Figs 5 and 6. The main difference from run No1 is the high differential pressure at the end of Run 4 which was about 1 bar, while the average differential pressure directly before receiving was still 0.5 bar. This was the first time the working differential pressure had been maintained to the end of the run. In line with these improved pressure levels, the tool brought out 7 m^3 of dust.

A comparison between the results of all four runs shows a strong correlation between tool differential pressure and cleaning performance: whereas the first few runs transported dust through parts of the line and dropped it occasionally, the final run brought out the already accumulated powder at the end of the pipeline.

In summary, the findings of these runs (supported by additional test results) are as follows. As

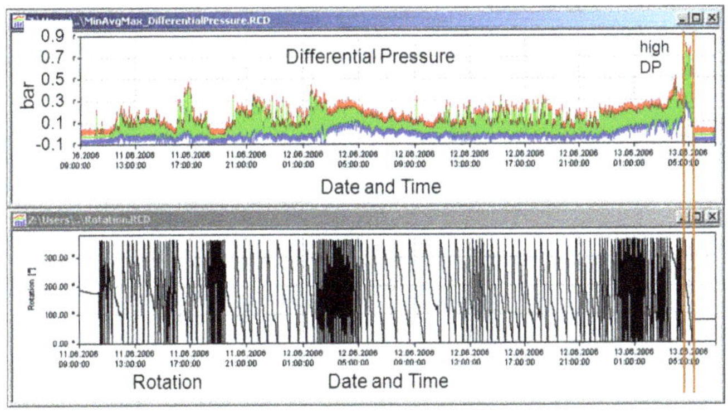

Fig.7. Run 4 produced 7.06m³ of dust. Top: tool differential pressure; bottom: tool rotation.

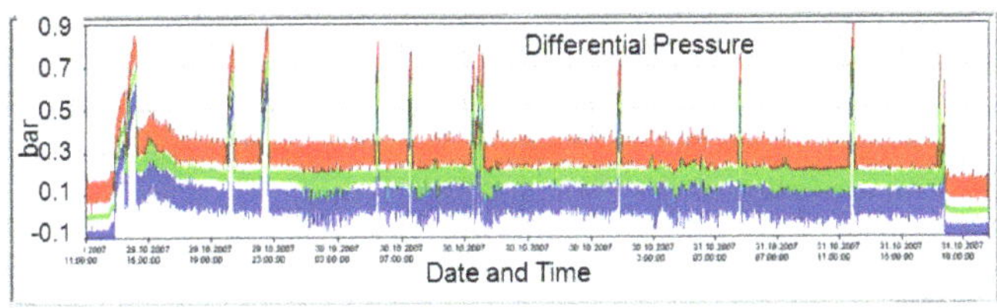

Fig.8. Differential pressure after tool modification produced 1.2 m³ of dust in the same 48-in segment.

expected, the differential pressure is the driving force behind tool performance. Therefore, to ensure that the accumulated dust is collected in the receiver, the pressure has to be maintained to the very end of the run. Tool friction behaviour is very inconsistent: although high differential pressure is built up, it tends to oscillate between high and low levels over time during the run (as, for example, in the middle part of Fig.4). These results suggest that the higher the differential pressure during a run, the more black powder is collected. This finding is confirmed by most other run test results. One baffling observation was made, however: since the tool was designed to create a differential pressure of about 0.35 bar as measured at the beginning of Run 1, it should have created significant differential pressure even in the absence of any dust or other debris. Nonetheless, Run 2 shows the differential pressure of a worn low-friction standard cleaning tool (CLP). An analysis of all available active cleaning PDL results revealed that for most of the runs the differential pressure created was very low from the start. Although it occasionally rose during the run, it remained low in most cases.

At first, this unexpected observation could not be explained. With further runs of the 48-in and 56-in tools, it was realized that the piston of the yoke spring setup could be blocked by the dust which in turn had a direct impact on the stroke of the yoke. For some of the 56-in runs, insufficient yoke / wall contact was subsequently confirmed and, in consequence, yoke maintenance was increased. After each run, the spring setup was checked and cleaned. However, since new dust accumulation cannot be avoided as it is the task of the tool, it was impossible to predict yoke support behaviour during a run. Inspection of the tools after the runs revealed that the yokes did not protrude beyond the edge of the guiding discs sized at the internal diameter of the pipeline. However, the yokes are designed for higher maximum stroke. Even if a certain abrasion of the brushes is assumed (which was not very high) the stroke of the yoke diameter was often reduced below the internal diameter of the pipeline.

Due to these findings, the design for the tools (30-in, 42-in, and 48-in) was modified. In addition to changes to the yoke kinematics, the most important added feature was a new yoke support and the disc spring piston was replaced by a number of tension springs. The new design was verified in the same pipe segment already considered in Figs 5 to 7. Compared to these results the DP record now remained constant at a level of about 0.2 bar besides the passage of the regular installations (Fig.8). The run removed about 1.2 m^3 of black powder and the subsequent inspection run proved the line to be clean. The most important finding, however, was the consistent differential pressure level achieved. This is the expected and required consistency needed for a controlled performance of the black powder cleaning tool. Additionally, the design changes meant that the maintenance effort required to keep the yokes moving was reduced to a minimum.

Conclusions

Presenting a new cleaning technology for the removal of black powder from gas pipelines, this article has shown the highly complex interdependence and interaction between pipeline surface, dust contamination, magnetic forces, brush friction, by-pass area, and operating conditions. Based on the empirical data from many cleaning runs, the behaviour and performance was evaluated for a better understanding of the tool's actual mode of operation. Tool design modifications made to overcome the weaknesses discovered subsequently led to more reliable and constant tool performance. Although Rosen's Technology and Research Centre continues to conduct research into the complex area of black powder removal to improve overall efficiency of the black powder cleaning tool, the newly developed technology already represents a low-effort solution for pipeline operators. More efficient than the laborious conventional cleaning procedures, the new tool produced very good to excellent cleaning results during the tests.

Outlook

The experience demonstrated conclusively that the black powder cleaning tool is able to remove large amounts of dust. While the development of an efficient dust-removal method is a great step forward, it also creates new challenges: operators now have to find ways to handle large quantities of black dust, not only what is collected in the receiver, but also the powder accumulated at the end of the pipeline system which has to be filtered out before the gas can be transferred to a plant or distribution system. This means that the question of collecting and filtering black powder in gas lines will have to be considered as early as possible during the planning phase in future. Similarly, tool behaviour will have to be refined to enable adaptation of powder removal activities to the new conditions posed by ever more sophisticated filtering systems.

References

1. R.M.Baldwin, 1998. Black powder in the gas industry - sources, characteristics and treatment. Report No TA97-4, Mechanical & Fluids Engineering Division Southwest Research Institute, Gas Machinery Research Council, May.

Enhancing pipeline efficiency through chemical cleaning

by Daniel Falabella and Dulce Gomez

Operations Department, Transportadora de Gas del Sur, Buenos Aires, Argentina

OVER TIME, pipelines in service lose efficiency and therefore transportation capacity. This is one of the reasons why TGS keeps an updated pipeline-simulation model that enables the identification of inefficient operations in the transportation system. As a result of the simulations we conduct, a decrease in the efficiency of one of the San Martin pipeline was detected.

In a first stage, TGS conducted field measurements of pressure and flow on the section involved, which were then compared to the data obtained in the simulation model, corroborating the accuracy of the simulation model. Later, conventional mechanical cleaning tasks were conducted without satisfactory results, which led TGS to explore several alternatives in the pursuit of pipeline efficiency enhancement. Chemical cleaning was preferred, as the use of this methodology presented a clear advantage: it allowed the cleaning process to be conducted while the transportation system remained in service.

Through several simulations conducted by means of the Gregg program, both the efficiency enhancement requested to the supplier and its result were determined. One of the challenges of the project was to keep the Cerri Complex liquid processing plant in service during cleaning tasks. For this, a further process simulation tool was required: Hysys was employed, which allowed us to define critical project variables, such as the solvent to be used, flow management in Cerri Complex to keep delivered gas within quality specifications, and dewpoint calculations.

This work reflects the simulation tasks conducted with the aim of enhancing operations in the pipeline, specifically increasing transportation efficiency. Besides, we would like to share the expertise and results we achieved in the implementation of this cleaning method, which had never been used before on an in-service transportation pipeline in Argentina.

WITH THE PASSING of time, pipelines basically loose transportation efficiency as a result of two factors: a roughness increase in the pipeline inner wall, and accumulations of dirt derived from daily operations (oil, rust, black powder, and other deposited products). The loss in efficiency shows in the decrease of the transported volume or in a significant pressure drop along the pipeline. We share with all transportation system operators our major concern which is to maintain high efficiency standards in our transportation system, thus ensuring an optimum transportation service and obtaining the best profitability.

Simulation programs tune the reality measured in the field to calculated values through the 'efficiency' variable. This parameter:

- considers the pipeline's own roughness
- takes into account potential dirt
- groups the non-relevant variables not included in the calculation
- estimates errors related to measurement variables used in the calculation.

Background

In 2001, with the goal to enhance TGS' transportation system (both pipelines and compressor plants) and to calculate the maximum transportation flow to be offered in the subsequent year, a 'maximum transportation' test was conducted. This test consisted in determining the maximum possible flow to be transported on a constant basis (without the effect of the demand cycle) for a period of 15 days; the test was also used to 'tune' the transportation system simulation model (length, flows, pressure, and efficiency). It was thus possible to detect several 'bottlenecks' within the system, which were later surveyed and analysed individually.

In a system as long as ours, with over 1000 km of pipelines, and with several compressor plants, a 'bottleneck' is the section between the compressor plants operating at full capacity, which allows the lowest transportation flow. One of these bottlenecks occurred in the Conesa – Río Colorado – Cerri section where a decrease in the transportation capacity was observed: the 'actual' transportation volume was lower than the 'simulated' volume calculated by the specific calculation software.

As a consequence of this, we ran several mechanical-cleaning processes, using mechanical scraper tools, endeavouring to reduce the capacity decrease, improve transportation efficiency, and verify the potential obstructions and reductions in the section. The tasks were conducted in line with our own procedures: by running two scraper tools fitted with cups and brushes and one polly-pig (foam pig).

Although the volume increased after the cleaning, it was not enough to meet our requirements. In the light of this, and after assessing many alternatives in the pursuit of flow and efficiency increase in the section, a chemical cleaning programme was proposed. According to the information supplied by the service supplier, the main advantage presented by this procedure was that it would not require any preparations: that is to say that normal operations could continue while the cleaning was performed; besides this, the process would not affect the operation of the liquid extraction plant downstream of the pipeline section to be cleaned. If this technique was proven to be viable, it would be used in other areas of our system affected with the same problem.

San Martin pipeline steady-state model

TGS has developed a base simulation model of the San Martin pipeline using the Gregg program. In this model, each section – from one compressor to another – has an associated efficiency value. This efficiency value is the tuning parameter with which the model represents the data obtained by field measurements.

In order to perform this adjustment with the steady-state model, we select a day of pipeline flows and pressures of maximum stability, and surveyed the system's measurement stations to obtain the following information: injection and delivery flows along the pipeline, head and discharge pressure of each compressor plant, and suction temperature at each compressor, and these data were then entered into the model. The information provided at the measurement stations was obtained from the SCADA system which TGS uses to monitor the performance of injection, delivery points, and compressors.

Once all these data had been entered into the simulation model, the suction pressure of each compressor plant was obtained. This value was compared with the suction pressure from SCADA for the surveyed day and, if required, the efficiency model was tuned to match this information.

The permanent updating of the transportation system model is critical, as it is used to define system expansions and to conduct daily studies. According to last San Martin pipeline simulation model, the efficiency values for the sections to be cleaned were:

Pipeline section	*Efficiency*
Conesa - Rio Colorado	0.91
Rio Colorado - Gral. Cerri	0.933

The efficiency increase expected from chemical cleaning resulted in a profitable investment, as it allowed an increase in the transportation capacity in the Chubut - Cerri section.

Chemical–mechanical cleaning

Overall procedure for pipeline chemical cleaning

A detailed description of the procedures involved in a chemical cleaning of a gas pipeline is given below.

A chemical cleaning programme removes deposits or solids such as black powder, millscale, or other solid elements from the inside of the pipe in order to enhance its cleanliness for in-line inspection, and improve its efficiency. The chemical cleaning products are added to the pipeline via the launching trap, and for this purpose it is necessary to make additional connections. The injection is made using a high-pressure pump, and the chemicals are then pigged through the line using the flow of the pipeline gas. For each section, we decided to run a minimum of five cleaning runs, being prepared to modify each run in line with the results of the previous one.

A high-pressure separator was installed in the collection area, and all the flow was diverted through the separator in order to separate solids from fluids. As the deposits were gathered, they were discharged to a storage tank (frac-tank), while the gas continued its normal flow, allowing operations to take place with a minimum of interruption.

Scope of the chemical–mechanical cleaning project

This cleaning project was carried out in two separate stages: the first consisted of the cleaning of the Conesa–Rio Colorado section, and the second involved the Rio Colorado–Cerri section. The company in charge of the cleaning service was Brenntag, and the operation was estimated to take two days for each section.

The mechanical-chemical procedure consisted of the injection of chemical products to remove deposits in the 30-in section of the main system (with closed loop). The cleaning project involved 140 km of pipeline in the Conesa–Rio Colorado section, and 80 km in the Rio Colorado–Cerri section. The products used for the cleaning were N-Spec 50 cleaning product, N-Spec 150 cleaner, and anti-foam product.

N-Spec 105 is a highly concentrated liquid blend of biodegradable surfactants and dispersants used to clean the inside of pipelines. It is non-corrosive and does not negatively affect metal surfaces, elastomer, or seals. The material has been designed to suspend oil-wet deposits such as compressor lubricating oil, sand, asphaltene, iron sulphide, and other harmful elements that might obstruct the flow.

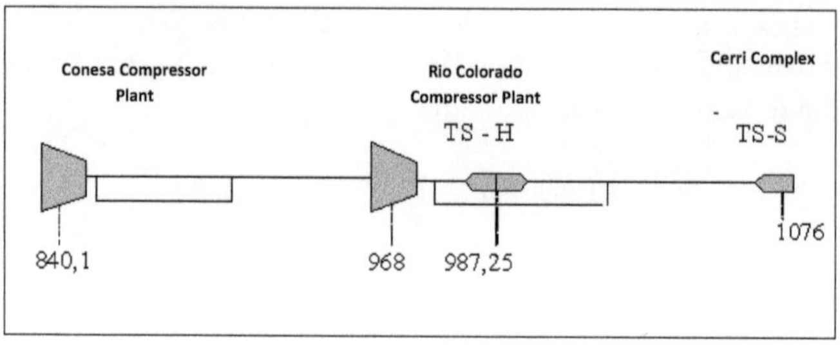

Fig. 1. Project schematic.

The products are injected in the liquid phase – blended with an additional fluid – into the natural gas in each section, and batching pig is run after each injection. The fluid, chemical products, and deposits that are loosened are separated in a three-phase separator installed by the cleaning service company at the discharge of each section. The cleaning process was carried out while the line was in service with a limited number of short and scheduled interruptions for the tool launching and receiving activities. The chemical cleaning runs were as follows:

1. Chemical injection (N-Spec plus solvent)
2. Pig type 1 run
3. Pig type 2 run
4. Pig collection
5. Removal of deposits and liquids using the separator

Five cleaning runs were carried out, each of them containing 3500 li of products along with 25,000 li of solvent. The difference between each run consisted in the type of pig launched as follows:

Run no	*Pig type*
1	30-in polly-pig
2	30-in polly-pig fitted with wire brush
3-5	30-in bi-di pig fitted with multi-discs and guides with wire brush

The cleaning task was deemed fulfilled when the procedure described above resulted in a maximum of 5% of solid sediments for the sample extracted in the liquid/solid separator located at the end of the line. Subject to pipeline conditions, this result was anticipated to be obtained by the fifth run.

Once this phase was concluded, a drying phase started. For this purpose, swabbing and foam multi-disc pigs were used.

Equipment installation

After the pipe sections were surveyed, the location of the cleaning equipment was confirmed, both in the launching and the receipt area. The high-pressure pump, the chemical products, solvent, diaphragm pumps, and a compressor were located in the launching area. In the receipt area, we installed a high-pressure separator, a frac-tank, and a tank truck in which the waste was stored. We also had a compressor and diaphragm pumps.

High-pressure pump

This pump was used for the injection of chemicals and solvents. For its connection we used high-

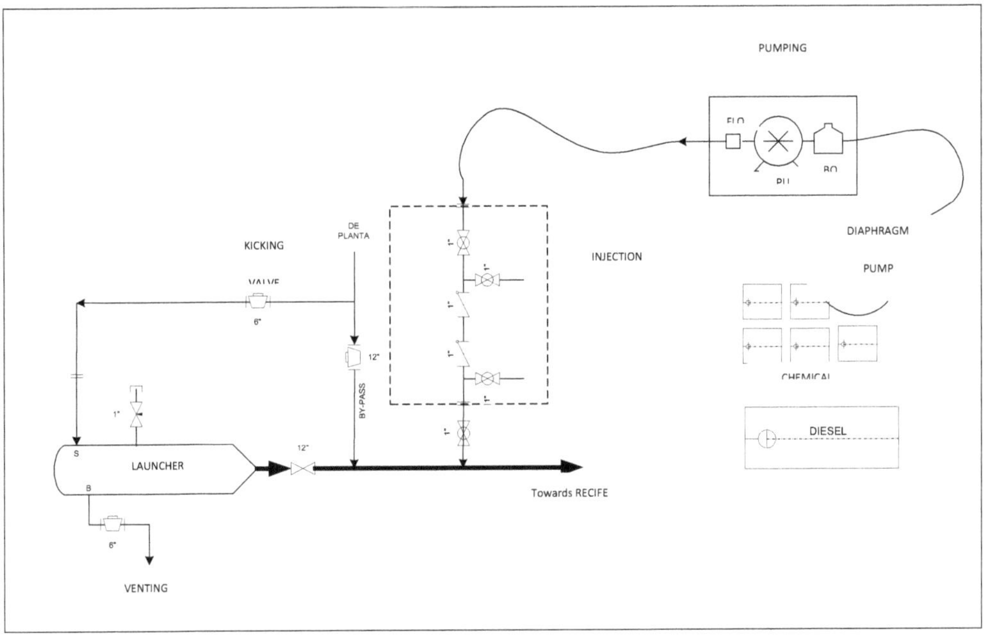

Fig.2. High-pressure pump.

pressure 2-in hoses. The pump inlet was connected to a skid-mounted polyethylene tank that acted as booster; this booster tank was supplied by diaphragm pumps.

At the outlet of the high-pressure pump we connected a flowmeter and a safety manifold by means of a flexible hose. This manifold, consisting of check and block valves, was connected to the injection point.

Chemical product containers

These containers store the injected chemical products and solvents. We used 1200-li capacity containers and a tank truck for the solvent, which was kerosene. At the launching area, N-Spec 50 and 105 containers were installed, with capacity enough to cover five cleaning runs, plus a further one, if required. As regards the solvent, it was located in tanks also with capacity enough to supply five runs, plus one extra if required.

Taking account of the number of runs, the volume of the injected chemical product was defined. As we kept a surplus to deal with any contingency, the unused product would be returned to the operation base. The handling of these products presented no problem, as the substances were non-corrosive, posed no health hazard, and our personnel had enough experience for its safe handling.

Flowmeter

The flowmeter was connected to the high-pressure injection pump. The meter was used as a guide; as we proceeded, we also measured the containers to ensure that the injected volume was as programmed. In case of meter failure, we could use container measurement.

Separator

The separator was isolated from the main line through valves. The connections to the separator were welded. The liquid outlet of the separator had a 3 in diameter, and was connected to the frac-tank. The separator was fitted with two liquid outlets.

The purpose of this 500-bbl tank was to receive the fluid/solid elements gathered by the separator. It was connected directly to the separator outlet using a high-pressure steel pipe. After each run, the service contractor measured all gathered fluids and solids and later reported these details; TGS played an important role in the monitoring of the operation.

The frac-tank was equipped with a meter to measure the stored volume. Once the received volume was determined, we proceeded to transfer all the contents to the storage tank. It is worth mentioning that below the frac-tank a canvas was arranged to protect the soil from any spill.

Tank truck for waste storage

The purpose of this tank was to store the fluid/solid deposits. It was connected directly to the frac-tank by means of 2-in flexible hoses and a diaphragm pump. As explained above, after each run the fluid was transferred to the tank truck, where it was stored. This tank level was permanently monitored. Once filled it was replaced with an empty one. The storage service was rendered by the company in charge of handling the administration and disposal of waste generated by this project.

Analysis of the solvent to be used

The cleaning procedure for the removal of deposits in the pipeline consisted of the injection of chemical products together with a solvent in liquid phase in the natural gas flow in the pipeline.

The supplier suggested the use of water as solvent. If water was to be used, the dewpoint of the gas at the discharge of the separator would be above the water content values in pipeline, and a drying process would be required. For that reason, we evaluated the use of other fluids as solvents: methanol, mono-ethylene-glycol, kerosene, stabilized gasoline, and butane.

For the determination of the most suitable fluid we considered the Cerri Complex's gas processing (cryogenic and absorption) trains. It was vital that liquid extraction activities continued throughout the cleaning process. Simulations were carried out in the El Estudio Conesa–Rio Colorado section, with the pipeline loop closed, and with a gas flow of 11 MM m^3/d. This low flow was attributable to the fact that during the cleaning process, the Canadon Alfa field was out of service due to scheduled maintenance activities.

The results obtained from the simulation of each of the fluids in our simulation programme were as follows.

1. Methanol

Inflow: 25,000 li in 2 hrs, equivalent to 9926 kg/hr.

> In the liquid phase at Rio Colorado 8659 li/hr would be separated, containing 6197 kg/hr of methanol; that is to say, 38% of the volume of the injected fluid would vaporize into the gas phase and continue as the gas to Cerri.
>
> With this fluid, the residual gas hydrocarbon dewpoint at Rio Colorado would be 22.2°C at 5500 kPa. The volume of the methanol content in the gas arriving at the Cerri

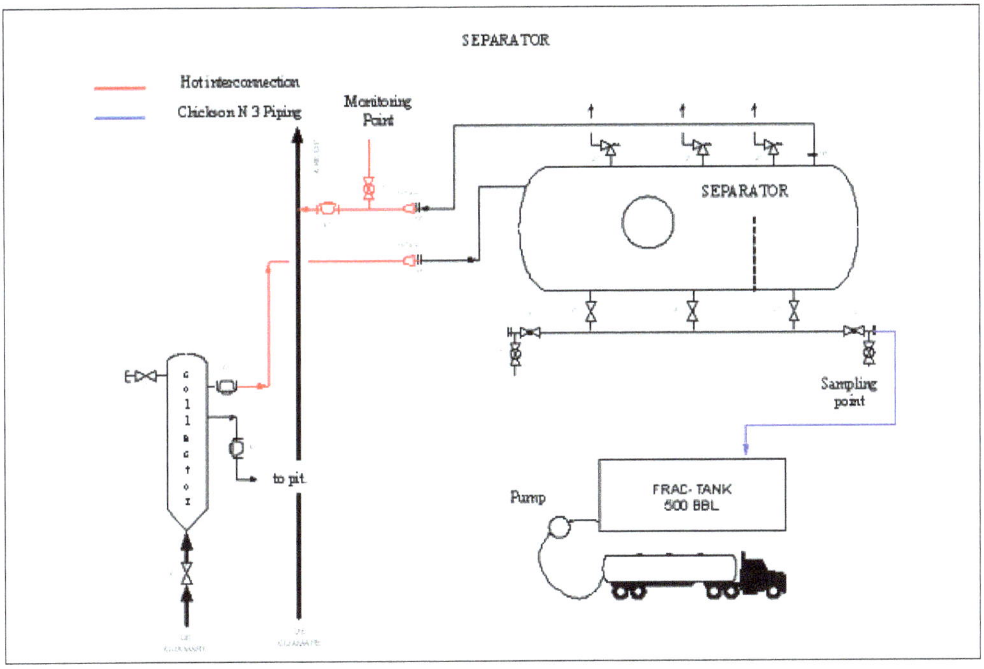

Fig.3. The frac-tank for waste collection.

Complex would be around 2794 kg/hr, equivalent to 3432 mgr/ m^3, which would be harmful for the molecular sieve in the cryogenic processing plant.

2. Mono-ethylene- glycol (MEG)

Inflow: 25,000 li in 2 hrs, equivalent to 13,554 kg/hr.

In the liquid phase at Rio Colorado 12,044 li/hr would be separated, with a content of 13,546 kg/hr of MEG.

This would result in a residual gas hydrocarbon dewpoint at Rio Colorado of -26°C at 5500 kPa, and upon arrival at Cerri the residual gas flow would have an MEG content of 4.6 kg/hr.

The approximate cost of the use of MEG is US$47,800.00 (25,000 li at $1.70/kg, and density 1.125 kg/m^3).

3. Light kerosene

Inflow: 25,0000 li in 2 hrs, equivalent to 9,389 kg/hr.

In the liquid phase at Rio Colorado 14,000 li/hr would be separated, with a hydrocarbon content of 10,114 kg/hr, part of which would be gas hydrocarbons which have been absorbed in the liquid phase.

The residual gas dewpoint at Rio Colorado is 30°C at 5,500 kPa, due to the content of the heavy hydrocarbon molecules that are vaporized into the gas phase. The estimated cost of this operation is $ 9,500.00.

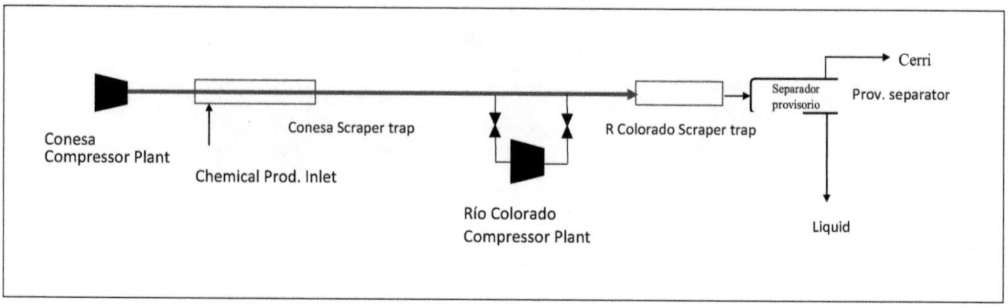

Fig.4. The simulated system.

4. Stabilized gasoline

Inflow: 25,000 li in 2 hrs hours, equivalent to 8,010 kg/hr.

As there would not be a liquid phase at Rio Colorado, sediments and debris would not be separated from the pipeline upon arrival at the separator. Therefore, the option to use gasoline was immediately discounted.

5. Butane

Inflow: 25,000 li in 2 hrs, equivalent to 7,170 kg/hr.

As there would not be a liquid phase at Rio Colorado, deposits on the pipe wall would not be separated. Therefore, the use of butane was immediately discarded.

6. Water

Inflow: 25,000 li in 2 hours.

In the liquid phase at Rio Colorado water is separated with some hydrocarbon content, but water molecules pass into the gas phase and result in a raised dewpoint of 26.1°C. The water content in the system renders it impossible to use this fluid for this purpose.

Choice of solvent

From the technical-economic assessment of the several fluids proposed, kerosene turned out to be the most suitable, although the processing of this in the cryogenic plants was ruled out, due to the potential effect it could have on the molecular sieve. However, there was a possibility of processing the gas at the absorption plant, as kerosene is used in this process; but a freezing test conducted on the cleaning solution determined that the product temperature was too close to the operating temperature of the plant, and it was thus concluded that it was inadvisable to process this gas at the complex.

The results of the simulation with kerosene were PRHC 8°C at 5500 kPa upon arrival at Cerri, so the required dilution operation was simulated at the Cerri Complex so that the product could pass through the Complex while remaining in-line with the quality specifications (PRHC -4°C at 5500 kPa), in accordance with flows scheduled by the gas dispatch department for the period involved in the cleaning operations. Figure 4 shows the result of the operation undertaken during the cleaning period.

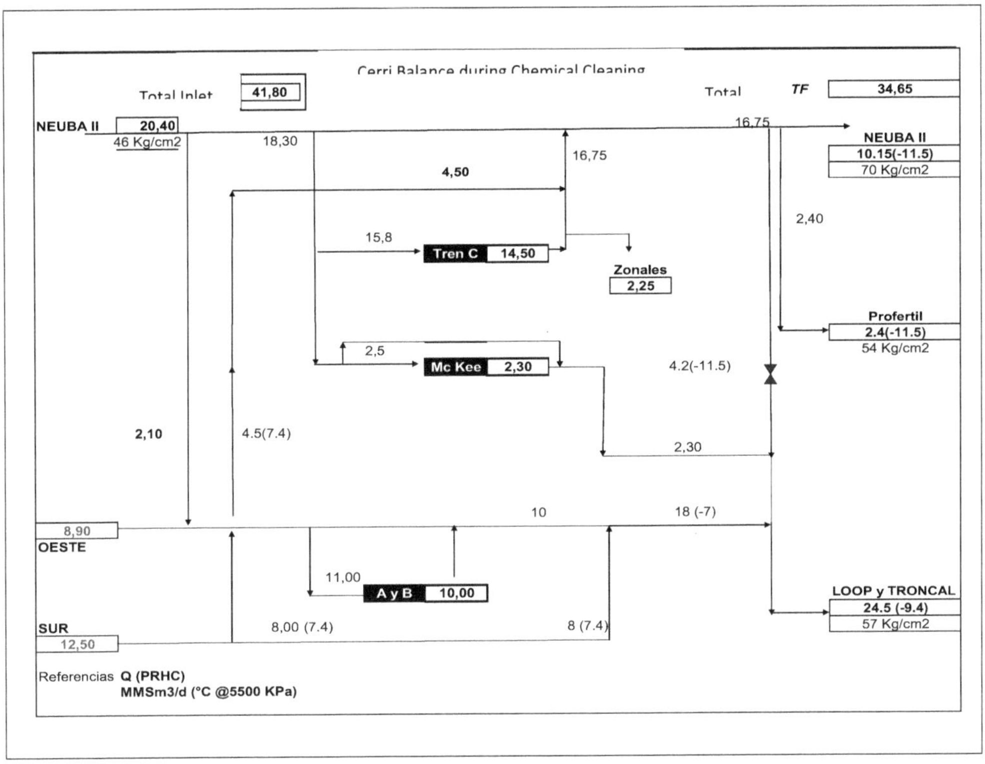

Fig.5. Cerri Complex balance during the cleaning procedures.

Operations required during the chemical cleaning procedures

The cleaning procedure was scheduled to coincide with the maintenance of the Canadon Alfa field, as the shutdown of this delivery point into the Sur pipeline allowed the cleaning to be undertaken.

As far as the speed of the run was concerned, there were no restrictions; the only parameter that affected the runs carried out for the cleaning procedure was the maximum capacity of the separators that received the liquids. The separator was designed for a volume of 14,000,000 m^3/d, with a retention efficiency of 100% for solid particles of 3 microns and higher and a 100% efficiency for liquid particles of 8 microns and higher.

While the runs were performed, the loop of each section remained closed to avoid the liquid being diverted; once the runs were completed, the loops were returned to service.

In the Conesa-Cerri section there were two offtakes (Medanos and Patagones) which had to be supplied by compressed natural gas as the San Martin pipeline gas in this section was out of quality specification.

For the runs performed in the first section (Conesa-Rio Colorado) the Rio Colorado plant was required to be out of service, as the pig trap was located downstream of this plant. It was therefore necessary for the Gral Conesa plant to discharge at its maximum pressure, allowing for a decrease in the flow due to the presence of liquids and pigs, and the shutdown of the Conesa loop.

Date	Injected kerosene (li)	N-SPEC injected (li)	Fluid received (li)	Solids (%)	Solids (li)
3/19/2006	21,000	4,000	796	69,5%	553.22
3/24/2006	21,000	4,000	15,399	22%	3,387.78
3/25/2006	21,000	4,000	15,390	11%	1692.9
3/27/2006	21,000	4,000	20,000	3%	600
Total	84,000	16,000	51,585		
Total injected fluid	100,000	Total received fluid	51,585	Total solids	6,233.9

Table 1. Results for the Conesa–Rio Colorado section.

Date	Injected kerosene (li)	N-SPEC injected (li)	Fluid received (li)	Solids (%)	Solids (li)
April 2					
run 1	21,000	4,000	11,542	28.8%	11,542
run 2	21,000	4,000	15,903	6%	954.18
run 3	21,000	4,000	28,984	2%	579.68
April 3			7,500	2%	150
Total	63,000	12,000			
Total injected fluid	75,000	Total received fluid	63,929	Total solids	5,007.98

Table 2. Results for the Rio Colorado–Cerri section.

Section	Original efficiency	Current efficiency	Benefit %
Conesa - Río Colorado	0.91	0.945	3.85
Río Colorado - Cerri	0.933	0.955	2.36

Table 3. Increases in efficiency.

Conclusions from the chemical cleaning

Samples taken at the separator had the results shown in Tables 1 and 2 for each section.

After the chemical cleaning was completed, and the transportation system was restored and in steady operation with flows arriving at Cerri the same or higher than 17 MM m^3/d, we proceeded examine the system by choosing a specific day, and using the same methodology used in the base model. The measured values for the selected day were entered into the simulation model, including injection and delivery flows along the pipeline, relative density, and suction temperatures in each compressor plant, and these were compared to the suction pressure obtained with Gregg simulation program and the values obtained by the SCADA system. As there was a difference between the measured and simulated pressures at the Rio Colorado compressor plant and the arrival pressure of the San Martin pipeline into the Cerri Complex, the efficiency was tuned for each section.

The results showed a clear efficiency increase in both sections, and are shown in Table 3. This efficiency increase can be translated into a 100,000 m^3/d increase in capacity along the route between Chubut and Cerri.

Chemical gel cleaning prior to MFL ILI of a natural gas transmission pipeline: a case study

by Brett Wakeham, Jeff Fleming, and Michael Cismaru

TransCanada PipeLines, Calgary, AB, Canada

MAGNETIC-FLUX leakage (MFL) is an accepted and reliable technology for inline inspection (ILI) of carbon steel pipelines. When an inspection tool is run under the parameters specified by the vendor, it is able to provide robust and reliable detection and sizing of metal-loss features.

Each year, TransCanada (the operator) performs multiple MFL ILIs on sweet, dry, natural gas transmission pipelines throughout North America. In the vast majority of cases, inspections are successfully completed on the first run, largely as a result of extensive preparation on the part of both the pipeline operator and the tool vendor. Unfortunately, preparation does not in itself ensure a successful inspection and factors outside the direct control of the pipeline operator and the tool vendor may interfere with what would otherwise be a successful inspection.

This paper examines a unique case where the MFL re-inspection of a NPS 30 natural gas transmission line produced significantly degraded data as a result of debris-induced sensor lift-off. A specialized gel-cleaning programme was required to remove the problematic debris from the pipeline prior to re-running the inspection tool.

Pipeline and inspection overview

The subject pipeline is a 130-km long, NPS 30 pipeline that transports sweet natural gas. The pipeline was previously inspected with an MFL tool in 2005, and was scheduled for re-inspection in 2010.

In 2005, the MFL tool was successfully run in the pipeline following two utility pig runs (standard cleaning protocol for the operator). In this case, a bi-directional disc/brush/magnetic-cleaning tool was run first and was followed by a gauge-plate tool. The cleaning tool removed 1 gallon of liquid and had a moderate coating of powder and thick sludge around the tool body. The gauging tool also removed a single gallon of liquid and it appeared exceptionally clean when it emerged from the trap. The 2005 MFL tool also emerged with a coating of sludge; analysis did not reveal any issue with debris-induced sensor lift-off.

2010 MFL re-inspection

The 2010 MFL re-inspection was scheduled for the first quarter of 2010 following the completion of one cleaning run and a gauge-tool run. The first cleaning tool (bi-directional disc/brush/ magnet) pushed out approximately 90 gallons of liquid and 20 gallons of heavy sludge, with dry, granular debris packed between the brushes and mandrel (Fig.1). Due to the large volume of debris received with the first cleaning tool, the decision was made to perform additional cleaning prior to the MFL run. Four more cleaning tools were run and progressively smaller volumes of debris were removed with each tool (see Table 1). Given that the volumes returned were consistently

Date	Tool type	Avg speed (kph)	Liquid debris volume	Heavy debris volume	Total debris volume
18-Jan-2010	Bi-di disc/ brush	9.8	90	20	110
19-Jan-2010	Bi-di disc/ brush	9	5	2	7
20-Jan-2010	Gauge	9	1	1	2
21-Jan-2010	Ring-brush / cup	9.7	0	0.5	0.5
22-Jan-2010	Bi-di disc/ brush	9.8	0	0.5	0.5
23-Jan-2010	Bi-di disc/ brush	9.6	0	3	3

Table 1. 2010 pre-inspection utility tool runs.

below 5 gals, the decision was made to proceed with the inspection after running five cleaning tools and one gauge tool. When the MFL tool emerged from the pipeline, the magnetizer body was covered in the same thick debris that was observed on the cleaning runs.

ILI data quality assessment

The field operations' report issued by the inspection vendor stated that an average of 30 adjacent sensor heads experienced intermittent, debris-induced, lift-off from the pipe wall between kilometres 5 and 40. Based on the tool's proximity sensors, 13% of the total data collected were impacted by moderate to severe sensor lift-off in the bottom quadrant of the pipe. This is shown in Fig.2, where the dark area represents sensor lift-off along the full length of the run (x-axis) and around the circumference (y-axis, where 12 o'clock is shown at the top).

Sensor lift-off has the effect of compromising the tool's ability to detect and size metal-loss features, although the extent of data degradation is dependent on the distance between the sensors and the pipe wall.

The inspection vendor provided the operator with data which were consistent with a large amount of debris in the pipeline and helped identify the specific areas affected by sensor lift-off. The main indicator of lift-off was the tool's proximity sensors. Plots of the proximity sensor data revealed that the issue was isolated to the bottom of the pipeline in a section beginning shortly after launch (at roughly 5 km) and ending approximately 40 km into the run. The vendor data also showed increased pressure differential (Fig.3) and start/stop behaviour throughout lift-off section (Fig.4), which indicates the presence of debris in front of the tool.

Historical pipeline information

In response to the pipeline debris issue identified by the inspection vendor, a complete review of the pipeline's operational record commenced. This information proved to be a valuable resource when assessing the severity of the debris problem and determining the most effective cleaning method.

Fig.1 (right). First NPS 30 cleaning pig run (2010).

Fig.2 (below). Sensor lift-off (dark) shown by plotting eddy data for full inspection (odometer = x-axis, orientation = y-axis).

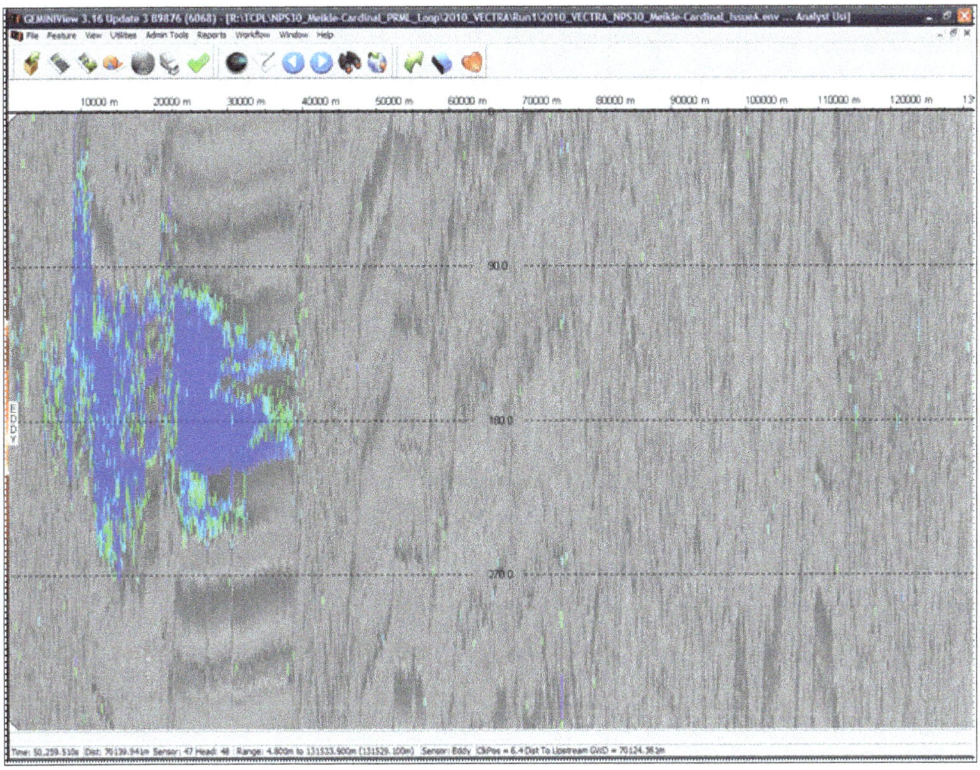

Previous inspections

Although the tools run in 2005 also emerged covered in a similar thick sludge, there was no indication in the data to suggest that they had been negatively impacted by pipeline debris. The only major difference observed during the cleaning runs in 2010 was the large liquid volume pushed by the first tool, and it was unlikely that the liquid alone would noticeably impact MFL data.

The difference observed by the proximity sensors was likely caused by a change in the volume and/or nature of debris in the first portion of the inspection segment. Despite this fact, the debris in the receive trap was relatively consistent between inspections, which may indicate that this debris is unrelated to that which caused the sensor lift-off. Perhaps this should not be surprising, given that the sensor lift-off ended more than 90 km from the receive site.

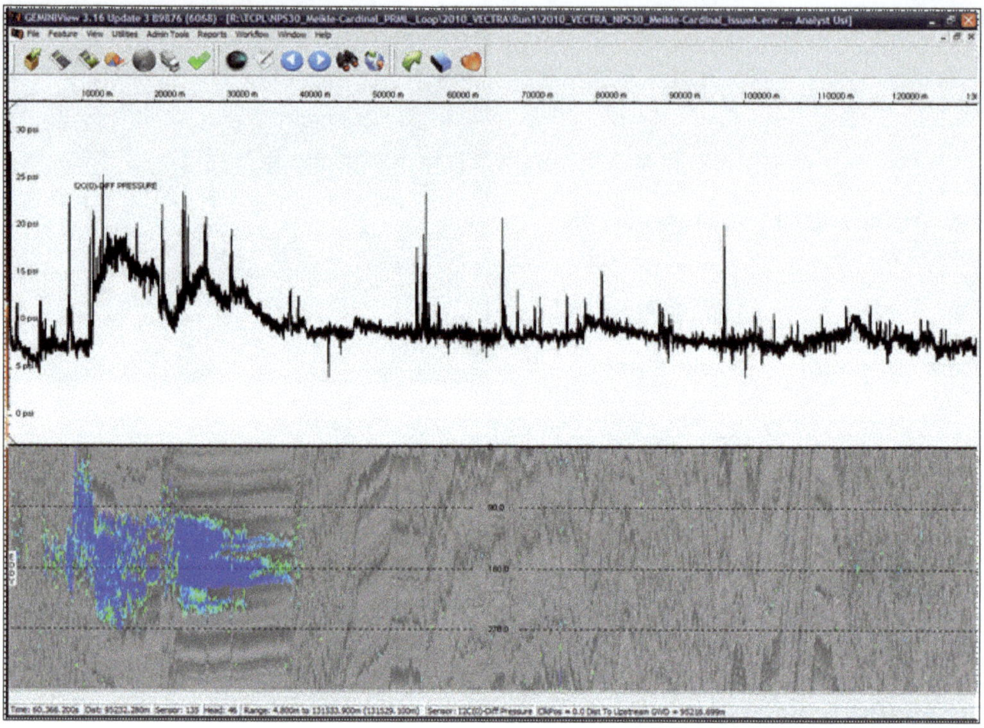

Fig.3. Differential pressure (top panel) increased in area of sensor lift-off (bottom panel).

Experience on upstream segment

In this particular case, operational experience from the upstream segment was especially valuable given that the sensor lift-off occurred only a short distance from the launch site and ended more than 90 km from the receive.

The upstream segment is a 20-in pipeline which has been in service for roughly 40 years. An issue was discovered in the 1980s, where black powder in the compressor stations was driving maintenance on the units. This problem was quickly resolved and consequently no issues for inline inspection arose throughout the 1990s and early 2000s.

In 2009, when this segment was last inspected, a problem was discovered with black powder once again. Every cleaning tool that ran in the line emerged with dry powder packed throughout the tool body and a relatively small amount of loose debris in front (Fig.5). Despite the cleaning effort on this upstream segment, three separate MFL tool runs encountered sensor-lift off of varying degrees, and data from multiple runs needed to be overlapped in order to obtain complete data.

In this case, the sensor lift-off occurred on the downstream end of the segment, where it connects to the 30-in pipeline of interest. This suggested that the debris from upstream may provide a better sample of the debris which caused the sensor lift-off in the 30-in segment.

Although, the debris was much drier than observed in the 30-in line, it is reasonable to infer that the sensor lift-off was, in both cases, caused by dry powder which likely originated in the 20-in segment. It is also likely that the liquid component observed in the 30-in section actually originated at some point mid-run. Laboratory analysis supported this conclusion as both samples contained iron sulphides, although the sample from the 30-in line contained significantly more hydrocarbons.

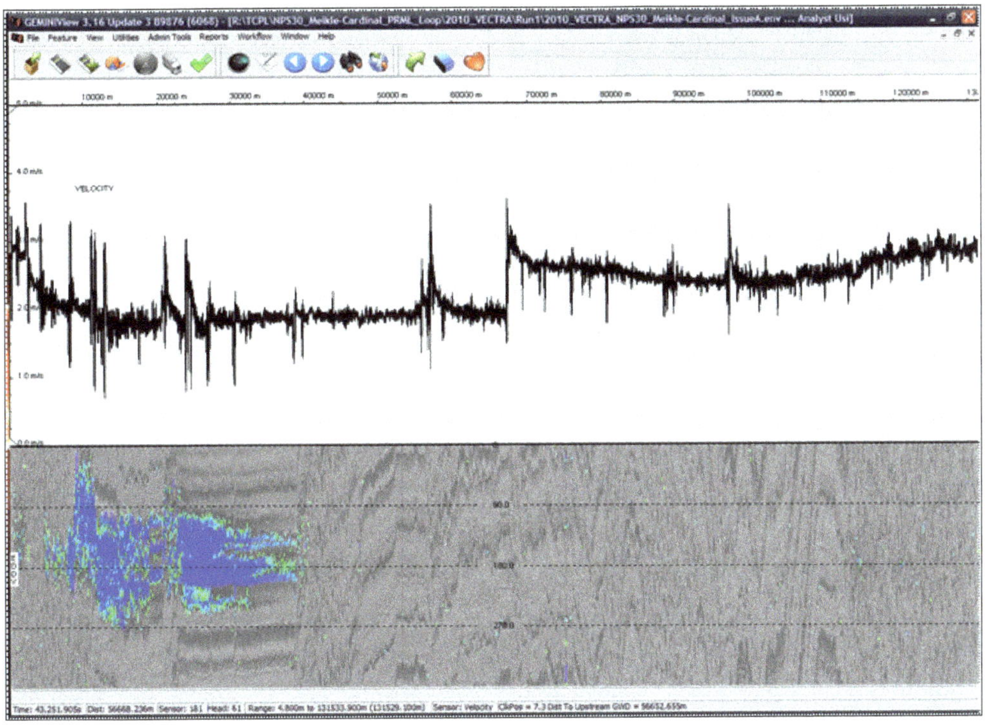

Fig.4. Inconsistent tool velocity (top panel) in area with sensor lift-off (dark in bottom panel).

Preparation for gel cleaning

After analyzing all available information, the operator was confident that the 2010 failed inspection was caused by black powder in the first 40 km of the inspection segment. The experience from the upstream pipeline in 2009 suggested that mechanical cleaning would likely be ineffective on the 30-in segment. In an optimistic scenario, cleaning tools may push the debris past the 40 km point after an unknown number of runs. In this case, the tool may collect data in the previous lift-off areas which would avert a second re-run; however, the debris would still reside in final 90 km, and the latter portion would probably be degraded.

Although mechanical cleaning provides a significant cost advantage in the near-term (likely 50% savings), the specifics of this case suggested that it would, at best, defer chemical cleaning until the next inspection cycle. In a less-optimistic scenario, mechanical cleaning may simply provide justification for the chemical alternative.

In accordance with the operator's procedures, failure to obtain new data in a timely manner would result in pressure restrictions and/or excavation of features which exceed the acceptable risk threshold. The decision was made to proceed with a chemical-cleaning project which would provide a high probability of success for the MFL re-run. Although the costs associated with chemical cleaning were substantially higher than mechanical methods, the operator believed that the investment was justified by the reduced risk of multiple failed inspections.

Project design and equipment

The cleaning programme used a five-pig cleaning train with 130 m^3 (130,000 li) of *Fracsol*, gelled

Fig.5. Cleaning pig received on upstream pipeline segment in 2009.

using the cleaning vendor's proprietary chemistry, and an additional 60 m^3 (60,000 li) of un-gelled *Fracsol* in the front compartment of the train. The un-gelled *Fracsol* was intended to act on the hydrocarbons that were binding solid particles in the debris samples. The belief was that this would provide a similar result as a separate solvent batch without extending the outage or adding significant logistical costs.

Running a liquid batch in a gas pipeline has obvious logistical and operational challenges. The launching operation required significantly more equipment than at the receive end and, in this particular case, it also offered less room to work. Equipment at the launch site included:

four 400-bbl tanks
blending unit
chemical van
high-pressure pumper
vacuum truck
iron truck
fire truck
data/lab van
picker truck

Over 100 rig mats were also required due to the tanker-truck traffic and the large footprint needed to accommodate all of the equipment. The equipment at the receive site was more limited but still included:

six 400-bbl tanks
separator
flare stack
vacuum truck
picker truck
fire truck
water truck

Procedure development and review

Prior to commencing any chemical-cleaning operation, it is prudent to ensure an adequate technical review has been undertaken in order to identify potentially adverse side effects of

Fig.6 (left). Pulling first tool of gel train from receive trap.

Fig.7 (above). Receiving breaker chemical batch.

introducing large volumes of chemical into the pipeline. The operator's ILI group engaged subject-matter experts and individuals representing pipeline integrity, operations' planning, engineering governance, and gas quality to consider chemical compatibility with various materials (such as valve components and internal coating) as well as problems related to residual chemical or debris which could remain in the pipeline or offtakes after the project was completed.

In this case, the proposed chemistry was not particularly harmful to any materials; however, there were obvious concerns about how debris and/or chemical remaining in the pipeline may impact gas quality. Since the gel was hydrocarbon based, the risks of encountering gas-quality issues were mitigated by developing a plan to monitor hydrocarbon dewpoints before, during, and after the project. This allowed for the project team to track how various activities were affecting the dewpoint and respond accordingly. Fortunately, the gas in the pipeline was blended with dry gas from another line downstream of the receive site. This helped to moderate dewpoints taken in the blended stream.

The risk of liquids entering a compressor is always significant when batching liquids in a gas pipeline. This risk was not only present during the run; there was also the potential for gel to remain in a tee or dead leg near a unit's suction and enter the compressor when it is restarted. These risks were mitigated by keeping compression off this line for the duration of the project and flowing gas through dead legs (by-passing the station) prior to restarting any unit.

The cleaning vendor's recommendation was to run the gel train at speeds under 3 ft/s (0.9 m/s, or 3.3 kph) to allow sufficient contact time for debris removal. The batch of breaker chemicals is able to run at much higher speeds because it acts quickly on contact with the gelled product. From the perspective of operations' planning, accommodating the extreme low speeds for the gel run effectively meant shutting-down the pipeline. All receipt and delivery points were isolated from this pipeline (in most cases they were switched to an adjacent line) which allowed the project team to control gas flow in the line directly from an upstream control valve.

Project execution

Loading and launch

Although the launch facility on this pipeline is fairly typical, it is unlikely that the detailed loading procedure would be applicable on another pipeline. Two connection points were used to inject liquid for this specific launch trap: the main injection point was a 2-in drain near the enclosure door, and an equalization line provided a second point to inject in front of the tool (this assisted in purging air from in front of the tool). The following is an ideal and simplified procedure for loading a tool in the train:

- load pig into barrel and ensure that it is in the nominal pipe;
- fill barrel behind the tool using the drain, and displace air through the blow-down in the launch barrel;
- inject additional liquid through an injection point downstream of tool and displace remaining air through a second blow-down, downstream of the tool;
- continue injecting liquid until the barrel pressure is equalized with the pipeline;
- open launch trap isolation valve;
- pump remaining liquid behind the tool (tool will push into the line);
- close launch trap isolation valve;
- depressurize barrel and drain liquid (vacuum truck may be required for gel).

This procedure was repeated for each tool in the cleaning train with the exception of the last tool which was launched with gas from the pipeline.

There were two main deviations from this procedure which occurred as a result of two circumstances that developed during the operation. First, when launching the tools into the line using the pumper and gel, the tools would stop in the bend and allow gel to by-pass as a result of relatively low pumping rates (compared to launching tools with product). This occurred after the first tool was pushed into the pipeline and over 20 m^3 of fluid was able to pass in front of the train. In order to prevent this from re-occurring, the remaining tools were launched from the trap with a small amount of gas. As a matter of interest, the batch pigs were 1.5-D compliant and the bend was 3D. It is possible that by-pass may not have occurred if 3-D compliant tools had been used instead.

The second unexpected issue developed while draining the barrel of gel. Due to the high viscosity of the gel, it took several hours for the gel to drain – even with the assistance of a vacuum truck. The cleaning vendor was able to remedy the problem by reducing the concentration of gelling agent (producing a thinner gel) near the end of each injection cycle.

After modifying the procedure to address these circumstances, the loading and launch of the train went smoothly and without event. The same process was followed to launch the breaker train after the gel was received. The only change to the procedure was that the breaker had only two batch pigs in the train.

Tracking and gel train control

Once the gel train was moving in the pipeline, the major challenge was to monitor the speed and position of the train. A control centre was set up to maintain communication with the trackers and to monitor the pressure differential in the line. As required, the control centre was able to adjust the flow rate in the line by changing the set point on the upstream control valve. Since all

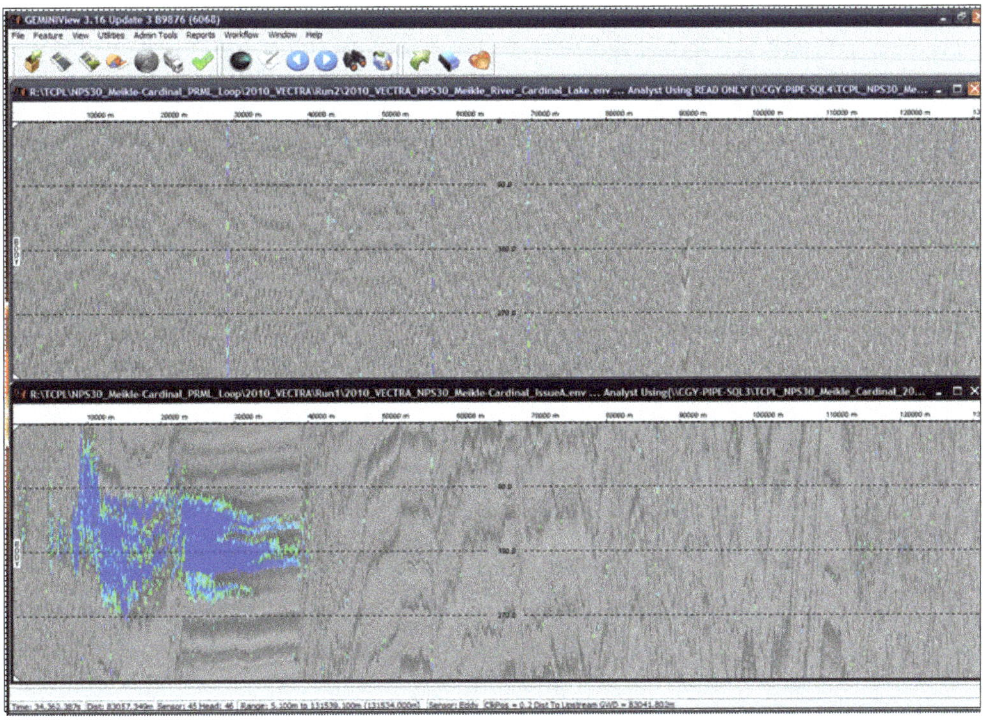

Fig.8. Comparison of proximity sensor data (dark represents lift-off) for re-run (top) and failed run (bottom).

receipts and deliveries were offline, the control valve and downstream pressure were the only two variables influencing the gas speed, although tool speed was still highly variable as a result of the static pressure head which fluctuated as the train travelled up and down hills.

The task of tracking the train was significantly complicated as a result of poor access in long stretches of the right-of-way and the unusual acoustics of five pigs travelling in over 190,000 li of liquid. Although the tools could be heard from more than 20 km away using geophones, it was extremely difficult, even for experienced trackers, to estimate their proximity to the train or to time beat counts on the welds. At some points during the run, the combination of the pressure differential and pipeline elevation data provided a better gauge on tool speed and location than the trackers were able to provide - particularly in areas where tracking sites were spaced further apart.

The gel train travelled at average speeds between 2.5 and 3.5 kph throughout the run. The pressure differential measured between launch and receive consistently reflected what was happening with the tool, and was generally between 200 kPa and 300kPa, although this fluctuated significantly whenever the train's speed was outside the typical range. For example, any time the train would slow or stop (confirmed by trackers), the pressure differential grew quickly (in some cases close to 600 kPa) as the obstruction caused gas to pack the line upstream of the train and the pressure dropped downstream.

Receiving the gel train

The gel train was stopped 1500 m from the receive trap in order to allow time to regroup trackers and organize the receive crew. When the line was restarted, trackers walked with the front tool while the gas was directed through the separator and back in-line. Since the line was effectively out of service already, the gas was flared once the train was 100 m away from the trap as a precaution to ensure that liquids and/or wet gas were not passed downstream.

More than 52 hours had elapsed from the time the train was launched until first pig entered the receive trap 130 km downstream. The train was stopped again after the second pig entered the trap so that both tools could be retrieved. After the trap-isolation valve was closed, the barrel was depressurized and partially drained into the separator through the kicker line. Once flow from the barrel into the separator stopped, a vacuum truck was attached to the 2-in drain on the bottom of the barrel and the drain valve was opened. Unfortunately, debris had accumulated around the drain and the 2-in valve was completely plugged. Since the barrel had only one drain, the only remaining option to drain the barrel was to open the seal on the enclosure door and allow the liquid to run into the catch tray where it could be collected by the vacuum truck.

As the tools were pulled from the trap, it was apparent that a substantial amount of debris had been removed as nearly a barrel of solids was piled in front of each tool (Fig.6). This is obviously a large volume considering that it only represents the amount of solids contained in a liquid volume roughly equal to half of the receive trap (the gel/liquid which did not drain through the kicker piping). As the remaining tools in the train were removed from the pipeline, there was a visible reduction in the amount of solids contained in the gel.

The receive process went very well without any significant incident. Although it was clear that the train had picked up a lot of debris, it was difficult to make any immediate conclusion about what may remain in the pipeline. When the breaker chemical was received two days later, the improvement relative to the gel run was clearly apparent. Although the tool and trap still had a coating of light oil, there was no sludge, the chemical was still somewhat translucent, and there was virtually no indication of solids in the liquid or on the tools (Fig.7).

Evaluation of success

The cleaning vendor took intermittent samples of the gel during the receive operation which were immediately sent for laboratory analysis. Based on the evaluation of the samples, it was estimated that more than 2000 kg of debris had been removed from the pipeline. It was also noted that the samples taken near the end of the train contained significantly less debris in comparison to those from the front compartments. This suggested that the cleaning was effective and that the vast majority of debris was removed. Based on these results, the decision was made to proceed with the MFL re-run which was scheduled for several days later.

Although the laboratory results were promising, the success or failure of this project relied on obtaining good data from the MFL re-run. After completing the tool run, the inspection vendor completed a comprehensive data-quality assessment which showed a tremendous improvement in data quality in which there was no indication of sensor lift-off or any other debris-related issue. Comparison of the proximity sensor data from the two runs clearly demonstrated that the issue with debris in this pipeline segment had been remedied and the MFL tool run was deemed successful (Fig.8).

Conclusion

The objective of this project was to ensure a successful re-inspection of the NPS 30 pipeline segment in a timely manner. Previous experience indicated that cleaning this pipeline would be a costly and difficult task. Although the cleaning required significant expenditure and resources, it was highly effective by all accounts. Comparison of the degraded MFL data to the data from the MFL re-run showed remarkable improvement, which would not have been possible using cleaning tools alone.

Chemical-assisted pipeline pigging cleaning operations

by Jonathan J Wylde

Clariant Oil Services, Houston, TX, USA

DETAILS ARE GIVEN on the development of a successful cleaning chemical for hydrocarbon transport pipelines. Elaboration on the formulation research of the new product and laboratory testing is summarized, with case histories of applications in Western USA and the Gulf Coast.

Hydrocarbon transportation can result in precipitation of paraffins, asphaltenes, and naphthenates which adsorb to the walls of the pipeline becoming associated with corrosion originated iron sulphides. Pigging operations alone do not always remove all these deposits due to compaction and a strong adherence to the walls of the pipeline. It therefore becomes necessary to add surfactant-based chemicals to assist in the break-up and removal of these deposits.

A literature review has been made regarding the current practice of pipeline cleaning, including the key properties required of cleaning chemicals, namely wettability, solubilization, emulsification, dispersion, detergency, and defoaming.

One case history details how the pipeline operator had previously tried to clean a 12-in diameter, 15-km long, section of pipeline with a pig. The pig was launched and became stuck. Application of the newly developed product was able to free the stuck pig and remove the significant debris that the pig has become lodged against. Details of the pigging programme, coupled with chemical solutions for this programme, are given.

INTERNAL PIPELINE deposits are a common observation. These deposits can restrict flow to the extent where shut downs and offline cleaning programmes become necessary. A plethora of solids can be found in pipelines and can come from a wide variety of sources and formation mechanisms. One method of characterization of the solids uses the medium that the pipeline carries as the classifier. It should be noted, however, that this is just a general rule and is governed by the fact that very few pipelines actually transport 100% of any single phase. For example, practically all oil export pipelines transport associated water between 0.2 and 5.0% by volume: this small amount of associated water can result in deposits such as mineral scales even though the dominant phase is hydrocarbon and would not be associated at all with such deposits.

The general rules, however, are as follows:

- A crude transportation pipeline becomes fouled with organic scales. Crude oil contains asphaltenes, naphthenic acids and paraffinic components, all of which during transportation can precipitate and adhere to pipeline walls [1].
- A gas transportation pipeline can also form organic scale deposits, condensed from gaseous state. Mineral based scales may also form of zinc, lead, arsenic, or mercury. Furthermore, if the gas is even slightly wet and sour conditions are present, sulphide scales will form [2].
- Water transportation pipelines most commonly form corrosion deposits, such as iron carbonate ($FeCO_3$), iron oxide / hydroxide (FeO, Fe_2O_3, $FeOOH$), and iron sulphide

(FeS, FeS2, etc.). A key factor of iron sulphide scales is that they are oil wetting (oleophillic) and when even low concentrations of liquid hydrocarbon are present in the water then a mixture of iron scale and hydrocarbon scale results [3].
- Multi-phase fluid and gas transport pipelines can have a combination of all the previous deposits described above. These deposits can often be the most compositionally complex resulting in complex removal and mitigation solutions.

The most common method of cleaning pipelines is through pigging, which can be performed whilst the pipeline is either on- or offline. Recently, focus has been made on chemically assisted pigging operations, as it has been recognized that both inorganic and organic scales can become compacted on the walls of pipelines. The addition of chemical surfactants assists in breaking up, softening, and transporting these adherent deposits [3].

Chemicals used to clean transportation pipelines

A literature search yielded very few results regarding compositional information of commercially available chemicals used during chemically assisted pigging operations – only references pertaining to very specific deposits such as paraffins could be found [4]. A review of oil-degreasing and solid-removal technology yielded several parameters that can be deemed essential to efficient chemical cleaning during pigging operations [5-7]. The key parameters described below show the different types of surfactant properties required in an ideal cleaning product:

- Wetting: the action of a surfactant to reduce surface tension of a medium. This reduction is achieved by molecular attraction towards a dissimilar surface. For pipeline cleaning, wetting agents help to remove hydrocarbon deposits from oil-wet scale, therefore allowing access to inorganic materials.

- Emulsification: surfactants enable the formation of a stable emulsion of two or more immiscible liquids - similar to micellular solubilization but with larger solubilized particles. During pipeline cleaning it is necessary to emulsify the hydrocarbon and solid particles that have been removed in order to prevent redeposition downstream.

- Solubilizers: surfactants that can affect otherwise-insoluble materials. When a surfactant concentration is high enough, micelle structures can form which incorporate the insoluble materials and bring them into an apparent solution. The best example of this is where it is required to recombine hydrocarbon and water.

- Detergency: the ability of a surfactant to remove particles from a surface. In pipeline cleaning it is a mandatory requirement to release hydrocarbons and other solids from a pipeline wall upon wetting to promote rapid release [8, 9]. Detergency is an essential component to mobilize hydrocarbon phases after wetting to remove them from the pipeline wall.

- Dispersion: surfactants that retain insoluble particles in suspension by preventing aggregation of particles with one another. Ideally, particles are small and this will lead to a more-stable dispersion. Similar to emulsification, this property of surfactants prevents redeposition of solid particles by maintaining them in suspension [10].

When these functionalities are combined to form an ideal pipeline cleaning chemical, the resultant product could become a complex blend of five to seven chemical components. The

Element	KeV	Weight %	Atomic %
Fe	6.403	83.55	58.88
Mn	5.898	0.86	0.61
S	2.307	0.70	0.85
Ca	3.691	0.40	0.39
P	2.013	0.12	0.16
Si	1.740	0.78	1.09
Br	1.480	0.87	0.43
O	0.523	5.04	12.41
C	0.277	7.69	25.19
Total		100	100

Table 1. Quantified elemental composition of the inorganic portion of the pig-trash sample used to evaluate the efficacy of newly developed pipeline cleaning chemical systems.

result, however, is a more purpose-driven product that gives good wetting, solvency, and detergency, and more readily frees solids from the walls of the pipelines. Surface-active components provide emulsification and dispersion characteristics that render insoluble deposits and multi-phase liquids as a single entity enabling more efficient transport and less secondary precipitation. As a final note, it may also be commonplace to add an antifoam chemical into a finished formulation as surfactants tend to display high foaming potential when agitated. Often, glycol or specialty antifoams are incorporated to bring this under control.

Although relatively well documented, using straightforward organic solvents for pipeline cleaning is less efficient than the previously described specialty blends. Base solvents do not provide an effective means to transport the mixed-composition slurries that would result after the organic components are dissolved, and this means that secondary deposition is very likely. Furthermore, it is common for aggressive organic solvents (such as toluene and xylene) to be incompatible with pig bodies.

Laboratory development and testing

Overview

All testing was performed using a variety of real solid pig-trash samples obtained from pigging operations in West Texas pipelines. The testing specifically involved:

- identification and characterization of samples
- solids' reactivity with specialty pipeline cleaning products vs standard organic solvents
- hydrocarbon solvency
- arsine and H2S gas generation propensity

Of note is that the specialty pipeline cleaning formulations all contained the same highly concentrated base surfactant-cleaning components. The difference between the products is in some of the more minor components in terms of odour control and chelating agents. The base organic solvents used as benchmarks for the specialty products included xylene, toluene, methanol, and acetic acid.

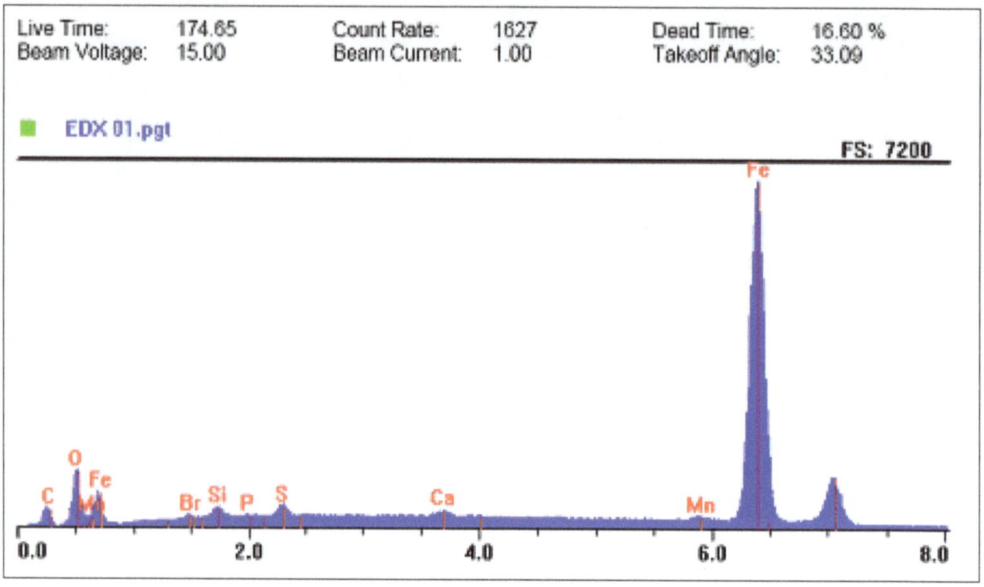

Fig.1. EDX analysis on the inorganic portion of the pig-trash sample used to evaluate the efficacy of newly developed pipeline cleaning chemical systems.

Fig.2. Neat and serial dilutions of specialty formulation 1.

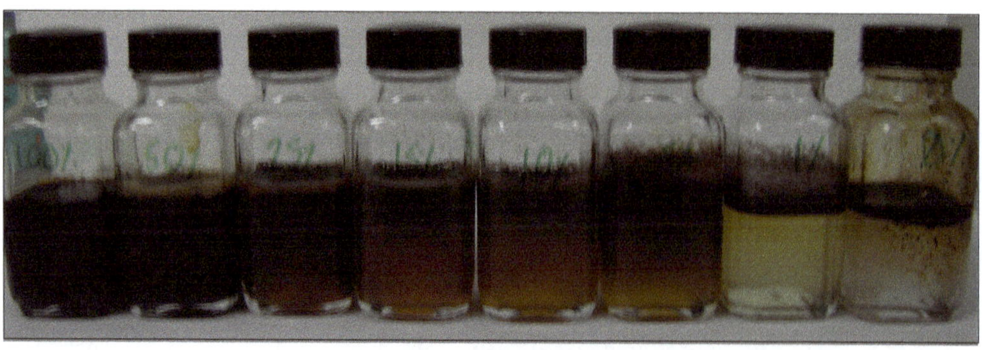

Fig.3. Neat and serial dilutions of specialty formulation 1 tested on crude oil dispersion and detergency.

Sample identification and characterization

A typical sample had a dark brown or black colour with a sulphurous odour. Weight loss on ignition showed that over 50% of the sample of organic and the residual inorganic components were analysed using energy-dispersive x-ray analysis (EDX). The EDX spectrum can be found in Fig.1, with the corresponding quantified composition in Table 1.

It can be seen that iron and sulphur dominate, as well as a very high phosphorous content (often associated with arsenic). Sodium and silicon were also detected, which are indicative of sand, silt or clay minerals, and residual salt. The dominance of iron sulphide can lead to evolution of H2S gas and the sample showed evidence of arsenic presence which can lead to the evolution of arsine gas.

Noted during the identification experiments was, that upon removal of the hydrocarbon component, it was possible to chemically mobilize the residual solids from the pipeline.

Hydrocarbon-solvency tests

Simple tests were performed to determine the ability of specialty formulation 1 to render organic components soluble and transportable. The same behaviour was exhibited by all the specialty formulations as they all had the same surfactant components with the same dissolution, emulsification, and dispersion properties.

Figure 2 shows the dilution of specialty formulation 1 in water to activities of 50, 25, 15, 10, 5, and 1%. To test efficacy, 10 parts of the dilution was added to 1 part crude oil, representing a worst-case test for the oil and grease expected to be encountered in an offline pipeline. Figure 3 shows the results of this test: dispersion and detergency were the key parameters observed. It can be seen from Fig.3 that the 15 and 10% concentration tests resulted in a single phase, and the crude oil was removed from the surface of the test vessel.

This test determined that a single wash of a 10% concentration of the various specialty formulations was appropriate for an applied concentration in the field.

Pipeline-cleaning efficacy tests

A range of solvents were ranked using the rolled-ball solvency test [12] and were tested alongside the specialty formulations. This test determined the efficacy each chemical displayed with respect to dissolution and dispersion of the pig-trash solid samples.

Pea-sized balls of pig trash were accurately weighed and placed in glass test jars. Equal volumes of the test chemicals were added and visual observations made over 12 hrs. A post-test analysis of the appearance was performed and then the residual solvent removed and the samples reweighed to determine solubility. The chemicals tested were as follows:

xylene
toluene
methanol
glacial acetic acid 1%
glacial acetic acid 25%
specialty formulation 1 – water soluble / oil miscible
specialty formulation 2 – water soluble / oil miscible with chelant

specialty formulation 3 - oil soluble / water miscible with odour control
specialty formulation 4 - oil soluble / water miscible with odour control and chelant

Photographs of the tests taken after 1 hr and 12 hrs contact time were taken and are shown in Figs 4 and 5, respectively. Figure 6 shows a photograph of the residual left over at the end of the test after the liquid component was removed.

The organic content of the pig trash was removed using a 50% dilution of specialty formulations 2 and 3. The ball of pig trash was broken down into a transportable slurry composed of granular particles. Weight loss indicated that all the specialty products had similar dissolution properties, comparable to methanol. Interestingly, toluene and xylene displayed no dissolution efficacy whatsoever.

Arsine and hydrogen sulphide gas generation

The unique challenge for the testing protocol required an evaluation of the arsine (AsH3) gas and hydrogen sulphide (H2S) gas evolved. The evolution of these toxic gases during pipeline cleaning has been documented in the literature [11].

It is possible for pipeline cleaning chemicals to evolve these gases, particularly when the pH is low, and this poses a health hazard. Thus, any chemical treatment needs to address this issue while still maintaining high efficiency at removing deposits within the pipeline to assist the pigging operation.

Specialty formulation 3 was used in this test as it was the highest performance product in previous tests, and it was benchmarked against a 1% and 25% active acetic acid solution. The pig trash was tested with a 2-hr contact time and the evolved gas tested for arsine and H2S, while the residual liquid left in the test vessels was tested for aqueous arsenic. The results of this test are shown in Table 2.

As expected, it can be seen that as the pH of the solutions decreased, the more arsine and H2S gases were generated and more residual arsenic was left in the test fluids. The gases evolved – using both concentrations of acetic acid – totally saturated the gas tubes and the actual gas concentrations were likely to be much higher than the minimum values stated. High phosphorous contents detected via EDX in the pig-trash samples are indicative of a high arsenic concentration. This also supports the field observations of high arsine gas generation when the slightly acidic commercially available pipeline cleaning chemical was used.

The most significant observation was that no significant arsine or H2S gas was generated when using the specialty formulation 3 at a 50% dilution in water. No soluble arsenic was detected either when the specialty formulation 3 was used, indicating that dispersion, not dissolution, was occurring in the tests.

Case histories

Case history 1

Specialty formulation 1 was deployed to clean a natural gas transport pipeline in Texas, in partnership with the integrity service division of a local pipeline pigging company. The 12-in diameter, 15-km long, section of this East Texas pipeline had previously been cleaned with a series

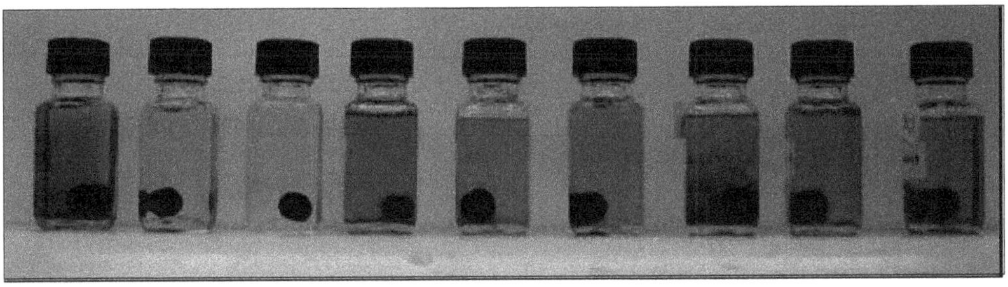

Fig.4. Solvency tests during chemical development after 1 hr contact time with test fluids. From left to right: methanol, toluene, xylene, specialty formulation 2, specialty formulation 2 - 50%, specialty formulation 3, specialty formulation 3 - 50%, specialty formulation 4, specialty formulation 4 - 50%.

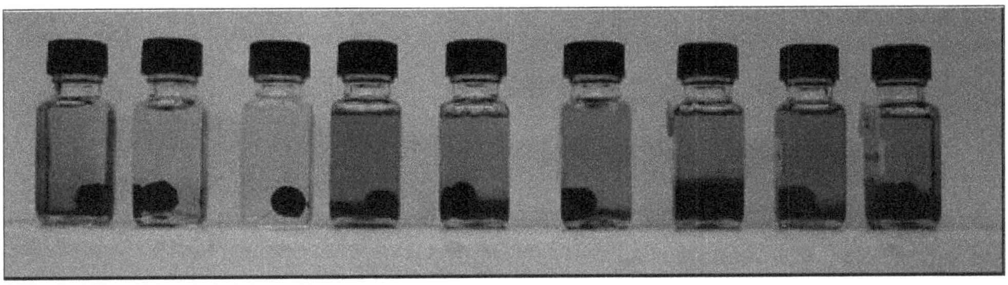

Fig.5. Solvency tests during chemical development after 12 hrs contact time with test fluids. From left to right, as in Fig.4.

Test fluid	pH	Soluble arsenic (ppb)	AsH_3 (ppm)	H_2S (ppm)
Acetic acid 1%	2.93	75	>2.0	>2000
Acetic acid 25%	2.24	100	>2.0	>2000
Specialty formulation 3 50%	7.20	0	0.1	0

Table 2. Results of tests determining the evolution of AsH3 and H2S gas during fluid contact with pipeline scale and residual aqueous arsenic in the test fluids.

of brush and seal pigs. One of the pigs became lodged in the pipeline, resulting in minimal fluid flow. A decision was made to use a chemically assisted treatment in an attempt to dislodge the stuck pig.

A total of 168 gals (4 bbl) of specialty formulation 1 was pumped neat, followed by 1,680 gals (40 bbl) of clean water. The product was pushed with a pig towards the lodged pig. The lodged pig was moved to the south then the flow was reversed and both pigs arrived at the northern junction and were removed from the pipeline. The water from the line contained large amounts of iron and hydrocarbons. When the two pigs arrived at the trap, a large amount of solids was recovered from the pipeline (Fig.7) and a small sample was obtained for analysis.

The second stage of the treatment was a 6% concentration treatment consisting of 250 gals (6 bbl) of specialty formulation 1 pumped in neat followed by 5,040 gals (120 bbl) of clean water into the

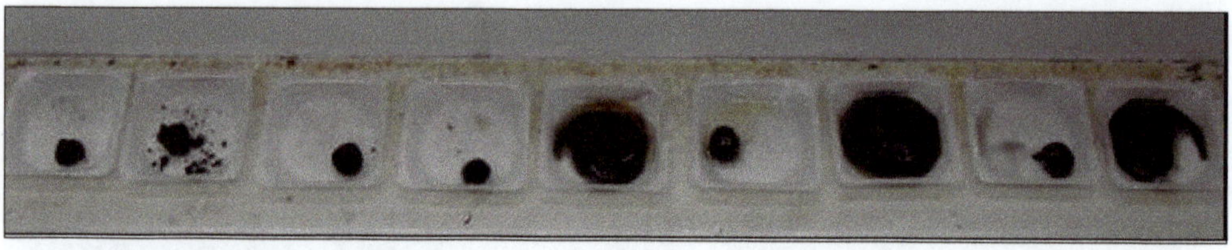

Fig.6. Solvency tests during chemical development after removal from the test fluids. From left to right, as in Fig.4.

Fig.7. Photographs of pig trash and pigs after removal at the southern end of the pipeline described in case history 1.

Element	KeV	Weight %	Atomic %
		A	
S	2.307	14.88	22.79
Ca	3.691	1.21	1.48
Mn	5.898	1.13	1.01
Fe	6.403	80.75	71.03
Cl	2.622	0.78	1.08
Na	1.041	1.03	2.20
Si	1.740	0.24	0.42
Total		100	100
		B	
Na	1.041	1.95	3.47
S	2.307	44.29	56.50
Ca	3.691	0.96	0.98
Fe	6.403	52.27	38.29
Si	1.740	0.53	0.77
Total		100	100

Table 3. Quantified elemental composition of the EDX analysis from case history 1: A = first stage sample, B = second stage sample. Note: C and O were not included in this quantification.

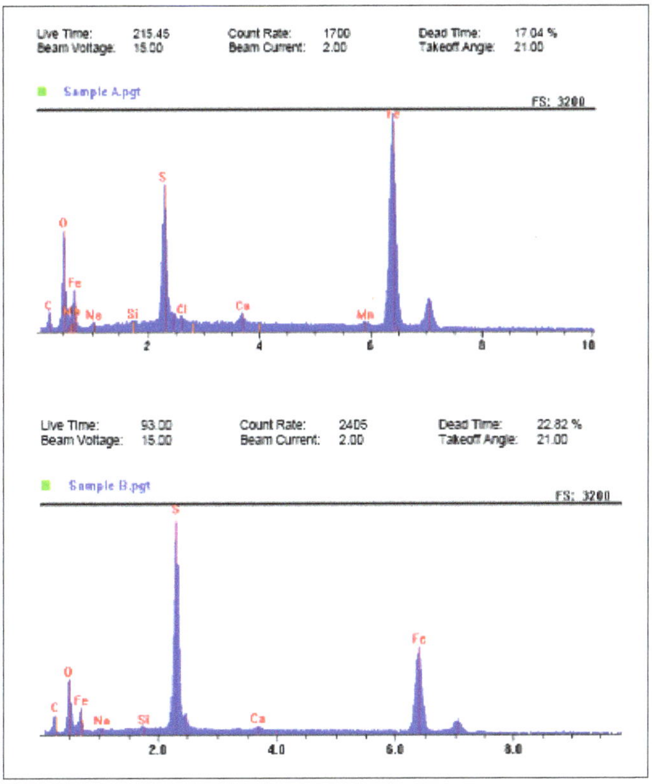

Fig.8. EDX spectra of the two pig-trash samples from case history 1: A = first stage sample, B = second stage sample.

southern end of the pipeline. A pig pushed the product the entire 15 km length of the line to northern trap. The water from the line contained large amounts of dispersed solids and hydrocarbons. This was followed by the arrival of the pig bringing even more solids. A further sample was obtained for a deposit analysis.

The pig-trash samples were analysed via EDX, and summaries are plotted in Fig.8 and the quantified compositions in Table 3. The analyses showed a dominance of iron sulphide with an associated 25 to 35% organic material.

This process yielded the following conclusions:

- Large volumes of soluble hydrocarbons were dissolved and removed.
- Removal of the hydrocarbons resulted in solids mobilization. Iron sulphide scale is very oil wet and can often be combined with 25wt% or greater organic material, therefore successfully removing the oil, grease, and wax will help to mobilize the iron scale [13].

Case history 2

Three parallel gas pipelines in South Louisiana required an oil-soluble product with odour control to chemically assist a pigging campaign. The pipelines were comprised of a 24-in diameter line and two 30-in diameter lines, all of which were 102 km long. A cleaning programme was required prior to an intelligent pigging run as the lines had been in service for 32 years and not undergone any offline pigging. Clearly, cleanliness and cleaning efficacy were a high priority.

Aromatic solvent was used to dilute specialty formulation 3 to 10% activity and this mixture was

	Weight %
Magnetite (Fe_3O_4)	1 - 10
Amorphous	> 50

Table 4. XRD analysis results on the inorganic component of pig trash in case history 2.

Element	KeV	Weight %	Atomic %
C	0.277	0.00	0.00
O	0.523	15.46	37.08
Na	1.041	1.03	1.72
Al	1.487	0.38	0.54
Si	1.740	2.42	3.31
S	2.307	3.61	4.32
Ca	3.691	1.09	1.04
Mn	5.898	0.43	0.30
Fe	6.403	74.92	51.50
Ba	4.465	0.66	0.19
Total		100	100

Table 5. Tabulated EDX results showing quantified elemental composition for the pig trash recovered in case history 2.

	Arsenic (mg/l)	Mercury (mg/l)
Pig trash from case history 2	36.3	11.4

Table 6. ICP analysis on the pig-trash sample from case history 2.

pumped into the pipelines and pushed with a series of brush pigs at a planned 17.6 kph (5 m/sec approx.). For each pipeline 500 gals (11.9 bbl) of mixture was used.

A significant amount of unexpected oil, grease, and solids was removed from the system. A sample of the pig trash was analysed using weight-loss, EDX, and x-ray diffraction (XRD). Figure 9 shows a photograph of the pig trash as it appeared in the trap. The thermal weight loss showed an organic content of 55.4% and this appeared to be heavy-end hydrocarbons such as paraffins and asphaltenes. The XRD analysis can be seen in Table 4 and this shows the inorganic portion to be poorly crystalline. The presence of magnetite (Fe3O4) suggests corrosion was occurring. The EDX analysis has been summarized in Fig.10 and Table 5, and this shows that the inorganic portion was largely composed of iron and oxygen. As well as magnetite (identified by XRD), there could also be other iron oxides (FeO, Fe2O3) and iron oxy-hydroxide (FeOOH). Other detected minor elements included silicon (siliceous material in the form of sand, silt, or clay), sulphur (suggesting iron sulphide minerals), and manganese (supports a corrosion origin for the solids).

Both arsenic and mercury were detected in an acid digestion of the sample followed by inductively coupled plasma mass spectrometry (ICP-MS). This has been summarized in Table 6 and showed the pig trash had the potential to generate arsine gas. This however did not occur due to the use of specialty formulation 3 to assist with cleaning instead of previously more acidic products.

The overall cleaning operation of the pipelines ensured success of the intelligent pig run and maximized value to the overall operation.

Fig.9. Photograph of the pig-trash sample from case history 2.

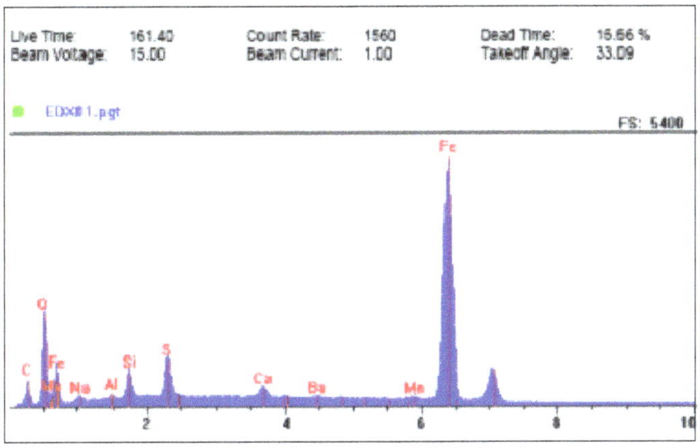

Fig.10 . EDX spectrum of the pig-trash sample after ashing.

Case history 3

This final case history concerns 10-in diameter US West Coat offshore in-field pipeline. The carbon steel pipeline is 9,330 ft in length and was required to be brought back into services after being mothballed for several years. There was a legislative requirement to determine the pipeline's integrity and therefore its ability to transport multi-phase production of 8,000 bbl/d of fluid (60% water cut and 14° API oil).

Existing deposits in the pipeline had already been determined through intelligent pigging prior to mothballing, and thus the cleaning campaign needed to be aggressive; hence, a chemically assisted pigging strategy was devised. The cleaning campaign was applied in three stages:

- Preflush using 300 gals (14.3 bbl) of specialty formulation 1 injected neat, followed by 5,400 gals (128.6 bbl) of treated seawater.
- Cleaning run 1 using 3,000 gals (71.4 bbl) of aromatic solvent, followed by 1,000 gals (23.8 bbl) of specialty formulation 1 injected neat, followed by 9,000 gals (214.3 bbl) of treated seawater.
- Cleaning run 2 was the most aggressive stage and used 1,000 gals (23.8 bbl) of aromatic solvent followed by 2,500 gals (59.5 bbl) of neat specialty formulation 1, followed by 22,500 gals (535.7 bbl) of treated seawater.

The final stage was never planned to be as aggressive as it was. This was optimized in response to observations during the campaign. Massive deposits were removed during the pre-flush, and

Fig.11. Photographs of the brush pig after removal during run 2 in case history 3.

during the first cleaning run the entire 30-ft trap was filled with trash. A further 20 ft of material had to be removed before the pig could be retrieved.

Following the final cleaning stage, smaller volumes of trash were recovered. Had chemical cleaning not been performed before running the intelligent pig, the information gathered would have not given the information necessary to satisfy the legislative requirements. Photographs of a typical pig after removal from the pipeline can be seen in Fig.11; a photo of the intelligent pig after it had completed its run is shown in Fig.12.

Conclusions and lessons learned

The experimental conclusions are as follows:

- Specialty engineered chemical pipeline-cleaning chemicals blended from surfactants in a synergistic way to address specific cleaning mechanisms display higher efficacy than commodity based solvent systems.
- The best pipeline cleaning chemicals address the following five key parameters: wetting, solubilization, emulsification, dispersion, and detergency.
- Laboratory evaluation of actual pig-trash samples allow for a more tailored solution and therefore more effective chemical cleaning product development.

The lessons learned from the case histories are:

- The specialty pipeline cleaning chemicals showed a high efficacy of treatment.
- Solids' removal was more efficient than previous treatments that did not use chemical cleaning chemicals to assist pigging.
- Arsine and hydrogen sulphide gas generation can be controlled using specialty cleaning formulations.

Fig. 12. Removal of intelligent pig after it was run – note cleanliness.

- The specialty formulations described here are recommended for use in any offline cleaning application and have particular applicability prior to intelligent pigging campaigns.

References

1. H.A.Craddock, E.Campbell, K.Sowerby, M.Johnson, S.McGregor, and G.McGee, 2007. The application of wax dissolver in the enhancement of export line cleaning. SPE 105049. Int. Symp. on Oilfield Chemistry, Houston, 28 Feb - 2 Mar.
2. H.A.Nasr-El-Din, A.Y.Al-Humaidan, S.K.Mohamed, A.M.Al-Salman, 2001. Iron sulphide formation in water supply wells with gas lift. SPE 65028. Int. Symp. on Oilfield Chemistry, Houston, 13 - 16 Feb.
3. J.L.Cordell and H.Vanzant, 2003. Pipeline pigging handbook. Clarion Technical Publishers.
4. G.Poole, G.Brock, S.Szymczak, and G.Casey, 2008. Successful pipeline clean out - lessons learned from cleaning paraffin blockage from a deepwater pipeline. SPE 115658. SPE ATCE, Denver, 21 - 24 Sept.
5. L.O.S.Buzelin and C.B.de Campos Lima, 2008. Innovative methodology for cleaning pipes - key to environmental protection. SPE Int. Conf. on HS&E, Nice, France, 15 - 17 April.
6. P.H.Javora, G.Baccigalopi, J.Sanford, C.Cordeddu, Q.Qu, G.Poole, and B.Franklin, 2008. Effective high-density wellbore cleaning fluids: brine-based and solids-free. SPE 99158. *SPE Drilling and Completions*, **23**, 1, pp 48-54.
7. S.N.Bordalo and R.C.Oliveira, 2007. Experimental study of oil/water flow with paraffin precipitation in subsea pipelines. SPE 110810. SPE ATCE, Anaheim CA, 11 - 14 Nov.
8. L.Thompson, 1994. The role of oil detachment mechanisms in determining optimum detergency conditions. *J. Colloid Interface Sci.*, **163**, 61.
9. K.R.Lange, 1994. Detergents and cleaners: a handbook for formulators. Hanser, Munich.
10. F.E.Friedli, 2001. Detergency of specialty surfactants. Marcel Dekker, New York.
11. D.O.Trahan, 2008. Arsenic compounds in natural gas pipeline operations. *Pipeline & Gas Journal*, March.
12. Clariant Oil Services, 2008. Procedure QPI 106 (Rev 2). Wax / asphaltene dissolver tests. In-house test procedure.
13. J.J.Wylde and A.W.Duthie, 2008. Root cause failure analysis, removal and mitigation of iron sulfide scale deposition in the BP Bruce produced water reinjection plant. Paper 08350. NACE, New Orleans.

Section 2: Corrosion and defect assessment

Development of a predictive model for pipeline external corrosion rates

by Dr Julia M Race[1], Sarah J Dawson[2], Leanne M Stanley[2], and Dr Shahani Kariyawasam[3]

1 School of Marine Science & Technology, Newcastle University, Newcastle upon Tyne, UK
2 PII Pipeline Solutions Business of GE Oil & Gas, Cramlington, UK
3 TransCanada, Calgary, Canada, and previously with *PII Pipeline Solutions Business of GE Oil & Gas, Calgary, Canada*

IN ORDER TO develop effective integrity-management plans for corroding pipelines, operators need to be able to estimate realistic internal and external corrosion growth rates. Indeed, corrosion growth rate data is an essential input into future integrity assessments, rehabilitation planning, and the determination of safe and cost-effective re-assessment intervals.

The rate of the external corrosion reaction in pipelines is influenced by a number of factors including the water content of the soil, the soluble salts present, the pH of the corrosion environment, and the degree of oxygenation. Therefore the prediction of external rates is complex and there is currently no method for estimating corrosion rates using empirical equations.

This paper describes a scoring model that has been developed to estimate external corrosion growth rates for pipelines where rates cannot be estimated using more-quantified methods, such as from repeat in-line-inspection (ILI) data. The model considers the effect of the different variables that contribute to external corrosion and ranks them according to their effect on the corrosion growth rate to produce a corrosion rate score.

The methodology has been validated by linking the calculated corrosion rate scores to known corrosion rate distributions that have been measured by comparison of the results from multiple ILI runs. The development of the corrosion-rate database and the results of the analysis of the database are reviewed and discussed.

Initial results from the preliminary corrosion rate model are presented in the paper and further planned developments in the model are outlined. The paper also demonstrates how the estimated corrosion rates can be used for the establishment of re-assessment intervals for direct assessment (DA), ILI, and hydrotesting, comparing the benefits of this approach with current industry recommended practice and guidance.

EXTERNAL AND internal corrosion have long been recognized as major threats to the integrity of offshore and onshore pipelines. In the presence of water (from either the product or the external environment) unprotected carbon steel will corrode. Corrosion defects reduce the load-carrying capability of the pipeline and, if they are allowed to continue to grow, may result in leak or rupture failures.

Pipeline operators mitigate against the effects of corrosion by the removal of water and/or the addition of an inhibitor into the product, the application of an external (or internal) coating and the application of a cathodic-protection (CP) system. If any of these protection systems fail then operators need to be able to identify where corrosion is occurring along the pipeline and how fast that corrosion is growing in order that appropriate monitoring and mitigation actions can be taken.

In particular, re-inspection intervals should be set on the basis of the known rate of degradation in the pipeline rather on a prescriptive timescale, and this requires the input of corrosion-rate data. If the corrosion rate selected is too high then this will result in an overly conservative inspection interval, whereas selecting a corrosion rate that is too low could threaten the integrity of the pipeline.

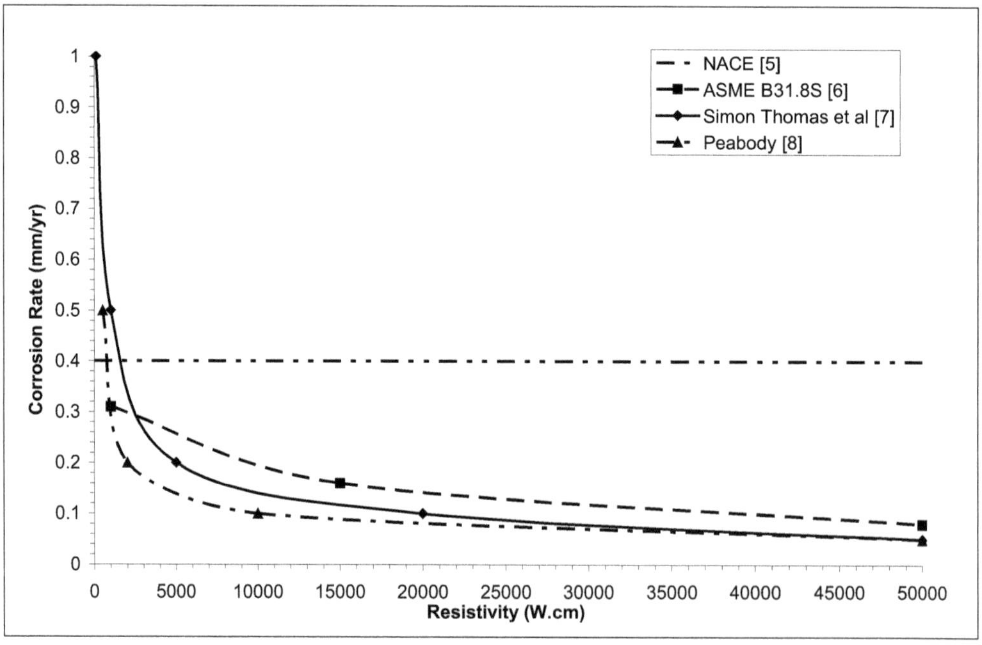

Fig. 1. Comparison of external corrosion rate prediction models.

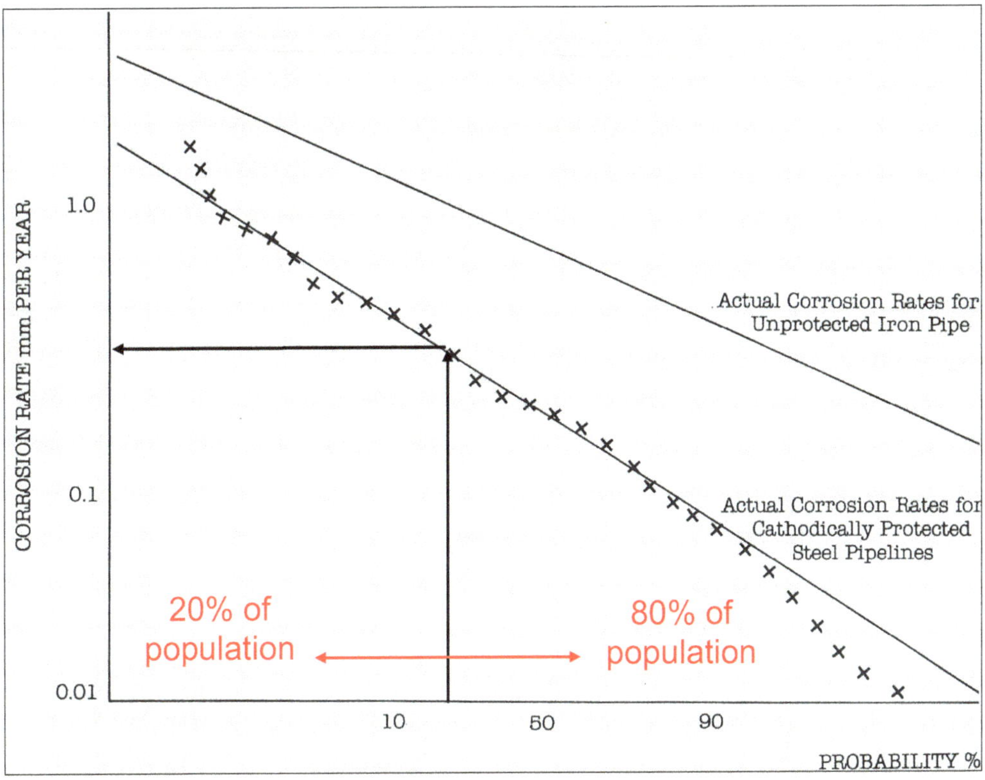

Fig.2. Probability plots of corrosion rates for pipelines in UK soils [9].

This paper focuses on the establishment of appropriate external corrosion rates for pipelines and discusses how external corrosion rates are currently estimated and measured before describing the development of a corrosion scoring model to estimate corrosion growth rates based on the pipeline parameters that most influence external corrosion.

Determination of corrosion growth rates

Pipeline corrosion growth rates can be estimated in a number of ways depending on the information available.

Internal-corrosion rate determination

Internal-corrosion growth can be measured using in-line probes and coupons. However, the results are highly dependent on the placement of the probes and coupons in the pipeline, and can only provide average growth rates. Predictive models such as De Waard and Milliams [1, 2] Cassandra [3], and Norsok [4] can also be used to estimate corrosion growth rates in 'sweet' oil and gas pipelines using operating data. These predictive models are either purely empirical (field experience) or semi-empirical (based on laboratory data, corrosion-rate data, etc.). The equations are assumed and fit values of constants to the experimental data.

External-corrosion rate determination

Unlike internal corrosion, which occurs in a closed system, the rate of the external corrosion reaction is influenced by a number of factors including the water content of the soil, the soluble salts present, the pH of the corrosion environment, and the degree of oxygenation. Therefore the prediction of external rates is complex and there is currently no method for estimating corrosion rates using empirical equations.

In the absence of any other data, the NACE recommended practice is to use a pitting corrosion rate of 0.4 mm/yr [5] to determine re-inspection intervals when using external direct assessment methodologies. This rate represents the upper 80% confidence level from long-term underground corrosion tests of unprotected steel in a variety of soils. ASME B31.8S [6] also contains guidance on estimating corrosion rates based on soil-resistivity measurements and site observations, which indicates that a maximum corrosion rate of 0.31 mm/yr (12 mpy) may be appropriate. Similar correlations between corrosion rate and soil type and resistivity have also been published by Simon-Thomas *et al.* [7] and Peabody[8]. All of these correlations are compared in Fig.1.

The effect of CP protection on the corrosion rate of steel is illustrated in Fig.2, which compares corrosion rates measured on protected and unprotected buried pipe. As would be expected, this data indicates that the CP reduces the corrosion rate; however, the rates measured under CP are comparable with the NACE pitting rate for unprotected pipe.

A comparison of all of this data indicates the range in the maximum corrosion rate that might be expected on buried pipeline steel (0.5 - approx. 1.5 mm/yr). In addition, the current guidance is not consistent, and therefore the selection of an appropriate rate for integrity-management planning needs to be considered carefully. One method for determining more-accurate measurements for corrosion growth rates is to use the data collected on the pipeline from an in-line inspection (ILI) tool.

Corrosion growth rates from one set of ILI data

Running an ILI tool in the pipeline provides the operator with a description of the internal and external corrosion located along the line. The ILI inspection vehicle will also provide depth, length, and width measurements for each corrosion feature. It is therefore possible to determine corrosion rates based upon the maximum defect depth detected in the pipeline and the difference between the corrosion initiation time and the time of the inspection.

In the determination of external corrosion rates, it is important to identify the cause of corrosion and estimate when it may have started by considering other sources of data, for example evidence that corrosion resulted from a known incident of third-party damage, or known incidents of CP underprotection on the pipeline. In the absence of such data it may be assumed that the corrosion has been active for some proportion of the pipeline life (the full-life, or the half-life). For internal corrosion, the corrosion rates can be estimated from the time at which the corrosive product was introduced into the pipeline.

Corrosion growth rates from two sets of ILI data

For pipelines where there have been successive ILI runs individual defects can be compared to identify the rate of corrosion growth. A run-comparison assessment provides a direct quantitative comparison of data from successive ILI inspections. The advantage of this method for corrosion growth determination is that the raw inspection data is compared for each defect individually, allowing any differences due to tool technology and analysis methods to be identified and minimized.

One of the most-common sources of error in determining corrosion growth rates using two sets

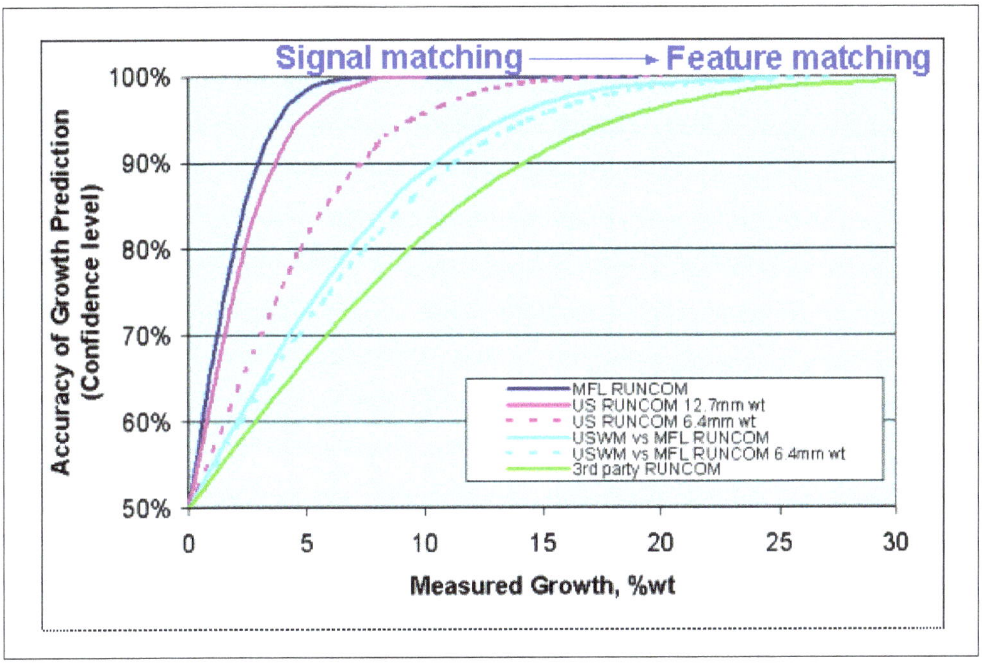

Fig.3. Accuracy of corrosion growth predictions for different ILI tools.

of inspection data is the incorrect matching of corrosion sites. The run-comparison assessment method eliminates errors in matching data sets by comparing raw inspection signals side-by-side, rather than using data that has already been processed by other software, and this ensures 100% accuracy in matching the individual corrosion sites. The use of signal-scaling tools allows technology effects (i.e. magnetic history, vehicle speed, top-to-bottom effect, tool repeatability) to be minimized. In addition, errors introduced through the defect shape, signal sampling, and human error are also minimized through the application of a rigorous and semi-automated process. It has been shown that the combined effect of reducing or eliminating these errors reduces the error on growth rate by a factor of more than three compared with box- or feature-matching approaches, as illustrated in Fig.3.

The accuracy of the corrosion-growth prediction obviously depends on the ILI technology used in each run and can be evaluated by statistical analysis of pull-through test data. Figure 4 shows the statistical distribution of the observed change in defect depth determined by comparing the same set of defects (of varying depth) in successive pull-through test runs conducted with a MFL tool. This data provides the repeatability accuracy of the tool, as the defects are identical in each test run. Further statistical analysis of the pull-through test data has been conducted to determine the accuracy of predicting actual corrosion growth. The following accuracy levels (for the run comparison of two sets of MFL data[1]) were determined:

- There is at least a 95% probability that measured growth greater than or equal to 4%wt at an individual defect is real corrosion growth and not associated with tool tolerances.
- This probability increases to at least 99% for measured growth of 5%wt and above.
- There is at least a 95% probability that a measured average growth greater than 3%wt for

[1] 48 inch GE PII Pipeline Solutions MFL tool.

a group of three or more defects is real corrosion growth and not associated with tool tolerances.

- The tolerance on corrosion growth at an individual defect is ± 3%wt with greater than or equal to 80% confidence.

- For a group of three defects, the tolerance on the average growth reduces to ± 1.7%wt at an 80% confidence level.

For example, for a 10-mm wall-thickness pipeline with a five-year interval between ILI runs the accuracy on corrosion growth prediction from two successive MFL runs (based on GE PII Pipeline Solutions' repeatability data) are as follows:

- At least 95% probability that measured growth rates greater than or equal to 0.08 mm/yr (3.1 mpy) at an individual defect is real corrosion growth.

- This probability increases to at least 99% for measured growth rates of 0.1 mm/yr (3.9 mpy) and above.

- There is at least a 95% probability that a measured average growth rate greater than 0.06 mm/yr (2.4 mpy) for a group of three or more defects is real corrosion growth.

- The tolerance on the corrosion growth rate at an individual defect is ± 0.06 mm/yr (2.4 mpy) with greater than or equal to 80% confidence.

- For a group of three defects the tolerance on the average growth reduces to ± 0.03 mm/yr (1.3 mpy) at an 80% confidence level.

The above statistics can be determined for other tool technologies and are summarized in Table 1.

Previous papers [10, 11, 12, 13] have demonstrated how GE PII Pipeline Solutions uses run-comparison software (RunCom)[2] to determine corrosion-growth rates and how this information is applied to assess the integrity of corroding pipelines with time, including the determination of repair needs and the optimum ILI re-inspection interval. To date, over 32,000 km of corroding pipeline worldwide have been assessed using run-comparison software and a vast database of corrosion-rate information has been built up.

In this paper, this database has been used to investigate the following aspects of external corrosion growth in pipelines against corrosion theory:

- the distribution of external corrosion rates (including the maximum rates detected)

- the relative rates of new corrosion and existing pipeline corrosion rates

- the relative rates of pitting corrosion and general corrosion rates

The distribution of all of the observed external corrosion rates is presented in Fig.5: this distribution has a mean rate of 0.36 mm/yr and a maximum rate of 2.27 mm/yr (Table 2). From

---

[2] Run comparison proprietary software developed and used by GE PII Pipeline Solutions.

Tool technology		Growth*** threshold for 95% probability	80% probability upper bound on growth***
Run 1	Run 2		
MFL*	MFL	5%wt	+2%wt
USWM**	USWM	0.6mm	+0.3mm
USWM	MFL	14%wt	+7%wt
Different vendor MFL tools		19%wt	+9%wt

Table 1. Corrosion growth prediction statistics by tool technology.

** GE PII Pipeline Solutions' magnetic-flux leakage (MFL) ILI tool.*
*** GE PII Pipeline Solutions' ultrasonic wall-measurement (USWM) ILI tool.*
**** Divide by interval between ILI runs.*

Rates (mm/yr)	All corrosion	Existing corrosion	New corrosion	Pitting corrosion	General corrosion
Mean rate	0.36	0.27	0.46	0.39	0.33
Standard deviation	0.23	0.16	0.25	0.23	0.20
Maximum rate	2.27	1.64	2.27	1.28	1.35
Number of readings	3165	1657	1508	358	2213

Table 2. Distribution of corrosion rates.

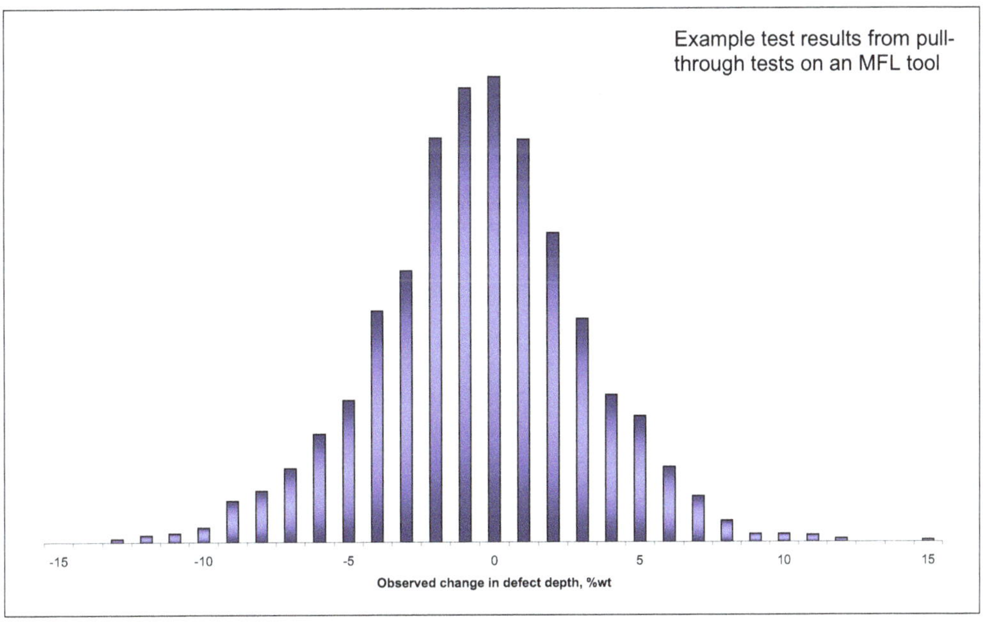

Fig.4. Statistical analysis of ILI pull-test data (assessment of the repeatability error).

the cumulative probability curve of this data (Fig.6), the 80% probability value was determined to be 0.52 mm/yr – i.e. there is an 80% probability of the corrosion rate being less than 0.52 mm/yr. It is highlighted that the run-comparison method for determining corrosion growth rates is

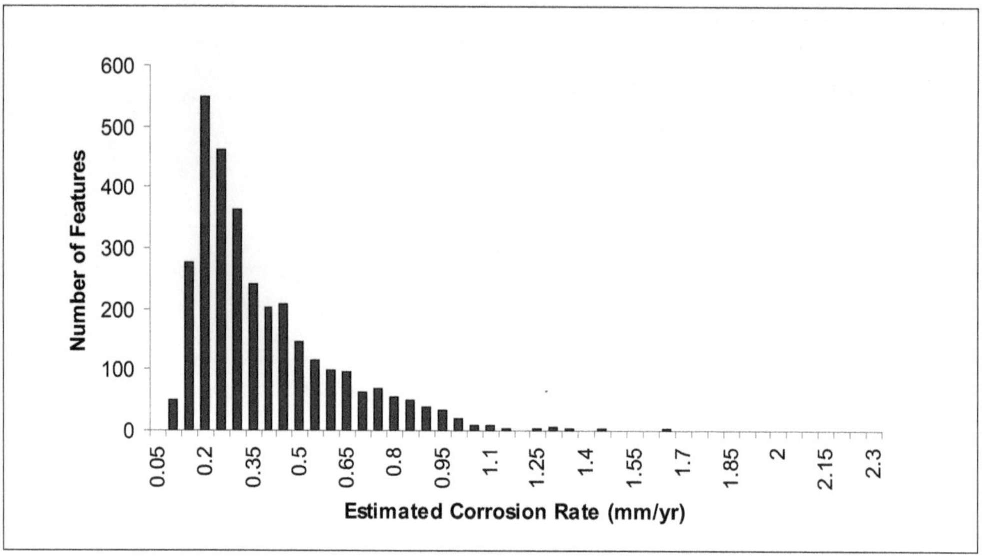

Fig.5. Distribution of all estimated external corrosion rates.

measuring the growth rate of the corrosion under the pipeline CP system and, indeed, this value is comparable with the distribution presented in Fig.2 for steel corrosion under cathodic protection. In addition, the database predicts that there is a 99.9% probability of the corrosion rate being < 1.5 mm/yr, which compares with the maximum rate presented in Fig.2. However, the 80% probability rate determined from this data is higher than the NACE recommended 80% upper bound of 0.4 mm/yr [5], which is for unprotected steel corrosion. Using a corrosion rate of 0.52 mm/yr in the absence of any other data would be a more-conservative estimate.

To investigate whether corrosion rates slow down with time, a comparison has been made between corrosion rates associated with new corrosion features (i.e. features which are only present in the second inspection) and corrosion rates associated with existing corrosion features (i.e. features which were present in the two inspection runs and have grown between runs). Corrosion theory suggests that corrosion rates should slow down with time due to the formation of protective oxide films, and therefore the corrosion rates of new corrosion features should be higher than the corrosion rates for existing corrosion. Figure 7 shows the difference in the corrosion rate distributions for new and existing features and these distributions are described numerically in Table 2: a statistical comparison of this data confirms that the new corrosion is growing at a faster rate than the existing corrosion (i.e. the two samples are different).

The database also allows the comparison to be made between corrosion rates and the depth of corrosion. Based on the assumption that newer corrosion is shallower than existing corrosion, it might be expected that there would be a correlation between the defect depth and corrosion rate (i.e. shallower defects would exhibit higher rates as they are newer features). Figure 8 illustrates that, based on the results from the entire database, there is no apparent correlation between the defect depth and the corrosion rate. However, a negative correlation between defect depth and corrosion rate has been observed on several pipelines in the database, and this relationship is shown in Fig.9. This shows other significant variables that vary among pipelines swamp the effect of depth on the growth rates. Within a pipeline these variables would be the same, and thus the depth versus growth rate relationship is evident.

To determine whether pitting corrosion occurs at higher rates than general corrosion, the rates associated with corrosion pits were compared against rates associated with general corrosion

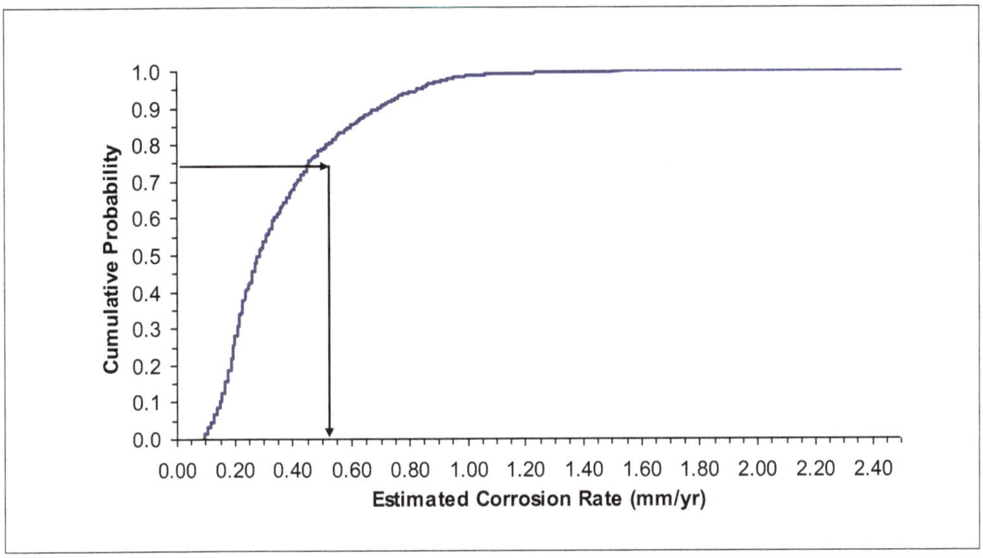

Fig.6. Cumulative probability curve for all estimated corrosion rates.

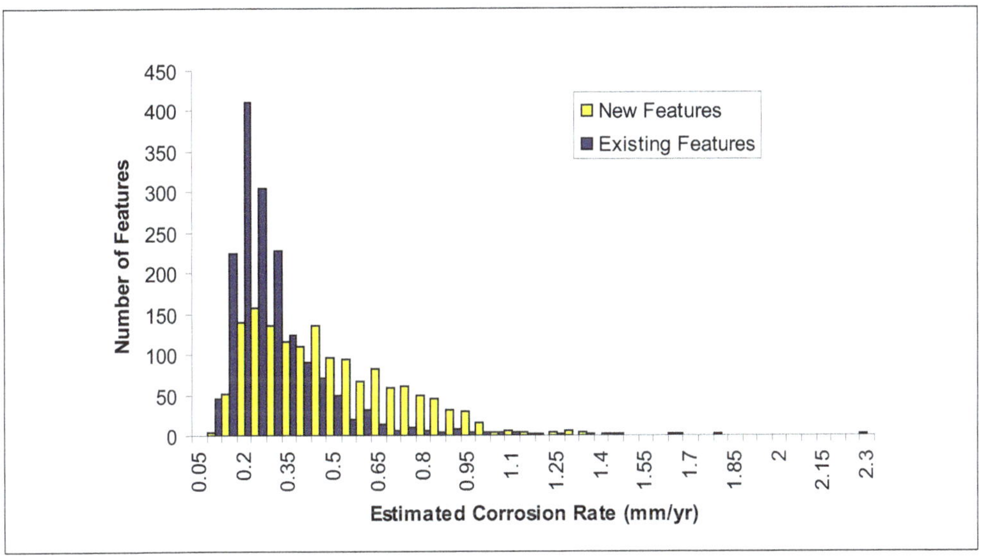

Fig.7. Comparison of corrosion rate distributions for new and existing features.

(Fig.10). The definition of pitting that has been adopted for this study is that corrosion is described as pitting if the length of the corrosion is less than three times the wall thickness. It might be expected that pitting corrosion would occur at higher rates than general corrosion, as the electrolyte in the pit becomes more concentrated (i.e. the pH increases). The result of a statistical analysis of these two distributions indicates that there is a significant difference between the rates measured for pitting corrosion and those measured for general corrosion (i.e. the mean pitting corrosion rate is greater than the mean general corrosion rate).

The above comparisons have been made to test that the observed behaviour of pipeline corrosion is consistent with corrosion theory. The conclusion of this study is that the basic trends are replicated in the database and that the maximum corrosion rates measured using the run-comparison software are comparable with the range predicted from published soil data models (0.5-1.5 mm/yr).

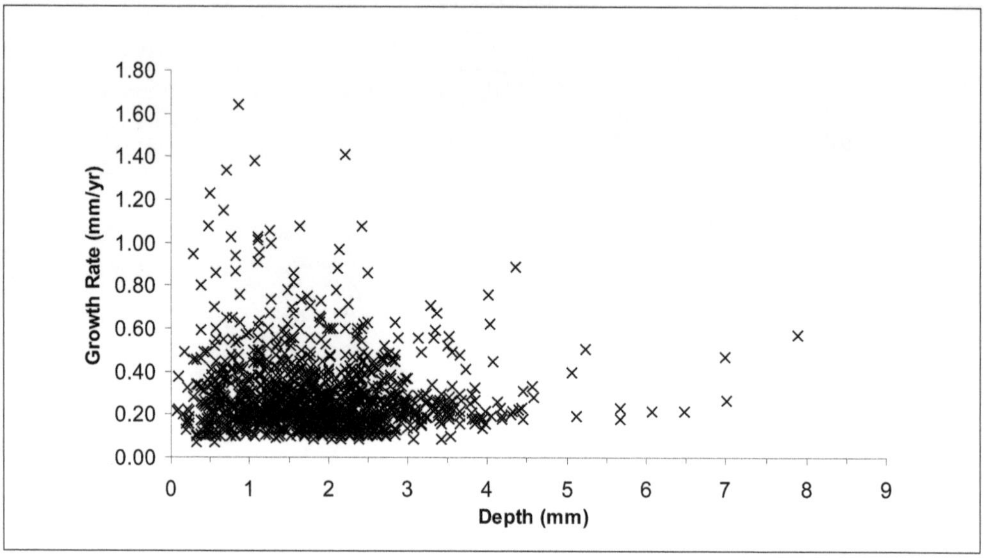

Fig.8. Comparison between growth rate and defect depth.

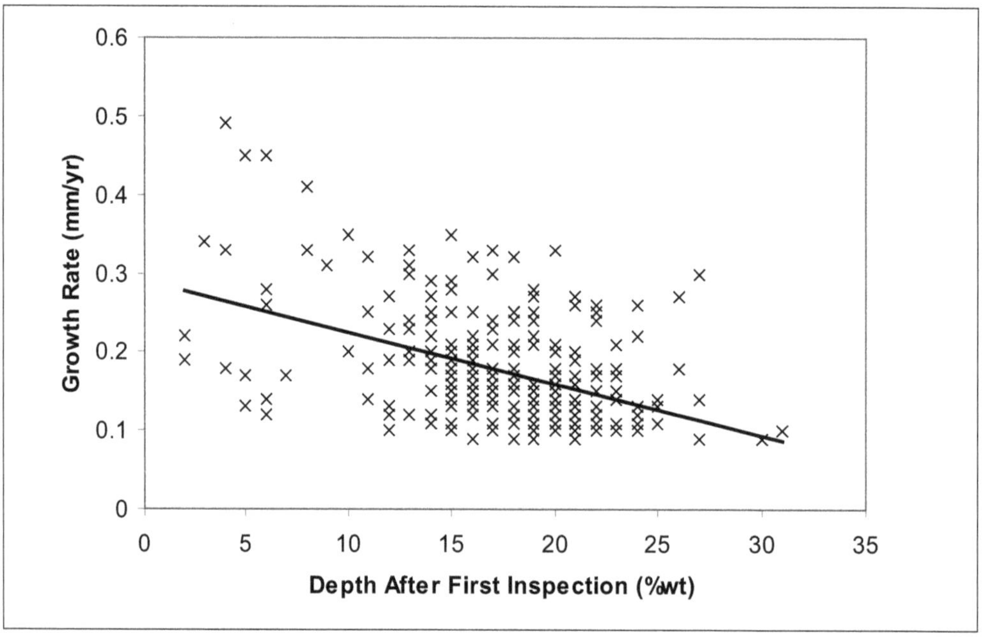

Fig.9. Distribution of growth rates vs depth for one pipeline.

Development of corrosion-scoring model

Although measurement by repeat inspection is one of the most-accurate methods for determining pipeline corrosion rates, this is not always possible for pipelines that have not been inspected or have only had one inspection. Therefore, a model has been developed to score a pipeline based on its susceptibility to external corrosion and the expected severity of that corrosion. This score is then benchmarked and validated against an external corrosion rate using the database of corrosion rates described in the preceding section.

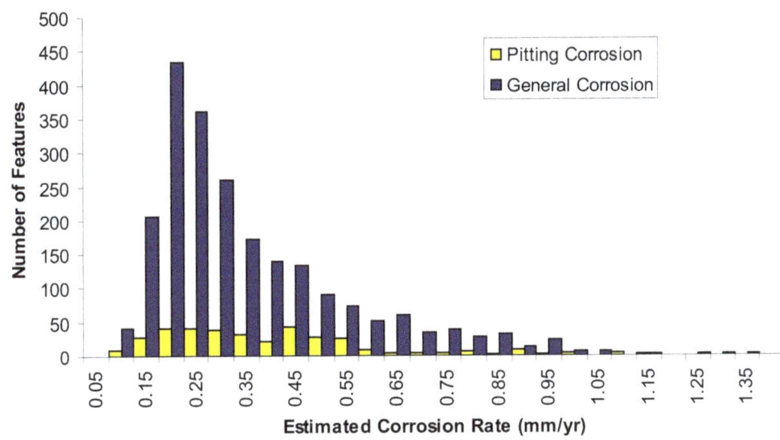

Fig.10. Distribution of growth rates vs depth for one pipeline.

Risk-ranking approach

The approach adopted for the development of the corrosion scoring model is based on a simple relative-risk ranking method developed by Kirkwood and Karam [14]. Further refined models will be considered subsequently. In this method, the probability of failure of a pipeline as a result of failure mode (iPF) is calculated using the formula:

$$iPF = iSSF \times iSVF \quad (1)$$

where:

iSSF is the susceptibility factor due to failure mode i
iSVF is the severity factor due to failure mode i

Each of the susceptibility and severity factors is dependent on a number of parameters which are weighted according to their relative importance.

The consequence of failure is calculated based on the damage or cost incurred when a pipeline fails, and is therefore a summation of all of the feasible consequence factors, CF (including fatality, damage to property, etc.). The total relative risk (RR) is then given by using the equation:

$$RR = \frac{1}{n_{PF}} \sum iPF x \frac{1}{n_{CF}} \sum iCF \quad (2)$$

where n_{PF} is the number of probability factors and n_{CF} is the number of consequence factors.

Extension to corrosion-scoring model

In the corrosion-scoring model developed during this work, the consequences of failure are not taken into account as only one threat is being considered. The three probability factors considered are:

- the probability that the coating will fail (COATPF)
- the probability that the CP system will fail and (CPPF)
- the probability that the steel will corrode in the event that it is unprotected in the soil environment (SOILPF)

Therefore, from Eqn (1), for each of these factors:

$$COATPF = COATSSF \times COATSVF \quad (3)$$

$$CPPF = CPSSF \times CPSVF \quad (4)$$

$$SOILPF = SOILSSF \times SOILSVF \quad (5)$$

and the total failure score (TFS) is given as:

$$TFS = (COATPF + CPPF + SOILPF)/3 \quad (6)$$

The TFS value is therefore a relative measure of the susceptibility of a pipeline to external corrosion and the severity of the resulting corrosion.

The parameters associated with the susceptibility and severity factors and the weighting indices applied were obtained by determining the conditions known to influence each individual event and assigning weighting factors on the basis of the influence of that factor on the event. This process used a combination of published information and engineering judgment, and the results were then reviewed and calibrated by a team of experts to ensure consistency. The parameters and weighting indices for each of the probability factors are discussed in the following sections.

Coating factor (COATPF)

The definition of pipeline-coating failure used in this model is that the coating is considered to have failed when the level of degradation is such that the CP system cannot protect the pipeline and active corrosion is occurring. This could be a result of either disbonding of the coating or the occurrence of a large area of exposed surface due to holidays in the coating. The susceptibility of a pipeline coating to failure is therefore dependent on the type of coating, the application procedure (whether in-field or factory applied) and how well the coating is maintained (measured by the number of coating surveys carried out). In the absence of coating survey data, the severity of the coating failure is dependent on a subjective view of the coating condition and the age of the pipeline. If coating survey data is available then the results can be used to determine the condition of the coating.

The weighting indices for each of these parameters were determined using the procedure mentioned above to give the following equations for determining the coating susceptibility and severity factors:

$$COATSSF = 50APP\_PRO + 30COAT\_TYP + 20COAT\_SUR\_FR \quad (7)$$

$$COATSVF = 80COAT\_COND + 20AGE \quad (8)$$

where:

Parameter	Input data	Parameter score
COAT_TYP	Single wrap tapes	1.0
	Asphalt, coal tar enamel, double wrapped tape	0.8
	FBE, liquid epoxy	0.3
		0.1

Table 3. Typical parameter scores for coating type.

APP_PRO = parameter score for coating application procedure
COAT_TYP = parameter score for coating type
COAT_SUR_FR = parameter score for coating survey frequency
COAT_COND = parameter score for coating condition
AGE = parameter score for pipeline/coating age

Each of the input parameters is then assigned a score between 0 and 1 to allow the susceptibility and severity factors to be calculated using equations (7) and (8). For example, the input parameter scores for coating type are provided in Table 3.

Cathodic protection factor (CPPF)

The CP system works synergistically with the coating system to protect the pipeline. In order to protect the pipeline the CP system must be available, well maintained, and regularly monitored and therefore these factors all contribute to the susceptibility of the CP system to fail. The severity of that failure is related to the level of protection on the pipeline. Criteria have been developed to determine when a cathodic-protection system is adequately protecting a pipeline. The most-common criterion is to maintain the pipe-to-soil off-potential above -850 mV (in aerobic conditions) as measured by a copper-copper sulphate reference electrode. A CP system is 100% effective when all areas of the pipeline meet the protection criterion.

The weighting indices assigned to the parameters affecting the CP susceptibility and severity are shown in the following equations:

$$CPSSF = 40CP\_AV + 30CP\_SUR\_FR + 30CP\_MAINT \quad (9)$$

$$CPPF = 100CP\_EFF \quad (10)$$

where:

CP_AV = parameter score for CP availability
CP_SUR_FR = parameter score for CP survey frequency
CP_MAINT = parameter score for CP maintenance
CP_EFF = parameter score for CP effectiveness

Soil corrosion factor (SOILPF)

Soil corrosion is an extremely-random process and variations in oxygen concentration, water content, soluble salts, microbial activity, and pH will affect the corrosion rate. Therefore corrosion rates will change along the length of a pipeline, and predicting how a buried pipeline will corrode is very difficult as all of these complex factors interact. In addition, the information required to

	Comment	Parameter score
APP_PRO	Factory applied - Fair	0.3
COAT_TYP	Tape	0.8
COAT_SUR_FR	Assumed none	1
COAT_COND	Fair	0.6
AGE	28 years	0.8
CP_AV	High	0.1
CP_SUR_FR	1 test post survey/year	0.5
CP_MAINT	On-off potentials measured	0.5
CP_EFF	Assume a few unprotected sections	0.5
SOIL_TYP	Assume compact loams	0.5
PIPE_CORR	0.2mm/yr (8 mpy)	0.2

Table 4. Typical pipeline data for one pipeline in the database.

make a prediction is generally not available, including parameters such as chloride and sulphate levels, pH, bacteria counts, and even resistivity measurements. As a result, in this model, the only parameter that is considered in determining the susceptibility of a pipeline to corrosion is the soil type.

The severity is determined by the corrosion rate of steel in that soil type as published by Simon-Thomas *et al.* [7]: the weighting index is therefore 100, and the soil susceptibility and severity factors are given by the equations:

$$\text{SOILSSF} = 100\text{SOIL\_TYP} \qquad (11)$$

$$\text{SOILSVF} = 100\text{PIPE\_CORR} \qquad (12)$$

where:

SOIL_TYP = parameter score for soil type
PIPE_CORR = parameter score for pipeline corrosion rate in the specified soil type

Calibration of corrosion-scoring model

In order to calibrate the corrosion-scoring model, 11 pipelines from the corrosion database were selected for which a corrosion score could be calculated and for which corrosion growth rates had been measured using the ILI run-comparison method. The maximum corrosion growth rate in the selected data set was 0.83 mm/yr (33 mpy), as it was considered that any corrosion rates greater than this could indicate either stray current or bacterial corrosion which are not included in the model calculations.

For each of the 11 pipelines a TFS was calculated based on known pipeline data, and a value between 0 and 1 assigned to each of the input parameters. As an example, the data for one of the pipelines in the database is provided in Table 4.

	Factor	Value
COATSSF	Coating susceptibility	59
COATSVF	Coating severity	64
CPSSF	CP susceptibility	34
CPSVF	CP severity	50
SOILSSF	Soil susceptibility	50
SOILSVF	Soil severity	20
COATPF	Coating probability	3776
CPPF	CP probability	1700
SOILPF	Soil probability	1000
TFS	Total failure score	2159
Max corrosion rate (mm/yr) (*determined using run-comparison software*)		0.37

Table 5. Calculation of total failure score.

Using equations (7) to (12) and the parameter scores from Table 4, the failure susceptibility and severity factors for each of the probability factors were calculated. The probability factors were then determined from equations (3) to (5), and the TFS was calculated from Eqn 6. The results of these calculations are presented in Table 5 for this example pipeline.

The total failure score was then calculated for each pipeline and plotted against the maximum corrosion rate, measured using the corrosion-rate database.

Inspection factor

The method described so far can be used for pipelines where there are no inspection data. However, if there are ILI data, then valuable information on the susceptibility and severity of corrosion on the pipeline can be provided. Therefore, the model also incorporates an inspection factor based on the density of external corrosion features (in terms of number of features per km), the depth distribution, and the calculated half-life corrosion rate. The half-life corrosion rate provides an estimate of the corrosion rate on a pipeline based upon the maximum defect depth and the difference between the corrosion initiation time and the time of the inspection. Therefore, for a half-life corrosion rate, the corrosion is considered to have been active for half the life of the pipeline. Although half-life rates will give an indication of the severity of corrosion, previous work has shown that they do not give a good prediction of actual corrosion rates [15].

The inspection factor is given by the equation:

$$\text{INSP\_FACT} = (50\text{NO\_DEF} + 50\text{DEF\_DEPTH})\,(100\text{HLF}) \quad (13)$$

where:

NO_DEF = parameter score for number of reported external corrosion defects
DEF_DEPTH = parameter score for defect depth distribution
HLF = parameter score for half-life corrosion rate

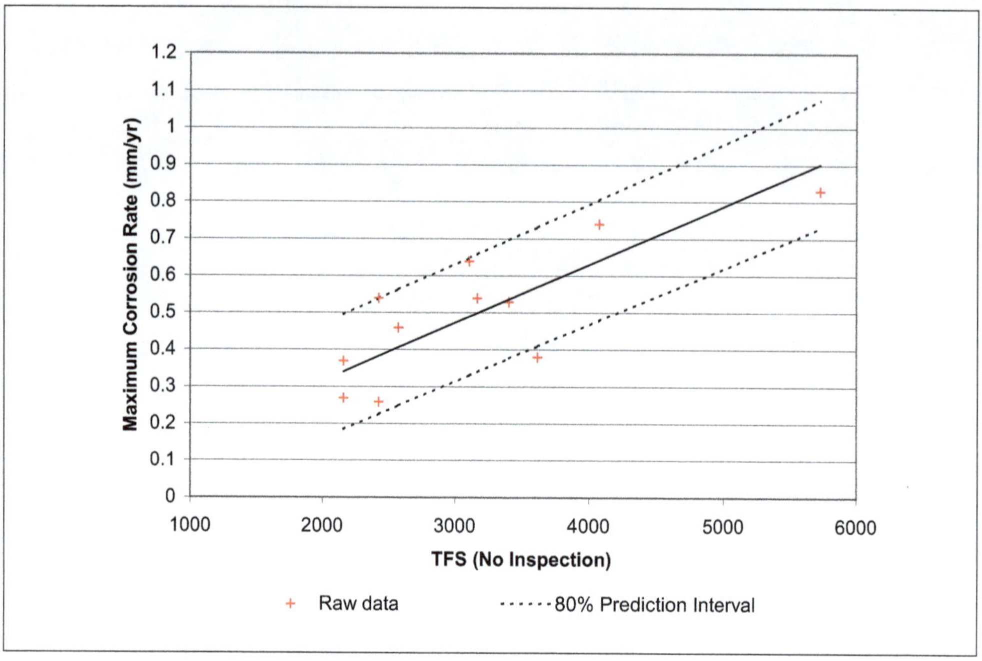

Fig.11. Plot of total failure score against maximum corrosion rate without the inspection factor.

	Comment	Parameter score
NO_DEF	93 defects /km	1.0
DEF_DEPTH	<5% defects ≥ 30%wt	0.1
HLF	Half life rate = 0.39mm/year	0.5

Table 6. Typical inspection data for one pipeline in the database.

The TFS after one inspection becomes:

$$TFS\_INSP = 0.2(TFS) + 0.8(INSP\_FACT) \quad (14)$$

Using the same example pipeline and the additional input from Table 6, the new TFS is calculated using equations (13) and (14) to be 2924.

Results

The results for the 11 pipelines used in this study are presented graphically in Fig.11, in which a linear regression has been applied to the data which gives a best fit equation of:

$$\text{Max corrosion rate (mm/yr)} = 1.58 \times 10^{4}\ TFS \quad (15)$$

The value of R^2 on this fit is 0.63. An 80% prediction interval has been added to the data which essentially means bounds of 0.16 mm/yr (6 mpy) either side of the linear regression line.

When the inspection factor is included, the results presented in Fig.12 are obtained; for this data, the linear fit is:

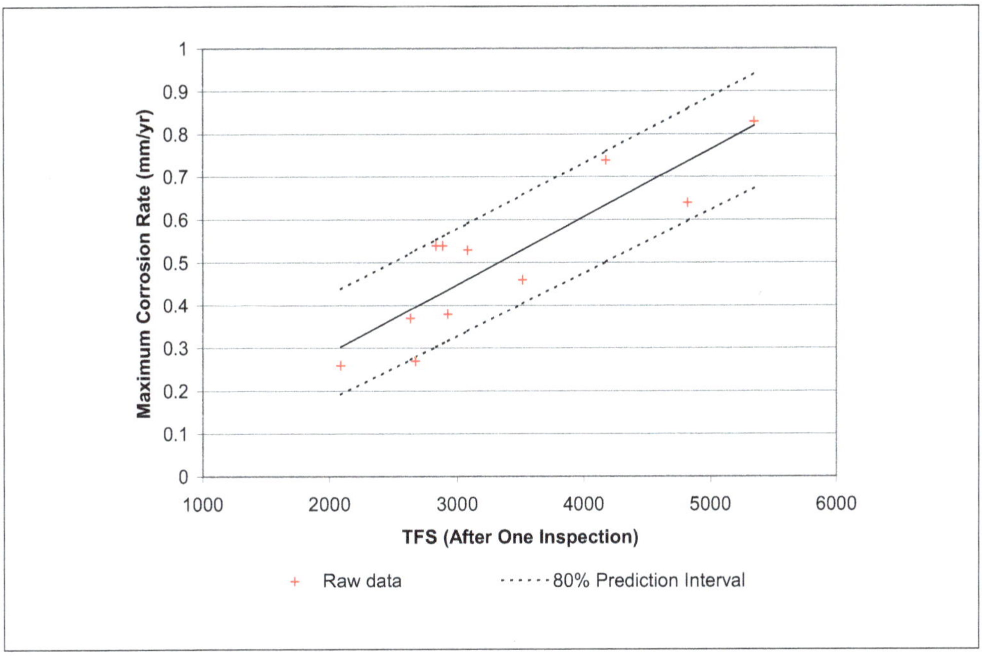

Fig. 12. Plot of total failure score against maximum corrosion rate with the inspection factor.

$$\text{Max corrosion rate (mm/yr)} = 1.51 \times 10^{4}\ \text{TFS\_INSP} \qquad (16)$$

The value of R^2 on this fit is 0.77, and the bounds become 0.13mm/yr (5mpy) either side of the regression line. Therefore, the inspection factor has increased the accuracy of the prediction and reduced the bounds on that prediction.

Equations (15) and (16) can now be used to estimate a maximum corrosion growth rate based on known parameters about the pipeline, and these estimated rates can then be applied in integrity-management plans to ensure that appropriate rates are selected for the establishment of repair plans and re-inspection intervals. It is highlighted that using this model, corrosion rates greater than the 0.3-0.4 mm/yr (12-16 mpy) recommended by B31.8S[6] and NACE RP0502[5] are predicted (and measured) for some pipelines. This highlights the need to be able to relate the selected corrosion rate to pipeline parameters.

Further planned model developments

It is recognized that the scoring models have been tested on only a small sample dataset, and further work is required to validate this model particularly for pipelines with maximum corrosion rates less than 0.25 mm/yr (10 mpy).

It is also recognized that the additive form of the risk equation used to calculate the TFS (Eqn 6), is an over-simplification, as it implies that corrosion occurs either because the coating fails or because the CP fails or because the pipe is in a corrosive soil environment. In fact, the corrosion rate is influenced by a combination of all of these parameters. For example, if the coating fails then the pipe may not necessarily corrode as long as the CP is adequately protecting the pipeline. Therefore the next iteration of the model will include the interaction of these parameters to calculate the TFS.

Establishment of re-assessment intervals

As part of a performance-based integrity-management programme, an operator can set the response times for the remediation of defects and the interval for re-assessment of the pipeline segment. In order to set a re-assessment interval, the pipeline operator has to be able to identify the threat that will control the degradation of the pipeline and the rate of degradation, and set an inspection interval accordingly. Thus the establishment of realistic corrosion growth rates is critical to this process.

Re-assessment intervals for DA

In order to calculate a re-assessment interval for DA, the remnant life of the largest flaw remaining in the pipeline after completion of the direct examination stage has to be calculated using information on flaw size and corrosion rates. In the NACE RP0502 guidance, the maximum re-assessment interval is taken as half the calculated remaining life (subject to limitations of other pipeline codes such as B31.8S).

When the operator has measured corrosion-rate data, actual rates may be used in the calculation of re-assessment interval; otherwise, an estimate of the corrosion rate has to be used. As mentioned previously, if no data is available then a rate of 0.4mm/yr (16mpy) is recommended. The external-corrosion rate model allows a corrosion rate to be estimated for use in the calculation of remnant life based on the pipeline parameters. In some cases, the model rate will be less than the recommended rate of 0.4mm/yr (16mpy), allowing the operator to increase the inspection interval. However, in other cases, the model rate may be higher than the recommended rate: in these cases, the operator may want to confirm or measure corrosion rates to ensure that the recommended rates will not result in premature failure.

Re-assessment intervals for hydrotest

The criterion for setting a re-assessment interval for hydrotesting is based on the requirement to prevent time-dependent failure, such as corrosion, before the next assessment. It is therefore assumed that defects exist in the pipeline that have just survived the hydrotest, and which then grow by corrosion to failure. Setting the re-assessment interval, therefore, requires an estimate of corrosion rate, and the model can be used to provide this estimate. As for DA, estimates less than the recommended rate will allow operators to increase the time interval between inspections.

However, it is highlighted that there are technical and practical difficulties with basing the future safe operation of a corroding pipeline on a hydrostatic re-pressure test:

- pressure testing to a high level cannot detect short deep corrosion pits that can subsequently leak, as it is a test for rupture and not imminent leaks;
- pressure testing is not an absolute guarantee of integrity;
- the pressure test provides no information on corrosion growth rates.

Re-inspection intervals for ILI

In order to set an interval for a repeat ILI run, the following approach can be followed:

Assumed corrosion rate	Optimum re-inspection interval
0.4 mm/yr (16 mpy) (NACE 80% UCI)	8 years
0.3 mm/yr (12 mpy) (ASME B31.8S)	12 years
0.55 mm/yr (22 mpy) (corrosion scoring model, 80% UPI)	5 years
0.54 mm/yr (21 mpy) (max. rate from run comparison study)	5 years

Table 7. Optimum reinspection interval.

- Assess the immediate significance of the corrosion defects reported from the current ILI run (taking into account tool tolerances) to identify any immediate repair needs. This could be achieved using a probability-of-exceedance approach [13].

- Apply the corrosion-growth information to the remaining corrosion defects. This may be in the form of a single corrosion rate (such as the NACE RP0502 recommendation), or estimated rates for individual pipe segments from the model described in the above sections, or individual corrosion rates obtained from a run-comparison analysis (if two sets of ILI data are available).

- Estimate the time for the corrosion defects to grow to critical dimensions that require remediation using the corrosion-growth information from above.

- Evaluate the optimum timing of the re-inspection taking into account the number and cost of scheduled repairs that would be required in the interval leading up to the ILI run vs the cost of the ILI run itself factoring in all the relevant costs (excavation, NDE, repair, ILI tool and operational costs, etc.). The re-inspection should be timed at the point when the combined (repair + ILI cost) is lowest and thus most cost-effective.

As an example of the influence that the corrosion-growth rate has on this analysis, a number of simple scenarios have been evaluated for a sample pipeline:

26-in x 11-mm x 75-km, X-60 pipe
MAOP equivalent to 72%SMYS
6,000 metal loss features reported by ILI
43%wt deepest feature
15%wt average feature depth

Four different corrosion rate scenarios were considered. The optimum timing of the re-inspection run was determined by taking into account the cost of scheduled repairs vs the cost of running the ILI tool vs time, and the results are shown in Table 7. In each scenario studied approximately 20 scheduled repairs were predicted to be required before re-inspection was shown to be cost-effective.

The above results highlight how sensitive the calculations are to the applied corrosion rate. Both the NACE and B31.8S rates are shown to be non-conservative compared to the actual observed maximum rate (obtained from a run-comparison study of repeat ILI data on this pipeline), thus underlining the importance of selecting a safe corrosion rate.

Summary and conclusions

The determination of external-corrosion rates is essential to ensure that pipelines are repaired and re-inspected in a safe and cost-effective manner. However, as there are many variables contributing to the rate of external corrosion for a buried pipeline, there are currently no mechanistic or empirical models to calculate corrosion rates.

This paper has described the development of a corrosion-growth rate database. This database has been tested against corrosion theory and observed external and internal corrosion rates. It is concluded that the observed corrosion rates and general trends are in agreement with other published sources of soil-corrosion data and corrosion theory.

Using the database of external-corrosion growth rates measured using repeat ILI data, a corrosion-growth scoring model has been developed which relates the measured maximum corrosion rate to a total failure score (TFS), calculated for a pipeline based on information about the coating, CP, soil, and inspection data (if available).

This work has demonstrated that a correlation can be derived between the TFS and maximum corrosion rate. The accuracy of the correlation can be increased and the level of uncertainty in the estimate can be decreased by including information from one ILI inspection run. This method can be used to estimate the external-corrosion growth rates for multiple segments within the same pipeline, i.e. wherever the parameters used as inputs to the model vary along a pipeline.

The validation set of data indicates that the default corrosion rates recommended in B31.8S[6] and NACE RP0502[5] may underpredict the maximum corrosion rates.

Finally, although a methodology for predicting external-corrosion rates (with or without ILI data) has been discussed, it is highlighted that the most-accurate rates are determined from the detailed comparison of repeat ILI data which provides rates on a defect-by-defect basis.

Disclaimer

The contents of this document are intended for information only and GE PII Pipeline Solutions does not authorize the reader -- or any other party – to use, copy, reproduce, or publish the said information for any commercial purpose. Accordingly, GE PII Pipeline Solutions accepts no liability whatsoever for any loss, expense, or damage arising from use or application of such information.

References

1. C.de Waard, U.Lotz, and D.E.Milliams, 1993. Prediction of CO2 corrosion of carbon steel. CORROSION/93, paper 69, Houston, NACE International.
2. C.de Waard, U.Lotz, and A.Dugstad, 1995. Influence of liquid flow velocity on CO2 corrosion: a semi-empirical model. CORROSION/95, paper 128, Houston, NACE International.
3. A.J.McMahon and D.M.E.Paisley, 1997. Corrosion prediction modelling: a guide to the use of

corrosion prediction models for risk assessment in oil and gas production and transportation facilities. Report ESR.96.ER.066, BP International, Sunbury.

4. NOROSK, 1998. CO2 corrosion rate calculation model. Standard M-506, www.nts.no/norsok, Norwegian Technology Standards Institution, Oslo.
5. NACE, 2002. Proposed standard recommended practice: Pipeline external corrosion direct assessment methodology. TG041, March.
6. ASME, 2004. B31.8S: Managing system integrity of gas pipelines. ASME Code for Pressure Piping.
7. M.J.J.Simon Thomas, L.H.Prager, C.V.M.Voermans, B.P.Pots, and I.J.Rippon, 2002. Deterministic pipeline integrity assessment to optimise corrosion control and reduce cost. CORROSION/2002, paper 02075, Denver, NACE International, April.
8. A.W.Peabody, 2001. Peabody's control of pipeline corrosion, 2nd Ed., Edited by R.L.Bianchetti, NACE International, ISBN 1-57590-092-0.
9. R.W.E.Shannon and C.J.Argent, 1988. A systems approach to the quantitative condition monitoring of pipelines. IGU 17th World Gas Conference, Washington, June.
10. S.J.Dawson, J.M.Race, S.Peet, and R.Krishnamurthy, 2001. Pipeline corrosion management. CORROSION/2001, paper 1627, Houston, NACE International, March.
11. B.Gu, R.Kania, S.Sharma, and M.Gao, 2002. Approach to assessment of corrosion growth in pipelines. IPC02-27263, Calgary, Canada, September 29-October 3.
12. B.Gu, R.Kania, and M.Gao, 2004. Probabilistic-based corrosion assessment for pipeline integrity. Corrosion NACExpo: 59th Annual Conference, New Orleans, paper 04164.
13. S.Kariyawasam and I.Colquhoun, 2005. Progressive management and engineering evaluation of pipeline integrity, paper 05159, Corrosion 2005, NACE International, Houston.
14. M.G.Kirkwood and M.Karam, 1994. A scheme for setting pipeline repair, maintenance and inspection priorities. Pipeline Risk Assessment, Rehabilitation, and Repair Conference, September 12-15, organized by *Pipes & Pipelines International* and Gulf Publishing Co.
15. P.Sofos, J.M.Race, and S.J.Dawson, 2004. Experience in the prediction of corrosion growth rates in oil and gas pipelines. 4th International Conference on Pipeline Technology, Ostend, Belgium.

Operator assessment of ILI defects

by Kevin W Ferguson

Panhandle Eastern Pipeline Co, Houston, TX, USA

WITH THE AGE of the original Panhandle Eastern Pipeline (PEPL) Co pipelines, it's not a matter of if anomalies will be found when an ILI tool is run, it's a matter of how many and how severe. When a final report is received from an ILI vendor, burst pressures are typically calculated using Modified B31G, 0.85dL. The results can seem unmanageable, but success has been had by doing further assessments on some anomalies without excavating them all. This assessment has been developed and performed by PEPL on three sets of Tuboscope ILI data and one set of Baker Hughes CPIG data. The method to be discussed was first employed in 2002. It provides a more accurate characterization of the defect and provides the company the ability to more effectively allocate resources.

Efforts have been made to review the colour scan of a vendor's raw high-resolution magnetic-flux leakage (HRMFL) data, and perform an assessment using effective area analysis without excavating hundreds of anomalies that prove no threat to the pipeline. This assessment is done by hand on the computer and in many cases returns a burst pressure higher than that calculated using Modified B31G, 0.85dL.

The following is a case study that shows how multiple defects have been assessed prior to excavation in an attempt to more accurately characterize the defect, and allow for a better allocation of resources. Digs have been performed to validate the process, and the results will be discussed.

THE ORIGINAL Panhandle Eastern Pipeline (PEPL) Co lines were installed back in the late 1920s and early 1930s,and some of these lines were in service for 20 to 30 years without cathodic protection (CP). During this time the lines corroded to varying degrees, but the corrosion was retarded to a significant degree with the application of CP. However, the years without CP, or with only marginal CP, left areas with corrosion that have since been assessed with the use of a high -resolution MFL tool. These tools provide a great deal of very useful information, but there are times when the Modified B31G, 0.85dL-calculated, rupture pressure is misleading.

When a new log is received, it is loaded into the database so that the newly identified anomalies can be aligned with the proper pipe properties. At this point, the properties of the pipe, along with the length and depth of the anomaly, are used to calculate a burst pressure using Modified B31G 0.85dL. Although used for complex shapes, this process is not accurate in predicting the actual burst pressure of a pipe with complex anomalies due in part to the simplification of the shape geometry. These complex anomalies are better characterized by the application of the RSTRENG effective-area analysis method.

Modified B31G 0.85dL on long interacting areas of corrosion that may have one deep pit and then a large area of associated general corrosion will not accurately characterize the anomaly. For more information regarding the various techniques for assessing corrosion defects, see PRCI project PR273-9803 [1].

One issue with this method is that long interacting anomalies with a single, small, deep pit can

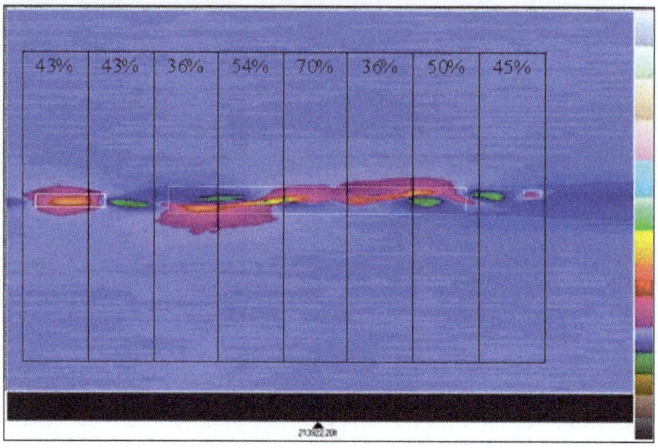

Fig. 1. Software view of an axial anomaly.

produce a very low rupture-pressure ratio or RPR (burst pressure divided by the MAOP). Then, when such an anomaly is investigated, it is discovered that it passes the very conservative B31G. At this point, the operator may decide to recoat the anomaly and may feel that the dig was a waste of time and resources. If this happens time after time, the operator may begin to lose faith in the results that are being produced.

The case with these pipelines is that there are a significant number of anomalies on the line. There may be short, deep anomalies interacting with more shallow general corrosion. The length of the interacting anomaly combined with the depth of a single anomaly can force an operator to investigate on a very aggressive, costly schedule when only using Modified B31G, 0.85dL.

The RSTRENG effective-area analysis (EAA) has proven to be less conservative than 0.85dL for complex shape defects, yet safe for evaluating defects in the ditch [1]. EAA provides a river-bottom profile of the defect, which credits for metal gain, and debits for metal loss. Using this method of assessment prior to digging the defects provides the operator with a more accurate representation of the actual defect, as it doesn't assume that the anomaly is a certain shape. This software reassessment method is a help to more accurately characterize defects so that limited resources can more effectively be allocated.

How can an operator more effectively assess the severity of an anomaly? Is it possible to conduct an EAA on the anomaly prior to deploying the construction crew to dig on the line? If an EAA can be used on the software, how accurate is this method and what are the limitations?

Basic ground rules

Some basic ground rules must be set prior to explaining the methodology that has been employed. First, the tool vendor will report interaction based on the customers preference. In the past 3t x 3t (where t is the wall thickness) has been specified to the ILI vendor, but for the purpose of this method, 1-in x 6t was used. The application of the more aggressive interaction rules required the one employing this method to review the various scans of raw data available and determine if more anomalies should be interacted. In some cases, more anomalies have been interacted, and in others, the interaction that was called by the vendor was used. Every anomaly must be reviewed individually. It has also been experienced that some anomalies appear to have no interaction in the software, but interaction is obvious after excavation. This has typically been found with either a deep pit masking an anomaly immediately downstream or with very mild general corrosion that the tool is not capable of accurately calling and characterizing.

Fig.2. Axially-aligned corrosion.

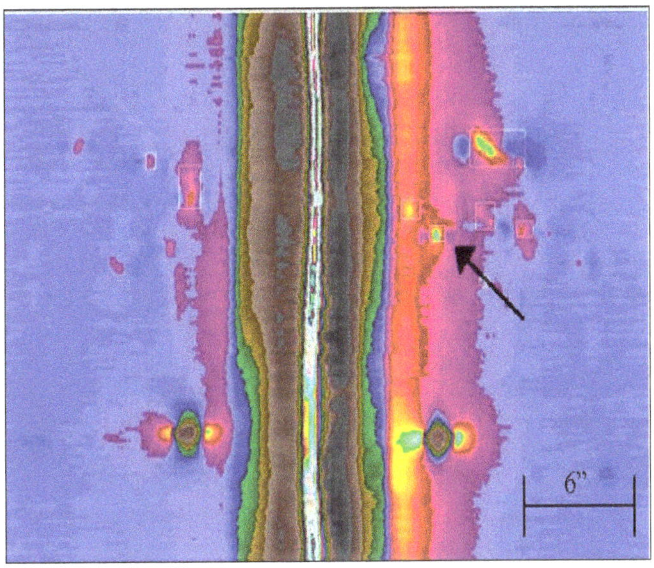

Fig.3. Anomaly downstream of a coupling.

There are several areas of conservatism that are built into the remaining-strength calculations, and the application of 1-in x 6t interaction is one. Knowing there is conservatism that is built into these equations also assists with the determination of how aggressive a schedule the reassessed anomalies need to follow.

There is a research paper sponsored by PRCI that studied the application of interaction rules. Two notable conclusions, based on a range of D/t ratios, from this research are:

> "Interaction of small-diameter (2t) axially separated pit-pit combinations is negligible (less than 5%), even when defects are spaced as close as 1t from each other. Predicted failure pressures change by less than 5% when the defect spacing is varied from 1t to 6t.
>
> "Interaction of larger-diameter (8t) axially separated pit-pit combinations is more significant. However, the difference in failure pressure for defects spaced 1t and 6t apart is still less than 10%."[2]

This research shows that the interaction rules are being more aggressively applied than what would be required. However, the more aggressive interaction rules are still being used to build additional conservatism into the method to be described.

There is also conservatism built into the equations. Effective-area analysis has shown during some digs that the defect has an RPR less than unity. If that were the case, the pipe would have failed prior to investigation. Some other factors that add conservatism can be:

line pressure at the location versus the MAOP
actual pipe wall thickness
actual pipe yield strength

Next, one must understand the abilities and inabilities of ILI tools. When using a normal ILI tool that senses flux leakage with magnetic poles that are axially aligned, it has been the company's experience that the tools/software/analysts can have difficulty accurately calling (identifying) anomalies that are axially aligned. This is not only referring to anomalies that are narrow and axially oriented, but also with anomalies that have multiple pits of varying widths that are axially oriented in relation to one another. An example of this is shown in Figs 1 and 2: when this anomaly was excavated, it was discovered that it interacted for approximately 13 in instead of the approximately 5 in that was called by the vendor, or the 8 in that was called during the reassessment using the software analysis. This is one example of this type of MFL tool inaccurately characterizing an axially oriented defect.

Caution must also be used when attempting to evaluate defects immediately downstream of an area covered by a sleeve. On the lines where EAA has been applied, caution has been taken to not use the method on anomalies that are immediately downstream of an existing sleeve or – in this case – a Dresser coupling. When the tool is moving out of the area of metal gain, the signal is distorted and can misrepresent the true characteristics of the anomaly. An example of this is shown in Fig.3, where the anomaly that is being called is in the echo of the coupling.

The overall accuracy of the tool should also be considered when applying this method or a similar one. Depending on individual experience with a certain vendor, if this method is employed, the company may wish to add the maximum tolerance to the depth of the anomaly; doing so will add some additional conservatism to the method. This has been done, at times, and it was found that the RPR is still more accurately characterized than through the use of Modified B31G 0.85dL alone. However, one must remember that the ILI vendors have a significant database of results that have led them to their current sizing algorithms, and the vendors are expected to provide accurate information. Therefore, the validity of this method is dependent upon accurate ILI data just as for any other remaining-strength calculation.

The tools that are being used are not 100% accurate, as one might wish. Rather, they provide an operator a look at the condition of the pipe with a relatively high degree of accuracy.

Locations method hasn't been used

The company has confidence with the results of the application of this method; however, it has not been employed in either HCAs or in Class 3 or 4 areas. In those areas, the company has taken a more aggressive stance on anomaly remediation.

Methodology

The methodology that has been utilized in an attempt to more accurately characterize these defects is described below. The company incorporates the use of the ILI raw data, Microsoft Word,

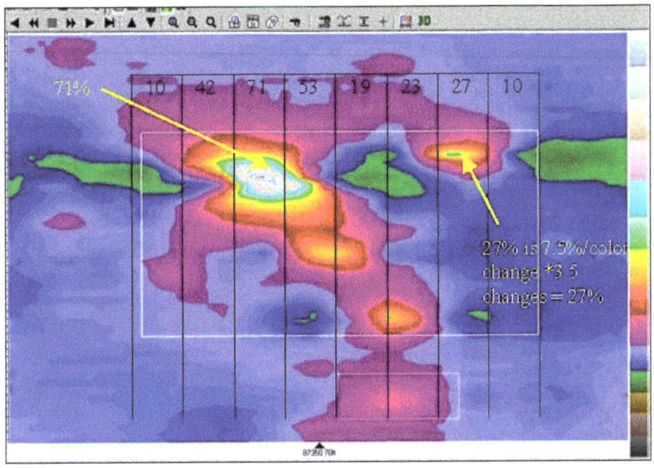

Fig.4. Reassement colour changes

Microsoft Excel, and RSTRENG2. The use of Microsoft Word in this process will assist the user in performing the analysis as well as enabling the user to document and save the results. The following describes how the analysis was performed.

1. Take the anomaly in question and create a grid for RSTRENG2 based on the length of the anomaly.
2. Find the deepest pit of the anomaly and note that number in the corresponding column of the grid.
3. Review the colour spectrum and determine the number of colours or shades the field goes through to go from nominal pipe to the deepest pit. Then, take the maximum depth and divide it by the number of colours: for instance, if a pit is 63%, and the field goes through six colour changes from nominal pipe to the deepest area, divide 63 by 6. The conclusion is then that each colour is approximately 10.5% of the spectrum. Always round, so in this case it would be 11%.
4. Determine the depth of each remaining column of the grid by multiplying the number of colour changes by the percentage determined above. The numbers should be noted, similar to a normal RSTRENG2 that would be performed in the ditch. During this stage, there will be times that a percentage seems too low or falls in a fraction of the way through a colour. The user can always add percentage or use half colours to multiply the percentage by, if the user feels the need. Depth percentage should never be taken away from an area. Also, if there are multiple pits that the user chooses to call interacting and that have known depths from the vendor, use the known depths.
5. Plug all of this information into RSTRENG2 (or some other EAA tool) and calculate the safety factor (RPR, in this case).

At the end of the analysis, if Microsoft Word was used, the screen will look similar to Fig.4, which also shows an example of taking the colour profile and using it to determine the depth of other pits/corrosion in the cluster.

When performing this type of analysis, the user must remember that the colour palette displays the strength of the magnetic field. The strength of the magnetic field is a function of depth and width of the anomaly, and this means that the colour changes are not linear, as is being assumed. However, it will be shown that the results using this assumption have been positive.

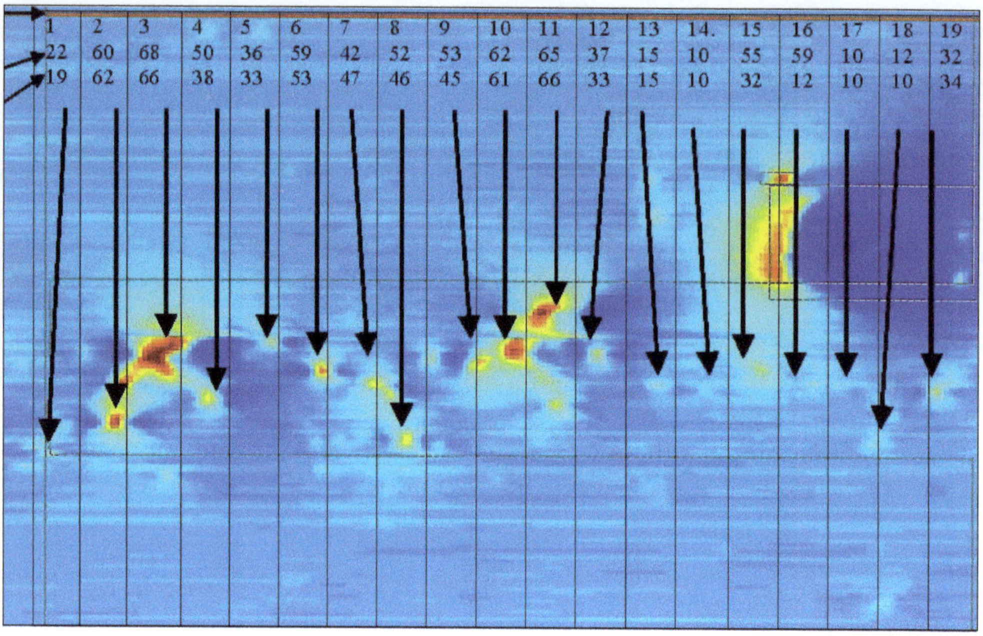

Fig.5. Operator results vs vendor results.

Explanation of colour profile

During the reassessment of these anomalies, one assumes that the strength of field is linear from pit to pit. For instance (see Fig.5) if the centre of a pit is called as 71% and there are 9.5 colour changes to get from nominal pipe to the centre of the pit, each colour change is 7.5%. When the in-the-ditch readings are taken, it is expected that they will not match up perfectly, but they should resemble what was displayed.

Discussion of results

During the discussion of these results, it is important to remember the goal of applying this method: it is not to find a loophole or an attempt to avoid digging anomalies that need to be investigated; the goal is more effectively to allocate resources. This method is being employed as an engineering critical assessment of the actual characteristics of the anomalies.

Table 1 shows the results of excavations that were completed for a series of anomalies over three different tool runs and two different lines. (A fourth run and third line will be discussed later.) In the table:

REA RPR = RPR of the software reassessment technique that is being described
0.85dL RPR = RPR calculated using tool run length and depth
Actual RPR = RPR calculated in-the-ditch using RSTRENG2
REA more accurate? – Notes if reassessment method described is more accurate than 0.85dL
Depth diff. = actual depth vs vendor-called depth
Length diff. = actual length vs vendor-called length

The desire was for the reassessment results to be more conservative in every case than the actual results. This proved not to be the case in many of the instances, and in fact 63% of the anomalies

#	Line	Wheel Count (ft.)	REA RPR	.85 dL RPR	Actual RPR	REA RPR vs actual	.85dL vs actual	REA more accurate?	Depth fiff.*	Length diff. *
1	L 200	135503.5	1.07	0.87	1.13	-0.06	0.26	Y	20%	-2.5
2	L 200	135503.1	1.31	0.87	1.22	0.09	0.35	Y	20%	-0.5
3	L 200	117684	1.12	0.63	1.08	0.04	0.45	Y	28%	-14.5
4	L 200	123650.2	1.48	1.25	1.2	0.28	-0.05	N	3%	-2.1
5	L 200	234821.4	1.19	0.61	0.99	0.2	0.38	Y	-4%	-4.4
6	L 200	77747	0.9	0.78	0.98	-0.08	0.2	Y	10%	-0.5
7	L 200	234914	1.16	0.83	0.99	0.17	0.16	N	12%	-1.3
8	O 200-02	237894	1.08	0.96	1.33	-0.25	0.37	Y	23%	0
9	O 200-02	232981.9	1.57	1.37	1.47	0.1	0.1	Y	10%	-1.25
10	O 200-02	235346	1.04	0.72	1.07	-0.03	0.35	Y	25%	0.5
11	O 200-02	23349	1.12	0.88	1.16	-0.04	0.28	Y	14%	-1
12	O 200-02	223740	1.06	0.75	1.26	-0.2	0.51	Y	21%	0.5
13	O 200-02	264125.1	1.13	0.78	1.01	0.12	0.23	Y	3%	1
14	O 200-02	41723	1.13	0.84	1.11	0.02	0.27	Y	20%	-17.5
15	O 200-02	235346	1.1	0.72	1.09	0.01	0.37	Y	28%	-0.3
16	O 200-04	213922.1	1.09	0.81	0.81	0.28	0	N	2%	-4
17	O 200-04	248639.5	1.41	1.00	1.49	-0.08	0.49	Y	27%	-0.2
18	O 200-04	9513.5	1.16	1.05	1.1	0.06	0.05	N	-1%	-12.1
19	O 200-04	9539.75	1.21	0.92	0.87	0.34	-0.05	N	0%	-5

* If the number is negative, the vendor called length or depth is lower than actual.

Table 1. Reassessment dig results.

#	Line	Wheel count	REA RPR	.85 dL RPR	Vendor predicted RPR
1	C 100	112799	1.38	0.78	1.54
2	C 100	86438	1.58	0.94	1.56
3	C 100	191369	1.36	1.16	1.46
4	C 100	261914	1.47	1.07	1.56
5	C 100	291725	1.27	0.82	1.25
6	C 100	294835	1.3	0.84	1.53
7	C 100	196156	1.44	1.06	1.43
8	C 100	297708	1.21	1.03	1.28
9	C 100	311095	1.35	0.79	1.47

Table 2. Software-only EAA results.

excavated proved to have a rupture pressure lower than predicted. There do not appear to be trends in the data that relate to depth error vs accuracy in RPR or length error vs accuracy in RPR. Of the two variables – depth and length – neither seems to have a larger bearing on the data burst pressure outcome. What does stand out is that the reassessment method does more accurately characterize the rupture pressure than does Modified B31G 0.85 dL. Of the anomalies that were dug, the software reassessment was as accurate or more accurate 74% of the time, and it was either more accurate or within 8 psig 84% of the time.

The following is an analysis of the three anomalies that were most severely misrepresented by the software reassessment:

#4 – this anomaly would have been accurately graded based, but the length was reported incorrectly.

#16 – this corrosion was axially oriented and some of the corrosion that was interacting was not being accurately represented on the ILI log (see Figs 2 and 3).

#19 – this corrosion was not accurately represented by the log. It was longer than called, and the general corrosion on the pipe did not show up in the raw data. Modified B31G 0.85 dL also returned a higher RPR than the actual in-the-ditch less conservative EAA.

Of all the anomalies that have been reassessed, investigated, and documented, there is reassurance that the method works. Note that even though the RPRs were different, only one could have been left without investigation based on RPR. The others would have all been remediated within three years based on RPR. And, due to the construction schedule, these anomalies would have all been remediated in two years based on ASME B31.8S-2001 Fig.4 [3]. Add to this analysis a review of close-interval survey and application of cathodic protection: the CIS survey was not reviewed in these areas prior to construction so that data is unavailable; however, cathodic protection is in place and – based on other digs on these lines – the corrosion is believed to be inactive.

Using the new reassessment RPR as described above and Fig.4 of ASME B31.8S-2001 [3], the scheduled response can be modified. Based on the above statements, is a two-year difference in a dig schedule significant? It is unlikely, considering the lines have been in the ground since the early 1930s, and the corrosion has been significantly retarded by the application of CP to the lines.

Even though a two-year difference is not significant, the desire will always be to reassess these anomalies to a lower RPR than actual. Over time, as more anomalies are reassessed and investigated, this method will continue to develop.

The reviewer should begin to take into consideration the width and depth of an anomaly affecting the strength of the field and not just the width. Also, a review of the line's CIS history should be done to get a feel for the activity of the corrosion in an area. Furthermore, the guidelines for reassessment schedule based on RPR are based on a relatively high rate of corrosion. Properly applied CP will prevent the pipe from corroding at such a high rate, which is further reason to believe that a two year difference in remediation schedule is not significant.

Software-based, vendor-backed results

One more set of results that needs to be discussed is on a new run with a different vendor that has not been investigated as of the preparation of this paper. The normal software reassessment was conducted and the data was sent to the analyst for validation; the information was sent back with results attached, and is shown in Table 2 and Fig.5.

Reviewing the results of this analysis shows that the RPR calculated using the software reassessment as described is much closer to the vendor-predicted RPR (using RSTRENG2) than to Modified B31G 0.85dL. The corrosion in the above analysis was either general corrosion over a significant length or multiple interacting pits over a significant length. In this case, 0.85dL was very low, due to a single deep pit. For example, anomaly #8 from Table 2 was called as 19 in long with the deepest pit being 68%. This produced an RPR of 1.03 which is a 90-day dig, according to the company's standard operating procedure. After reviewing this anomaly with the software reassessment, the calculated RPR was 1.21. This type of result is typical for a line such as this one with large areas of interacting corrosion including a small deep pit. It is much simpler to plan a dig two years away as opposed to a dig in 90 days. The 90-day dig will cost more both in money and resources; it also may come at a time when the gas is needed to support the customers downstream. Figure 5 shows the depth predictions of both the company's software-reassessment method and the depth predictions of the ILI vendor. The arrows were drawn on the screen by the ILI vendor analyst to note the pit corresponding to the depth shown.

Conclusions

Industry has known for some time that Modified B31G 0.85dL is more conservative than RSTRENG effective-area analysis. However, most tool vendors running HRMFL tools offer only the length and width of an anomaly for an operator to calculate a burst pressure and a rupture pressure ratio. The data presented above are from actual tool runs and show that effective area analysis can be applied prior to physically touching the pipe based on the tool vendor's ILI data. This method of assessment prior to digging also proves to be more accurate than the operator's other alternative of the RPR produced with Modified B31G 0.85dL.

Is this software method always more conservative than the actual dig results? No; however, in the majority of cases, it still revealed the anomalies that needed attention and provided a timeframe based on RPR that was reasonable. As has been mentioned, the reason for researching this method was so resources could be effectively allocated. Digging anomalies with a raw-data 0.85dL calculation of less than unity (i.e. immediate digs) is not effective if 95% of those prove to have actual RPRs that are in the 1.2 to 1.5 range. One may say that such anomalies needed investigation, but why should the resources be pulled away to investigate an anomaly that proves to have an RPR of 1.5 if other anomalies are delayed which, after investigation, have an RPR that is much lower. This method aggressively pursues knowledge about the actual characteristics of each anomaly without having to dig them all.

The data presented show that this reassessment method works, and provides results that are acceptable and believable. The data and method are validated by in-the-ditch dig results and, in the latter cases (Table 2), by a tool analyst performing a direct analysis on the individual pits comprising the anomaly. The RPR numbers may be off due to misrepresentation of the anomaly by the magnetic field, missed length, and/or due to missed depth; however, the trends in the data prove that an analysis of the anomaly by the operator using effective-area analysis on the ILI data provides an accurate characterization of the actual defect. This software reassessment is another tool in an operator's toolbox to assist in the decision to allocate resources.

References

1. Fu, Stephens, Ritchie, and Jones. Methods for assessing corroded pipeline - review, validation, and recommendations. PRCI Report PR273-9803.
2. Chauhan, Vinod, and W.Sloterdijk. Advances in interaction rules for corrosion defects in pipelines. PRCI Report.
3. Anon., 2002. ASME B31.8S-2001 (Supplement to ASME B31.8): Managing system integrity of gas pipelines - A supplement ASME Code for Pressure Piping, B31. The American Society of Mechanical Engineers, New York.

Acknowledgements

Jerry Rau, Director of Pipeline Integrity, Panhandle Eastern Pipeline Co.
Ross Cummins, Senior Pipeline Integrity Specialist, Panhandle Eastern Pipeline Co.
Lindsey Morisse, Senior Pipeline Integrity Specialist, Panhandle Eastern Pipeline Co.
Steve Atkinson, Senior Pipeline Integrity Specialist, Panhandle Eastern Pipeline Co.
Mike Smith, Senior Corrosion Technician, Panhandle Eastern Pipeline Co.
Justin Shedd, Corrosion Technician, Panhandle Eastern Pipeline Co.

ILI performance verification and assessment

by Guy Desjardins[1], Randy Nickle[2], and Mike Reed[2]

1 Desjardins Integrity Ltd, Calgary, AB, Canada
2 Alliance Pipeline Ltd, Calgary, AB, Canada

API 1163 recommends that operators verify the accuracy of ILI measurements, following an inspection by comparing the results to excavation results. However, the number of excavations required for this verification is left open to interpretation. This paper presents an optimization method for determining the number of excavations, based on the accuracy necessary to maintain the integrity of the pipeline. This method balances the number of excavations required based on ILI accuracy and the increased proven accuracy from an increased number of excavations. This optimum number of excavations enables the operator to demonstrate an accuracy of the ILI tool at level necessary to ensure the continued integrity of the pipeline.

THIS PAPER IS the authors' attempt to address the question of how many excavations are required to verify or validate an in-line inspection (ILI) programme. The context of this question is contained within the ultimate goal of maintaining pipeline integrity in a cost-effective manner.

The objective of a pipeline integrity-management programme (IMP) is to maintain safe and reliable operations. ILI can play a vital role in an IMP by enabling the operator to identify and assess corrosion and other anomalies on the pipeline, so that they may be addressed in a timely fashion. For the operator to have confidence in its IMP, it needs to have confidence in each component of that plan, and ILI is no exception. To build confidence in the ILI tool, the operator needs to confirm the results by excavating the pipeline and comparing the reported anomaly severities with those reported by the tool. The greater the number of comparisons, the greater the amount of confidence the operator has in the assessed performance of the tool.

If the operator has little or no confidence in the sizing accuracy of the ILI tool, as may have been the case with older technology, then the operator might want systematically to excavate all indications after every ILI run. With improved technology, high-resolution tools can reliably detect and assess very small metal-loss anomalies. Because of the sensitivity of the tools, the number of indications can be quite large, and the option of excavating them all is neither feasible nor, from an integrity perspective, necessary. The data delivered by high-resolution MFL (magnetic-flux leakage) ILI affords the operator the option of determining, in advance, which are the most severe indications warranting investigation and leaving the remainder to be monitored.

The goal of this paper is to verify the accuracy of the tool so that the operator can have confidence in the maintenance programme. The verification of the ILI is usually done in conjunction with a number of excavations and repairs on the pipeline.

While the primary goal of an excavation is usually to maintain pipeline integrity, a by-product of the excavation is the verification of the ILI-tool accuracy. The level of accuracy which can be verified depends on the number of anomaly comparisons. The operator is interested in the ILI

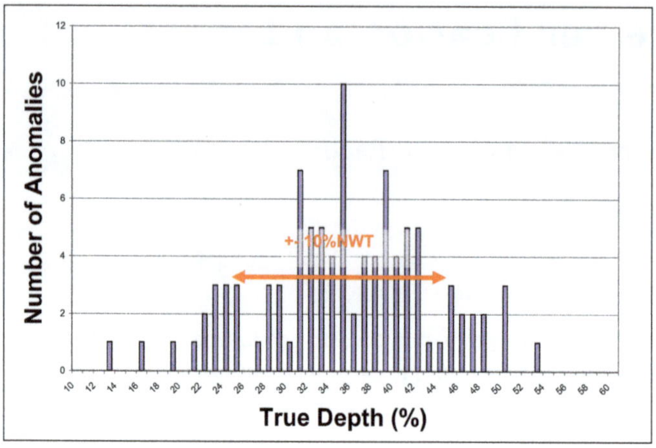

Fig. 1. An example of the scatter that the true depths of 100 anomalies might have, given that they all have a reported depth of 35%NWT.

accuracy for the whole population of anomalies. The excavations typically only expose a sample from that population. The performance of the tool on the sample can be a good indicator of the performance on the total population, but because of random variability, the global accuracy can only be calculated within some confidence interval.

As part of this project, we want to determine the optimum number of excavations. For this paper, the optimum number of excavations is the number of excavations needed to sufficiently assess the accuracy of the ILI tool and to maintain the safe operation of the pipeline. The safe operation of the pipeline is ultimately the primary goal.

The general procedure to determine the required number of excavations on a pipeline is finally applied to the Alliance Pipeline system.

ILI accuracy

The main subject of this paper is the assessment of the accuracy of the ILI data. ILI accuracy is typically stated in terms of a tolerance and a certainty; for example, in the stated accuracy of "±10% of nominal wall thickness (NWT) 80% of the time", the tolerance is "±10%NWT", and the certainty is "80% of the time".

Figure 1 illustrates an example of the scatter that the true depths of 100 anomalies might have, given that they all have a reported depth of 35%NWT. If the operator were to excavate and examine each of these anomalies, he would expect that 80 anomalies would have a true depth of between 25%NWT and 45%NWT, and the remaining 20 anomalies would have a depth outside this interval. The certainty (80%) is the ratio of the number of anomaly measurements that are within tolerance to the total number of measurements. A certainty of 80% of the time is more accurate than 70%, but less accurate than 90% of the time, for a fixed tolerance. Similarly a tolerance of ±10%NWT is more accurate than ±15%NWT but less accurate than ± 5%NWT, for a fixed certainty.

Without further assumptions about the distribution of tool error, it is difficult to compare accuracies when both the tolerance and certainty differ: for example whether ±15%NWT 95% of the time is more or less accurate than ±10%NWT 80% of the time.

In order to compare and convert accuracies, we need make some assumption about the distribution of ILI errors. If the distribution of tool error is normal, as illustrated in Figure 2, (that

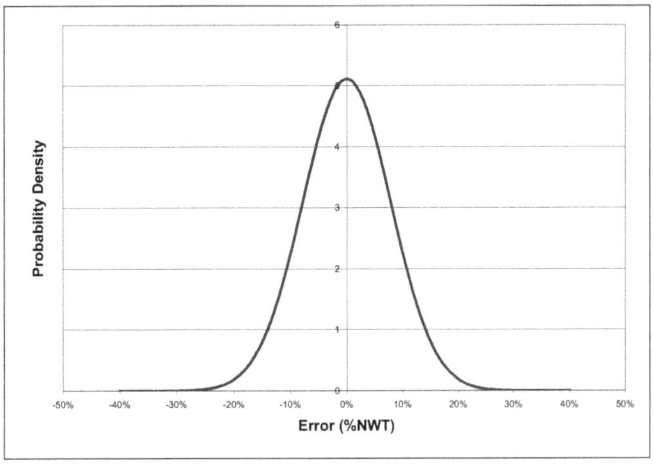

Fig.2. A normal distribution of tool error.

is it follows the typical bell-curve distribution) then various ways of stating ILI accuracy can be compared and converted.

If we can assume that the distribution of ILI error is normal, then we can compare and equate different ways of stating accuracy. For example ±10%NWT 80% of the time is equivalent to:

±7.8%NWT 68% of the time; and
±15.3%NWT 95% of the time.

In this paper, we will generally state accuracy in terms of a constant tolerance (that is ±10%NWT) with a variable certainty 70, 80, or 90% of the time. With a normal assumption these accuracies can also be converted into a fixed certainty and variable tolerance, if we are more comfortable with that form.

Benefits of accurate ILI data

While it should be intuitively obvious that more-accurate ILI data are better than less-accurate data, the benefits can also be quantified. With greater accuracy, the operator has confidence in the accuracy of the ILI data; he trusts the reported severity of anomalies and can use the ILI data to make integrity decisions. If the operator lacks confidence in the accuracy of the data, then he can't trust the reported depths to the same degree. The result is that, with less-accurate data, the operator tends to excavate more anomalies to account for ILI uncertainty.

In the past, low-resolution MFL tools reported relatively few anomalies, and the sizing accuracy of these tools could not be relied upon. Thus many operators typically excavated all indications reported by the ILI tool.

Today, high-resolution tools are much more accurate and report much larger numbers of indications. The excavation of all indications is no longer practical on most pipelines. Fortunately the accuracy of the tools has improved, so that the excavation of all anomalies is not necessary.

The decision about which anomalies need to be excavated and possibly repaired should be partly based on the accuracy of the ILI tool. Figure 3 illustrates the relationship between the excavation threshold and the accuracy of the ILI tool: the excavation threshold, in this example, is the maximum reported anomaly depth which the operator is willing to leave unexcavated.

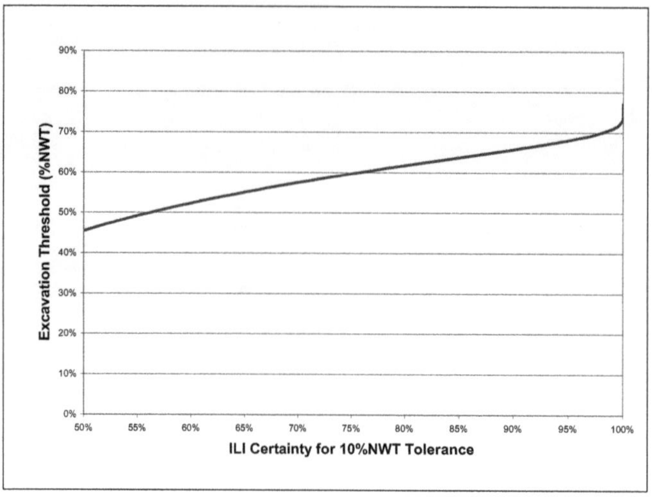

Fig.3. The relationship between the excavation threshold and the accuracy of the ILI tool.

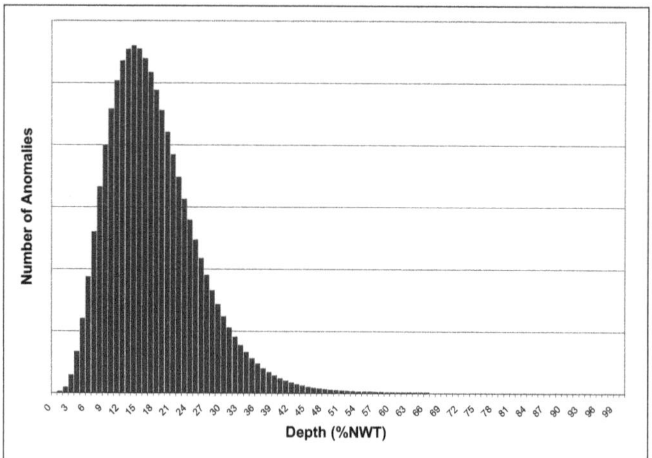

Fig.4. A typical distribution of ILI reported corrosion depths on a pipeline.

In Fig.3, the line shows the excavation threshold as a function of ILI tool accuracy. The threshold is based on 1.8 times tool tolerance at 80% certainty, and is equivalent to a 1% POE (probability of exceedance) threshold. If the tool tolerance is ±10%NWT 80% of the time, then any anomaly within 18%NWT of 80%NWT requires excavation. The x-axis is the accuracy of the ILI tool in terms of the certainty. With a tool accuracy of ±10%NWT 65% of the time, the operator would need to excavate all anomalies with a reported depth deeper than 55%NWT. However, with a tool accuracy of ±10%NWT 90% of the time, the operator can set the excavation threshold much higher at a reported depth of 65%NWT. The reason for the change in excavation threshold is that the higher accuracy gives the operator confidence that a corrosion anomaly reported at 60%NWT, for example, is not significantly deeper than reported and does not exceed 80%NWT. Conversely, with a lower accuracy, the operator does not have that same confidence.

The tangible benefit of highly accurate ILI data can be assessed by considering the number of excavations required with highly accurate data versus less-accurate data. Figure 4 shows a typical distribution of ILI reported corrosion depths on a pipeline.

The number of anomalies which would need to be excavated is a function of the excavation threshold. The relationship between the number of anomalies to be excavated and the accuracy of the ILI tool is illustrated in Fig.5. With accurate ILI data, the number of anomalies which need

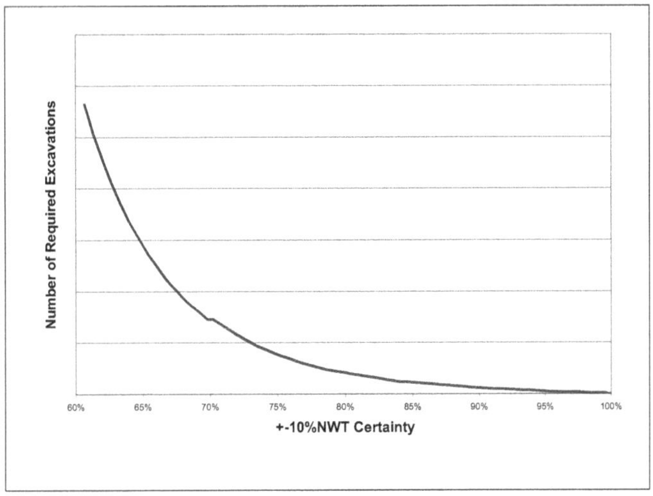

Fig.5. The relationship between the number of anomalies to be excavated and the accuracy of the ILI tool.

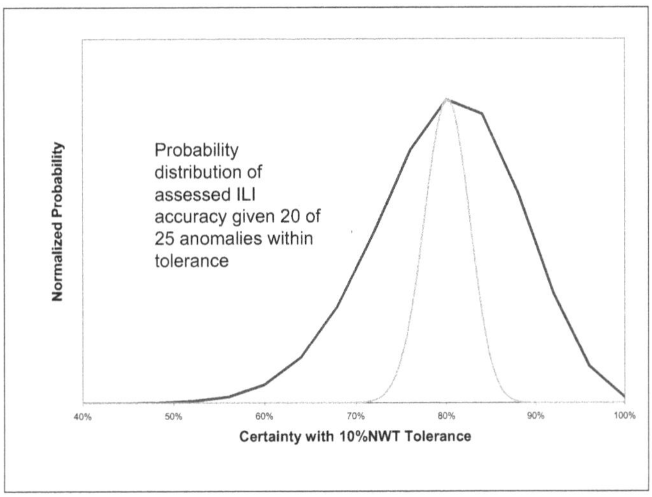

Fig.6. The location of the peak illustrates that the best estimate of the accuracy is ±10%NWT 80% of the time.

to be excavated is relatively small. However with less-accurate data, the number of anomalies needing excavation increases quickly.

ILI accuracy assessment and the effect of the number of excavations

A typical quoted accuracy for a high-resolution MFL ILI is ±10%NWT 80% of the time. API 1163 requires operators to verify the accuracy of their in-line inspections. To validate the ILI run, the operator typically compares the reported anomaly sizes to their actual sizes, usually from an excavation. (Special care must be taken when the field measurements have significant measurement error.) Statistically, the uncertainty in the assessed accuracy is dependent on the number of excavated anomalies.

To verify the accuracy of an ILI run, the operator needs to estimate two parameters: tolerance (±10%NWT, for example) and the certainty (80% of the time). Increasing the number of excavated anomalies increases the accuracy of the estimate of these two parameters.

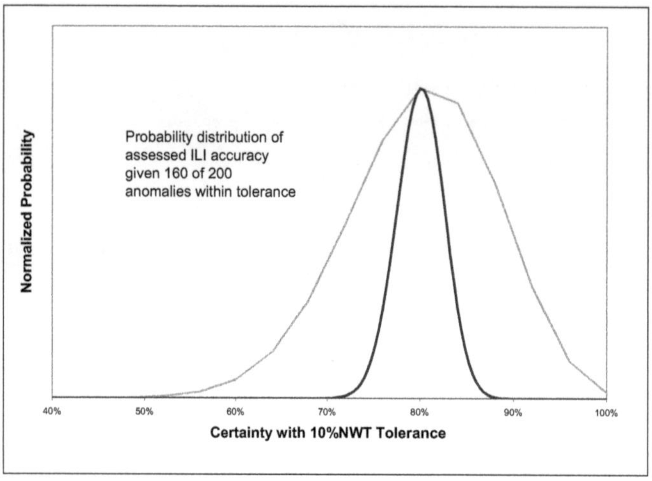

Fig.7. The narrowing of the dark blue probability curve illustrates higher confidence in the best estimate of the accuracy.

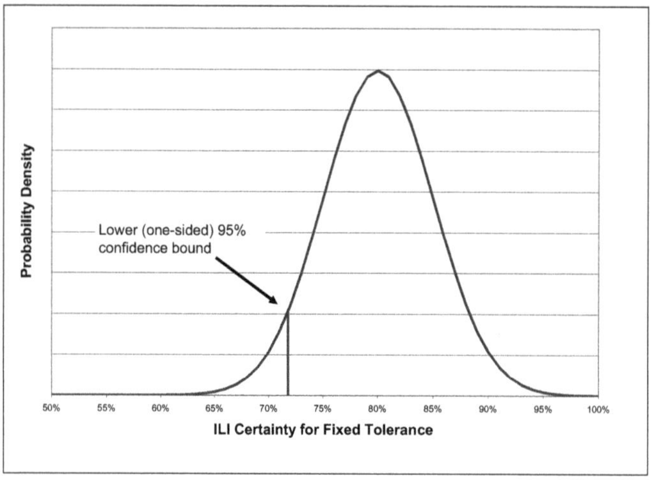

Fig.8. The lower 95% confidence bound.

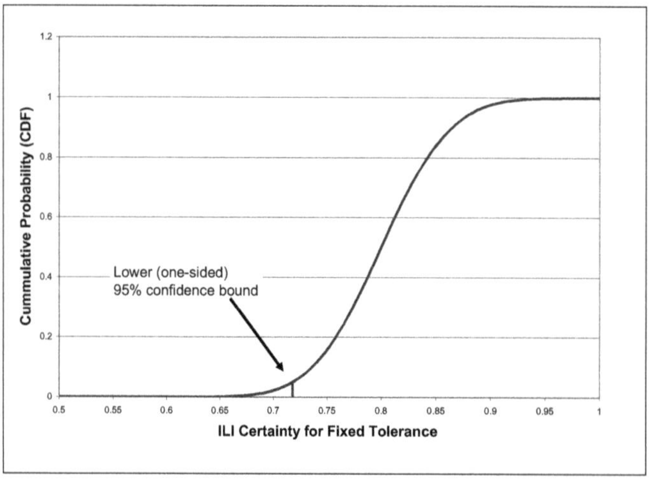

Fig.9. The lower 95% confidence bound.

To illustrate the significance of the number of excavated anomalies on the assessed accuracy, Figs 6 and 7 show the difference in the confidence of the assessed accuracy for 25 and 200 excavated anomalies, respectively. If an operator excavates only 25 anomalies – of which 20 are within tolerance of 10%NWT – then the best estimate of the accuracy is ±10%NWT 80% of the time, which is indicated by the location of the peak in Fig.6. The width, however, of the distribution

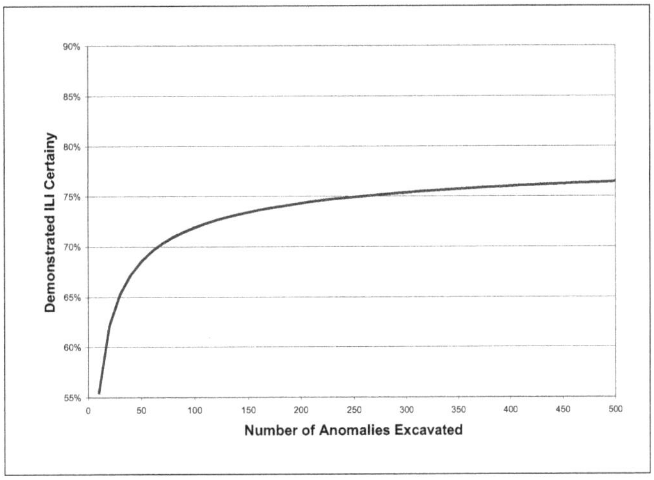

Fig.10. The increase in the lower 95% confidence bound with increasing numbers of excavated anomalies.

is an indicator of the confidence in that estimate. Thus, because of random variation, the true accuracy might be anywhere within the probability distribution in the dark blue line.

If the number of excavated anomalies is increased to 200 - with 160 anomalies within tolerance - then the remains at ±10%NWT 80%, but the confidence of that estimate is much higher, as indicated by the narrowing of the dark blue probability curve in Fig.7.

The width of the probability curves in Figs 6 and 7 indicate the level of confidence in the assessed accuracy: a wide probability curve indicates low confidence and a narrow sharp probability curve indicates a high level of confidence. The width of the curve decreases with increasing number of excavated anomalies.

The goal of this paper is to determine the number of required excavations to verify an ILI run. The number of excavations depends on the level of certainty the operator requires in the assessed accuracy of the tool. The question remains, however, of how much certainty is required.

Pipeline integrity engineers tend to make conservative assumptions about the integrity of their pipelines. For example, the actual wall thickness tends to be thicker than nominal wall thickness; and actual yield strength tends to be greater than the SMYS (specified minimum yield strength). Thus it seems reasonable that if we are faced with some uncertainty about the true accuracy of the ILI tool, we should take a conservative approach and assume an accuracy which the true accuracy of the tool is very likely to exceed. One approach would be to assume the lower 95% confidence bound on the assessed certainty. The lower 95% confidence bound is illustrated in Figs 8 and 9.

The effect of increasing the number of excavated anomalies is to reduce the uncertainty in the accuracy assessment of the ILI data. Reducing uncertainty causes the probability distribution of the assessed certainty to become narrower. If the location of the central peak remains fixed, then as the probability curve narrows, the lower 95% confidence bound on the ILI accuracy will increase towards the central peak. Figure 10 illustrates this increase in the lower 95% bound with increasing numbers of excavated anomalies.

This lower 95% confidence bound on the certainty of the ILI reported depths increases with the number of excavated anomalies. So with only 20 excavated anomalies, (assuming that 16 of those anomalies have depths within a ±10%NWT tolerance) the lower bound accuracy is ±10%NWT 60% of the time. With 160 of 200 within tolerance, the lower 95% confidence bound on the ILI

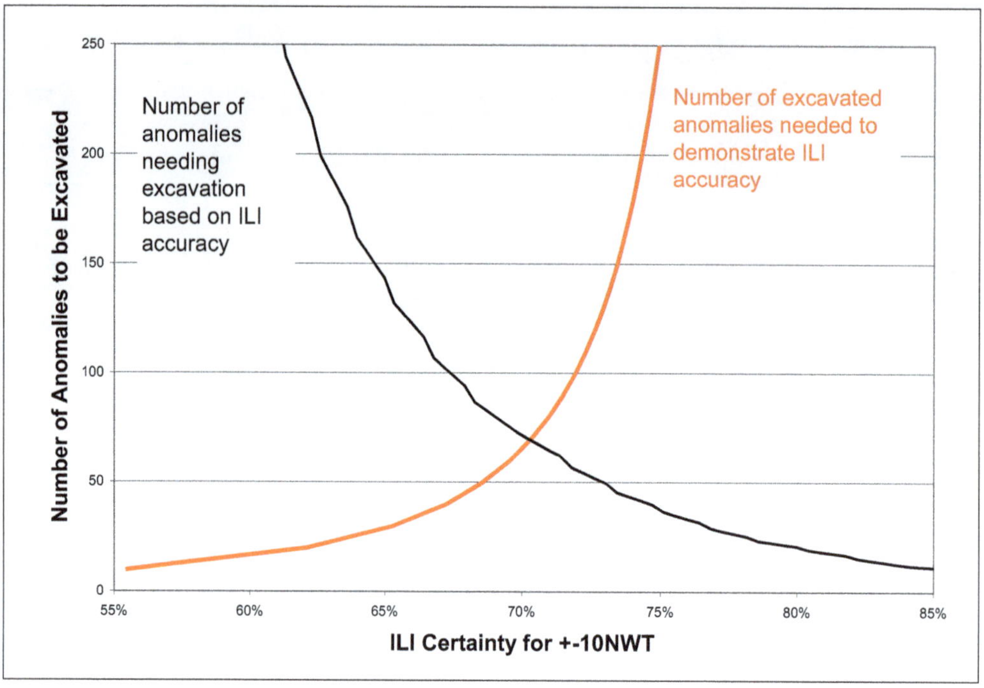

Fig.11. The concept of the optimized number of excavations.

accuracy increases to ±10%NWT 74% of the time. Note that no number of excavations can demonstrate that the tool is more accurate than it actually is. Thus the curve in Fig.10 asymptotically approaches 80% certainty, with increased number of excavated anomalies.

Instead of asking how many excavations we need to verify the accuracy of the tool, we now ask "What level of accuracy is required to ensure pipeline integrity programmes are properly managed?" The reason for this change is that we can relate the accuracy of the tool to the benefit of high accuracy ILI data, which can reduce the number of excavations. Ultimately, we can relate the accuracy of the tool to the development of a program meto manage pipeline integrity.

Optimum number of excavated anomalies

The two sections above discuss two aspects of ILI accuracy and the number of excavations. On one hand, highly accurate ILI data allow the operator to excavate fewer anomalies because of the confidence in the assessed severity. On the other hand, the number of excavated anomalies enables the operator to demonstrate or verify greater accuracy of the data (assuming that the tool is, indeed, accurate). These two competing effects may be balanced so that the number of excavations simultaneously satisfies all of our integrity concerns and also proves the accuracy the tool necessary to confidently leave all remaining anomalies in the ground for future monitoring.

Figure 11 illustrates the concept of the optimized number of excavations, and is a combination of two previous figures, Figs 5 and 10. (The axes of Fig.5 have been transposed to conform to Fig.10.) The blue line in the figure shows the number of anomalies which need to be excavated for a given ILI tool accuracy: the number of anomalies needing excavation decreases with increasing accuracy. The orange line shows the number of excavated anomalies needed to demonstrate a given ILI tool accuracy: the number of excavated anomalies needed to verify a given

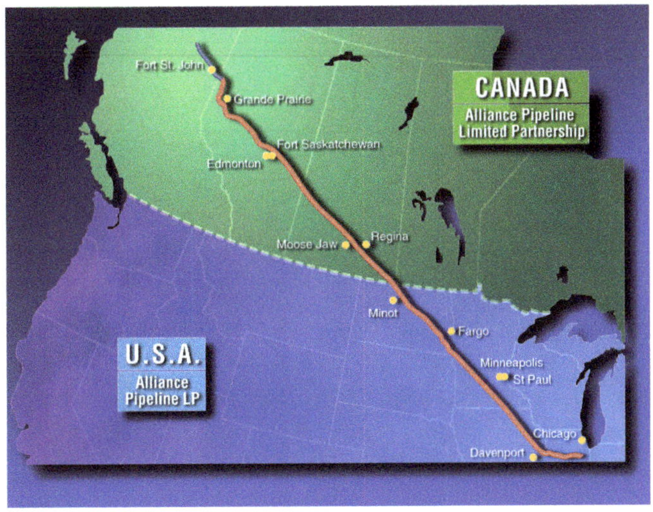

Fig.12a. The Alliance pipeline system.

accuracy increases with ILI accuracy. At the intersection, the operator simultaneously satisfies all integrity concerns and proves the tool accuracy necessary to confidently leave all remaining anomalies in the ground for future monitoring.

Practical considerations

Thus far in this paper, the optimization procedure has been idealized somewhat. The implementation of this procedure in practice is likely to require some adaptation. The procedure works best if the anomalies are all excavated in decreasing order of severity, and the accuracy is reassessed after each excavation. However, from an operations' point of view, the operator may need to excavate all or most sites in a short period of time. Also, random variability of the accuracy assessment may cause the assessed accuracy of the tool to initially increase and decrease randomly with increased excavations. Eventually the assessment will settle at or near the true accuracy of the tool.

Alliance Pipeline

This analysis was applied to the Alliance pipeline which runs from Ft St John, BC. to Chicago, IL. The Alliance Canadian and US mainline systems were completely baseline inspected with the high-resolution BJ *Vectra* MFL tool between 2002 and 2005. As of the spring of 2006, a total of 19 anomalies were excavated.

Assessment of accuracy on the Alliance system

The unity graph of the field and ILI results is shown in Fig.12. The comparison of the field-measured depths and the ILI-reported depths found 16 anomaly depths within tolerance. However, we noticed that the ILI tool over-stated the depth of all the anomalies. The average over call is approximately 6%NWT.

Assuming that the difference between the ILI and the field depths is solely due to the ILI tool, we subtracted the difference from the ILI depths, and Fig.13 shows the unity graph of the field and adjusted ILI results. After the adjustment, the comparison of the field-measured depths and the ILI-reported depths found 15 anomaly depths within a tolerance of ±5%NWT. These results yield

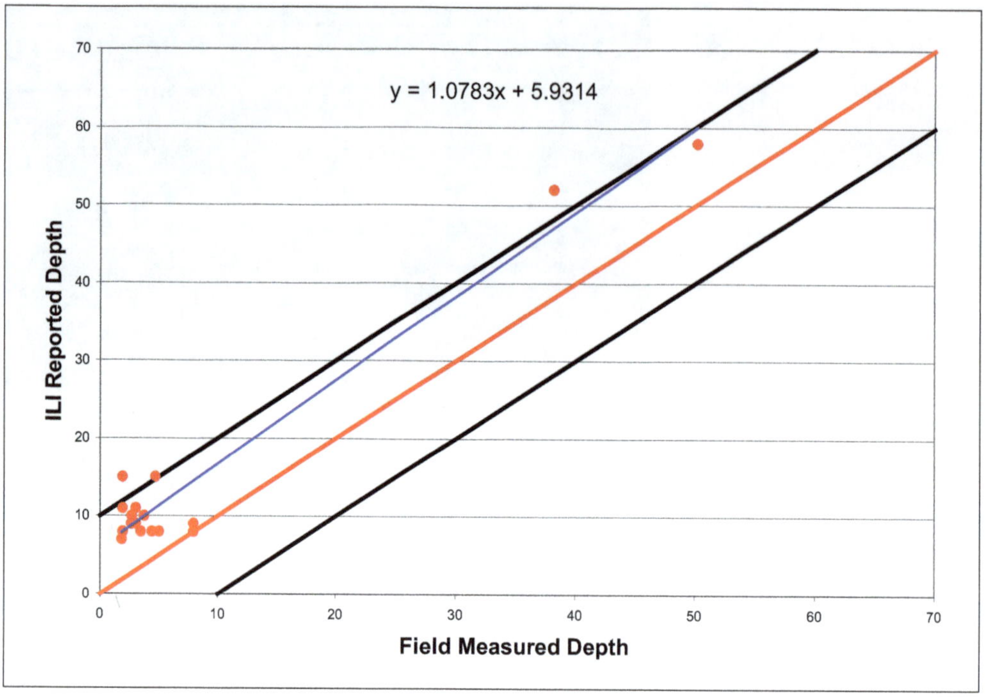

Fig. 12b. Unity graph of the field and ILI results for the Alliance pipeline.

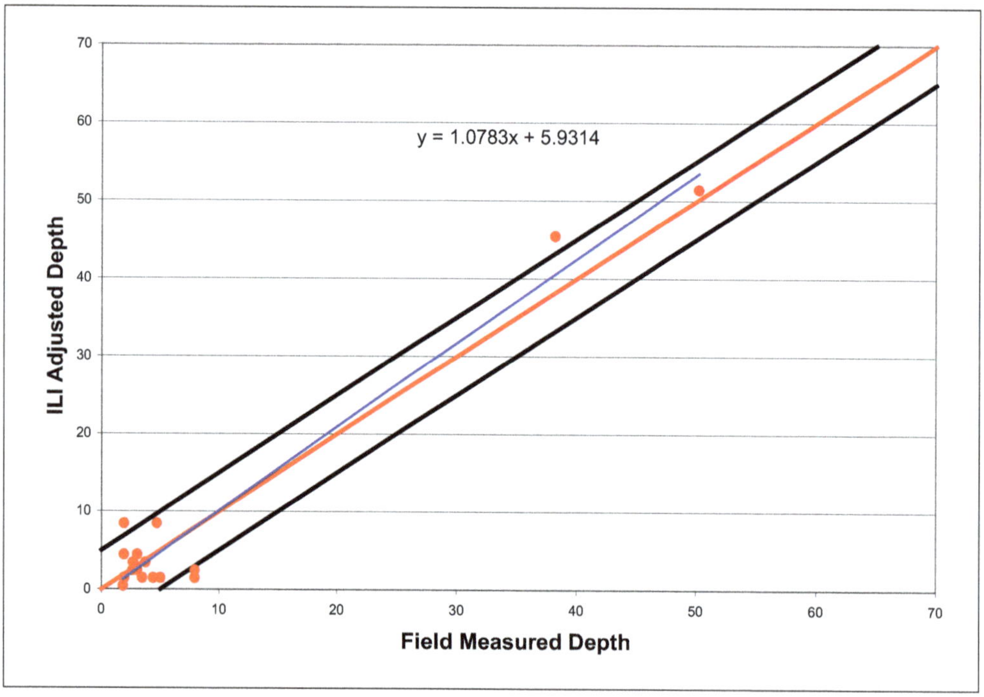

Fig. 13. Unity graph of the field and adjusted ILI results for the Alliance pipeline.

a best estimate of accuracy of ±5%NWT 78% of the time. The 95% lower-bound estimate is ±5%NWT 64% of the time, which is equivalent to approximately ±6%NWT 80% of the time.

With this analysis, Alliance is able to use the demonstrated accuracy, ±6%NWT 80% of the time, to plan and conduct its integrity-maintenance programme.

Conclusions

Increased accuracy of ILI provides the confidence in the data when developing an excavation programme to manage pipeline integrity. Increasing excavations provides greater certainty in the ILI accuracy assessment. By balancing these two effects, the operator can develop an excavation programme that addresses ILI anomalies with greater certainty.

Future work

Since the writing of this paper, Alliance has investigated six additional anomalies, and the results of these assessments will be incorporated into this analysis. Alliance also plans to further refine this analysis to assess the accuracy separately of the various wall thickness ranges on the mainline pipe.

Acknowledgements

The authors wish to thank Alliance Pipeline for its support of this work.

References

1. API 1163, 2005. In-line inspection systems qualification standard. American Petroleum Institute, First edition.
2. R.V.Hogg, J.W.McKean, and A.T.Craig, 2005. Introduction to mathematical statistics. 6th Edition, Prentice Hall.
3. A.Bhatia, N.S.Mangat, and T.B.Morrison, 1998. Estimation of measurement errors. Proc. International Pipeline Conference, 1, pp 315-325, Calgary, Alberta, May.
4. G.Desjardins, M.Reed, and R.Nickle, 2006. ILI performance verification and assessment using statistical hypothesis testing. Proc. International Pipeline Conference, Paper 10329.
5. G.Desjardins, 2005. Assessing ILI tool performance. NACE Corrosion, Paper 05164.
6. R.McCann, R.McNealy, and M.Gao, 2007. In-line inspection performance verification. NACE Corrosion, Paper 07132.

Development and application of local corrosion growth rates for pipeline integrity assessments

by Pamela J Moreno[1], Neil A Bates[2], David A R Shanks[2], William V Harper[3], David J Stucki[3], Clifford J Maier[4], and Dr Thomas A Bubenik[4]

1 Det Norske Veritas, Katy, TX, USA
2 Det Norske Veritas, Calgary, AB, Canada
3 Otterbein University, Mathematical Sciences Dept, Westerville, OH, USA
4 Det Norske Veritas, Dublin, OH, USA

PIPELINE-INTEGRITY assessments are often based on conditions that are assumed constant over long sections of pipeline – perhaps entire pipeline systems. Such assumptions generally lead to conservative but unrealistic corrosion-growth-based results. As integrity-assessment methodologies continue to evolve, so does the ability to account for local conditions. When multiple in-line inspections of a given pipeline segment have been performed, statistically active corrosion (SAC) methods may be used to estimate local corrosion growth rates.

By incorporating local growth rates into the analysis, fewer features will require mitigation. It is also possible that the reinspection frequency can be extended. These cost savings can be recognized by operators that use corrosion-growth rates determined using statistical multi-inspection comparisons.

This paper presents one SAC method that has been used to reduce the number of excavations and extend the reinspection interval for several pipeline operators. A case is presented in which the local corrosion-growth rates from an SAC analysis will be compared against growth rate values traditionally used in probability of exceedance (POE) analyses. Additionally, verification of SAC growth rates by examination of the raw signal data is addressed.

REMAINING-LIFE ASSESSMENTS are often based on assumptions about corrosion rates that, while conservative, can lead to unrealistic results. Excess conservatism can also lead to short reassessment intervals and unnecessary or misguided mitigation. This paper discusses how data analyses can be used to identify and verify areas where corrosion is actually taking place. By identifying and addressing these areas, operators can minimize unnecessary mitigation measures while maximizing reassessment intervals.

An in-line inspection identifies metal loss such as corrosion but does not determine if the corrosion is active (i.e. growing) or inactive (i.e. mitigated). Conversely, above-ground cathodic protection (CP) surveys reveal areas where corrosion activity may exist, but they reveal nothing about corrosion depth or severity. Both in-line inspection and above-ground surveys present a mere snapshot in time that doesn't necessarily reflect future conditions.

Statistical comparisons of two or more sets of inspection data are sometimes used to identify areas of possible corrosion growth, but they may not identify all areas of corrosion activity. As a result, pipeline operators cannot readily gain an understanding of where and how quickly corrosion is taking place.

This paper discusses an integrated approach to identifying corrosion activity using a combination of statistics, inspection-signal comparisons, and engineering analyses. The approach relies on a full understanding of the mechanisms that cause corrosion and its growth. Pipeline operators can use this approach to calculate remaining lives (thus preventing failure), prioritize repairs and mitigation, and (at times) extend reassessment intervals.

The approach uses statistical analyses to identify areas where growth may be occurring, while non-statistical approaches are employed to identify locations that may be missed by the use of statistics alone. Inspection signal comparisons confirm where real change has taken place, and a good understanding of corrosion mechanisms helps in determining remaining life by estimating mean and maximum corrosion growth rates. Ultimately, local corrosion rates are determined, which can help operators better prioritize repairs and set re-assessment intervals as compared with approaches where uniform corrosion growth rates are assumed.

This process is collectively known as statistically-active corrosion (SAC). The SAC output is a robust set of locations where change is occurring along with estimates of corrosion-growth rates. The SAC results can then be used in calculating probabilities of exceedance (POE) and subsequent development of mitigation plans. Here, uncertainties in growth rates and defect depths and lengths are used to estimate the likelihood of a release as a function of time and location. A case study is given to illustrate the practical methodology and its potential to generate cost savings.

The statistically-active corrosion methodology

Identifying corrosion activity

Corrosion identification and growth estimation benefits from a combination of statistical analysis and engineering assessment of raw signal data from the inspections. Statistical methods can be used to quickly analyse an entire pipeline and identify specific areas for raw signal assessment for validation. Additionally, spot signal assessment of some areas where statistical techniques did not find active corrosion provides validation concerning potential false negatives.

Statistical comparison of inspection data

Matching pit-to-pit depths over multiple in-line inspections is a common technique that is not easy and is fraught with potential difficulties. One challenge relates to orphan features (features reported by one inspection and not another) and how those are treated in the analysis. Historically, attempts to identify active corrosion growth were focused on investigation of only portions of the pipeline where 'sufficient' data were available on all runs. Conversely, the approach described in this paper (known as a statistically-active corrosion assessment) considers all data. In the SAC approach, various 'safety nets' are developed based on the individual inspections to allow statistical comparisons over time, even when ideal conditions do not exist.

The SAC methodology is an evolving process blending engineering assessment of raw inspection signals, along with the associated statistical analysis of data generally provided by inspection vendors. Thus, while the statistical methods are generally more global in perspective, the engineering components of SAC do incorporate pit-to-pit comparisons where appropriate. When signal data are analysed, this parallel analysis provides a critical quality feedback loop to both validate results and ensure completeness. While the main focus is often on corrosion growth based on depth, the methodology can be applied to other metrics of interest such as length growth or volume of metal loss.

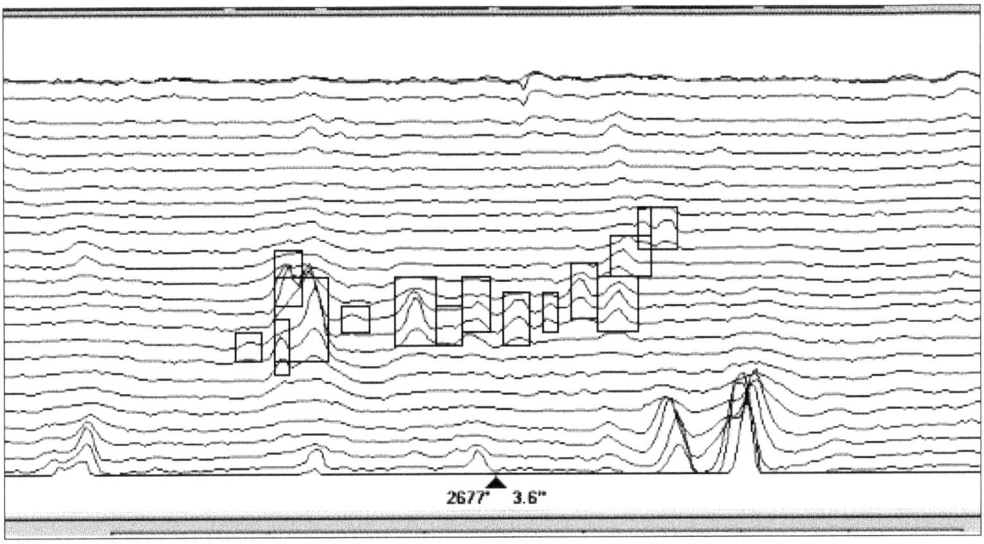

Fig. 1. Box-by-box comparison.

A variety of statistical methods is used, as appropriate to the given situation. The analysis is performed both on moving windows (of usually 30-m or 100-ft length) and on joints. Depending on the operator's needs to either establish general corrosion-growth rates over contiguous areas, or to pinpoint specific joints of concern, the output options are numerous, including potential summary information such as km/mi ranking, worst 25 joints, etc.

Results are based on average depth changes over time (for joints or windows), maximum pit depth change over time, or items such as whether there is a statistically significant increase in the number of reported features over time along the pipeline. The desired confidence level may be specified for statistical significance, which can be important when identifying areas of the pipeline for further investigation. For example, in a pipeline with numerous features, the operator may want to focus only on those areas where it is 95% confident that there is active corrosion. For a pipeline with less data in a risk-averse situation (perhaps in a high-consequence area), the operator may want to be in a more exploratory preventive mode using a lower confidence level to alleviate potential future issues well before they might materialize.

The statistical comparison is improved by reviewing the alignment of box dimensions (shown in Fig. 1), as provided by the ILI vendor in the length, width, and depth measurements provided, and these are typically provided in a spreadsheet format. Through a comparison of these anomaly dimensions, small localized areas of corrosion growth can be characterized for further investigation.

In addition to being able to characterize corrosion growth rates along the pipeline for subsequent use (such as a probability of exceedance (POE)) analysis, SAC can be used for remaining useful life analysis, providing not only point estimates but also the associated confidence intervals. Having such analysis information provides a safety factor that may be used to extend the life of a pipeline or to help establish sound re-inspection intervals.

Comparisons using raw ILI data

In most cases, an automated approach alone is very challenging and prone to misconceptions. In such cases, comparing the actual signals recorded in each inline inspection run can improve the

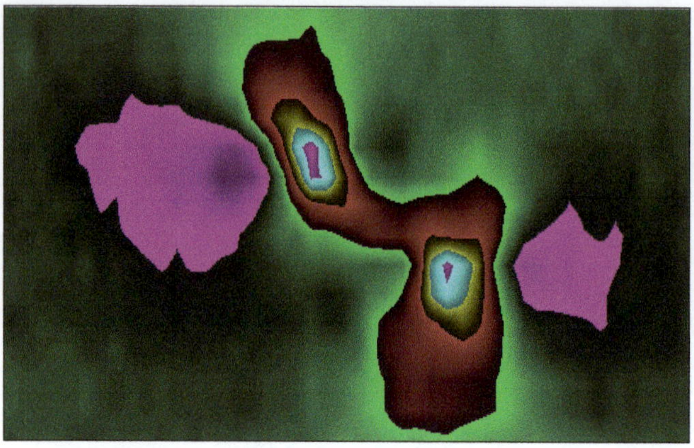

Fig.2. Anomaly-by-anomaly comparison.

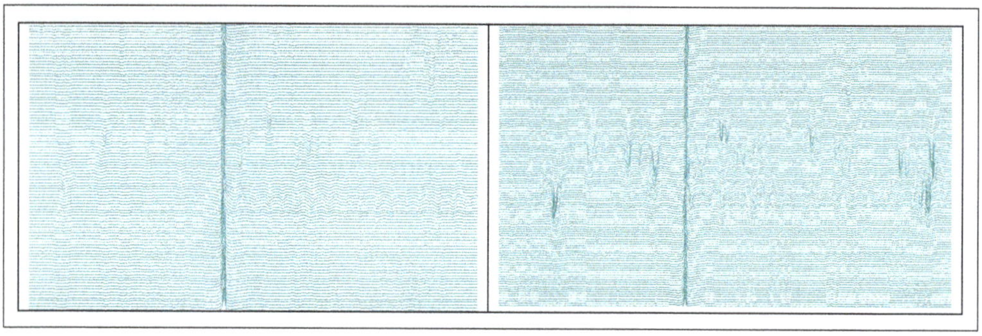

Fig.3. Comparison of same the portion of line from and older inspection (left) with a more-recent inspection (right).

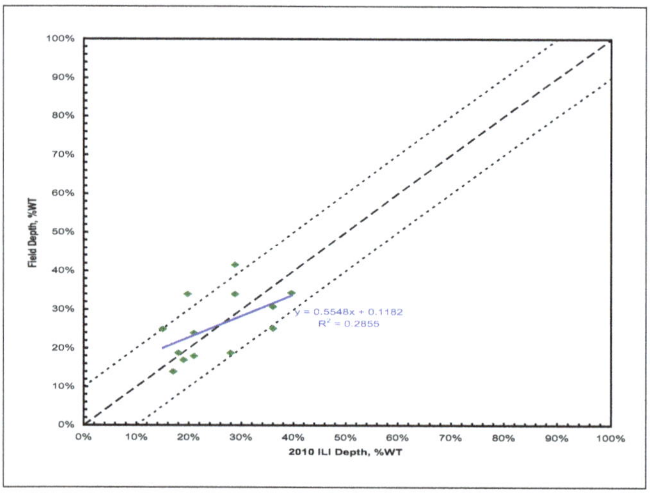

Fig.4. Simple unity plot between ILI depth and field depth.

automated approach. By comparing actual signals (see Fig.2), low levels of corrosion growth can be verified or removed from consideration. This is often useful in determining differences in tool recording capabilities versus actual corrosion growth on a pipeline segment. Anomaly-by-anomaly comparison may also be useful when a particular anomaly needs to be reviewed over several inspections to determine its severity and/or origin.

There are many aspects to the evaluation of raw signal data. Figure 3 shows the change in raw

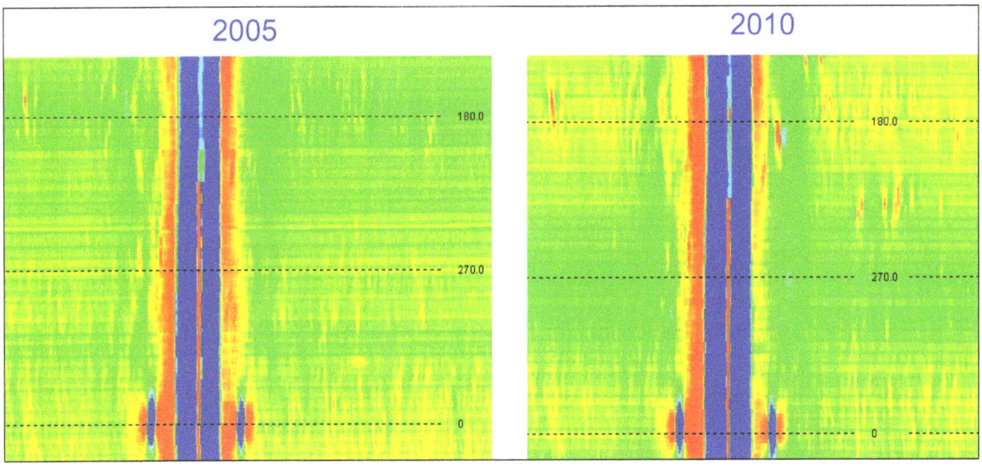

Fig.5. Comparison between 2005 and 2010 data representing probable significant growth.

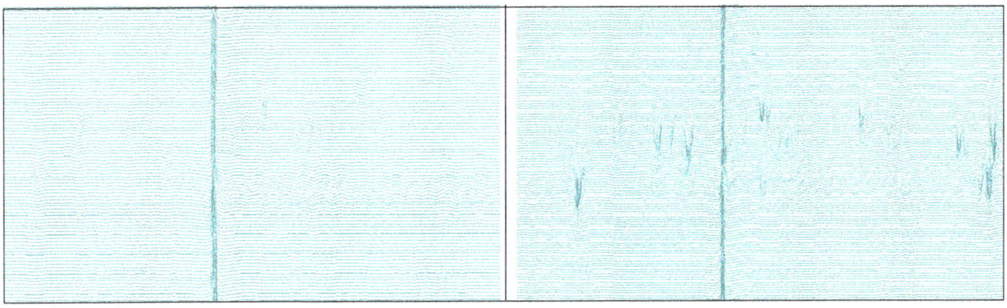

Fig.6. Comparison between 2005 and 2010 data representing possible significant growth.

Fig.7. Comparison between 2005 and 2010 data representing possible growth.

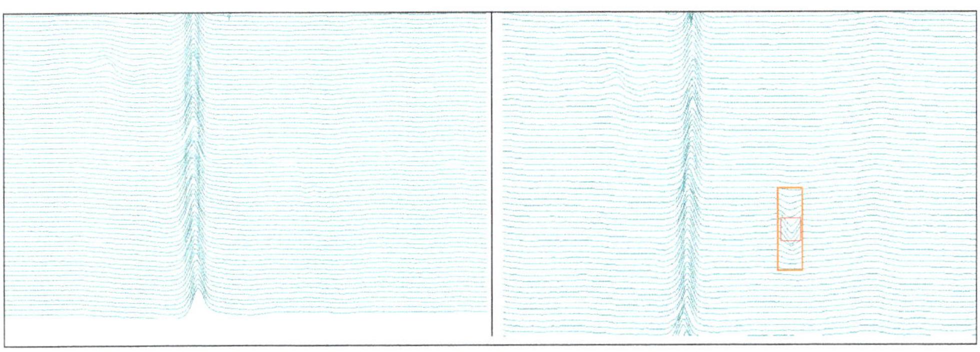

Fig.8. Comparison between 2005 and 2010 data representing possible growth.

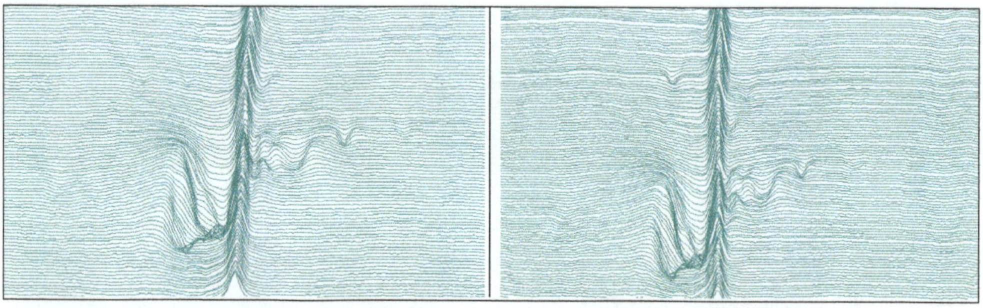

Fig.9. Comparison between 2005 and 2010 data representing possible minor growth.

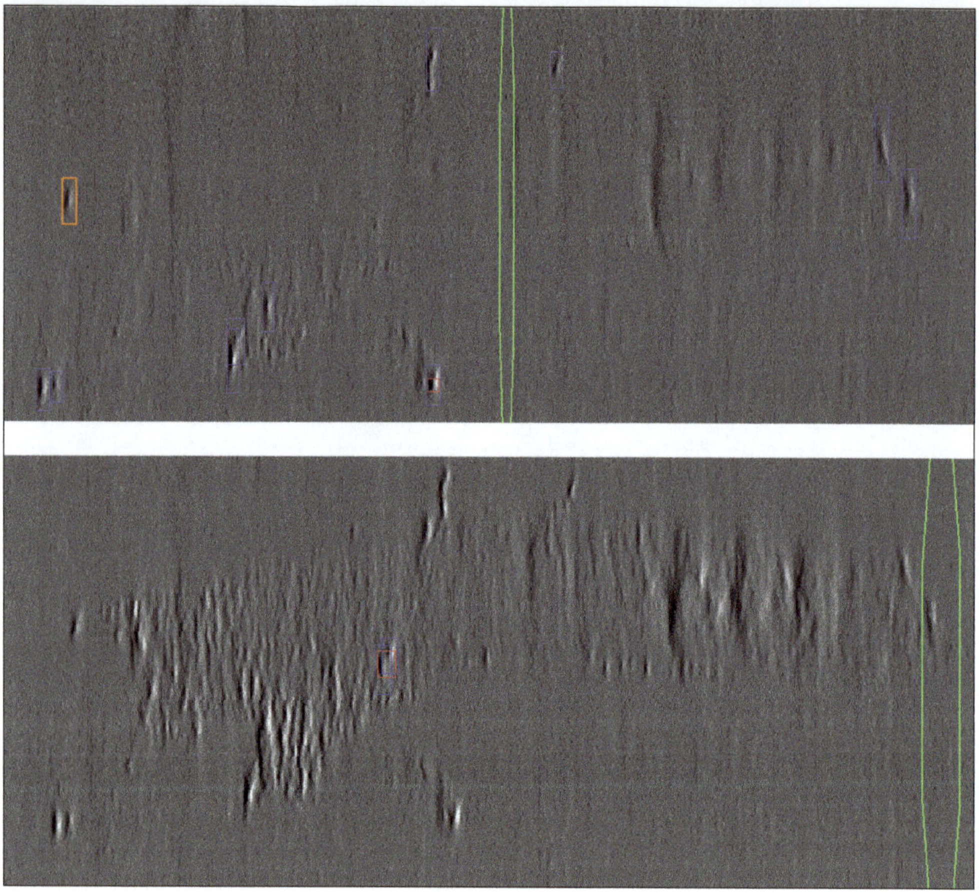

Fig.10. Comparison between 2005 and 2010 data representing possible significant growth.

signals over a four-year time horizon for one pipeline section. This figure verifies the SAC analysis that found this portion of the pipeline to have statistically active corrosion.

Raw ILI data is also used to review previous excavation results from both the previous and the current ILI data. Unity plots, as shown in Fig.4, can then be created using the verified anomalies from each data set.

Once the accuracy of the survey is verified, the sensitivity of surveys can be matched to represent the actual condition of the pipeline as closely as possible. This results in a good ILI representation of the actual condition of the pipeline. These results can then be used to match the ILI data sets

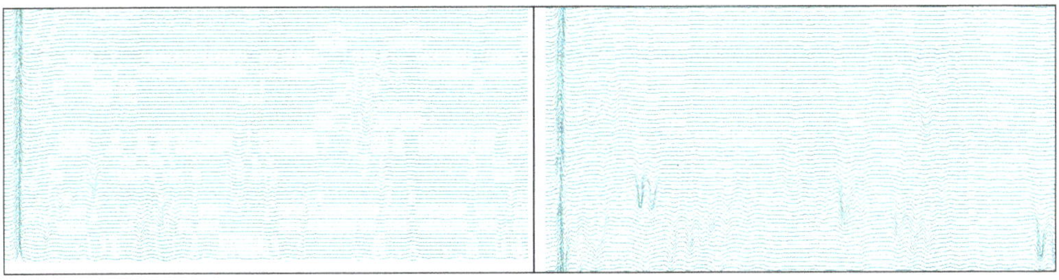

Fig.11. Comparison between 2005 and 2010 data representing possible significant growth.

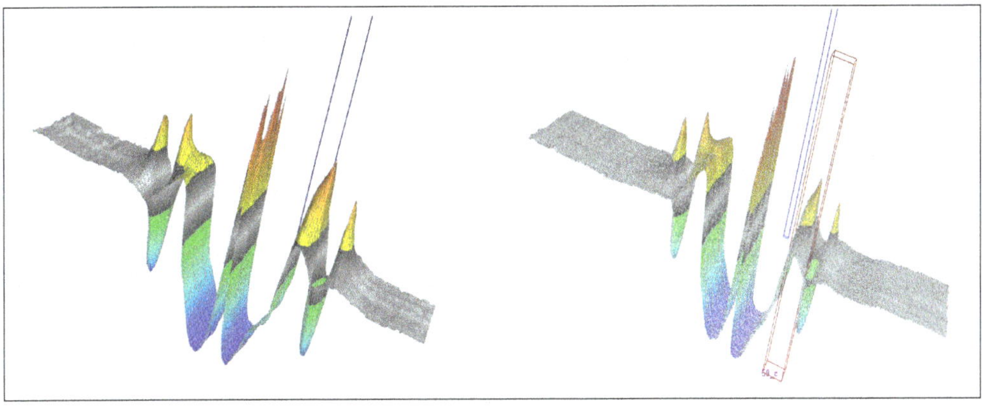

Fig.12. Comparison between 2005 and 2010 data for anomalies near girth weld.

in sensitivity to ensure that standard tool differences have been removed prior to the statistical processing.

The statistical work can now be completed. Here the potential hot spots of corrosion growth are identified utilizing multiple statistical comparison methods, such as:

- Statistically significant differences in the mean depth in 2010 versus 2005.
- Unusual differences in the numbers of anomalies graded per joint in 2010 versus 2005.
- Unusual differences in the maximum depth in 2010 versus 2005.
- Overall highest depths in 2010.
- Areas with small numbers of anomalies but high SAC growth rates.
- Areas that have appeared to have 'healed' themselves.
- Other joints which stood out in the statistical analysis as unusual or likely to have had growth.

Figures 5-11 show various ILI vendor software representations of areas identified in this type of procedure. These areas are identified as active corrosion through the comparison of the multiple ILI raw data sets.

Common issues that can result in 'false' hot spots are:

- The two ILI tools may have a different number of sensors, which could cause differences in grading of some anomalies.

- Many anomalies, especially near welds, may be reported on one survey but not the other. The actual signals associated with these anomalies may not show evidence of significant growth (see Fig.12).

- The algorithms used on the two surveys may indicate different depths for signals that did not show evidence of significant growth. These algorithms are proprietary and could not be reviewed in this report.

- The interaction criteria for interacting two anomalies axially may be more conservative in one year or the other. This could cause anomalies to be represented differently in the boxed data, whereas they are the same in the raw data.

As viewable in Figs 5-12, the ILI raw data are an important data set for validation of the identified statistically active areas.

Determining corrosion-growth rates

A common approach for comparing multiple in-line inspections is to perform a 1-to-1 match between reported anomalies. This matching is often difficult, due to variability between analysis techniques used from inspection-to-inspection or vendor-to-vendor. In addition, 1-to-1 matching often results in wide variations in corrosion growth-rate estimates. It is not uncommon to find extremely high growth rates in either a positive or negative direction. Alternative methods typically use only the peak depth of reported metal loss over some area (for example a joint, or perhaps an area with multiple reported features) with the expectation this approach captures the worst-case situation and provides a better estimate of expected corrosion-growth rates. However, these methods tend to focus on the extremes as opposed to incorporating trends evident in the data sets.

One of the key concepts in the SAC process is the use of all the data in each inspection and not just isolated features. The SAC process does not exclude any data. The SAC process results in estimates of the local corrosion growth rates along the full pipeline and provides cumulative distribution-based probabilities as well, such as P(corrosion d • 0.13 mm/year) = 88%. The growth units are provided in the units desired by the operator. The SAC process is used to filter the noise and identify site-specific locations where there is statistical evidence (typically at the 95% confidence level) of active corrosion growth. Results may be summarized in any manner desired by the operator, for example by kilometre if the pipeline company has a desire to prioritize its corrosion programme at a more macro level for CP enhancements.

There are multiple ways in SAC to assess corrosion-growth activity over time. Without going into specific formulas, techniques such as two-sample t-tests, one-sample t-tests, and Poisson ratio tests, are part of the family of methods used. For example, if there are sufficient data in two inspections, a two-sample t-test is used to assess if there is a statistically significant increase in average corrosion growth over time for a window or joint. If one inspection has no data for the given window/joint whereas the other does, a one-sample t-test is used to evaluate if there is significantly more corrosion than some specified default such as 10% wall loss. Count data, summarizing the density of reported features over time, are analysed using a Poisson-ratio approach to appraise whether sufficient evidence exists to find a statistically significant increase in the number of reported features over time for a given location of the pipeline.

In earlier applications involving corrosion growth over time, default values such as those given in Table 1 might be used. While such analyses provided value in identifying possible areas for either action or additional study on the pipeline, the estimation process was found to be too conservative and not cost effective. Using global corrosion-growth estimates results in over-prediction and is no longer necessary, since local corrosion-growth estimates are now possible and verifiable using SAC-based methodologies.

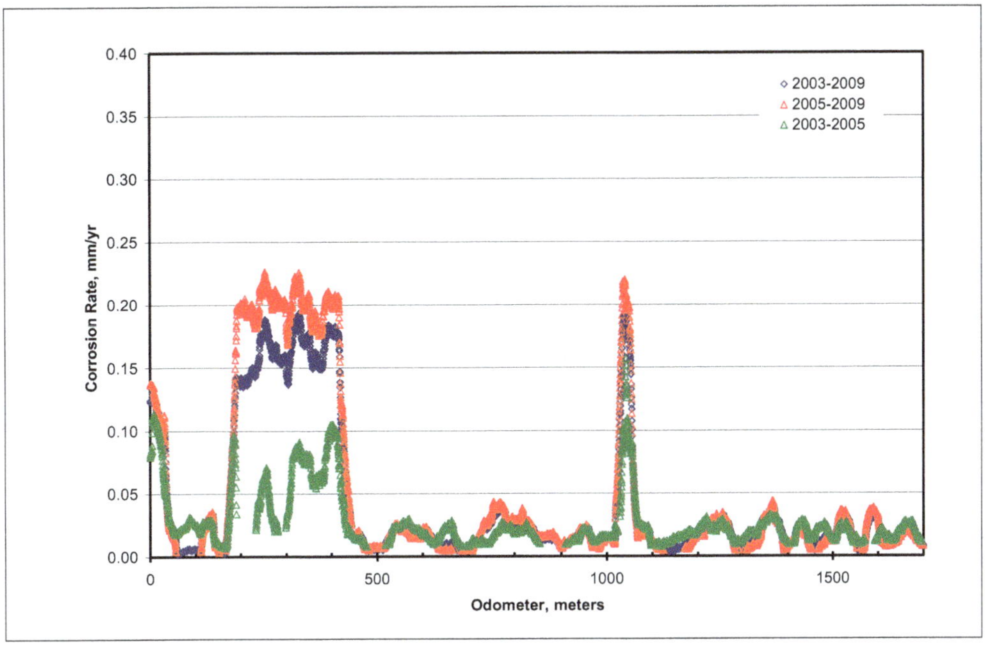

Fig. 13. Mean corrosion-growth rates for a bitumen pipeline.

Since the SAC process estimates corrosion-growth rates when there is statistical evidence of active corrosion (either on a sliding-window or joint basis), the raw data can be filtered such that the inherent variability from the inspection data is accounted for.

Figure 13 shows the calculated SAC corrosion-growth rates from a bitumen pipeline. Green symbols represent the SAC mean growth from 2003 to 2005, and red symbols represent the growth from 2005 to 2009. Blue symbols reflect the rate derived from 2003 to 2009. The plot shows that the 2003 to 2009 rates are between the rates for the other two time periods, as expected. Additionally, the trends are reasonably consistent – another positive attribute. Other observations include:

- Stretches of significant growth are readily apparent when the rate exceeds 0.05 mm/year. Values below 0.05 mm/year may not be relevant.
- The growth rate is accelerating. Rates are higher from 2005 to 2009 than from 2003 to 2005.
- There is a fair amount of variability within active regions.

For this particular application involving a government oversight board, it was desired to use local corrosion-growth rates as shown in Table 1 while applying the most conservative rate. This involved not only the comparisons of the inspections as partially illustrated above, but also

Table 1. Typical external corrosion-growth rates used in early corrosion-growth assessments.

ILI reported depth (% WT)	Typical corrosion growth rate (mm/year)
0 to 20%	0.10
20 to 40%	0.20
> 40%	0.30

involved the development of upper 95% confidence bounds on the estimated corrosion-growth rate. This information will be used in the next section to compute the estimated remaining lives.

Application of corrosion science

The corrosion-growth rates previously discussed are then reviewed with respect to corrosion mechanics. Here, for example, the presence of very high rates might suggest microbiologically influenced or stray-current corrosion. Similarly, corrosion rates are compared to values typically found in the field to ensure they are realistic.

Estimating remaining life and determining reiinspection interval

Deterministic and probabilistic methods are used to estimate the remaining lives of metal-loss anomalies and identify safe reinspection intervals. The POE methodology proposed by Mora *et al.* [1] and Vieth *et al.* [2] is one of the ways this may be used. This methodology considers both the leak and rupture failure modes. Further, the reported depth and length of the anomalies are adjusted using the field-tool regressions and then grown into the future using the SAC-estimated growth rates. The failure year for each anomaly is determined based on the preferred failure criteria – typically 80% of the wall thickness for depth and 100% of the maximum operating pressure (MOP) for predicted burst pressure. Using these failure criteria and the uncertainty from the field-tool regressions (i.e. prediction/standard error), a POE value is calculated for each anomaly in each year included in the assessment.

The critical anomalies are prioritized based on their failure year, and combined into excavation sites according to the preferred dig length. From these prioritized sites various options of excavation/repair and re-inspection intervals are prepared by considering the cumulative POE values for the entire pipeline. When a particular option reaches the defined probability thresholds, the reinspection interval is assigned by applying a 1 to 2 year safety buffer. The cumulative POE values for each option are then used to predict the most likely worst depth and lowest predicted burst pressure at the time of the assigned re-inspection intervals. A cost-benefit analysis is then performed to provide an economic comparison of the various options. Finally, the preferred limits for reinspection interval are considered in selecting the recommended option with the smallest net present value, while maintaining pipeline integrity.

By applying corrosion growth rates in a targeted manner based on the SAC analysis, those anomalies in areas that did not show indications of statistically significant growth will have less impact on the future integrity of the pipeline. This allows operators to focus efforts on the areas with greater likelihood of active corrosion, thereby more effectively using integrity resources.

Examples of applications and tailored solutions

One case study pertains to a 323.9-mm diameter, 4.8-mm wall thickness, dry natural gas transmission pipeline that was built in 1970 and was coated with polyethylene tape. A high-resolution magnetic-flux leakage (MFL) inspection was performed in 2002, and subsequent excavations revealed anomalies corresponding with mostly external corrosion, with field-measured depths of up to 77% of the wall thickness. In 2008, another MFL inspection was performed by the same vendor and two distinct differences were noted: (1) that the number of external corrosion anomalies had increased by a factor of 3.5 (3,684 in 2008 vs 1,044 in 2002); and (2) that the number of manufacturing anomalies had increased by a factor of 4.8 (1,272 in 2008 vs 266 in

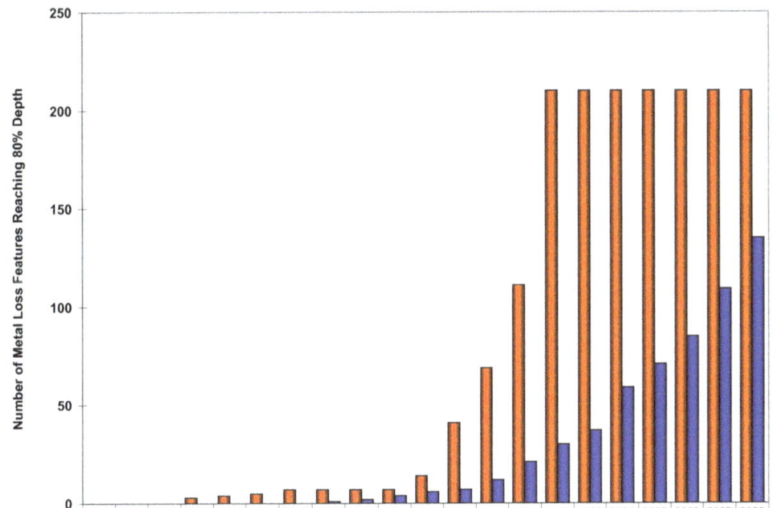

	2008	2009	2010	2011	2012	2013	2014	2015	2016	2017	2018	2019	2020	2021	2022	2023	2024	2025	2026	2027	2028
Traditional Growth Rate	0	0	0	3	4	5	7	7	7	7	14	41	69	111	210	210	210	210	210	210	210
SAC Growth Rate	0	0	0	0	0	0	0	1	2	4	6	7	12	21	30	37	59	71	85	109	135

Year

Fig. 14. Deterministic comparison of corrosion-growth rates for the case study.

2002). In addition to calculating growth rates along the line, the operator questioned whether these two issues were due to improvements in technology (increased sensitivity) or new corrosion occurring along the pipeline.

To investigate the large change in the number of corrosion and manufacturing anomalies between the inspections, an SAC assessment of the 38 excavated (and subsequently recoated) areas since the 2002 inspection was used to compare the average and maximum corrosion-growth rates. First, the number of reported anomalies was compared to determine if there was a statistical difference between the 2002 and 2008 inspections. This analysis removed 33 of these areas from the analysis. Then, the average and maximum corrosion-growth rates were compared to check if there was a statistically significant increase in the corrosion depths between the two inspections. Of the five remaining recoated areas, only one had a statistically significant increase in corrosion depth. It was concluded that the increase in the number of reported corrosion anomalies was due to improvements in the tool technology rather than new corrosion.

The nature of the mill anomalies was investigated by comparing the results of a SAC analysis without these anomalies against one with the anomalies. A 28% increase in the number of areas (SAC windows) exhibiting corrosion growth with a statistically significant increase in the average depth was found when these anomalies were included. In addition to the SAC analysis, data from past excavations were reviewed, which showed that some of these manufacturing anomalies were in fact external pitting. MFL signal analysis was performed for a sample of the manufacturing anomalies and it too showed that some of the anomalies did not appear in the 2002 inspection. It was concluded that many of these anomalies could actually correspond with external corrosion, so a decision was made to include them in the SAC and POE assessments as corrosion.

The external corrosion-growth rates of the SAC assessment were then compared with those that an operator would typically apply (given in Table 1). Figure 14 shows the cumulative number of external corrosion anomalies that would be expected to grow to a depth of 80% of the wall thickness as a function of time for both of the corrosion-growth rates: there is a difference of four

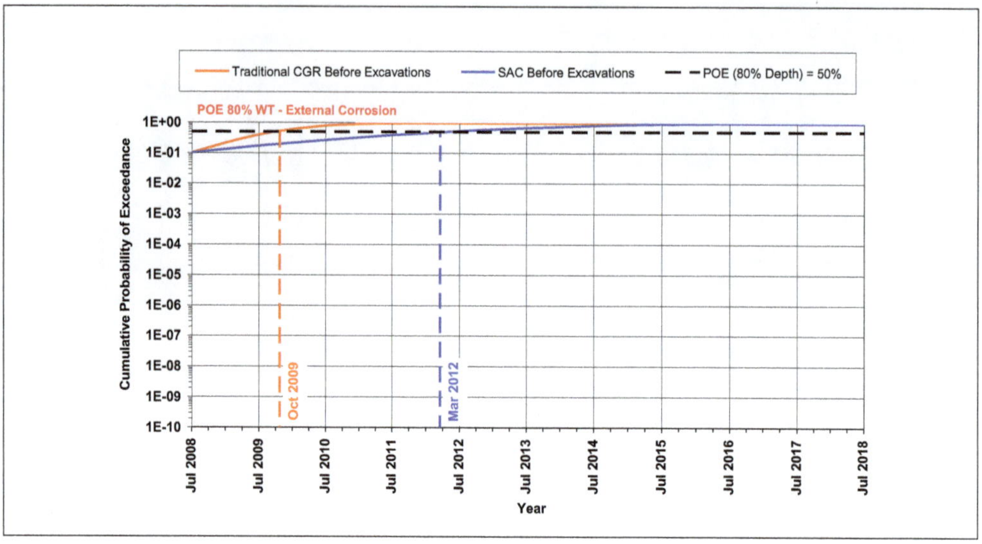

Fig.15. Probabilistic comparison of corrosion-growth rates for the case study.

years (2011 for the traditional rate and 2015 for the SAC rate) when the first anomaly would be predicted to reach 80% depth. After taking into account the tool accuracy from a field-tool analysis, the date for an anomaly at the traditional rate to reach 80% depth would be October, 2009, and for the SAC rate would be March, 2012 – a difference of 2.4 years, as shown in Fig.15. These results demonstrate how the reinspection interval can be increased by performing an SAC assessment.

Additional considerations

While most pipelines have a long design life, others carrying corrosive products may have short design lives. For the bitumen pipeline example provided in the previous section, it was desired to determine whether the life of the pipeline might be extended beyond the 10-year design life. Three in-line inspections had been performed on this pipeline. SAC was used for a remaining-life analysis to estimate which portions of the pipeline needed remediation to achieve this goal. For this specific case, the remaining life was defined to be when the 95% upper-bound confidence interval on the maximum estimated corrosion-growth rate would cause the deepest pit on a joint to exceed a depth of 80% of the pipe-wall thickness.

These in turn led to lower 95% confidence bounds on the estimated remaining life of each joint. In this manner, the operator was able to pinpoint joints requiring remediation in order to extend the pipeline life another three years while satisfying the oversight group. Figure 16 shows the predicted remaining-life point estimates (the circles, where seen) and the accompanying lower 95% bound on the remaining life as the bar at the lower end of each vertical line segment. These results, along with additional specific rankings of joints, potentially saved millions of dollars in both line maintenance and maintaining a high throughput beyond its design life.

Conclusions

This paper presents a methodology that can be used to produce more-accurate remaining-life assessments for corroded pipelines. Statistical methods are useful in identifying areas of active corrosion growth, based on data readily provided by the inspection vendors. Combined with non-

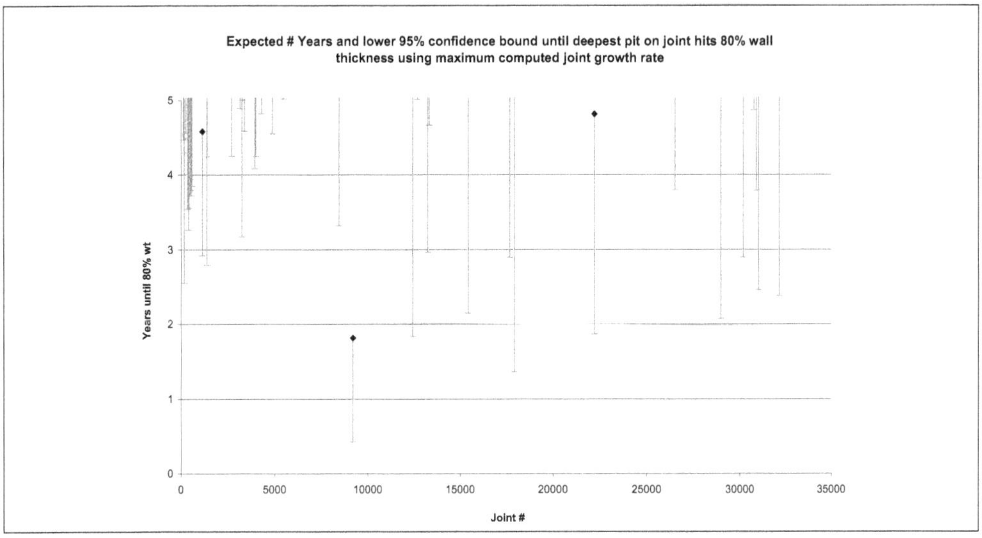

Fig. 16. Expected number of years and lower 95% confidence bound until the deepest pit on a joint achieves a depth of 80% of the wall thickness using the maximum computed growth rate (0-5 years).

statistical techniques for reviewing the raw signal data, corrosion-growth rates are determined, which are more accurate than traditional growth-rate estimation methods.

Subsequently, remaining-life and reinspection intervals may be computed based on these growth rates. The case study illustrates how this approach can benefit pipeline operators. The improved accuracy generally results in a longer reinspection interval. Further, mitigation efforts can be more effectively implemented since the areas exhibiting corrosion growth are identified.

Acknowledgements

The authors acknowledge the support of Det Norske Veritas (USA), Inc., DNV Energy Canada Ltd, and selected clients in carrying out the work needed to prepare this paper.

References

1. R.G.Mora, C.Parker, P.H.Vieth, and B.Delanty, 2002. Probability of exceedance (POE) methodology for developing integrity programs based on pipeline operator-specific technical and economic factors. Proc. 4th International Pipeline Conference, Calgary.
2. P.H.Vieth, S.W.Rust, and B.P.Ashworth, 1999. Use of in-line inspection data for integrity management. NACE International, Proc. Corrosion 99 Conference, Houston.

Section 3: EMAT

ILI with high-resolution EMAT technology: crack detection and coating disbondment

by Hamad Al-Qahtani[1], Thomas Beuker[2], and Dr Joerg Damaschke[2]

1 Saudi Aramco Pipelines Department, Dhahran, Saudi Arabia
2 Rosen Technology and Research Centre, Lingen, Germany

THE VARIOUS AND complex cracking processes that can occur on a pipeline have made accurate and reliable crack detection a great challenge. Different conditions give rise to different cracking mechanisms, which result in different crack types. In many cases, coating disbondment occurs as a precursor to cracking, as does stress-corrosion cracking (SCC). The associated challenges for a pipeline operator in the complex and dynamic oil and gas industry are continuous, and require thorough, short-, and long-term solutions.

An in-line inspection tool for the detection of cracks, and in particular SCC and coating disbondment, has been developed. The system is equipped with electromagnetic acoustic transducers (EMAT), following a high-resolution approach. After successfully testing this 16-in crack-detection tool thoroughly in sample pipes containing real SCC and various types of artificial defects, first runs – one in a gas pipeline and another one in an oil pipeline – were performed that proved the performance of the approach under operational conditions. This article introduces parts of the data-evaluation process and presents results obtained from these two field tests.

SAUDI ARAMCO IS one of the world's leading international oil and gas companies. It is also a major pipeline operator, which owns and operates a vast and scattered hydrocarbon transportation network within Saudi Arabia. The network comprises over 17,000 km of pipelines ranging from 3 to 56 inches in diameter, operating in many different terrain conditions. This network originates at the oil, gas, and NGL production plants, and terminates at the export terminals, processing plants, or domestic users.

Fig.1. The 16-in RoCD2 inspection tool designed for detection of cracks and coating disbondment.

The safe and reliable operation of this pipeline network is essential to Saudi Aramco's operation and the prosperity of the country. The associated challenges facing pipeline operators in the complex and dynamic oil and gas industry are continuous and require thorough, short- and long-term solutions.

Saudi Aramco constantly researches and tests various related technologies to overcome challenges, such as the detection of cracking and coating disbondment. Traditionally, non-destructive in-line inspection (ILI) tools are based on technologies including magnetic-flux leakage (MFL), ultrasonic testing (UT), or eddy current. However, none of these techniques is applicable to the detection of stress-corrosion cracking (SCC), particularly in gas pipelines. Recently Rosen has developed a new type of ultrasonic sensor that is based on an electro-magnetic acoustic transducer (EMAT) [1]. Unlike conventional UT, through using physical effects such as the Lorentz force and magnetostriction, this technology allows a contact-free generation and observation of ultrasonic signals. It is independent from a coupling medium between the sensors and the pipeline to be inspected: the pipeline serves as its own transducer.

For this project, a 16-in tool was manufactured and equipped with EMAT sensors (Fig.1). First field test were performed, proving the performance of this technology under operational conditions.

Field testing

As a part of Saudi Aramco's programme to encourage technical innovations, the use of the Rosen EMAT technology was commissioned for the inspection of two 16-in liquid and gas pipelines for detecting the occurrence of SCC and external coating disbondment. These two pipelines were specifically selected due the known presence of SCC and coating damage.

Both runs were carried out following the normal ILI procedure, and following the specific operating parameters shown in Table 1.

EMAT findings and verification	Pipeline anomalies	Coating anomalies	Selected anomalies	Verification digs
Sour gas	10	73	13	13
Sour crude	34	37	18	18

Table 1. Operating parameter of the inspected 16-in pipelines.

EMAT findings and verification	Pipeline anomalies	Coating anomalies	Selected anomalies	Verification digs
Sour gas	10	73	13	13
Sour crude	34	37	18	18

Table 2. Summary of the anomalies reported from the EMAT survey and the verification digs.

Both lines were inspected in May, 2006. Data collected during the runs were complete and of good quality. Both runs were evaluated using automated algorithms developed during this project. For example, girth welds can be detected quite easily since they cause typical signal characteristics in different data channels (the transmission channel and the echo channel). Long-seam welds can be observed in the echo channels (increase) and transmission channels (decrease).

The anomalies identified in the data were divided into pipeline anomalies and coating anomalies. A total of 44 pipeline anomalies and 110 coating anomalies were reported. From these indications, 31 locations were chosen for the dig and verification programme outlined in Table 2.

Based on the preliminary report, the field work was started. The maintenance and repair work on both lines were concluded by January, 2007, after submission of the final inspection report. Details about the inspection technology supported by findings from the field work are given in the subsequent sections.

Inspection technology

The EMAT modules are arranged on the in-line inspection tool following a high-resolution approach (Fig.2, right). In contrast to a low-resolution approach (Fig.2, left), a complicated evaluation of the UT travel time to locate an anomaly on the pipeline perimeter is not required. Figure 3 shows the basic arrangement of one EMAT module used to inspect a distinct area (pixel) on the pipeline.

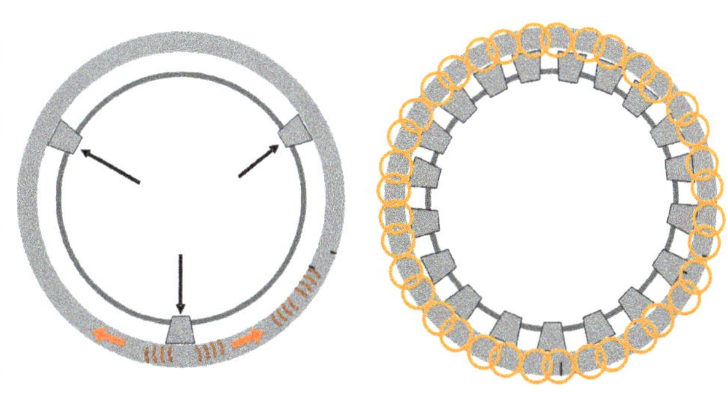

Fig.2. EMAT sensor arrangement. Comparison between low-resolution (left) and high-resolution approach. The high-resolution approach overcomes the complicated analysis of the UT-travel time to locate cracks on the pipe perimeter.

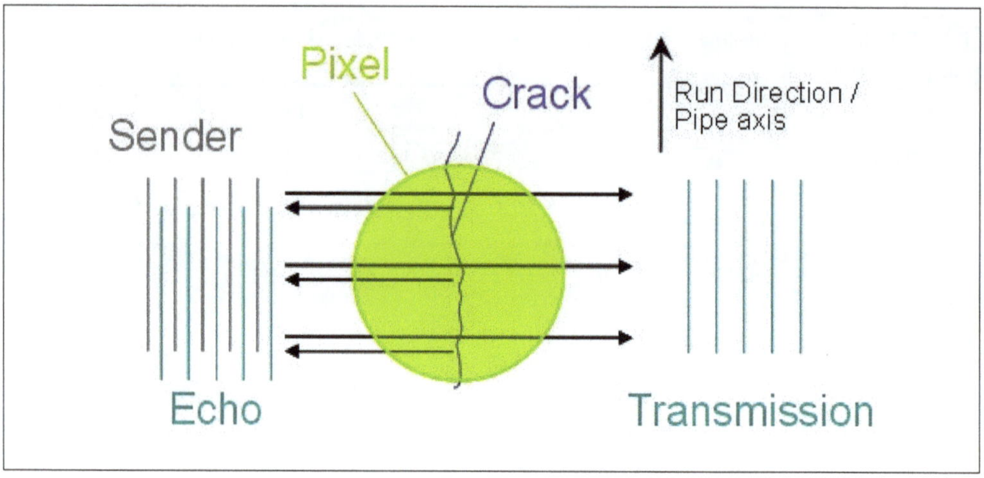

Fig.3. Basic arrangement of three EMAT modules comprising one sender module (left) and two receiver modules (one left, one right). The transmission signal is used for detection of coating disbondment, while the echo signal allows the identification of crack-like indications.

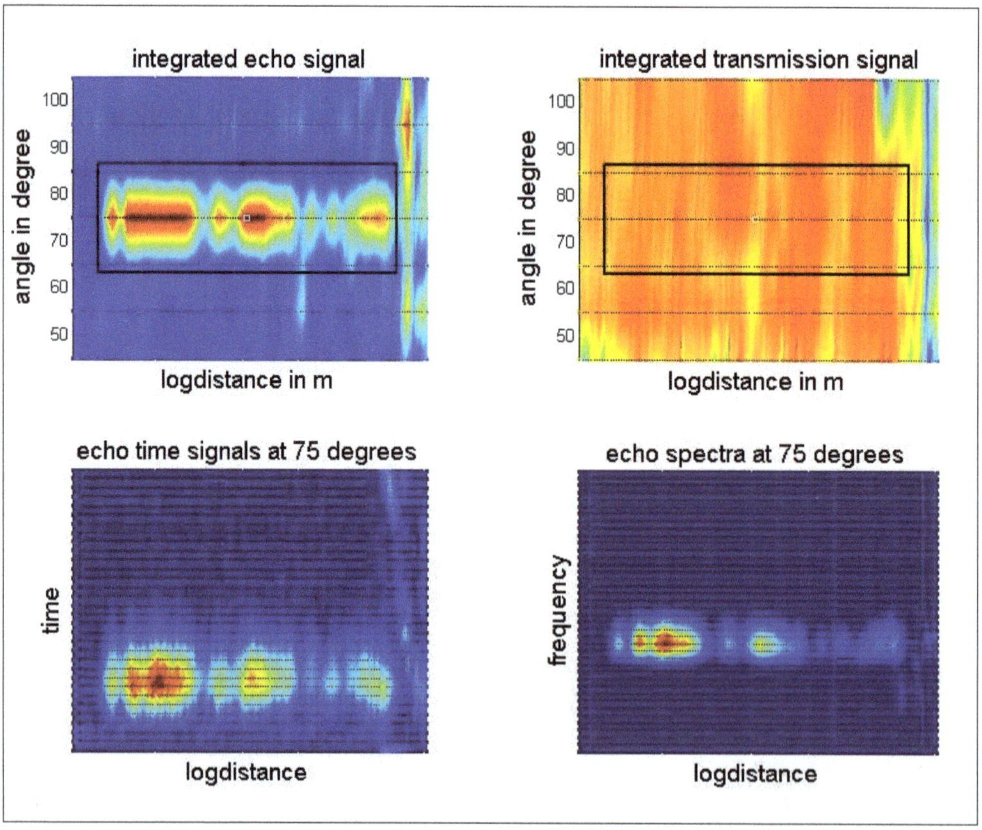

Fig.4. Detailed views of a single anomaly. The upper two panels contain c-scan views of six individual inspection channels (the echo signal on the left and the transmission signal on the right). The two lower panels show non-integrated echo data as functions of the log distance of the channel at 75°. The left panel shows the time signals and the right panel shows corresponding spectra.

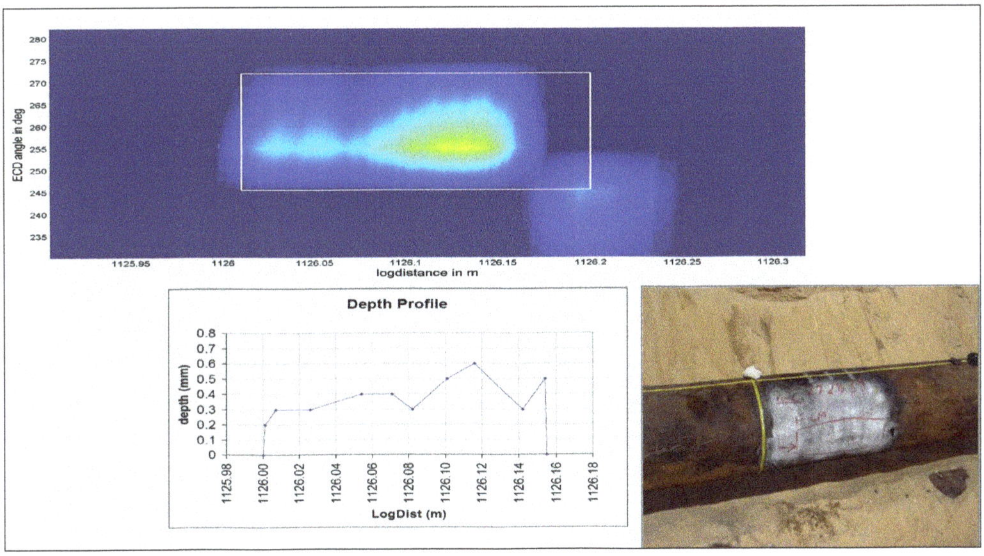

Fig.5. Top: RoCD2 data obtained from an oblique linear indication. The example is demonstrating the high sensitivity of the chosen EMAT method. Bottom, left: the location as verified in the field with a hand-held 10 MHz TR-probe; bottom, right: the dig site.

The ultrasonic waves do not travel around the whole circumference of the pipeline before they are observed by a receiver. Rather, the acoustic waves only travel a short distance between the EMAT sender and the receiver, allowing comparatively simple data evaluation and avoiding false alarms.

The sensor arrangement required to inspect one pixel on the pipeline comprises one EMAT sender (Fig.3, left) and two EMAT receivers (Fig.3, one on the left and one on the right). The EMAT sender generates a tailored horizontal shear wave that contains distinct frequencies and is particularly sensitive to near-surface axial-oriented linear defects. The transmission signal is monitored for changes in the coating quality.

Data evaluation

From Fig.3 it can be seen that an echo signal will only be recorded if a significant amount of energy is reflected into the EMAT echo receiver. Since the echo receiver is active only for a short time interval, only signals that are reflected from a specific sensor-related position on the pipeline are detected. Hence, other signals emitted from adjacent EMAT senders, or late reflections emitted from other positions on the pipeline, can easily be excluded during the data-evaluation process. Due to the arrangement of the EMAT modules, the features that are primarily detected have an axial dimension. A detailed analysis of significant echo signals including signal amplitude, arrival time, and frequency content, provides valuable information about the type of the defect detected.

In Fig.4, the four panels show additional information about one particular anomaly. While the two upper panels show integrated data of the echo (*left*) and the transmission (*right*) data as a function of the circumferential position and the log distance, the two lower panels show non-integrated vector data of one specific channel (the channel at 75°). The lower left panel shows the echo time signals as a function of the log distance, and the lower right panel corresponding signal spectra.

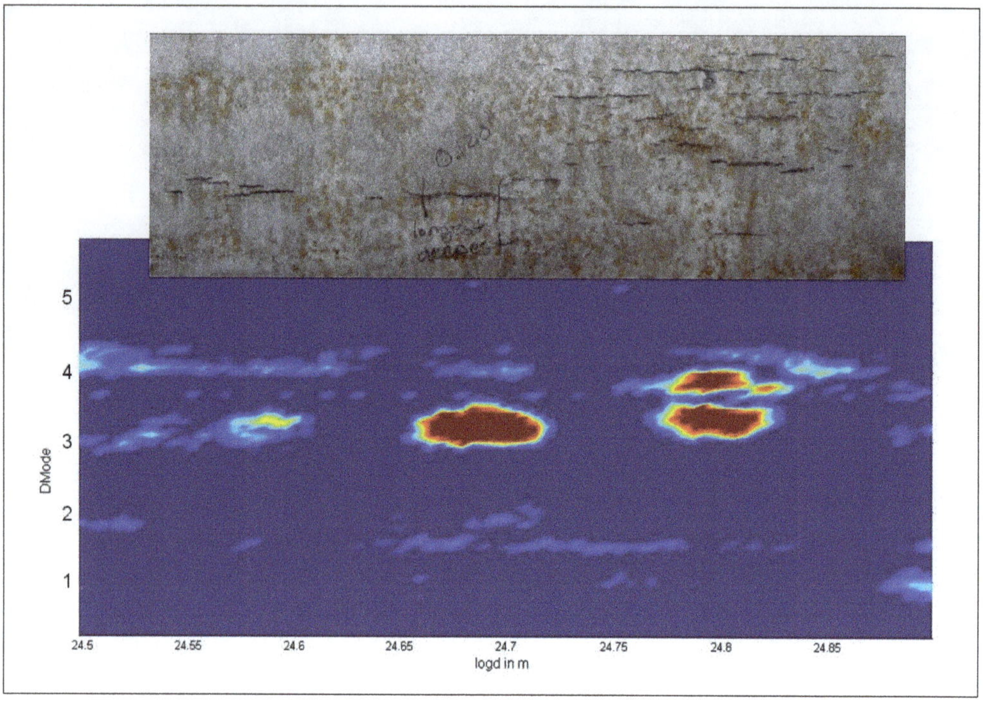

Fig.6. RoCD2 data obtained from a SCC sample during an extensive test programme. Top: grit-blasted and MPI-tested pipeline surface; bottom: five individual channels showing the SCC threat of the pipe-section

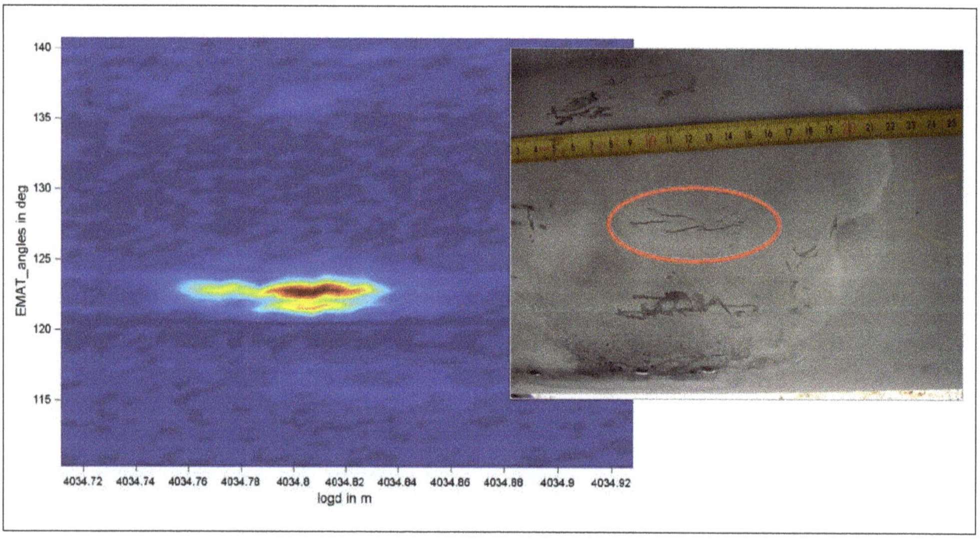

Fig.7. RoCD2 data obtained from an SCC location, confirmed during verification work conducted during the course of the project.

By analysing the signal time domain, information about the defect orientation is gained as it relates to the pipe axis. This means that the echo channels are sensitive to defects in both the axial and the circumferential directions.

Crack detection

The UT-wave propagates from the EMAT sender on the left-hand side towards the EMAT receiver on the right-hand side (Fig.3). In a no-crack-condition this wave reaches the receiver and is recorded as a so-called transmission signal. On the other hand, if there is a crack-like defect between the EMAT sender and the opposite EMAT receiver, a part of the signal energy is reflected in direction of the EMAT sender. This signal is recorded as a so-called echo signal by the second EMAT receiver. Hence, two acoustic data channels exist for each pixel: namely, one echo and one transmission channel.

From these data channels, numerous signal parameters can be extracted: signal frequencies, signal amplitude, travelling time of the acoustic wave, etc. Unlike an MFL measurement, not only one value (magnetization level) is recorded at one particular pipeline position, but several vectors (time signals, spectra, etc.) providing much more information.

The sensitivity of the system was demonstrated in the field during this project, and this is shown by data obtained during the detection of an oblique shallow linear indication (Fig.5, top). The obtained reflection for this 0.012-0.020-in (0.3-0.5-mm) crack was well above the noise level. The location was part of the dig programme conducted during the project. The linear indication feature has been verified with a hand-held 10-MHz TR-probe. A corresponding depth profile was taken (Fig.5).

The detection capability of the in-line inspection system was demonstrated during an extensive pull-test programme (Fig.6), and during the verification work in the field. Figure 7 represents a crack colony, 2-in in length, found in the field during the course of this project.

Coating disbondment detection

The transmission channel contains information about the wave directly propagating from the EMAT sender to the transmission receiver. The overall amplitude of this wave depends on the lift-off, the presence of a defect, and the presence and type of an external coating. The latter dependency can be used to classify and distinguish between different types of coating, such as fusion-bonded epoxy, tar, or tape-wrap coating (Fig.8).

Coating disbondment is detected by a substantial local increase in the transmission amplitude, since coating generally dampens the acoustic wave. Hence, if the damping effect is missing due to a reduction in the bonding quality of the coating, a significant increase of the signal amplitude can be observed. An example of an area with disbonded coating is shown in Fig.9.

Conclusion

The new EMAT sensor and the high-resolution approach proved its feasibility in the first inspection surveys in Saudi Aramco's gas and oil pipelines. Both pipeline and coating-related features were found. The high-resolution approach gave accurate results and offers further

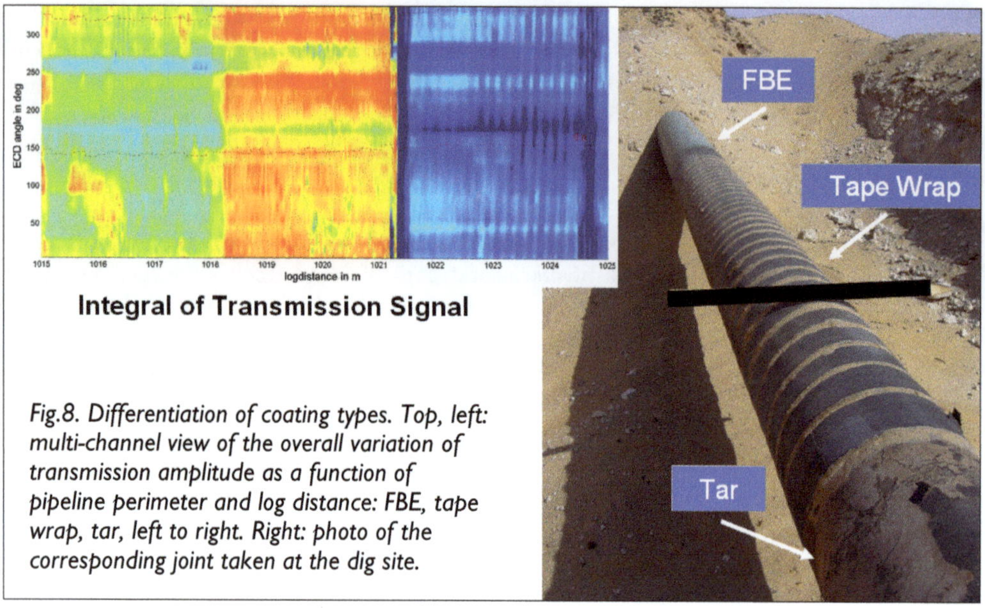

Fig.8. Differentiation of coating types. Top, left: multi-channel view of the overall variation of transmission amplitude as a function of pipeline perimeter and log distance: FBE, tape wrap, tar, left to right. Right: photo of the corresponding joint taken at the dig site.

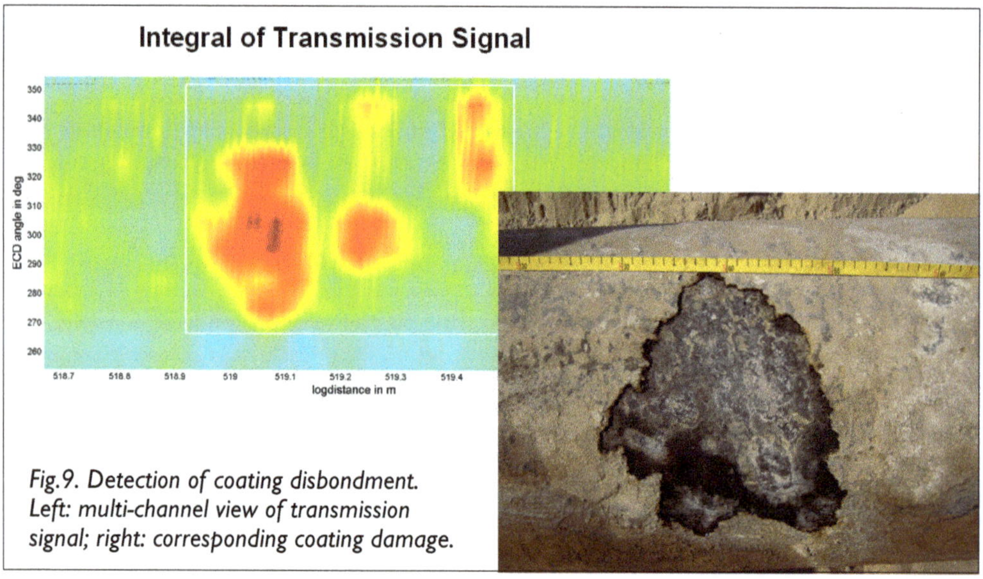

Fig.9. Detection of coating disbondment. Left: multi-channel view of transmission signal; right: corresponding coating damage.

potential for continuous improvements. The promising results of the first inspection survey are being further validated within Saudi Aramco. The data evaluation can rely on multi-dimensional data sets and 100% sensor coverage. This allows good characterization of the anomalies found.

References

1. M.Klann and T.Beuker, 2006. Pipeline inspection with the high resolution EMAT ILI tool: report on full-scale testing and field trials. Proc. 6th International Pipeline Conference, ASME, Calgary.

Validation of the latest generation EMAT ILI technology for SCC management

by Jim E Marr[1], Elvis San Juan Riverol[1], Gabriela Rosca[1], Jeff Sutherland[2], and Andy Mann[2]

1 TransCanada, Calgary, AB, Canada
2 PII Pipeline Solutions, Calgary, AB, Canada

TRANSCANADA MANAGES the integrity of its gas transmission pipelines that are susceptible to stress-corrosion cracking (SCC) by periodically performing hydrostatic testing. Interest in an alternative approach to manage pipeline integrity in the presence of severe SCC and other forms of longitudinally oriented defect resulted in the endorsement of the latest generation of dry-coupled in-line inspection (ILI) tool. PII's (PII Pipeline Solutions, a GE Oil & Gas and Al Shaheen joint venture) ILI tool uses the electromagnetic-acoustic-transducer (EMAT) technology to meet this requirement.

This paper will summarize field experience results of the latest-generation EMAT ILI tool, which has been commercially available since September, 2008. This ILI programme review demonstrates the challenges that have been overcome, targets that have been achieved, and that the tool delivers the specification functionality to detect, size, and discriminate which are key parameters to support an effective SCC pipeline-integrity programme.

TRANSCANADA PIPELINES HAS been collaborating with PII Pipeline Solutions for over 10 years on the development of an ILI tool to locate and determine the severity of SCC in dry, sweet, natural gas pipelines. The PII EMAT ILI is now a third-generation tool. This paper will present some of the most recent results from the TransCanada and PII EMAT SCC programme.

TransCanada SCC overview

TransCanada has had a history of SCC primarily within tape- and asphalt-coated pipelines. In the case of tape-coated lines, there is the presence of both toe cracks in the crotch of the double-submerged-arc-weld (DSAW) longitudinal seam and in the associated tented disbonded region across the long seam. Five of six failures from 1986 in Canada have been associated with tape coatings and were toe cracks. For the Canadian assets over the past 25 years, asphalt-coated lines were in a state of condition monitoring. In the United States, all in-service and hydrotest failures have been in the body and associated with asphalt-coated lines.

The results of these failures and ongoing maintenance activities have resulted in an extensive, repetitive, hydrostatic testing programme over the past 25 years. Hydrostatic testing may be potentially harmful to the pipe but in many cases has been the only reliable option to remove injurious axial defects from the pipeline. As some research indicates, consecutive pressure tests may cause the sub-critical cracks to propagate thus worsening the condition of the pipeline. Another observation has been the coalescence of SCC may have changed the severity signature of a valve section resulting in a shortened hydrotest re-assessment interval.

Recent advancements in ILI technology have made it possible to assess for cracking and the overall SCC severity of a pipeline. At the present time for liquid pipeline systems, the leading-edge technology is ultrasonic (UT) crack-detection tools which have enjoyed success in locating and classifying the severity of SCC. The major obstacle for natural gas operators is the required use of a liquid slug that envelops the tool to ensure a continuous sound wave between the sensor and the pipe wall. A more recent technology that has now moved past validation is the utilization of EMAT.

In the management of SCC, TransCanada has also had an extensive programme of data integration utilizing the predictive models, elastic-wave ILI, UT/ILI, and extensive investigative excavations. Initially, the predictive soils' models enabled the recognition of susceptibility but could not delineate severity until an excavation or series of sites were available for inspection. When utilized in conjunction with EMAT, the predictive SCC model can provide locations that are deemed susceptible and, with time, improve the analytical reliability of the tool. This combination effort is simpler and less disruptive than the implementation process required for a hydrostatic testing or conventional liquid ultrasonic ILI operational challenges.

In another application, the data obtained from historical elastic-wave SCC ILI have been integrated into current SCC planning activities. These historical runs have enabled some success with multiple run-to-run comparisons to determine potential crack locations and potential severities.

Another initiative is the utilization of historical and present MFL ILI results to identify areas of 'low-level' corrosion which infers an area of coating disbondment. Coating disbondment is required for SCC to initiate and propagate.

EMAT and TransCanada history

Listed below is a summary of the TransCanada and PII EMAT history.

- 2000 - PII delivers 36-in EmatScan crack-detection tool, first-generation
- 2004 - release of second generation – TransCanada ran in 2005 with excavations between 2005 to 2006 (small success, POI issue)
- 2005 - decision to build third generation; first run in TransCanada 30-in inch (approx. 40km) in 2008
- 2010 - the latest generation of the 24-36-in EMAT crack-detection tool was the subject of the last IPC in Calgary 2010 [1].

Further collaboration is ongoing to improve the tool's capabilities to detect and identify SCC accurately and reliably for different types of similar-appearing defect and signal loss (attenuation) for various coating systems and pipe-surface anomalies. This past year the tool's detection ability for both tape- and asphalt-coated pipelines, delineating toe and body cracks, has been very promising. Listed below is a brief summary of recent EMAT modifications:

- The PII EMAT third-generation modifications include a decreased spacing of sensors (15°) which improves the coverage and redundancy.
- There has been an increase in the number of carriers from second- to third-generation which improves the redundancy and coverage of the inspections.
- Additional UT sensors to advance discrimination have been added to the tool.

Property	EMAT GEN III Tool
Size range (in)	24 to 36
Inspection range (km)	170
Speed range (m/s)	0 - 2.5
Bend passing	1.5 D
Minimum defect size* (mm)	2 x 50
POI (%)	> 66
POD (%)	> 90
Detection redundancy	5
Disbondment detection	All coating types
*Base material and seam weld for all coating types	

*Table 1. EMAT third-generation specifications. Note: *base material and seam weld for all coating types.*

- Operationally, modifications were done to the sensors to reduce signal-to-noise ratios aiding the ability to detect and discriminate SCC.

PII EMAT tool specifications

A primary goal is to continue to work with PII to improve its EMAT tool and enable the better detection of cracks. Table 1 summarizes the current EMAT ILI tool's specifications as reference for an evaluation of performance.

The objective of the EMAT ILI was to detect and size longitudinal cracks and related crack-like defects with lengths greater than or equal to 50mm and depths greater than or equal to 2mm. PII's EMAT tool is designed to identify and size cracks and crack-like defects both in the plate material and weld areas having a 90% probability of detection (POD) and 66% probability of identification (POI) on or above the detection threshold. As described below, these specifications in some cases have been exceeded.

The crack depth sizing specification is reported as a depth band of ±0.5mm at 80% certainty (all defects within sizing specification). Length sizing specification is ±10mm or ±10% of reported length at 80% certainty, whichever is greater.

In time, quite significant cost-saving opportunities may be achieved if hydrostatic testing can be selectively removed from the integrity programme (mostly likely following a few years of EMAT, direct examination, and hydrostatic testing) taking into account that hydrostatic testing can be one of the most expensive mitigation options available.

Recent TransCanada and PII EMAT collaboration

The PII EMAT tool has now completed over 800km of inspections with TransCanada in both the USA and Canada. The results of these inspections have been confirmed with over 31 field verifications. Comparatively, the results from the in-line crack inspection provide far greater information relative to a hydrostatic test.

Through a collaborative effort consisting of an extensive engineering assessment and multi-department company review process, it is believed that the majority of injurious cracks have been detected and mitigated (for the sections analysed), but also that all the colonies from sub-critical downwards to insignificant were addressed, aiding in the progression of the reliability and maturity of the tool. This ability to detect colonies within tool specifications makes it possible to prioritize the defects, allowing for a planned mitigation action and to monitor their growth by repeating the inspection in a desired time period.

TransCanada SCC EMAT management philosophy

TransCanada uses a risk-based system and has developed performance-based integrity plans to manage its pipeline assets. EMAT's recent promising results are encouraging, but TransCanada is most likely going to continue to use EMAT plus direct examination, followed potentially by hydrotesting in the near term, to manage SCC. TransCanada has proposed EMAT runs where:

- one or more valve sections are on the hydrostatic test programme (possibility of EMAT as a hydrostatic test replacement);
- SCC-susceptible valve sections, where limited or no information is known about the presence or severity of SCC; and
- lines with no company experience but subject to regulatory compliance.

Some of the additional advantages of running the EMAT tool are:

- move towards to a probabilistic defect management process;
- provide more data for targeted dig-site selection: improve models and SCCDA process to address susceptibility;
- should not create a major outage impact; and
- expanded opportunities with MFL, caliper, or other ILI programmes

Excavation and correlation programme results (2008 – present)

During the last couple of years TransCanada has conducted a series of EMAT ILI runs across the TransCanada system. Analysis of the EMAT data suggested sites which may fail prior to a hydrostatic retest. Conversely, PII reported a number of significant ILI features as 'non-decidable' which will require further investigation for future tool development and refinement of the analysis and discrimination capabilities.

Consequently, 31 excavations were completed to confirm both the integrity of the line and the validity of the ILI inspection. All excavation sites were verified in the field by the SCC threat-management team.

The excavations were intended to:

- remove assumed near-critical features from the line;
- enable TransCanada's pipeline-integrity group to develop an understanding of the ILI tool tolerance and nature of the features;
- establish correlations among ILI calls (detection and sizing of SCC features) and non-

System	TQM	FHZ8	Canadian ML	GLGT	Total
ILI Year	2008	2009	2009-2010	2010	
Excavation year	2009-2010	2010	2010-2011	2011	
Reference wall thickness (mm)	8.4 - 12	8.9	9.1	9.525	
Total accepted ILI length (m)	39.2	38.3	387.1	112.2	576.8
Total length analysed (km)	39.2	38.3	210.85	38	326.35
No. of digs to date	10*	10	11	-	31
No. of digs planned to date	1	4	12	4	21
No. of joints excavated	10	14	14	-	38
Total excavated length (m)	120	168	161	-	449
POD % (Field excavations to date)	100	91	100	-	93
POI % (Field excavations to date)	70	79	77	-	76
POD - No. features above spec. present	5	22	19	-	46
POD - No. features above spec. detected	5	19	19	-	43
POI - No. features reported by EMAT	10	42	31	-	84
POI - No. features correct classification	7	33	24	-	64

*Table 2. TransCanada third-generation EMAT summary results, 2008 – present. Note: * three digs were done in the 30-in system to prove feature classification.*

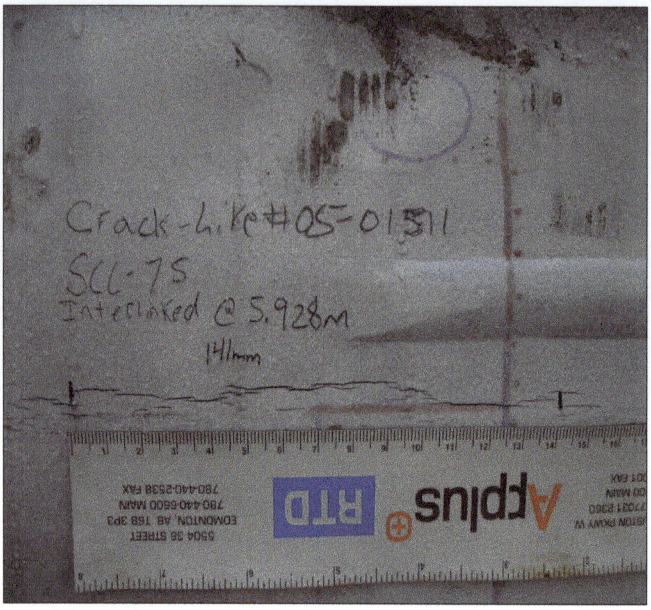

Fig.1. 2009 site (141mm max. interlinking length and maximum depth of 43.5% WT).

Fig.2. 2010 excavation toe-crack (256mm max. interlinking length and maximum depth 66.3% WT).

Fig.3. 2010 excavation SCC in corrosion (100 mm max. interlinking length and maximum depth 60.2% WT).

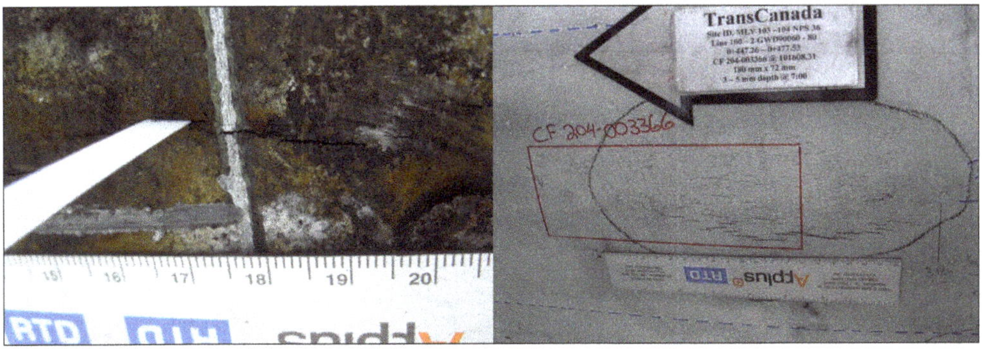

Fig.4. 2010 excavation shows accuracy of ILI call box (120mm max. interlinking length and maximum depth 75.8% WT). Note: white straight edge is a piece of pH paper.

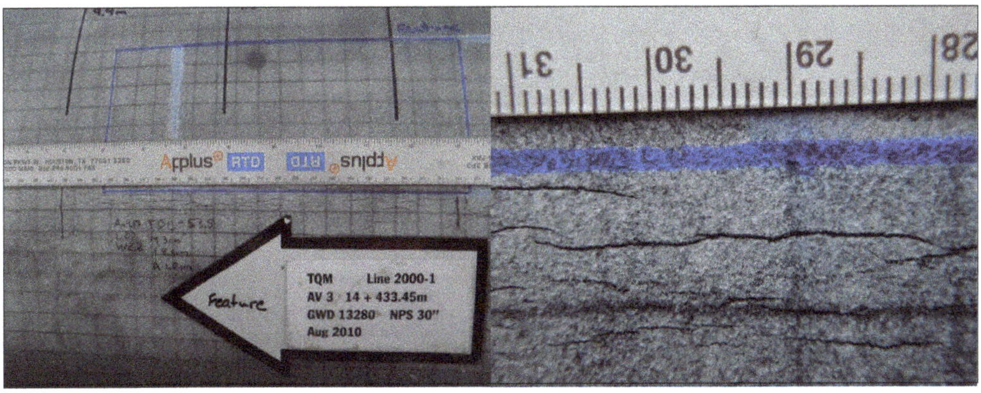

Fig.5. 2010 excavation adjacent to long-seam weld (85mm max. interlinking length and maximum depth 33% WT).

destructive examinations (NDE) to prove and improve the EMAT technology related to feature classification;

- enable the reliable calculation of the failure pressure of the features that will be left in the line and predict when they will need to be repaired;
- allow TransCanada to improve an already robust integrity-management plan for both inspected pipeline segments and to further support integrity decisions for the entire system.

Table 2 shows a summary of TransCanada third-generation EMAT results since 2008 until the present. To date, the PII EMAT system has shown a 93% POD and a 76% POI inspection performance based on field excavation results, with ongoing cooperative excavation activities in progress. Some specific examples of field results and correlation are discussed in the following sections.

Eastern Canada

In 2009, TransCanada conducted five investigations in this area. During these excavations the tool was successful with the discrimination of mid-wall indications from SCC. This was a milestone in EMAT ILI as this discrimination development overcame one of the bigger analysis hurdles (SCC from non SCC) but functionally saved TransCanada a costly replacement.

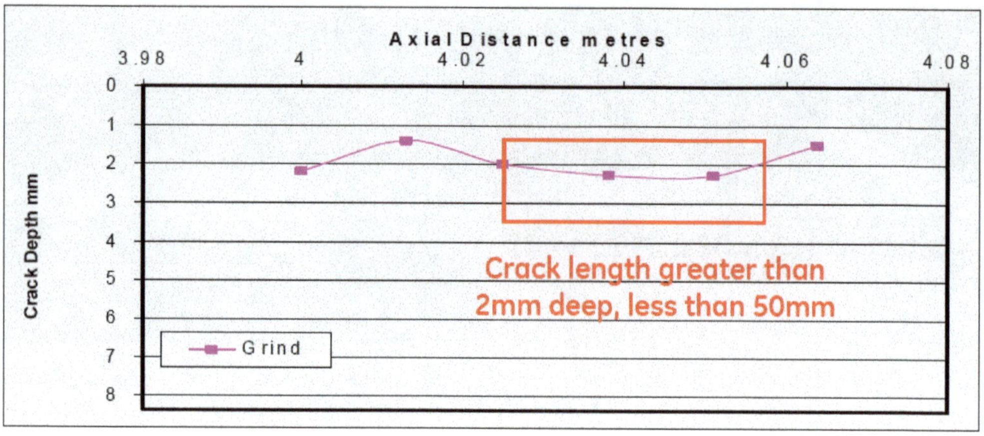

Fig.6. Example of crack length and depth below threshold or detection specification [1].

Figure 1 illustrates one of the colonies detected by the EMAT tool. Five SCC colonies from this programme were classified as significant. This programme had 182 grind repairs and one sleeve applied to the pipeline [1].

Interestingly, the direct-examination programme completed in the mid 1990s never detected a colony greater than 15% in depth.

All Canada

In 2010, TransCanada conducted 27 investigations based on the EMAT analysis, and a total of 33 joints with an approximate length of 390m was inspected. Some examples of the SCC detected during these excavations are presented in Figs 2-5.

Field NDE practices and limitations found in correlation

During the 2009 and 2010 excavations, the following limitations in NDE evaluation techniques for crack sizing were noted:

- average crack depth and maximum crack depth from the EMAT analysis differs from field NDE techniques due to the fact that the crack classification is in ranges or buckets (2-3mm; 3-5mm; and > 5mm);
- EMAT crack-length measurement could be affected by the effective length that corresponds to a crack depth deeper than 2mm. So the conditions of a 50-mm length by 2-mm depth by the tool specification must be achieved.

Figure 6 illustrates the correlation between crack length and crack depth from a grinding profile. The EMAT tool can only really see crack depths below 2mm and the tool should only be able to discriminate the area within the rectangular area, although in reality the crack length exceeds the rectangular area of Fig.6.

Figure 7 illustrates the crack profile of a colony measured using phased-array techniques. In this example, the field NDE would have recorded a total colony length of 400mm. The EMAT tool would have only seen the area within the rectangle box representing 300mm. There is also a NDE evaluation point noted on the relative coarseness of the grinding method compared to the phased-array examination to determine crack depth.

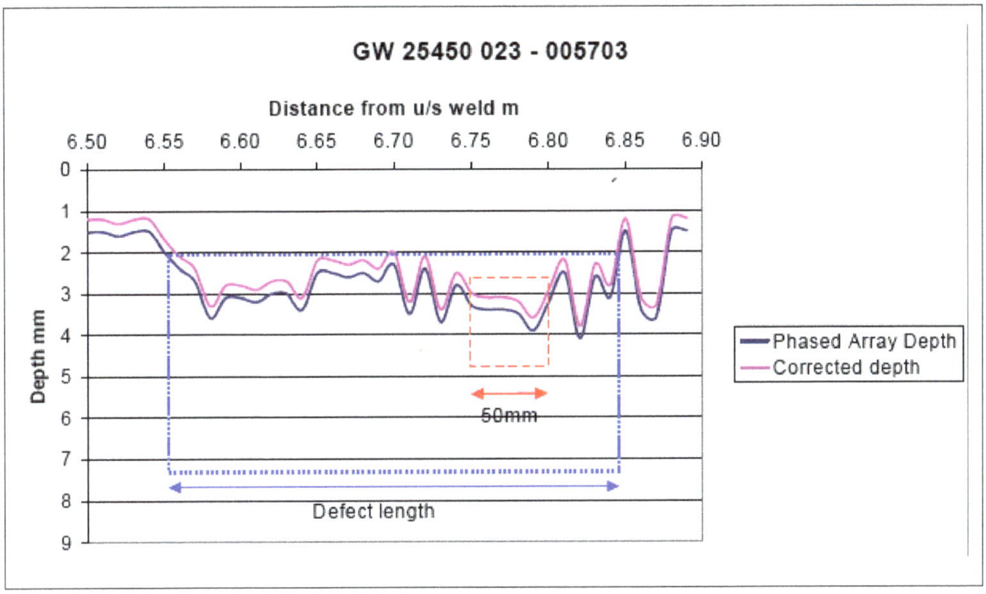

Fig.7. Example of crack length using phased-array techniques.

Programme lessons and developments

This paper presents and summarizes the most recent findings of the EMAT programme. Overall, 38 joints, totalling 449m of inspected pipe, were evaluated between 2009 and 2010. In one asset evaluation there were nine cut-outs and one sleeve applied to mitigate the SCC detected by the EMAT tool across 11 excavations. Described below are some of the 'lessons' and developments from the past two years.

During the validation of results, few excavations showed that some crack-like and crack-fields were incorrectly classified. These classification anomalies included:

- Situation A: a crack-like feature was found after the NDE but not reported by the EMAT tool.
- Situation B: crack-like or crack-field reported by the EMAT tool. There was no colony detected by the NDE.

These two groups of features were challenging and were collaboratively investigated in order to provide clarification of these issues, enabling the refinement of the EMAT tool analysis.

Situation A

Some cracks were initially classified as geometry feature during the analysis and were not reported for any further field investigation. After the NDE was performed on the same joint for a confirmed colony, a number of other features under this misclassification of geometry were found to be intermittent SCC that fluctuated between being either over or under the tool depth specification. These features were and can be detected by the EMAT tool but were originally classified as geometry following the existing company procedures. Based on the field confirmation and improvement of the discrimination analysis, all similar features have been subsequently reanalysed and re-classified. The investigative programme will continue to evaluate and refine this type of feature.

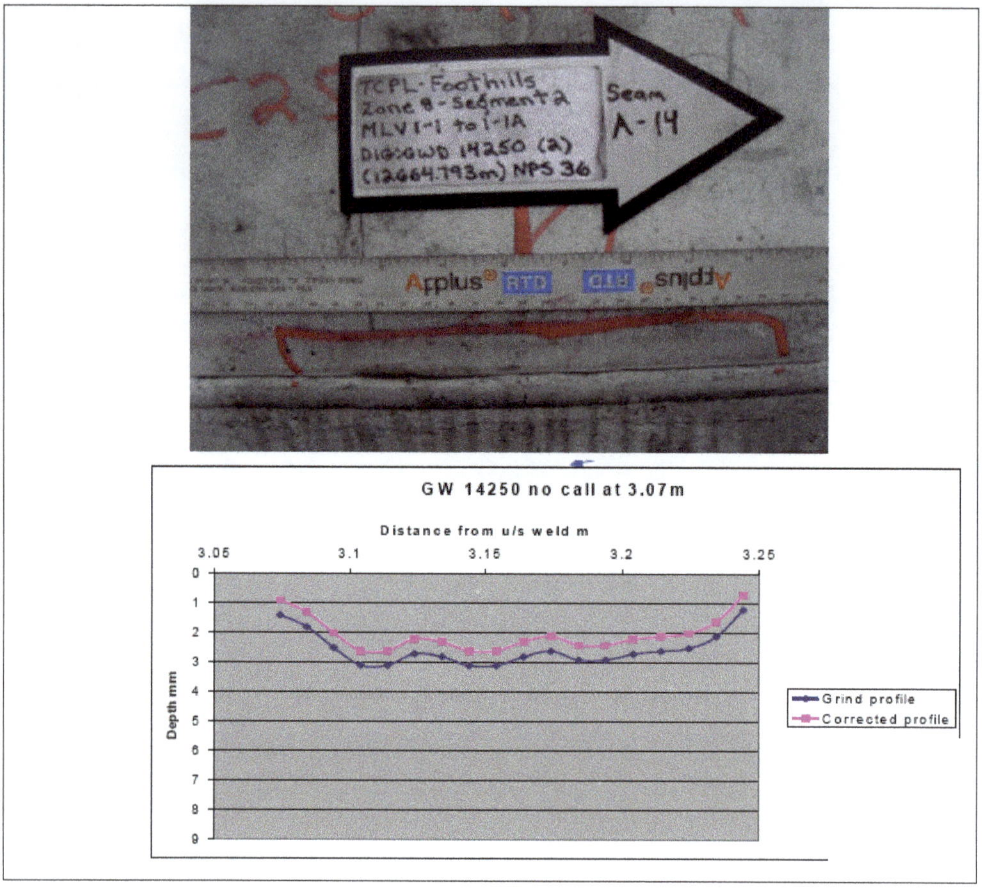

Fig.8. 2010 no-call feature classified: top – MPI; middle – B-scan data, cross section profile after NDE.

Figure 8 is an example of this type of call. Some sensor indications are coincident with this feature but could be not be originally resolved during analysis to be classified as a crack.

Situation B

There were three situations across the system over the past two years, although most of these misclassifications occurred during the 2010 programme. This type of misclassification consisted of the following types:

- 'non-decidable' features
- external corrosion miss-call
- external corrosion deposits masking EMAT signals

'Non-decidable' features

Following the excavations, TransCanada and PII discussed the need to report some specific features that do not fully meet the existing classification criteria. One crack with a relatively short length-vs-depth ratio was identified as a non-decidable feature based on PII's original classification, although upon excavation it was discovered to be a through-wall leak. The EMAT tool detected strong signals during the analysis of this indication but the existing procedures guided the decision

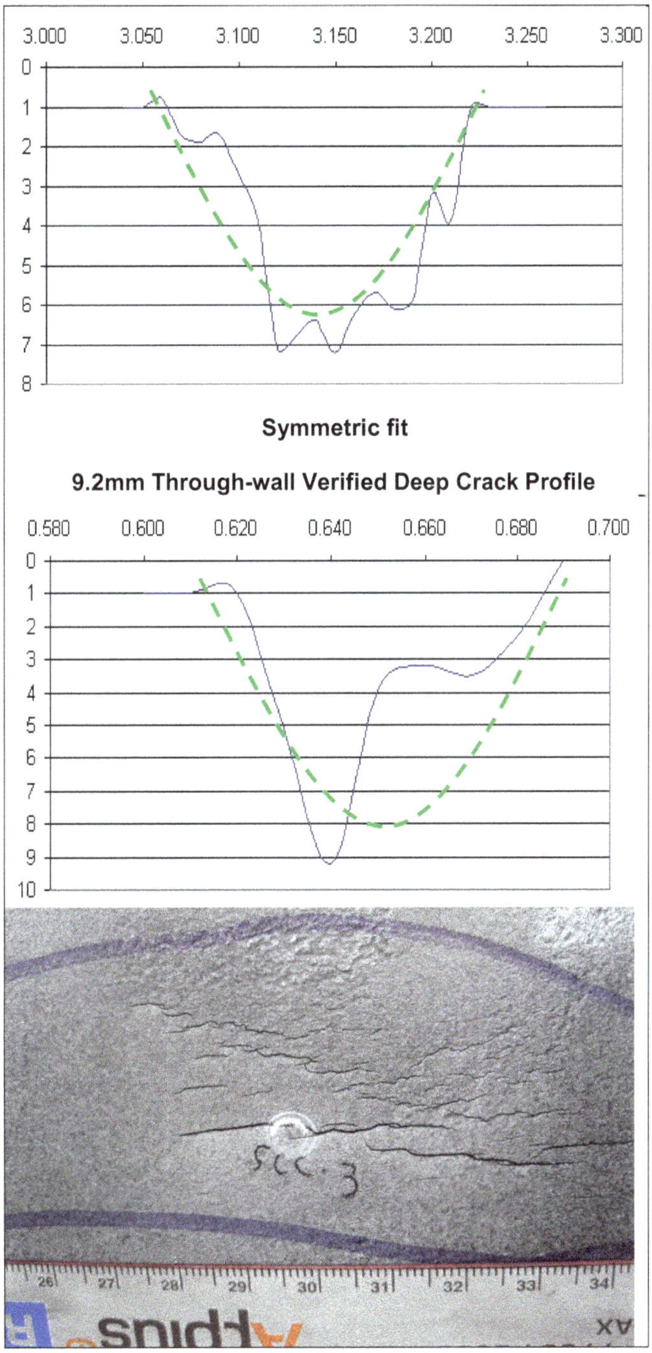

Fig.9. Excavation results through-wall leak, 'non-decidable' feature: top – symmetric fit example; middle – non-symmetric fit example; bottom – MPI of the feature found at the non-decidable location.

of the reported call. Originally, the EMAT analysis classified it as an inclusion, based upon the relatively strong shear- and Lamb-wave classification signals.

The lesson established from this feedback was to refine the guidance in analysis, as this pattern of cracking results in a differing disruption to the ultrasonic energies than expected. In the past, signal characterization was based upon long, deep (symmetric) crack profiles. Short and deep (non-symmetric) profiles were not considered in initial testing, but now will be considered as possible cracks. Figure 9 illustrates the difference between a symmetric and non-symmetric crack profile:

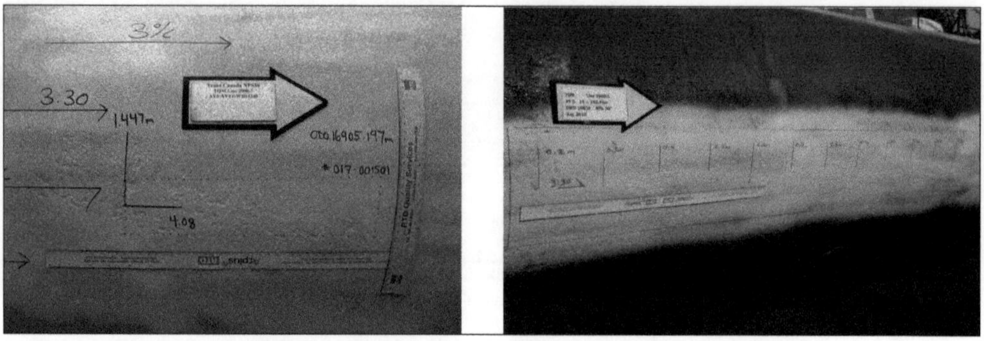

Fig.10. Examples of misclassified crack-like features within external corrosion areas.

these non-symmetric deep/short features were originally 'non-decidable' features as they had a typical aspect ratio and signal response.

TransCanada and PII have decided that whenever there are conflicting signal characteristics, PII will apply a more-conservative approach and classify the indication as a crack-like feature (for example, 'non-decidable' to be characterized as a crack with depths provided). Therefore a 'non-decidable' feature classification has been created and included in all future reports.

Misclassified external corrosion (corrosion coincident with crack-like indications)

In some circumstances conservative calls were made in reported feature areas. The following NDE showed that there was no cracking associated with the reported EMAT features. The misclassified features were located at, or coincident with, the worst areas of external corrosion. The external corrosion was characterized as being steep sided and narrow and was aligned axially in an area of general wall loss associated with a disbonded coating. Each feature had numerous areas of external corrosion indications (see Fig.10). Although the EMAT data did have some characteristics normally associated with corrosion, some indications had high amplitudes and were linear which indicated they could be cracking and hence were conservatively reported.

Misclassified external corrosion deposits: EMAT signal masking

In two cases, one in tape and the other in asphalt, corrosion deposits were found at the location of the reported features. In one example, very hard cathodic-protection-derived (assumed) deposits with yellow, black, and brown colouration were found in a disbonded area underneath the asphalt-coated pipe (Fig.11). The measured on-potential (pipe-to-soil) was -2.330mV. The NDE showed that there was no cracking associated with the reported EMAT features.

It seems that the density of these iron-dominated deposits may attenuate the EMAT signals and could be interpreted as a possible colony. Signals may be enhanced by coating variation or deposit thickness and chemistry, but the EMAT data indicated something physically different about this location. In these cases the iron-rich deposits seemingly causing data mis-interpretation.

Summary

Listed below is a summary of both the results and expected future actions based on the most recent programme:

Fig. 11. Misclassified crack-like features: top – deposits as found; bottom – MPI of the ILI reported feature area.

- TransCanada has extended the excavation programme to 2011 in order to address the remaining features from one of PII's 2010 reports. A total of 21 excavations are planned for 2011.

- With confidence, the EMAT tool is anticipated to delineate valve section severities within tool specifications and have the ability to locate and measure SCC features existing within the line [1].

- TransCanada and PII will continue with the improvement in analysis, software sizing, and classification and discrimination. The results of the excavations are returned to PII upon field discovery and they are immediately incorporated into the analysis process. Training sessions have taken place with the analysis team to teach how to use the excavation information to improve classification. Quality-control procedures have also been modified to take into account the results of these investigative excavations.

- Based on excavation results, it has been proved that the EMAT tool is able conservatively to define valve-section severities and locate severe SCC features present on the line.

- The tool identified 62 crack-like or crack-field features, with the majority exceeding tool specifications and indicating a heightened integrity-threat awareness. The results supported the decision to add more sites for excavation, and to complete the analysis for the entire length of one of the EMAT runs.

- The recent results from the PII EMAT tools are most encouraging. The EMAT tool can discriminate between mid-wall laminations and SCC; it also can find SCC in the body and seam welds, as well as locating SCC in both tape and asphalt coatings. The 2010 programme had several sites with immediate sleeves and cut-outs. The tool is improving, with the lessons-learned being applied on mis-calls and results that are not SCC within EMAT data analysis.

Acknowledgements

Thanks are given to the efforts of the EMAT PII group in Stutensee, Germany, and Calgary, and to TransCanada personnel in Calgary.

Reference

1. J.E. Marr and E.Sanjuan Riverol (TransCanada), S.Jiangang, A.Mann, and S. Tappert (GE), and J.Weislogel (PII), 2010. Validation of latest generation EMAT in-line inspection technology for SCC management. IPC 2010-31091, ASME.

Evaluation of EMAT tool performance by monitoring industry experience

by Ming Gao, Samarth Tandon, and Ravi Krishnamurthy

Blade Energy Partners Ltd, Houston, TX, USA

DESPITE THE FACT that electromagnetic acoustic transducer (EMAT) technology has become available in recent years, there is limited information, experience, and field validation on their capabilities, limitations, and potential for characterizing SCC cracks in gas pipelines. In this paper, advances in EMAT technology and its performance with time are summarized. Various experiences of performance with various EMAT tools are evaluated with currently available data, and discussed. Statistical methods, including binomial probability distribution analysis, binomial confidence interval analysis, and least square linear regression analysis, are used for evaluating probability of detection (POD), probability of false calls (POFC), probability of identification (POI), and sizing accuracy.

A methodology is proposed to assess EMAT tool performance against hydrostatic testing. The results demonstrate that EMAT can be used not only as a reliable tool for SCC susceptibility detection in gas pipelines, but also potentially as an alternative integrity tool to hydrostatic testing for gas pipeline SCC management. Case studies on EMAT performance vs hydrostatic testing are illustrated in detail. Gaps between current EMAT technology and industry needs are identified. Finally, issues for continued research and technology development of EMAT are discussed.

CRACK OR CRACK-LIKE anomalies are common feature in a pipeline system. For gas pipelines, cracks are detected and mitigated through ILI tools such as ultrasonic crack detection (USCD/UTCD) by filling the pipeline with a liquid couplant, and/or through hydrotesting. These methodologies for crack mitigation in a pipeline cause lengthy service interruptions, which turn out to be economically unviable for the pipeline operation.

Consideration of electromagnetic acoustic transducer (EMAT) inspection technology started in the 1970s, with pilot projects throughout the 1980s and 1990s. With the innovation of commercial EMAT ILI tool in 2000, a gas pipeline may be inspected with ILI crack-detection technology without the need for a liquid medium couplant and consequent overall service interruption.

However, it is important to know how well can a tool perform in terms of detecting, discriminating, and locating cracks or crack-like features. API 1163 provides a measure to gauge the tool performance by in-ditch validation in terms of POD, POI, POFC and location accuracy [1]. There have been at least 15 pipeline segments, operated by different companies, which have been inspected with various implementations of EMAT-based inspection tools. However, since its inception, there has been limited data available on validation of the performance of the tool. The aim of this paper is to summarize inspection performances and experiences known to date.

In this paper, advances in EMAT technology with time are presented. The methodologies used to measure the tool performance and improvements in tool performance are then described. A comparison of the tool performance with hydrotesting is illustrated in detail. It is shown that the EMAT may be ready to move up from a severity tool to a mitigation tool.

Background

Cracks are one type of anomaly which account for failures in a pipeline system. The pipeline industry has several methods to counter this problem, one way being detection through ILI, and a second being mitigating critical stress-corrosion cracking (SCC) through hydrotesting. ILI tools such as UTCD/USCD can be used for crack detection, although they require a liquid couplant to transmit signals for this purpose. For liquid pipelines, these tools are well suited and may be run in the line without service interruption. However, for gas pipelines, these tools require the pipeline to be filled with a liquid couplant such as water, or require batching the tool in a liquid slug, both causing lengthy service interruption to the pipeline which may not be viable economically. On the other hand, mitigating SCC through hydrotesting causes service interruptions and environmental issues such as contamination or erosion. Moreover, it only eliminates critical SCC features and does not provide information on the sub-critical features existing in the pipeline.

In all possible cases, the viable option for crack detection in a gas pipeline was to develop a tool which can be run in the pipeline without a liquid couplant. The basic working concept of the EMAT technique is based on the principle that a metal grid of steel can be excited by electromagnetic waves to oscillate and generate ultrasonic pulses and waveforms.

The EMAT technique has been elusive in the past due to the ineffective nature of electromagnetic induction and the practical application of the guided-wave technique [2]. An improvement on the magnetization capabilities and a more thorough understanding of the guided-wave technique changed the situation. This motivated two major pipeline inspection vendors to develop in-line inspection tools which work without a liquid couplant [2-4].

Commercial tools ranging from 16-in to 48-in are now available for inspection of SCC and coating defects in gas pipelines [5, 6]. Significant progress has been made commercially to detect, discriminate, and size cracks. Experience has been gained, but not fully reported, from many pipeline runs performed by these two pipeline inspection service vendors with different technologies. Very limited information is available to the public about the actual in-field performance, mainly because of its relatively short history. The degrees of impact on the reliability of ILI results have not been evaluated, in particular, using both exploration and validation excavations.

There is a need to quantitatively evaluate the effectiveness of the current technologies using various pipeline inspection and pipeline operator excavation databases and pull tests, in term of their POD, POI, POFC, and sizing tolerance. Critical factors that contribute to the tool effectiveness need to be identified. Further improvements of the current technologies, and both short- and long-term strategies, need to be established.

Current EMAT technologies and claimed capabilities

The EMAT technologies and associated in-line inspection tools currently available for crack detection and characterization are as follows:

GE: technology and ILI tool
Rosen: technology and ILI tool

A brief review of current EMAT technologies and claimed capability is given below based on the available data in the public domain.

GE: technology and ILI tool

In 1997, TransCanada PipeLines teamed-up with GE PII to develop a new ILI tool using EMAT technology for its 36-in pipeline [2, 7]. The technology consists of multiple arrangements of various sensor types, based on guided-wave ultrasonic transmission and reflection. Figure 1 is a schematic of the initial design concepts used in GE's 36-in crack-detection tool, showing details of the sensor block that contains three different type of sensors and the arrangement of three sensor blocks on each of the four carrier modulus [7, 8].

For this first-generation technology, 450 pull tests were conducted to closely monitor the performance of the components and optimize their properties. The tests were performed both on real and artificial defects including SCC, laminations, inclusions, and machined defects with varying lengths, depths, orientations, and circumferential positions in the pipe wall. As reported in 2002, the technology was demonstrated as capable of resolving better than 30-mm x 1-mm defects [2, 7].

In the autumn of 2002, the GE first-generation EMAT tool was run on a 64-km section of the TransCanada system on a line previously run with an *Ultrascan CD* tool. The *Ultrascan CD* tool run data were correlated, and validated the tool. A POD of 92% and a POI of 46% were reported.

In 2004, GE released a second-generation tool that consisted of enhanced sensors for both sensitivity and robustness. The tool was run in-field in 2005, with excavations in 2005-2006 [9]. One reported experience of an approximately 700-km inspection programme using the EMAT 36-in tool was accomplished for one gas transmission pipeline operator [9], and a total of 15 toe cracks were successfully verified. The results were limited to light and uncoated pipe.

The tool/technology showed that it can distinguish insignificant pipe-wall features (stringers, laminations, and inclusions) from SCC defects, and internal/external pipe-wall features. Crack depth reporting was provided in three depth categories in the first generation tool (depth < 2mm, depth = 2-5mm, and depth > 5mm), and extended to four categories within the second-generation tool (1-2mm, 2-3mm, 3-5mm, > 5mm).

In 2008, GE introduced its third-generation EMAT tool [8]. The newer technology targeted better overall inspection and operational performance for a wider range of diameters, longer run distances, and 1.5-D bend passage, and is summarized in Table 1. As with the first-generation design, the third-generation tool emphasized the use of longer-distance guided-wave ultrasonics, with fewer, wider, sensor spacing over the pipe circumference to ensure wave-mode purity and wave propagation between the sensors.

This design includes high redundancy sensor coverage of the pipe wall to improve upon POD, POI, and sizing performance including SCC-susceptible 'heavy' coatings such as bitumen. The underlying analysis methodology was also significantly updated over the first generation to encompass the new sensors' ultrasonic modes and better visualization of crack features, anomalies, and coating.

In pull testing, features down to < 0.5mm depth were detected repeatedly. Similarly a key focus on discrimination of features was developed and validated against actual non-crack features in blind tests [22]. With the third-generation tool, the overall approach to present to industry was to ensure a full operational validation with a partnered operator to consider as many conditions and defects as possible, and hence an interim 2-mm x 50-mm detection size was initially set and published, as noted in Table 1.

Property	EMAT (Tool)	
	Generation I	Generation III
Size range (NPS)	36	24-36
Inspection range (km)	150	170
Speed range (m/s)	0-1.2	0-2.5
Bend passing	3D	1.5D
Minimum defect size (mm)	2x50*	2x50
POI (%)	50	>66
POD (%)	>90	>90
Detection redundancy	2	5
Disbondment detection	All coating types	All coating types

Table 1. Specification of GE EMAT tool [9].

Property	Specification
Range @ max. speed	105.6 miles*
Max. speed	8.2 ft/sec
Max. pressure	2,756 psi
Temp.	32-122°F**
Min. bend radius back-to-back	1.5D 90°
Min. ID in straight pipe	27.01° in round 25.67° in oval
Min. ID in bend	28.43°
Tool length	26.41 ft
Tool weight	7,445 lbs
*longer range and ** higher temperature available on request	

Table 2. Detailed specification of the GE EMAT ILI tool [6].

	Radial crack-like defects with longitudinal orientation	
	In-plate material, min. length 1.969in	In longit. weld area, min. length 1.969in
Min.depth extension of POD 90%	0.079in	
Depth gouging in 3 classes	0.079-0.118in 0.118-0.197in >0.197in	
Lenght sizing accuracy at 80% confidence	0.394in or 10% oflength	
Deviation from longitudinal orientation	+/- 10%	
Internal/ external discrimination	yes	

A major objective of the third generation development was to advance the identification and classification specification (POI), and overall to reduce an operator's experience regarding false calls (POFC, i.e. probability of false calls) [8].

In an inspection and validation programme between 2008-2010, the tool was validated with a POD of greater than 90%, and POI of 81% [10, 11]. The POI improvements were higher than 35% over the previous generation reporting.

The specifications for both the tools are discussed in Table 1 [9] and Table 2 [6]. More detailed information can be found from GE PII website.

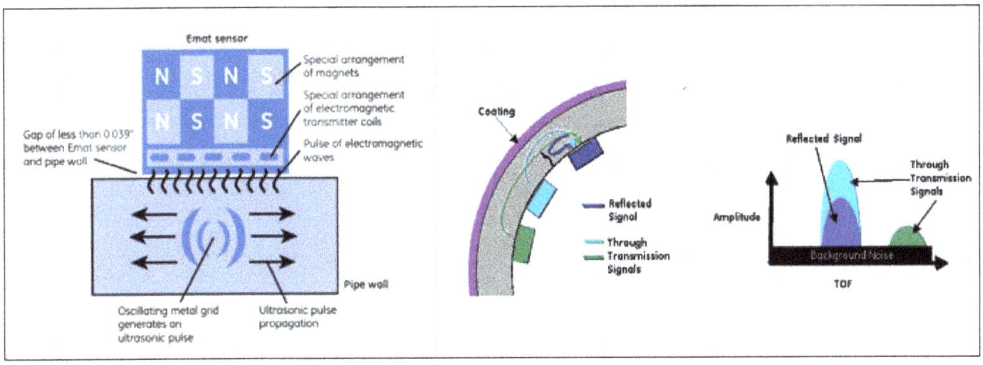

Fig.1. Schematic of the initial design concepts used in the GE 36-in EMAT crack-detection tool [7, 8].

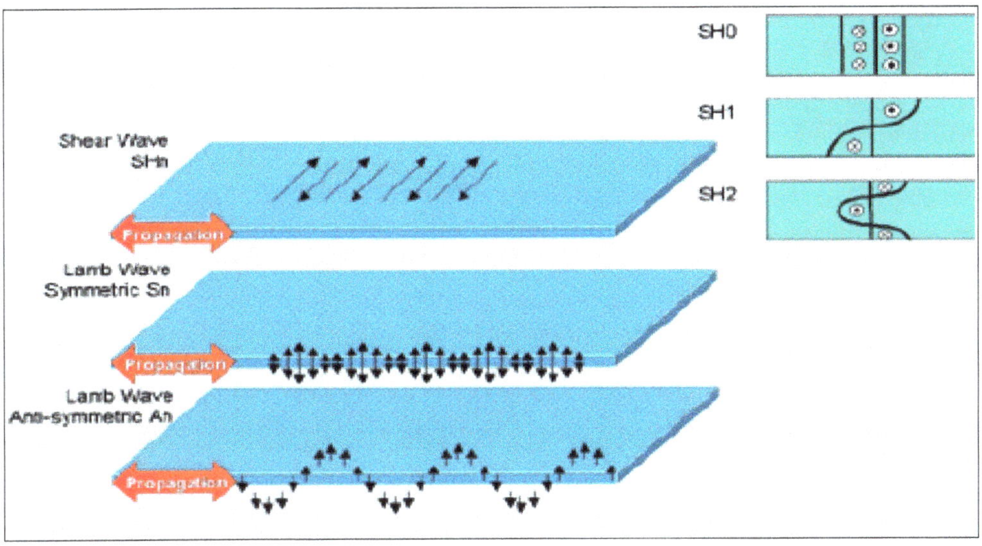

Fig.2. Schematic of the wave type used in the Rosen EMAT crack-detection tools.

Rosen: technology and ILI tool

After GE, Rosen teamed with Sonic Sensors to develop another tool using the EMAT technology of guided waves. The guided wave is a mechanical-elastic wave whose propagation depends on the dimensions and properties of the material itself. A guided wave as generated by an EMAT transducer propagates within the external and internal pipe surface as a boundary condition. The presence of SCC disturbs the guided wave, and a 'significant' change in the dimensions of the wave guide, such as that from a crack, reflects the wave and causes an echo, which may then be detected [3].

The guided waves can be categorized into Lamb-waves and horizontal shear waves of a different order, Fig.2. If guided waves are properly selected, an attracted signal can be obtained from the SCC location independent of the existing external surface coating.

Rosen incorporated a high-resolution design in its tool, which enabled improved lift-off behaviour and coating detection [12]. The magnets were placed outside the sensors to allow for a light-weight design [13]. Figure 3 shows the advances in the high-resolution EMAT ILI tool [3], which include: (a) improvement in the POD and characterization using shear wave from both directions; (b)

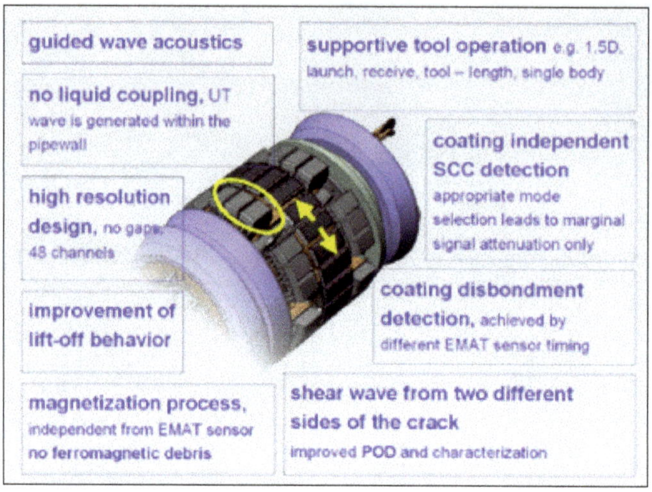

Fig.3. Advances in the Rosen EMAT ILI tool.

coating disbondment detection; (c) coating independent of SCC detection; (d) improved lift-off behaviour; and (e) light-weight design of the sensors.

In 2005, full-scale pull tests were conducted with prototype EMAT sensors in a pull-test line containing artificial features as well as disbonded coatings and natural SCC. The 6-m (19.7-ft) long test joint was taken from a coal-tar coated large-diameter natural gas pipeline. The overall sensitivity of the high-resolution EMAT prototype was determined on a set of EDM notches introduced into the test pipe. Full-scale tests on the pull rig showed high sensitivity: notches of 15mm in length and 10% depth were detected, and all the areas with SCC were detected. The dimensions of the SCC colony can be analysed from the measured data, although individual cracks could not be distinguished from the detection signal. The disbonded coating could be detected clearly [3].

In 2007, a 16-in tool was manufactured with a high-resolution approach, in which a large number of EMAT modules were arranged on the ILI tool. In this configuration, the ultrasonic waves do not travel around the circumference of the pipe before they are observed by the receiver. Rather, the acoustic waves only travel a short distance between the EMAT sender and the receiver, allowing comparatively simple data evaluation and avoiding false alarms [13].

The EMAT was tested on the two 16-in gas pipelines, both of which had FBE coating and operated at 250 psi, and with lengths of 2 km and 5.92 km, respectively. The long-seam weld, girth weld, linear anomalies, and weak coating could be identified.

In 2009, a combination of artificial and natural crack-like indications was studied by Rosen after the EMAT tools had gone into service. The minimum dimension found for the EMAT technology was 20 mm in length and 0.65 mm in depth with POD of 92%. Crack-like anomalies 20 mm in length and 0.42 mm in depth were detected with a POD of 44%. A multi-parameter correlation model was used which takes into account the distribution of the response of the individual parameters to a particular feature type. The POI for crack-like features vs other features was found to be 91% [14].

EMAT depth sized a population of artificial and natural crack-like flaws with an accuracy of ±0.64 mm with a confidence level of 90%. The length-sizing accuracy determined using EMAT on artificial crack-like defects from multiple passes during a pull-test programme showed larger

System Specifications

Tool sizes		14" – 36"
Technology and application		EMAT crack detection EMAT coating disbondment detection
Special data	EMAT (SCC, cracks) Spatial resolution	35 mm (1.4") 64 – 168 channels
	EMAT (disbondment) Spatial resolution	35 mm (1.4") 32 – 84 channels
	Quality channel	35 mm (1.4") 32 – 84 channels
	Pressure	1 channel
	Temperature	1 channel
	Acceleration sensor	3D
	Weld identification	yes

Standard Operating Specifications

Pipeline product	gas or liquids
Product temperature range	0 °C – 65 °C (32 °F – 149 °F)
Maximum operating pressure	15 MPa (2175 psi)
Operating tool speed range	0.3 – 5.0 m/s (0.67 – 11 mph)
Inspection tool speed range	0.3 – 2.0 m/s (0.67 – 4.4 mph)
Minimum bend passage	1.5D
Maximum operating time	50 hours
Maximum inspection length	330 km (205 miles)

Performance Specifications

Crack detection	Wall thickness range	up to 20 mm (0.79")
	Minimum depth (in parent material)	1 mm (0.039")
	Minimum depth (in long seam)	2 mm (0.079")
	Minimum length	20 mm (0.79")
	Orientation to pipe axis	±18°
Crack sizing	Length sizing	±10 mm (±0.39")
	Depth sizing	precision estimation model
Coating disbondment detection	Type	coal tar enamel (or comparable)

NOTES:
Active speed control recommended
Contact ROSEN for operating conditions outside the standard range

Table 3. Specification of the Rosen EMAT tool [5].

scattering for short features. The tool demonstrated that it can identify the crack lengths of individual cracks in the colony, thus enabling the application of clustering rules, for determination of significant length on the crack colony [15, 16]. The tool can also identify the disbonded areas by a change in the transmission amplitude and reports them as individual features. The lateral dimensions and position of disbonded areas can also be reported in detail. The tool can differentiate between coatings, and identify the disbonded areas and their corresponding dimensions.

The tool current specifications as listed on Rosen website are shown in Table 3 [5].

Methods for tool-performance assessment

Determination of in-line tool performance is straightforward if the complete population of tool predictions can be directly measured and validated, one example of which is the laboratory pull test for performance evaluation. However, for field verification, the tool performance must be determined from direct measurements of a small size of sample of indications from the overall population. Statistical methods such as binomial distributions, confidence intervals, and other methods for hypothesis testing are referenced in API 1163 [1] for the purposes of determining the tool performance in terms of POD, POI, POFC and depth/length sizing tolerance. In the following section, the methods used for the present investigations are described.

Binomial distribution analysis

The binomial probability distribution method is one of the most useful statistical methods for characterizing count data, such as the number of ILI measurements that satisfy a performance specification. This method can be directly applied to POD, POI, POFC, and sizing-tolerance evaluations.

In a binomial experiment there are two possible outcomes – 'success' and 'failure' – regardless of the nature of the observations. In an ILI validation process, a fixed number of excavations (measurements) are made. An ILI measurement, for example detection of a crack, will be called a success if it is predicted by ILI and found in the field measurement according to the tool's specification, and a failure otherwise. Once the number of successes, x, is determined, a binomial distribution based on the inspection certainty, p, as defined in the performance specification, is then used to determine the probability $p(x)$ of finding x cases out of a total of n measurements:

$$p(x) = C_x^n p^n (1-p)^{n-x} \qquad (1)$$

where

$$C_x^n = \frac{n!}{(n-x)!x!}$$

n = total number of measurements

x = number of successes, for example the number of anomalies above the detection threshold that are successfully detected and reported by the ILI tool, etc.

p = hypothesized probability of inspection (i.e. certainty); for example, $p = 0.80$ for detection means that an anomaly above the specified detection threshold will be 'certainly' detected by the tool 80% of the time.

Probabilities (p) are commonly expressed in two ways: as a number between 0 and 1, such as 0.80, and as the percentage equivalent to that number, such as 80%. In this paper whichever terminology seems more natural in the context it is used.

The cumulative probability of x, i.e. $\sum_{i=0}^{x} p(i)$, defines the confidence level of the inspection tool for the given inspection certainty:

$$\sum_{i=0}^{x} p(i) = p(0) + p(1) + ... + p(x) \tag{2}$$

With the established binomial distribution, the certainty p (such as POD, POI, etc.) can be back calculated based the on the number of successful measurements and the given confidence level, or the confidence level can be calculated for a given POD with the same set of measurements. Then the tool performance can be evaluated against the tool specification provided by vendors.

Clopper-Pearson confidence-interval method

In the above section, we introduced the binomial distribution analysis. The analysis calculates certainty p from n measurements. Considering the randomness of sample selection, the number of success x from n measurements would not be the same for repeating random-selection tests. Therefore, the calculated p will be different. To account for this uncertainty, confidence-interval methods have been developed [17-22].

The confidence-interval method computes the interval for p, i.e. the lower and upper ends of the interval P_L and P_U, using the number of successful measurements, x, and the total number of measurements n. The interval having its ends p_L and p_U contains the true certainty p_{true}, with 'true' POD, POI, etc., of the population with the given confidence level. Therefore, the tool performance can be evaluated with the lower and upper ends of the interval of p.

One of the confidence interval methods, namely the Clopper-Pearson confidence-interval method, is selected for the present performance study. The Clopper-Pearson confidence interval is known as 'exact' in terms of binomial confidence interval, and 'conservative', which has coverage at least satisfying the specified confidence level for the analysis. API 1163 defines the confidence interval based on the standardized normal probability distribution, which in general is different from the binomial confidence interval, specifically for small sample size n.

The confidence interval for certainty p_L (lower end) and p_U (upper end) are solutions of

$$\sum_{i=0}^{x} C_i^n p_U^i (1 - p_U)^{n-i} = \alpha \tag{3}$$

and

$$\sum_{i=x}^{n} C_i^n p_L^i (1 - p_L)^{n-i} = \alpha \tag{4}$$

Table 4 provides the confidence interval (lower and upper ends) of certainties at 95% confidence for a fixed number of measurements, $n = 25$, and x success using the Clopper-Pearson methodology. The table can used to find upper and lower ends of POD or POI for 25 observations with x success varying from 0 to 25.

x	0	1	2	3	4	5	6	7	8	9	10	11	12
P_L	0.000	0.002	0.014	0.034	0.057	0.082	0.110	0.139	0.170	0.203	0.236	0.270	0.305
P_U	0.113	0.176	0.231	0.282	0.350	0.375	0.420	0.462	0.504	0.544	0.583	0.621	0.659
x	13	14	15	16	17	18	19	20	21	22	23	24	25
P_L	0.341	0.379	0.417	0.456	0.486	0.538	0.580	0.625	0.679	0.718	0.788	0.824	0.887
P_U	0.695	0.730	0.764	0.793	0.830	0.881	0.890	0.918	0.943	0.966	0.988	0.998	1.000

Operator	Segment	Inspection yr	Digs	Cracks	Other features	Grand total
O1*	L1	2003	10	460	17	477
	L7	2005	33	2118	26	2144
	L8	2005	8	193	18	211
	L4	2006	10	293	1	294
	L5	2006	10	113	47	160
	L2	2007	10	306	23	329
	L3	2007	5	91	5	916
	L6	2007	3	10	11	21
O2	L1	2007	10	5	7	12
	L2	2008	15	2	8	10
	L3	2008	4	82	0	82
	L5	2008	13	13	NA	13
	L4	2009	72	147	17	164
O3	L1	2008	5	6	21	27
	L2	2009	15	146	7	153
Total		2005-2009	223	3985	208	4193

* More insepctions and excavations after 2008 will be collected.

Table 4 (above). Endpoints of 95% confidence intervals for certainty, n = 25 (Clopper-Pearson method).

Table 5 (right). Year of ILI inspection and corresponding number of anomalies found in-ditch.

Tool performance evaluation (POD, POI, POFC, and sizing)

EMAT inspection and excavation data from a total of 15 pipeline sections were collected and analysed, as shown in Table 5. The data contain the pipeline sections inspected during the year 2003-2009, and a completed excavation investigation in 2010. The lines inspected during the earlier years were inspected with older model tools, whereas the ones recently inspected in 2009 were inspected with newer models, having better capability and performance. 223 excavations were done in total, finding 3,985 cracks, and 208 other features.

In general, POD in the initial years of the launch of the old tools was high while POI was low due to numerous other types of linear indications with similar signals to cracks (such as laminations) being detected and identified as cracks. The low POI resulted in unnecessary excavations. The low POI drove ILI vendors to make extensive efforts to improve the tools' capability for discrimination of cracks from other types of defect, and as a result, the POI has been significantly increased.

For practical interest, the evaluation of tool performance is focused on the newer tools with recent inspection and excavation data, and is presented in the paper.

Performance evaluation for probability of detection (POD)

POD is a measure of the ILI tool's ability to find anomalies existing on the pipeline. POD in this paper is presented in the following three ways:

1. Success rate of detection: calculated from the number of anomalies (x) successfully detected and confirmed by the ILI tool and excavation in terms of the total number of anomalies with same type of signal (n) found in the ditch. POD is expressed as success rate = x/n.

2. Certainty (or probability) of detection: with the same set of x and n data but calculated using the binomial-distribution method for a given confidence level, such as 95%, reflecting the confidence with which the probability of detection is satisfied. POD is expressed in percentage or fraction at the 95% confidence level.

3. Confidence interval for POD: with the same set of x and n data but calculated using the Clopper-Pearson method at a given confidence level, for example 95%, reflecting the confidence with which the confidence interval for POD is satisfied. POD is expressed as lower and upper ends of probability of detection, p_L and p_U.

For assessing the number of anomalies successfully detected by the ILI tool, two counting criteria are used:

- Criterion A: all the anomalies that are reported by the ILI tool and confirmed in the ditch, regardless of whether the anomalies are above or below the specification.

- Criterion B: only those anomalies that meet the threshold for detection and that are reported by ILI and are confirmed in the ditch are counted as success x. The threshold of detection is defined as "a continuous length over which the depth and length criteria are met" in accordance with vendors' contracted specifications.

For assessing the number of ILI missed calls, only one counting criterion is used: the number of anomalies (cracks) that meet the threshold of detection (for example 1mm x 30mm) but are not

Year of inspection/ excavation	Pipeline section	Crack/crack-like reported by tool and confirmed by excavation (x)	Crack/crack-like found during excavation (n)	Detection success rate (x/n) (%)	POD based on binomial analysis @ 95% confidence interval (%)	Clopper Pearson confidence interval @ 95% confidence (%)
2008-9	O2-L2-2008	10	10	100.0	*	*
2008-9	O2-L3-2008	2	15	13.3	5.7	2.4-36.3
2008-9	O3-L1-2008	11	13	84.6	68.4	59.0-97.2
2008-9	O2-L5-2008	12	13	92.3	79.4	68.4-99.6
2009-10	O2-L4-2009	40	47	85.1	76.4	73.8-92.8
2009-10	O3-L2-2009	39	41	95.1	88.9	85.4-99.1

*Sample size too small for binomial and confidence interval analysis.

Table 6. Pipeline sections and their corresponding PODs calculated using counting criterion A.

Year of inspection/ excavation	Pipeline section	Total cracks indentified correctly by tool (x)	Total crack/ crack-like features found during excavations (n)	Identification success ratio (x/n) (%)	Certainty (POI) based on binomial analysis @ 95% confidence interval (%)	Clopper Pearson confidence interval @ 95% confidence (%)
2008-9	O2-L2-2008	2	8	25.0	*	*
2008-9	O2-L3-2008	1	1	100.0	*	*
2008-9	O3-L1-2008	6	10	60.0	*	*
2008-9	O2-L5-2008	11	11	100.0	*	*
2009-10	O2-L4-2009	22	29	75.9	63.3	59.4-88.1
2009-10	O3-L2-2009	22	29	75.9	63.3	59.4-88.1

*Sample size too small for binomial and confidence interval analysis.

Table 7. Pipeline sections and their corresponding PODs calculated using counting criterion B.

detected by the ILI tool. Cracks that do not meet the criterion and not reported by ILI will not count as ILI missed calls.

In addition, errors in sizing and the influence of the time gap between the ILI run and the excavation on crack size are considered for correction:

- For phased-array ultrasonic technology (PAUT), an error of ±0.25 mm is estimated based on the direct comparison with fracture surface measurement
- For grinding-out measurement technique, an error of +0.25 mm for 'over grinding' is estimated based on the direct comparison with fracture surface measurement
- For the influence of time gap between ILI run and excavation on the sizing, a depth growth

rate of 0.25 mm/yr is considered. This growth should be subtracted from NDE measured depth

Combining the above three factors, the following criteria are applied:

- For PAUT depth, no correction is made because crack growth cancels the possible depth under-estimate by the technology.

- For grinding-out measurement technique, a -0.5 mm correction is applied to the field depth measurement to account for crack growth and over-grinding.

With the above criteria, data collected in 2009 and 2010 from six pipeline sections and two operators were analysed and are presented in Tables 6 and 7.

Table 6 shows that the success rate of the latest EMAT technologies for crack detection is high: all are above 80% except for Section 02-L3-2008. The reason for the low POD of this section might be attributed to the in-field protocol for this pipeline section, for which interlinked length and maximum depth of the colony was used for the POD analysis

The Table also shows both binomial and confidence-interval PODs that are lower than the success rate in the statistical sense; however, they are higher than, or close to, the commonly acceptable POD = 80% at 95% confidence level.

It is noted when changing the counting criterion from Method A to B (i.e. only those anomalies that meet the specified threshold for detection (depth over continues length) and confirmed in ditch were counted as successfully detected by the ILI tool) that the success rate and binomial/ confidence-interval PODs decreased, Table 7. The decrease in POD results from removing all the features that are below tool specification from *x* and *n*. Nevertheless, the PODs are high for all the pipeline sections except Section O2-L3-2008.

Probability of identification (POI)

POI is a measure of an ILI tool's ability to properly discriminate an anomaly from the other types of anomalies that exhibit similar signals. The probability of identification (POI) is defined as the probability that an anomaly, once detected, is correctly classified at a certain confidence level. Similar to POD, POI is presented in the following three ways:

- Success rate of identification: the number of anomalies is successfully classified by the ILI tool (x) to the total number of anomalies (n) having similar signals as reported by ILI. POI is presented as success rate of identification = x/n.

- Certainty (or probability) of identification: with the same set of x and n data but calculated using the binomial-distribution method at a given confidence level, usually, 95%. POI is expressed in percentage or fraction at 95% confidence level.

- Confidence interval for POI: with the same set of x and n data but calculated using the Clopper-Pearson method at a given confidence level, usually 95%. POI is expressed as lower and upper ends of probability of identification, p_L and p_U

The same counting criteria as for POD are used for POI:

Year of inspection/ excavation	Pipeline section	Crack/crack-like reported by tool and confirmed by excavation (x)	Crack/crack-like found during excavation (n)	Detection success rate (x/n) (%)	POD based on binomial analysis @ 95% confidence interval (%)	Clopper Pearson confidence interval @ 95% confidence (%)
2008-9	O2-L2-2008	2	10	20.0	*	*
2008-9	O2-L3-2008	2	2	100.0	*	*
2008-9	O3-L1-2008	7	11	63.6	*	*
2008-9	O2-L5-2008	12	12	100.0	*	*
2009-10	O2-L4-2009	38	54	70.4	60.5	58.5-80.4
2009-10	O3-L2-2009	33	40	82.5	72.6	69.6-91.5
*Sample size too small for binomial and confidence interval analysis.						

Table 8. Pipeline sections and their corresponding tool POIs calculated using counting criterion A.

Year of inspection/ excavation	Pipeline section	Total cracks indentified correctly by tool (x)	Total crack/ crack-like features found during excavations (n)	Idnetification success ratio (x/n) (%)	Certainty (POI) based on binomial analysis @ 95% confidence interval (%)	Clopper Pearson confidence interval @ 95% confidence (%)
2008-9	O2-L2-2008	2	8	25.0	*	*
2008-9	O2-L3-2008	1	1	100.0	*	*
2008-9	O3-L1-2008	6	10	60.0	*	*
2008-9	O2-L5-2008	11	11	100.0	*	*
2009-10	O2-L4-2009	22	29	75.9	63.3	59.4-88.1
2009-10	O3-L2-2009	22	29	75.9	63.3	59.4-88.1

Table 9. Pipeline sections and their corresponding tool POIs calculated using counting criterion B.

- Criterion A: discrimination applies to all the anomalies that are reported by the ILI tool and confirmed in the ditch, regardless of whether the anomaly is above or below the specification.

- Criterion B: discrimination only applies to anomalies that meet the threshold for detection and are confirmed in the ditch.

- Table 8 shows the success rate for identification that is in the range between 63%-100%. The Table also shows both binomial and confidence-interval POIs that are lower than the success rate in the statistical sense. Though significant improvement has been made recently, there is a small gap between the current tool performance and the commonly acceptable POI of 80% at 95% confidence level.

Year of inspection/ excavation	Pipeline section	False calls (x)	Tool calls (n)	Fasle call rate (x/n) (%)	Certainty (POFC) based on binomial analysis @ 95% confidence interval (%)	Clopper Pearson confidence interval @ 95% confidence (%)
2008-9	O2-L2-2008	12	22	54.5	68.9	35.3-72.9
2008-9	O2-L3-2008	1	3	33.3	*	*
2008-9	O3-L1-2008	0	11	0.0	*	*
2008-9	O2-L5-2008	2	14	14.3	29.6	2.6-38.5
2009-10	O2-L4-2009	28	82	34.1	42.5	25.5-43.7
2009-10	O3-L2-2009	1	41	2.4	7.2	0.1-11.1

Table 10. Pipeline sections and their corresponding tool POFCs calculated using counting criterion A.

Year of inspection/ excavation	Pipeline section	False calls (x)	Tool calls (n)	Fasle call rate (x/n) (%)	Certainty (POFC) based on binomial analysis @ 95% confidence interval (%)	Clopper Pearson confidence interval @ 95% confidence (%)
2008-9	O2-L2-2008	12	20	60.0	74.2	39.4-78.3
2008-9	O2-L3-2008	1	2	50.0	*	*
2008-9	O3-L1-2008	0	10	0.0	*	*
2008-9	O2-L5-2008	2	13	15.4	31.8	2.8-41.0
2009-10	O2-L4-2009	28	57	49.1	59.1	37.6-60.7
2009-10	O3-L2-2009	1	30	3.3	9.5	0.2-14.9
*Sample size too small for binomial and confidence interval analysis.						

Table 11. Pipeline sections and their corresponding tool POFCs calculated using counting criterion B.

- Table 9 presents the POI results when counting criterion B is applied. It is observed that the POIs changed, resulting from removing all the features that are below specification from x and n for discrimination (POI) analysis.

Probability of false call (POFC)

POFC is a closely associated measure with POD, which is the frequency that the tool falsely reports an anomaly where no anomaly exists. Obviously, POFC would be better when it is small. Similarly to POD and POI, POFC is presented in the following three ways:

- Rate of false call: the ratio of the tool falsely reporting non-exiting anomalies (x) to the total number of this type of anomaly (n) reported by the ILI tool. POFC is presented as rate of false call = x/n.

Depth ILI	Depth excavation	At 95% confidence level	
12.5-25.0%	0.6, 18.2, 45.4, 33.2, 24.0, 39.7, 33,23, 46.15	Tolerance	Certainty
		+/- 10% wt	49%
25.0-40.0%	34.0, 49.7	+/- 15% wt	60%
		+/- 22% wt	>80%

Table 12. (a) ILI-reported and field-measured crack depth; and (b) depth-sizing tolerance calculated using binomial-distribution analysis.

- Certainty (probability) of false call: calculated using the binomial-distribution method.
- Confidence interval for POFC: calculated using the Clopper-Pearson confidence-interval method.

Table 10 shows that the false-call rate can be as low as 0% and 2.4%, and range from 0% to 55%. The Table also shows both binomial and confidence-interval POFCs that are higher than the success rate in the statistical sense; however, they have been significantly improved compared to the old tools. One of the inspections has achieved a POFC of 7.2% at 95% confidence level.

Table 11 presents the POFC results when counting criterion B is applied, showing an increase in POFCs. The increase in POFC results from removing all the features that are below specification from x and n for false call (POFC) analysis. Finally, a gap is still seen between the current tool performance on POFC and industry expectation of approximately POFC = 5%.

Sizing

Accuracy of sizing is the measure of tool's ability to predict an anomaly's dimensions, which are typically depth and length for cracks. Establishing sizing tolerance based on the correlation between ILI tool prediction and field excavation is one of the important components of fitness-for-service and life-prediction assessments.

Two types of statistical method are used for the sizing analysis: (a) linear-regression and (b) binomial-distribution or confidence-interval analysis.

In the pipeline industry, a unity graph plot of ILI and field data with linear regression is often used to determine the error bands at the desired confidence level. The linear-nf:regression analysis describes the sizing accuracy with the following two parameters:

tolerance, for example ±10% wall thickness (wt) for corrosion
confidence level, for example 80%

The advantage of using the unity graph plot approach is that the plot provides an opportunity to investigate ILI system error, possible error sources, and appropriate calibration and adjustment. However, this method does not provide complete information on how good or bad the evaluation could be when using a small sample size of field excavations (n) to represent large population of anomalies (N) on the pipeline. The results of analysis are valid only within the data set used for regression, and predictions should not be extended beyond the range of the data set that is used.

API 1163 also recommends using the binomial-distribution or confidence-interval methods for

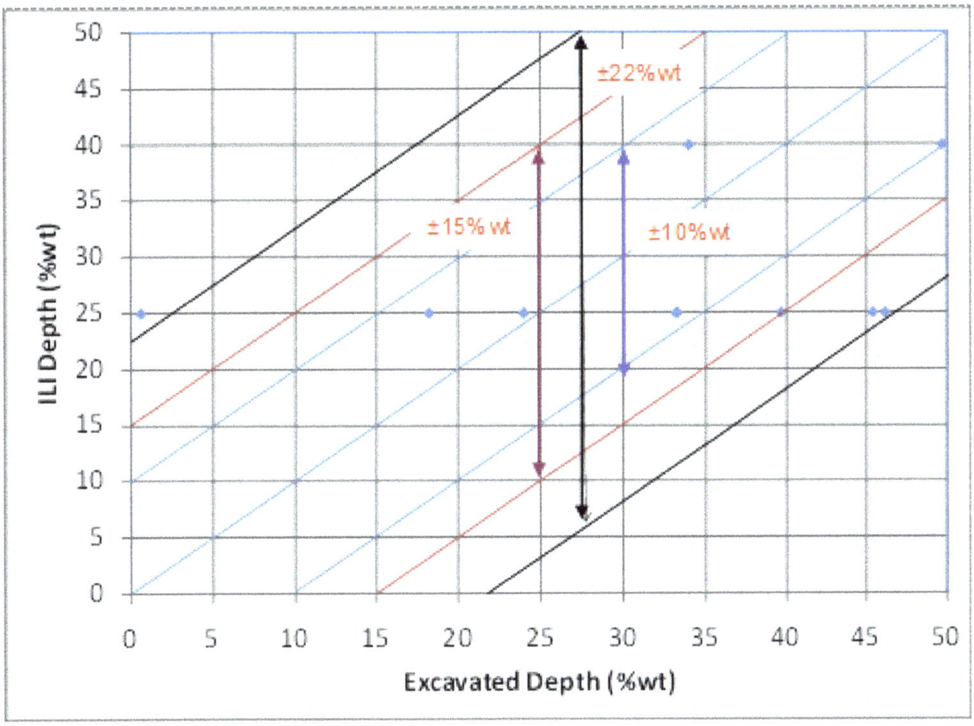

Fig.4. Unity graph plot showing length correlations for the tool run O2-L5-2008.

sizing analysis. With these methods, the sizing accuracy shall include the following three parameters when a small sample size of excavations is used for tool performance validation:

- a tolerance, for example within ±10% of wt
- a certainty, i.e. the probability (for example 80% of the time) that a reported anomaly depth is within the specified tolerance
- a confidence level indicating the confidence, for example 95%, with which the tolerance and certainty levels are satisfied

Since sizing analysis is still ongoing during the preparation of the paper, only one experience (pipeline section O2-L5-2008) is presented here to illustrate depth and length tolerance considerations.

Depth-sizing tolerance

Ten cracks (in pipeline section O2-L5-2008) were sized in-ditch with phased-array UT and compared to the ILI prediction. No error correction for the phased-array UT reported depth was made.

Figure 4 is a unity graph plot of these ten data points. Since the ILI tool reported a range of depth for each of crack groups (for example 12.5-25% wt, 25%-40% wt), only the upper end of the depth for each range is used. Therefore, linear regression is not applicable due to the nature of the ILI-reported depth. The error bands (±10% wt, ±15% wt, and ±22% wt) in the figure are not calculated from linear regression but from binomial-distribution analysis.

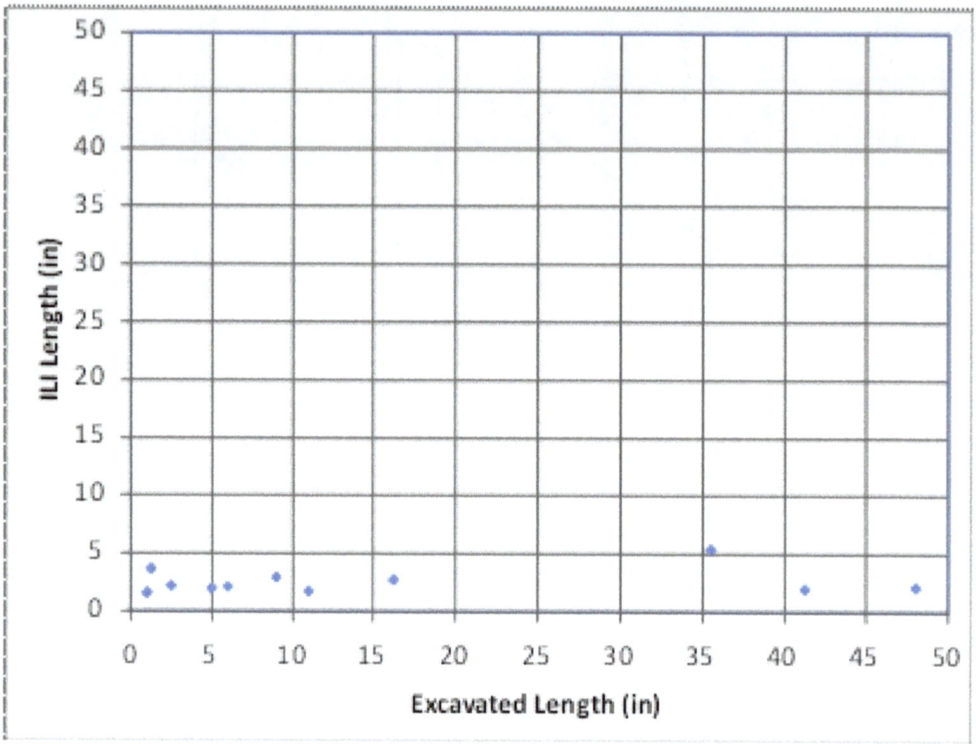

Fig.5. Length correlation for the tool run O2-L5-2008.

For binomial-distribution analysis, the upper end of the depth range is used to compare with the in-ditch measurement. The three tool tolerance (± 10%wt, ± 15%wt, and ± 22%wt) are estimated with three certainties, 49%, 60% and > 80%, respectively, for a given 95% confidence level. The results are presented in Table 12 (b). It is seen that for a certainty greater than 80% at 95% confidence level, the tool depth sizing tolerance is ±22% wt.

It should be noted, however, that the sample size of ten used for binomial analysis is not sufficient for a meaningful statistical analysis; therefore, the results presented here are informative. More detailed analysis of the recent data is in progress and will be presented in the future.

Length-sizing tolerance

Crack-length sizing is more uncertain and difficult to assess than depth sizing. It is quite often that in-ditch NDE reports envelope dimensions, while ILI reports either total length seen by the tool or interlinked crack length based on the ILI vendor's criteria. Therefore, the correlations between ILI and in-ditch measurements are often poor. However, better correlations were observed from other pipeline sections.

Even though the impact of length on the pipeline's integrity is less sensitive than that of depth, additional work – for example, a consistent protocol for length sizing in-ditch – is needed to minimize the error between ILI and in-ditch NDE. Figure 5 is the unity graph plot between one ILI and in-ditch measurement experience, showing poor correlations.

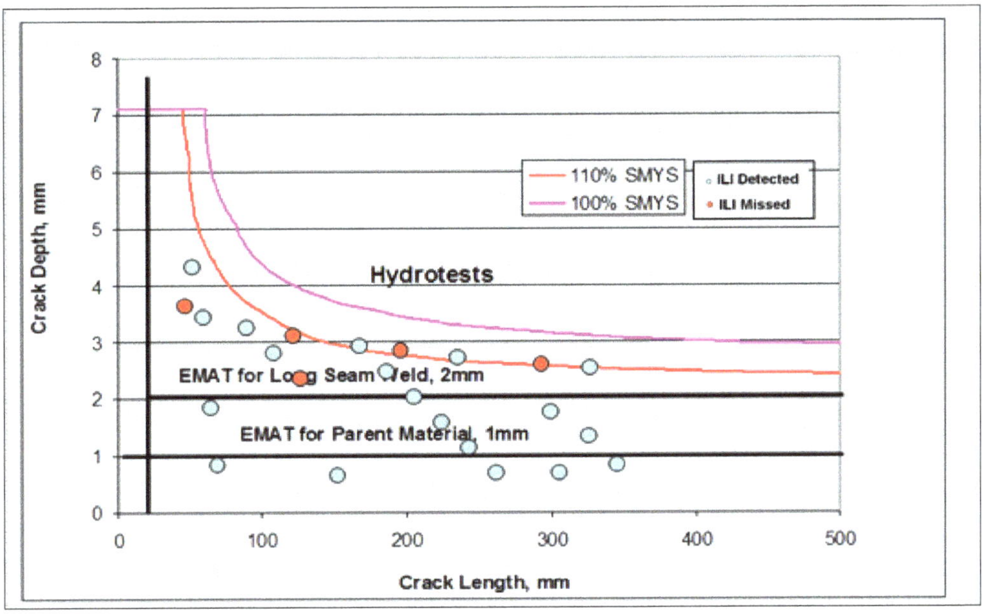

Fig.6. A sketch of hydrostatic testing sentence plots at pressures of 100% and 110% SMYS. The dark lines in the figure represent the detection limits of EMAT tool. The red and blue circles represent cracks in the pipeline.

Evaluation of EMAT performance against hydrotesting

In the initial years of EMAT development, even though the tool's POD was generally high, the reliability of detecting significant features was not rigorously verified. Therefore, EMAT was often treated as a method to determine SCC severity rather than mitigation. Pipelines in which severe SCC was found by EMAT were eventually hydrotested to ensure that the SCC threats were mitigated.

With the combined efforts made by ILI vendors and operators in recent years, EMAT tool performance has been improved. As shown above, the success rate for crack detection is better than 84% with a statistically determined POD greater than 78% at 95% confidence level based on 'depth over continuous length criterion'. The highest success rate achieved was 95.1% with a statistical determined POD better than 88.9% at 95% confidence level. It therefore appears to be the time for EMAT to move from an 'SCC severity evaluation' tool to an 'integrity mitigation' tool. An evaluation of current EMAT performance against hydrotest will be useful for understanding and providing quantitative insight into the feasibility for this movement.

Concept

Hydrotesting is used to remove all types of defects that might threaten a pipeline's integrity at MAOP prior to next hydrotest, or to show that none exists. Hydrotesting has been used for decades for crack mitigation: the pipeline is filled with water and pressurized to desired pressures, such as 100% or 110% SMYS. Critical anomalies would rupture or leak at these pressures. The cracks that survive the test and remain in the pipeline subsequently depend on two factors: testing pressure and material properties, and can be estimated using a fracture-mechanics' based approach with actual measured or estimated material fracture toughnesses (K_{IC} or J_{IC}) and yield/tensile strengths. For the purpose of demonstration, the API 579/ASME FFS-1 FAD (failure-assessment diagram)

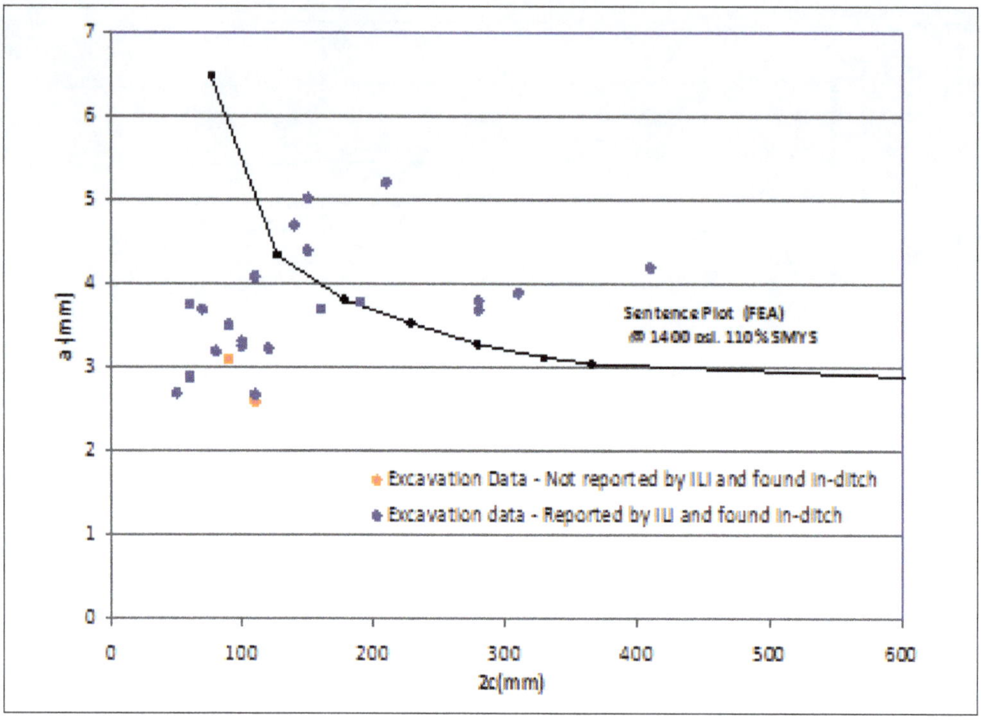

Fig.7. Sentence plots overlaid with excavated cracks for pipeline section O3-L2-2009.

method [23] is used to calculate the maximum survived cracks (i.e. critical cracks) at a given hydrotest pressure.

The maximum survived cracks or critical crack sizes for hydrostatic testing can be graphically plotted. The plot shows a locus of critical length vs its paired depth for a particular hydrotest pressure, which is commonly known as the sentence plot for hydrotest. Figure 6 is a sketch of two typical hydrotest sentence plots along with the assumed ILI detection limits and crack features in the pipeline:

- *Hydrostatic testing sentence plots*: two coloured curves representing crack critical depth as a function of length at two hydrotesting pressures, i.e. 100% and 110% SMYS. Cracks with their combined length and depth on or above the sentence plot(s) would be detected by hydrotesting and removed from pipeline for service.

- *EMAT detection limits*: three (black) straight lines representing EMAT detection limits (thresholds) that are below or on the left-hand side of the hydrotest-sentence plots. This defines that cracks equal or greater than the detection threshold lines would be detected by the tool at a certain confidence level, for example 80% of the time.

- *Crack features in the pipeline*: light coloured circles representing crack features in the pipeline.

Since the confidence level of the EMAT detection limits is not 100%, a certain amount of cracks above the detection threshold might be missed by the tool. Moreover, for the purpose of integrity assessment, the feature length used for assessment is the interlinked or effective length, not the 'continuous length over which the depth criterion is met' used for POD, POI, and POFC analyses.

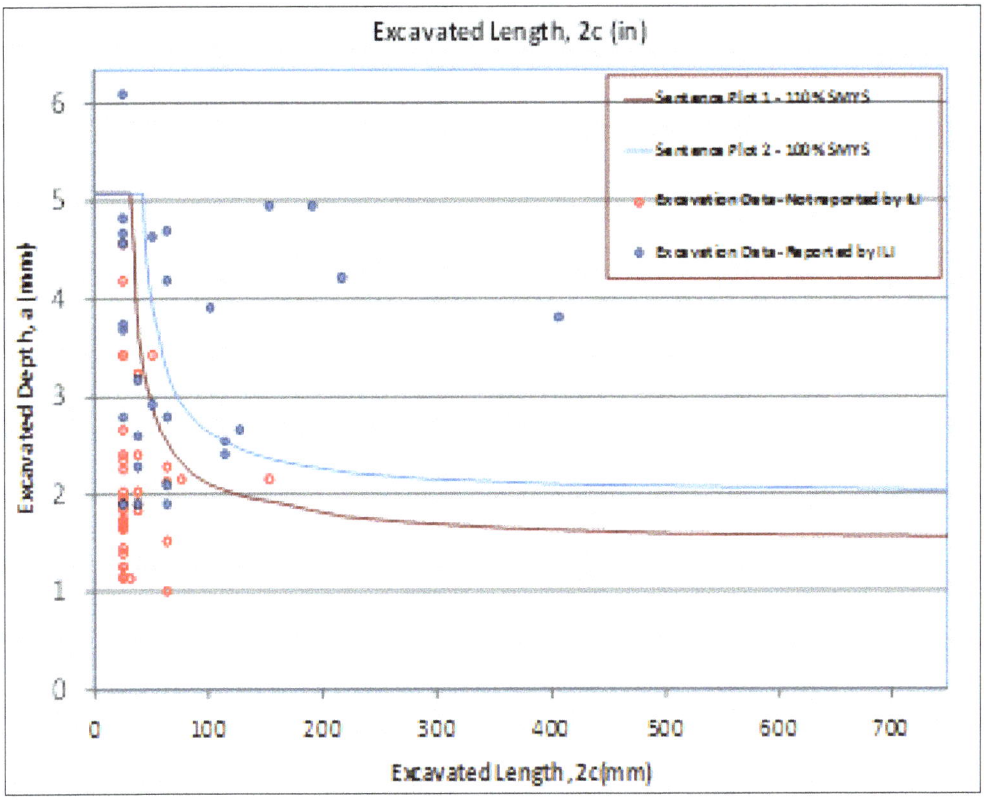

Fig.8. Sentence plots overlaid with excavated cracks for pipeline section O2-L4-2009.

Therefore, the number of features not detected or reported by the tool based on the POD definition may not be the same number of the features reported here based on the interlinked or effective length for integrity assessment.

From Fig.6 it is seen that all the missed features by ILI are below the 100% SMYS hydrotest sentence plot, suggesting that even if these features were not detected by EMAT tool, they would also not be detected by hydrotesting. In this case, the performance of the EMAT is equivalent or even better than that of hydrotesting at 100% SMYS. EMAT can be used as an alternative method for crack mitigation.

For hydrotesting at 110% SMYS, two ILI missed features are above the sentence plot, suggesting that these two features would be detected by hydrotesting but missed by EMAT. In this case, EMAT cannot be used as an alternative method for a 110% hydrotest.

From the above discussion, the concept of evaluating EMAT performance against hydrotesting is established. There follow three case studies to demonstrate the feasibility of using EMAT as an alternative method to hydrotesting.

Case study 1: Operator 3 – line 2

The pipeline section was inspected with EMAT in 2008. Ten excavations were performed, and 153 total features were found, out of which 146 were cracks. 51 SCC features were ground to get the profile. Figure 7 shows the sentence plot and the crack dimensions: the sentence plot was

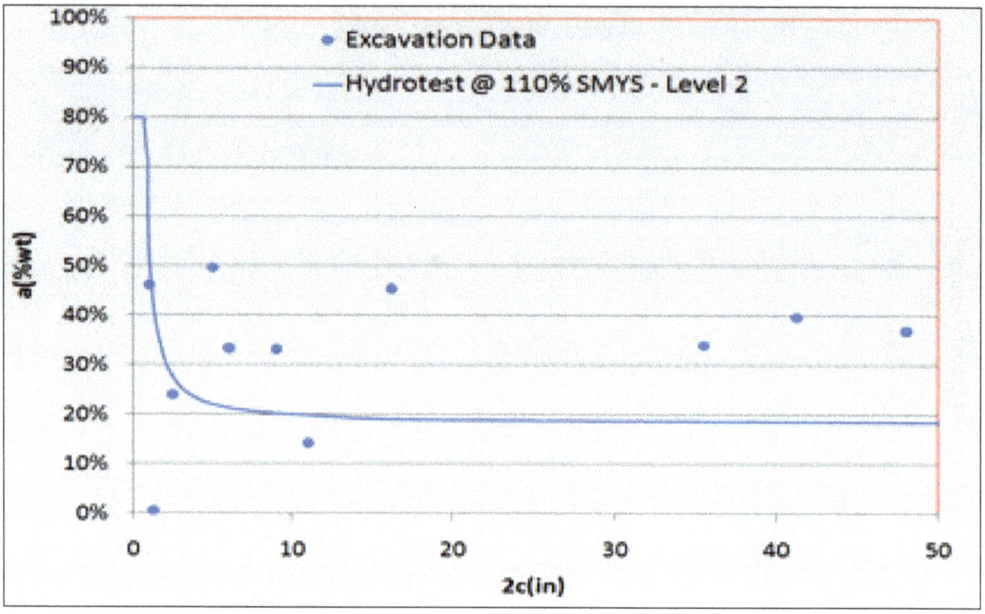

Fig.9. Sentence plots overlaid with excavated cracks for pipeline section O2-L5-2008.

established using finite-element analysis at 110% SMYS. Nine features above the sentence plot were observed in the field, out of which all were reported by the tool. The ILI tool performance was at par with hydrotesting at 110% SMYS.

Case study 2: Operator 2 – line 4

The line was inspected with EMAT in 2009. 72 excavations were made in which 164 features were found, 147 of which were cracks. The depth was measured using phased array. Since there is no material data available for API 579 Level 3 analysis, the sentence plot was determined using API 579 Level 2 at 100% SMYS and 110% SMYS. Ten features above the sentence plot at 100% SMYS were observed in the field, out of which all were reported by the tool. The ILI was as good as hydrotest at 100%SMYS, and the detection ratio is 100%. For hydrotesting at 110% SMYS, 15 features were above the sentence plot at 110% SMYS were observed, out of which 13 were found in the field, Fig.8. The tool performance was not at par with the hydrotest at 110% SMYS.

It is noted, however, that the sentence plot established using API 579 Level 2 is very conservative. The actual critical crack sizes would be larger than those predicted by API 579 Level 2 [23]. Therefore, the two features above the Level 2 sentence plot at 110% SMYS might actually be below the sentence plot if API 579 Level 3 material-specific FAD and tearing-instability analysis is used. Therefore, a Level 3 assessment is essential to determine if the performance of EMAT is at par with hydrotesting at 110% SMYS.

Case study 3: Operator 2 – line 5

The line was inspected with EMAT in 2008. 13 excavations revealed 13 features which were all cracks. The depth was measured using phased array. The sentence plot was determined using API 579 Level 2 at 110% SMYS because of the lack of material data. Eight features above the sentence plot at 110% SMYS were observed in the field, out of which all eight were reported by the tool, Fig.9. The ILI tool performance was at par with hydrotesting at 110% SMYS. The success rate for detection is 100%.

From the above case studies, it is demonstrated that the EMAT tool performance is at par with hydrotesting at 110% SMYS for two pipeline sections and at par with hydrotesting at 100% SMYS for one pipeline section. Moreover, EMAT inspection provides the operator with information about the subcritical and critical cracks, and coating disbondment, whereas hydrotesting only provides information on critical cracks alone.

Finally, proof tests are essential to validate the performance of EMAT against hydrotesting. This may be done by selecting one or more small section(s) of a long pipeline inspected by EMAT. The selected section(s) contain critical or significant cracks for repair/removal based on fracture-mechanics' assessment. After repair/removal of these critical/significant features, the pipeline is reassessed with the calibrated tool performance (POD/POI) and sizing tolerance to ensure no critical features remain in this small section(s) of the pipeline. Then hydrotesting follows. If there are no failures, EMAT performance is validated; otherwise, a lesson would be learned for further tool improvement.

Summary

The advances in EMAT technology and its performance are reviewed with the available information in the public domain, and summarized. The current EMAT technologies and claimed capabilities are presented. EMAT ILI performance is evaluated with excavation-validation data collected from three pipeline operators and 15 pipeline sections.

In recent years, significant improvement of EMAT technologies and design is noted over earlier generations.

The success rates of detection of the recent runs in 2008 and 2009 are in the range between 84% and 95%, which corresponds to POD (binomial-distribution analysis) in the range between 68.4% and 88.9% at 95% confidence, respectively.

The success rate of discrimination between crack and lamination and other linear defects in 2009 increased to 69% and 82%, corresponding to the probability of identification (POI, binomial-distribution analysis) of 59% and 72%. The increase in the identification may be attributed to the recent improvements in the tools for their respective classification technologies and/or algorithms.

The POFC in the previous years was high, but recently has been performing at 0-54% in 2008-2009 and 2.4% - 34% in 2009-2010. There are still perceived gaps in POI/POFC between the current tool performance and industry expectations at a commonly acceptable level.

A methodology is proposed to assess EMAT tool performance against hydrostatic testing. Comparisons of the tool performance with hydrotesting were performed. Three case studies on various EMAT performance vs hydrostatic testing are discussed in detail. The EMAT tools performed at par with hydrotesting at 100% SMYS for one pipeline run and with hydrotesting at 110% SMYS for two pipeline runs.

These results demonstrate that EMAT technology can be used not only as a reliable tool for SCC susceptibility detection in gas pipelines, but also potentially as an alternative integrity tool to hydrostatic testing for gas pipeline SCC management. An approach to validation of EMAT performance against hydrotesting is discussed.

Finally, issues of continuing research, such as developing a consistent field NDE protocol for sizing, are discussed.

References

1. API, 2005. 1163: Inline inspection system qualification standard. American Petroleum Institute.
2. M.Kothari, S.Tappert, U.Strohmeier, J.Larios, and N.Ronsky, 2004. Validation of EMAT in-line inspection technology for SCC management. Proc. International Pipeline Conference, ASME, Calgary.
3. T.Beuker, B.Brown, R.Alers, and G.Alers, 2004. SCC detection and coating disbondment detection improvements using the high resolution EMAT ILI technology. Proc. International Pipeline Conference, ASME, Calgary.
4. B.Ashworth, H.Williams, N.Uzelac, and A.O.Barbian, 2000. Detection and verification of SCC in a transmission pipeline. Proc. International Pipeline Conference, ASME, Calgary.
5. Rosen Inspection Technologies. EMAT crack detection and coating disbondment tool. www.roseninspection.net.
6. GE PII. EmatScan helps lower costs and raise crack-detection confidence for gas-pipeline operators. www.geoilandgas.com.
7. M.Yemoans, B.Ashworth, U.Strohmeier, A.Hugger, and T.Wolf, 2002. Development of 36in EmatScan crack detection (CD). Proc. International Pipeline Conference, ASME, Calgary.
8. S.Tappert, D.Allen, A.Mann, M.Balzer, and G.Boven, 2008. Inline inspection for cracks in gas pipelines – enhancements derived from 5 years experience. Proc. International Pipeline Conference, ASME, Calgary
9. S.Tappert, D.Allen, A.Mann, M.Balzer, and G.Boven, 2009. Third generation EMAT tool enhanced for finding SCC and disbanded coating in dry gas pipelines. *Pipeline and Gas Journal*, **236**, 6, June.
10. J.Marr, E.San Juan Riverol, J.Weislogel, S.Tappert, A.Mann, and J.Sun, 2010. Validation of EMAT in-line inspection technology for SCC management. Proc. International Pipeline Conference, ASME, Calgary.
11. J.Marr, E.San Juan Riverol, G. Rosca, J.Sutherland, and A. Mann, 2011. Validation of the latest generation EMAT ILI technology for SCC management. Pipeline Pigging and Integrity Management Conference, Houston, USA, organized by Tiratsoo Technical and Clarion Technical Conferences.
12. A.Fahad, 2009. Detection of pipeline coating failures and stress corrosion cracking (SCC) using electro-magnetic acoustic transducer (EMAT) technology. Saudi Aramco Journal of Technology, Spring.
13. A.Al-Oadah, W.Borjailah, J.Damaschke, T.Beuker, and M.Jaarah, 2007. In-line inspection with high-resolution EMAT technology crack detection and coating disbondment. NACE, Corrosion 2007.
14. B.Thomas, C.Doescher, and B.Brown, 2009. Acceptance of EMAT based in-line inspection for the assessment of stress corrosion cracking and other forms of cracking in pipelines. NACE, Corrosion 2009.
15. L.Sergio, D.Katz, T.Beuker, D.Claus, and B.Brown, 2008. A framework for managing the threat of SCC and other forms of cracking in pipelines using in-line inspection tools. Proc. International Pipeline Conference, ASME, Calgary.
16. I.M.Klann and T.Beuker, 2006. Pipeline inspection with the high resolution EMAT ILI tool: report on full-scale testing and field trials. Proc. International Pipeline Conference, ASME, Calgary.
17. M.Gao and R. Krishnamurthy, 2009. In-line inspection performance verification POD, POI, POFC and sizing. China International Oil & Gas Pipeline Conference, November, Langfang, China.
18. R.McCann, R.McNealy, and M.Gao, 2007. In-line inspection performance verification. NACE Corrosion 2007, Nashville, TN.
19. R.McCann, R.McNealy, and M.Gao, 2008. In-line inspection performance verification II: validation sampling. NACE Corrosion 2008, New Orleans, LA.
20. L.D.Brown, T.T.Cai, and A.DasGupta, 2001. Interval estimation for a binomial proportion (with discussion). *Statist. Sci.*, **16**, 101-133.
21. L.D.Brown, T.T.Cai, and A.DasGupta, 2002. Confidence intervals for a binomial proportion and asymptotic expansions. *Ann. Statist.*, **30**, 160-201.
22. W.W.Piegorsh, 2004. Sample sizes for improved binomial confidence intervals. *Comp. Statist. & Data Anal.*, **46**, 309-316.
23. API, 2007. 579-1/ASME FFS-1: Fitness for service evaluation of pressure vessels and equipment. American Petroleum Institute.

Combining EMAT ILI and multiple data sets for crack detection in natural gas pipelines to reduce validation costs

by Jim Marr[1], Richard Kania[1], Gabriela Rosca[1], Rahim Ruda[1], Elvis San Juan Riverol[1], Stefan Klein[2], Nikola Jansing[2], Thomas Beuker[2], N Daryl Ronsky[3], and Ralf Weber[4]

1 TransCanada Pipelines Ltd, Calgary, AB, Canada
2 Rosen Technology and Research Center, Lingen, Germany
3 Rosen Canada Ltd, Calgary, AB, Canada
4 Ralf Weber ILI Consulting, Karlsruhe, Germany

IN-LINE INSPECTION (ILI) by electro-magnetic acoustic transducer (EMAT) technology for crack detection in natural gas pipelines has been utilized for more than a decade. Identification and sizing of stress-corrosion cracking (SCC) and other critical crack-like defects in pipelines involves a complex data integration and analysis process. This process is aided by using multiple data sets during the analysis to eliminate uncertainties and reduce unnecessary investigative excavations and validation costs.

This paper describes the integration and analysis process and how conventional ILI tool data, coating data, soil data, and pipeline construction data, combined with EMAT ILI data, can promote an exceptionally high probability of detection (POD) and probability of identification (POI). The effectiveness of this integration approach is illustrated by case studies of two 20-in natural gas pipelines that have an SCC history.

IN-LINE INSPECTION (ILI) of pipelines by smart tools provides a lot of information to a framework for managing the threat of crack-like defects such as stress-corrosion cracking (SCC) [1]. Several technologies based on magnetic-flux leakage (MFL), eddy current, or ultrasound are applied to address a wide range of different types of defects to support the discrimination and sizing of SCC. However, the most promising technology for direct detection and sizing of SCC has emerged in the past few years. The electro-magnetic acoustic transducer (EMAT) technology allows for generation of ultrasonic horizontal shear waves in the pipe wall by either of two physical phenomena resulting from alternating currents in a static magnetic field: Lorentz force, and magnetostriction. The EMAT ILI system is set up to generate ultrasonic waves consisting of lower- and higher-order modes which propagate in circumferential direction of the pipe wall.

Fig. 1. 24/26-in RoCD2 EMAT tool at launcher.

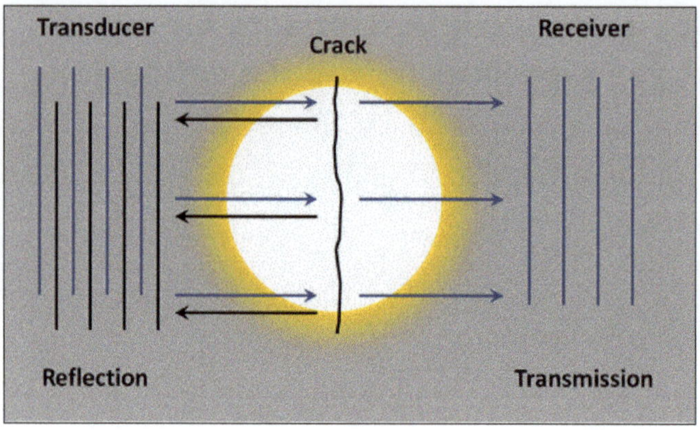

Fig.2. RoCD2 EMAT sensor arrangement. An ultrasonic shear wave is generated in the pipe wall travelling from transducer to receiver. An obstacle, such as a crack, situated in the sensitive area of the EMAT sensor results in reflection of the ultrasound.

The crack-detection and coating-disbondment (*RoCD2*) inspection fleet based on EMAT technology can be applied to detect linear anomalies in the pipe wall as well as determine and identify the condition of external pipeline coatings. Figure 1 shows the 24/26-in dual-diameter Rosen EMAT ILI tool during the launching process. The company's current tool fleet covers all pipe diameters ranging from 16 to 48in; by the end of 2011, more than 10,000 km have been successfully inspected in North, Central and South America, the Middle East, Europe and the Commonwealth of Independent States.

EMAT operating principle

Figure 2 shows a schematic representation of the EMAT arrangement. A single EMAT probe inspects a small, well-defined area between transducer and receiver. Transmission and reflection signals are captured by means of two separate receiver sensors within the EMAT sensor arrangement.

For a *RoCD2* inspection tool, sensors are arranged to allow for a high-resolution image of the pipeline. Due to the limited propagation distance of the waves between the measuring elements, this design ensures high signal-to-noise ratios as a basis for accurate determination of the position and dimensions of features.

Waves which propagate from transmitter to receiver through the pipe wall without hindrance are used to assess the external pipe coating. The ultrasound is attenuated by intact coatings, and lower signal amplitude is captured by the receiver. In case of coating disbondment or, for example, coating holidays, the attenuation is reduced. Pipe anomalies situated in the sensitive EMAT measurement area reflect part of the ultrasonic wave. Information on frequency, time of flight, and modes are used for discrimination of cracks and volumetric features and for determination of length and depth of the features. The quality of EMAT signals obtained from crack and coating measurements is supported by the quantification of possible lift-off effects and magnetization measurements. Further details on the concept of the high-resolution EMAT technology are described in references [2-4].

Data integration and analysis

The following case study has been generated by the data acquired from EMAT inspections of two 20-in natural gas pipelines – a 300-km inspection for which 150 km have been selected for evaluation. Both lines have an SCC and corrosion history and are part of continuing repair and excavations programmes.

Due to the complexity of identification of crack-like defects in pipelines, analysis and correlation of multiple data sets has been carried out on each *RoCD2* ILI indication. Highly effective prioritization has become possible by following a distinct data-evaluation procedure based on known SCC susceptibility conditions. Specific pipeline history and operator experiences have influenced the prioritization that has been carefully set-up in terms of rating each single parameter. The overall prioritization of each ILI indication has finally been determined by a weighting process as a final step of the data evaluation.

As described above, the leading dataset used for analysis and anomaly classification is the ultrasonic shear-wave echo reflected by an anomaly situated within the sensitive area of the EMAT sensor. Evaluation of echo amplitude, time, and frequency balances the classification. In accordance with the requirement of an ILI inspection, an unambiguous crack-like EMAT signal lead to a corresponding call even if all other data sets do not indicate presence of a crack-like feature. This case can easily be explained by taking into account local variations of the pipeline conditions, or the limitations of the sensitivity of other data sets.

As part of an SCC-management approach, predictive soil model categorization allowed for sectioning of both pipelines. The number of potential crack indications detected from the ILI data by the anomaly search algorithm has been determined for areas of interest and correlated to the soil model prediction of pipeline susceptibility to SCC. Verification of sound parameterization at each step of the fully automated data processing ensured highest sensibility and a probability of detection according to published specification.

Prior to the EMAT ILI survey, a circumferential MFL (CMFL) ILI tool was launched to acquire MFL data for correlation of corrosion, prominent crack-like defects, and further indications of both pipeline sections. CMFL data are of high interest for detection of corrosion by itself, and are of additional value in terms of combined evaluation of EMAT data for identification of crack-like features. By accessing both data sets at the same time, the discrimination and identification process of each indication is enhanced and supports the prioritization and assessment process.

As described earlier, the ILI tool comes with an intrinsic transmission data set of the ultrasonic shear wave generated by the EMAT transducer inside the pipe wall travelling to the receiving sensor. The complex variation of the transmission signal amplitude, time of flight, and frequency allows for identificatioo:n of different types of coating-repair material and detection of areas of coating disbondment. Identification of coating type ensures correlation to the pipe book or areas which have previously been excavated, and is helpful in feature prioritization as some coatings are more prone to SCC susceptibility [5]. Additionally, the evaluation of coating disbondment provides useful information about the general, as well as the very local, condition of the pipeline. For correlation purposes it supports the comparison to external corrosion at locations detected by CMFL, which in turn is unaffected by the coating or its condition. The two independent data sets provide valuable information on the same location and mechanism. Correlation of both data sets requires careful evaluation and parameter selection by experienced analysts, since adjustment and accuracy influences prioritization and assessment.

The 20-in pipeline segment's SCC history and operating experience, combined with pipeline construction and EMAT data, proved invaluable for the project. Geospatial data such as latitude, longitude, and elevation, of the pipeline also supported identification of local variations of the pipeline environment.

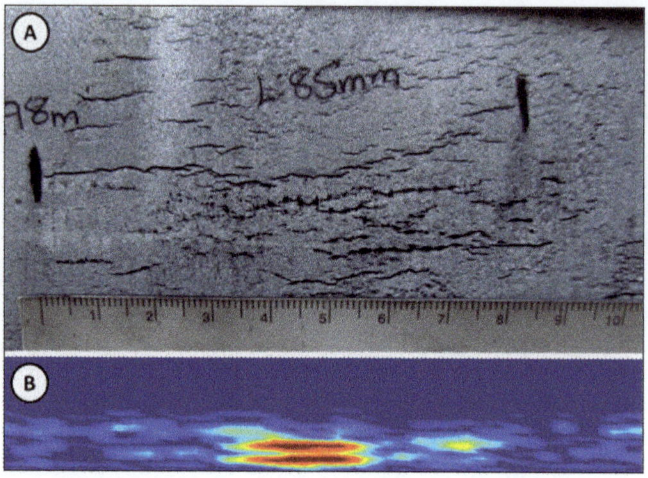

Fig.3. Field verification (a) vs BSCAN of EMAT time; (b) of a verified SCC colony. The colony has been reported as a crack-like anomaly associated with corrosion at a depth of 40% and 50 mm length. Field verification confirmed the classification and sizing at 42% depth and an interlinked length of 85 mm.

The main outcome from the criteria described above is a prioritization of crack-like indications based on EMAT ILI, soil, CMFL ILI, coating, and pipeline construction data. Confidence in the call as a measure of coincidence of criteria was very beneficial for the evaluation of *RoCD2* data and selection of verification sites. Site selection for validation of the classification and crack sizing was also carried out by the pipeline operator using a secondary analysis of all available signal data together with the data analysts at the ILI vendor office. Timely feedback of results from the in-field correlation and assessment process was also critical in further improvement of feature identification and sizing during the project.

RoCD2 *sensitivity and sizing*

The minimum crack and crack colony dimensions in the pipe body specified for the EMAT technology are 40 mm in length and 2 mm in depth, with a probability of detection (POD) of 90% [6]. The minimum crack dimensions in the longitudinal weld area are 40 mm in length and 3 mm in depth at a 90% confidence interval. The depth and length sizing accuracy in the pipe body and the longitudinal weld area at 80% confidence, and for the 20-in pipelines are therefore 0.95 mm for depth and 10 mm for length, respectively.

Sensitivity of the EMAT technology is influenced by the signal-to-noise-ratio of the time-integral of the EMAT echo amplitude. A sub-critical flaw can be detected if its effective cross section is above the detection threshold of the applied EMAT ILI sensor system. The specification has been derived from artificial and natural crack-like indications. Since the first commercial EMAT ILI runs in 2006, the number of natural defects used to derive the specification increases continuously. The total length of pipe containing crack and crack-like flaws available for testing and verification nowadays exceeds 400 m ; furthermore, over 2,000 historic excavation results and corresponding ILI data have been gathered in a database to continuously improve and test latest sizing improvements. The collection of different pipes and field results enabled the development and improvement of sizing models for commercial applications.

Results of the validation

In total 66,694 anomalies have been initially detected by the *RoCD2* anomaly search algorithm in the pipe body (29,839 anomalies in the longitudinal weld area). By applying all criteria described above, 755 (500) crack-like indications have been reported. The initial result of the automatic

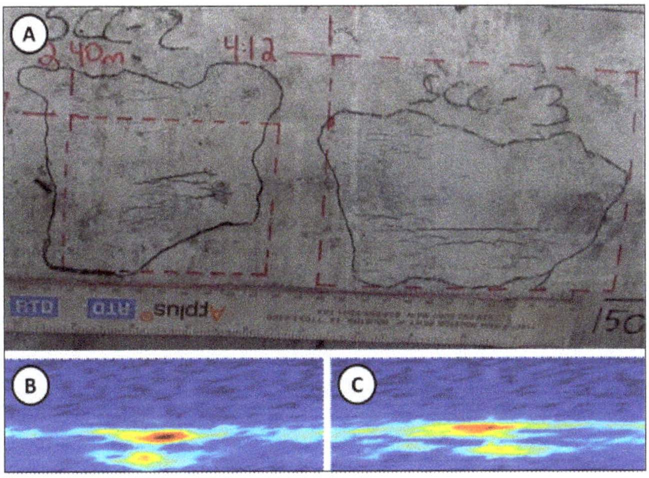

Fig.4. Field verification (a) vs BSCAN of EMAT frequency (b, c) of two verified SCC colonies. The colonies have been reported as crack-like anomalies at a depth of 52% and 46%, and 88 mm and 142 mm length. Field verification confirmed the classification and sizing at 40% and 43% depth and an interlinked length of 35 mm and 87mm.

search emphasizes the sensitivity of the EMAT technology to a variety of superficial and sub-critical pipeline anomalies. However, application of distinct procedures is required for semi-automated classification of anomalies to meet industry accepted reporting times.

At the time of this publication, the pipeline operator selected 26 joints for verification of anomaly classification and sizing. By the end of 2011, verification of 16 joints and 51 reported crack-like anomalies in the pipe body, and five in the longitudinal weld area, had been conducted. Multiple pipe joints have been removed from the pipeline to allow for NDT analysis to improve detection and sizing of flaws, as well as EMAT ILI pull-through testing.

Figure 3 shows an in-field photography of a verified SCC colony after magnetic-particle inspection (MPI) and corresponding EMAT data. In-field NDT depth sizing was carried out using a phased-array ultrasonic device. The crack length and interlinked length were determined in-field by the MPI length, and application of the pipeline operator's interlinking rule, respectively.

The colony shown in Fig.3a has been reported as a crack-like anomaly associated with corrosion at a depth of 40% and 50 mm length. Coating disbondment and metal-loss corrosion has been reported for this indication. The area and pipe steel were both determined as being highly susceptibility to SCC. Field verification confirmed the classification and sizing at 42% wall thickness depth, an MPI length of 140 mm and an interlinked crack length of 85 mm. The EMAT time signal is shown in Fig.3b. During semi-automated sizing of the indication, the analysts capture time and frequency of the EMAT signal which are used to determine the crack depth and length. Comparison of the EMAT and NDT phased-array ultrasonic (PAUT) depth shows only slight variation of the depth by 2% of the local wall thickness. The difference in length originates from the fact that the EMAT signal corresponds to the effective cross section of the corresponding anomaly at the EMAT detection threshold inside the pipe wall. As a consequence, the length determined from the EMAT signal corresponds to the maximum length of the anomaly at a depth equal to the detection threshold. MPI and interlinking length are determined at the outer surface of the pipe wall. Consequently underestimation of the EMAT ILI length when compared to the MPI or interlinked length is be observed.

Figure 4a-c shows the in-field verification result and corresponding EMAT frequency data. The colonies have been reported as crack-like anomalies at absolute depth of 52% and 46% and length of 88 mm and 142 mm. Field verification confirmed the classification and sizing at 40% and 43% depth, MPI length of 170 mm and 145 mm and interlinked lengths of 35 mm and 87 mm. Again,

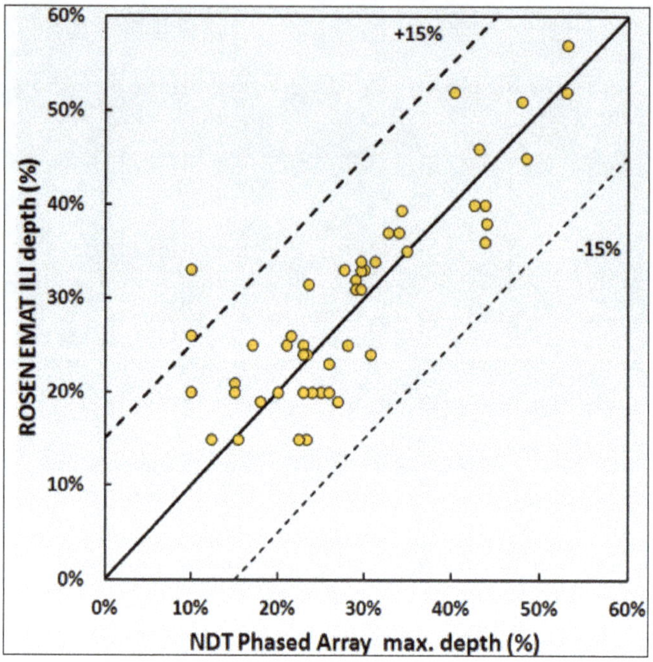

Fig.5. Unity plot of Rosen EMAT ILI depth vs phased-array depth. Specified accuracy is given by the dashed lines.

there is little difference between EMAT ILI and PAUT depth. Although the EMAT length is for the second colony similar to the MPI length and greater than the interlinked length, the difference for the first colony is obvious. In agreement with the discussion above, the ILI reported length shows an underestimation of the length when compared to the MPI length. Since both colonies are separated by only about 30 mm influence of pipe or tool can be neglected. PAUT profiling in comparison to EMAT data will provide very useful information to support the current understanding of feature discrimination and sizing, and will be published in further studies. Furthermore, these findings might influence the strategy to assess crack-like features and provide useful information for definition of a relevant flaw length with regards to the pipeline integrity assessment.

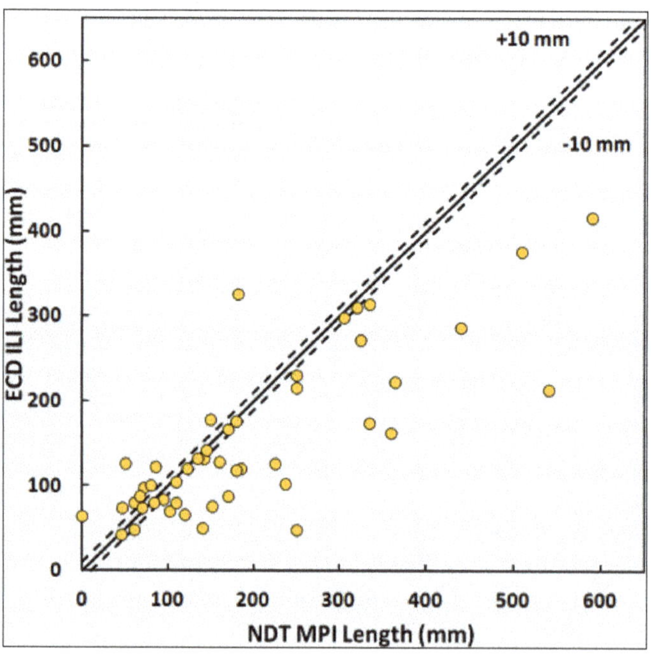

Fig.6. Unity plot of Rosen EMAT ILI length vs MPI length. Specified accuracy is given by the dashed lines.

The overall result of the verification findings achieved by the end of 2011 is presented in Figs 5 and 6. The overall POD being equal to the number of detected anomalies divided by the total number of anomalies multiplied by 100 is 56/56 and equal to 100%. In other words, all anomalies meeting the published specification have been detected. The overall POI is calculated as the number of correctly identified anomalies divided by the total number of anomalies multiplied by 100 is 48/56 and equal to 86%. There have been six anomalies verified to be as being metal-loss corrosion and two mid-wall pipe-manufacturing related anomalies.

Figure 5 shows the unity plot of the reported ILI EMAT depth vs the PAUT maximum depth. The boundary of specified accuracy of 15% at 80% confidence is indicated by two dashed lines: 96% of the crack-like indications are within that tolerance. This result clearly demonstrates the successful application of the sizing approach and implementation of the algorithms based on experience with real crack-like features. Figure 6 shows the unity plot of the reported ILI EMAT length vs the MPI length. As already stated, a tendency of underestimation of the superficial crack length can be determined. This is even more pronounced as the crack length extends to lengths beyond 150 mm. This finding is in agreement with the current understanding of the influence of the effective anomaly cross-section at the EMAT detection threshold.

Conclusion

This paper has summarized the process and results of data integration and analysis of various data sets in order to further promote the POD and POI of EMAT ILI data, based on the case studies of two 20-in natural gas pipeline inspections and verification excavations. It showed that the EMAT technology has improved and has become a reliable and accurate method for detection, identification, and sizing of SCC cracks and crack fields, to support the management of SCC threat in natural gas pipelines.

Outlook

The very encouraging results of the 2011 verification excavation programme triggered extension of the validation to 2012. Results of this ongoing study will be subject of further reports. EMAT depth sizing will be investigated with respect to crack morphology and shape. Comparison of EMAT crack and crack-colony lengths will be conducted using non-destructive phased-array ultrasonic depth profiling and destructive investigations. At the end of this process, the EMAT depth-sizing performance will be used for direct comparison of the crack-depth profile and EMAT data and determination of crack-like feature length for integrity purposes.

Acknowledgements

The authors would like to acknowledge the assessment, verification, and correlation work done infield and in shops, by Spencer Blomquist and his team from Applus RTD in Edmonton, Canada; Derek Spitzmacher, Pinnacle Integrity Engineering Ltd, Edmonton Canada; and Mathias Friedrich, Rosen RTRC, Lingen, Germany.

References

1. The Canadian Energy Pipeline Association (CEPA), 2007. Stress corrosion cracking: Recommended

Practices 2nd Edition, Canada, December.

2. T.Beuker, R.Alers, B.Brown, and G.Alers, 2004. SCC detection and coating disbondment detection using the high resolution EMAT ILI technology. Proc. International Pipeline Conference, ASME, Calgary.
3. M.Klann and T.Beuker, 2006. Pipeline inspection with the high resolution EMAT ILI tool: report on field experience. Proc. International Pipeline Conference, ASME, Calgary.
4. J.Damschke and T.Beuker, 2006. First surveys run with electromagnetic transducer. *Pipeline & Gas Journal*, October.
5. National Energy Board, 1996. Report of the inquiry concerning stress corrosion cracking. Canada, December.
6. Rosen, 2010. RoCD2 - Rosen EMAT crack detection and coating disbondment performance specification. August.

Section 4: Failure assessment

A methodology for the prediction of pipeline failure frequency due to external interference

by C Lyons[1], Dr Jane V Haswell[1], Dr Phil Hopkins[2], R Ellis[3], and N Jackson[4]

1 Pipeline Integrity Engineers, Newcastle upon Tyne, UK
2 Penspen, Newcastle upon Tyne, UK
3 Shell, Stanlow, UK
4 National Grid, Solihull, UK

THE UK Onshore Pipeline Operators' Association (UKOPA) is developing supplements to the UK pipeline codes BSI PD 8010 and IGE/TD/1. These supplements will provide a standardized approach for the application of quantified risk assessment to pipelines.

UKOPA has evaluated and recommended a methodology: this paper covers the background to, and justification of, this methodology.

The most relevant damage mechanism which results in pipeline failure is external interference. Interference produces a gouge, dent, or a dent-gouge. This paper describes the fracture-mechanics' model used to predict the probability failure of pipelines containing dent and gouge damage and contains predictions of failure frequency obtained using the gas industry failure frequency prediction methodology (FFREQ), and operational failure data from the UKOPA fault database. The failure model and prediction methodology are explained and typical results are presented and discussed.

Introduction

Risk and regulations in the UK

Most pipelines operate under strict regulations. The UK Pipeline Safety Regulations, PSR [1], are risk-based and goal setting, and place the duty on the operator to ensure that risks are 'as low as reasonably practicable' (ALARP) [2]. This duty applies at all stages of the pipeline life, from design through operation to decommissioning.

Risk and standards in the UK

Pipelines such as natural gas are classed as 'major accident hazard pipelines' (MAHPs), under the UK's PSR [1]. The UK pipeline standards and recommendations are within BSI PD 8010-1 [3] and IGE/TD/1 [4]: they recommend the use of quantified risk analysis (QRA) to evaluate the risks posed by these pipeline to the surrounding population.

QRA enables the analysis of the frequency and consequences of pipeline failure and the subsequent calculation of risk of harm to the population in the vicinity of the pipeline, and therefore assessment of the individual and societal risks to specific populations in proximity to pipelines [5]. The calculated risk levels can then be assessed with respect to defined acceptance criteria [2, 6].

This QRA may be carried out as part of the design safety evaluation, and during operation following route surveys carried out to assess changes in infrastructure, population and land use in the vicinity of the pipeline, or to assess the acceptability of developments planned in the vicinity of the pipeline.

QRA in the UK

The use of QRA for the safety evaluation of pipelines is now accepted practice in the UK [5]. It is used at the design stage of a new pipeline, and also to assess changes in risk during the life of existing pipelines, which occur primarily as a result of developments in the vicinity of the pipeline. The assessment of pipeline safety using QRA, rather than simple-code compliance assessments, allows the effects of actions taken to reduce risks to be evaluated and applied.

The role of UKOPA

The UK is a small, densely populated, and well-developed land area which relies on MAHPs to transport a range of hazardous products including natural gas to industrial, commercial, and domestic users, and petrochemical products between industrial facilities.

Land-use planning controls are operated in the UK; risk-based land-use planning controls are set by the safety regulator, and therefore affect the pipeline operators, local authorities responsible for land development, and developers with commercial interests.

The United Kingdom Onshore Pipeline Operators' Association (UKOPA) represents the views and interests of the UK pipeline operators responsible for the MAHPs regarding safety, legislative compliance, and best practice. A strategic aim of UKOPA has been to achieve agreement with all stakeholders regarding pipeline QRA methodology, and the inputs and assumptions applied in the analysis, so that consistency in decisions on land use can be achieved.

UKOPA and risk supplements to standards

UKOPA has therefore drafted risk-assessment supplements to the UK pipeline standard and guidelines IGE/TD/1 Ed 4 [4] and PD 8010 Part 1 [3]. These supplements, which were scheduled for final publication in 2008, will give guidance on:

- determining failure frequencies
- consequence modelling
- standard assumptions to be applied in the risk-assessment methodology for land-use planning zones
- conducting site-specific risk assessments
- risk-reduction factors to be applied for mitigation methods.

The supplements include specific guidance on the prediction of failure frequencies due to external interference (i.e. dents, gouges, and combinations of dents and gouges), which is of particular importance in assessing the residual risk levels of pipelines. This damage mechanism is of concern as it is random in nature, and the likelihood of failure is not based on the age or condition of the pipeline.

Methodology used in supplements

To provide guidance on pipeline failure frequency due to external interference, UKOPA required a methodology for the prediction of pipeline failure frequencies due to dent and gouge damage. The methodology used for the work was a reconstruction of that developed and published by British Gas for the risk management of the UK gas pipeline network [7, 8, 9, 10, 11]. This methodology is encompassed in the gas industry pipeline failure frequency prediction software FFREQ [7, 10, 11, 12, 13], which has been used in pipeline QRA for over 25 years. The methodology can be summarized as:

- The modelling of the failure state of a specific pipeline subject to dent-gouge damage, using a fracture-mechanics' failure model. Pipeline damage due to external interference occurs in the form of gouges and dents or combinations of these. This type of damage is random in nature, and operational failure data are sparse; consequently, a predictive model is required to calculate failure frequencies for this type of damage for specific pipelines.

- Prediction of the likelihood of occurrence of the dent-gouge damage which results in failure for specified pipeline conditions. The failure frequency prediction methodology uses damage probability distributions developed from operational damage data recorded in the UKOPA pipeline fault and failure database [14]. Predictions obtained have been compared to predictions obtained using industry failure frequency prediction methodologies and operational failure data from the UKOPA fault database.

- Modelling of the incidence rate of external interference. Predictions obtained have been compared to predictions obtained using the gas industry failure frequency prediction methodologies FFREQ and operational failure data from the UKOPA pipeline fault and failure database [14].

The failure model and prediction methodology are explained, and typical results are presented and discussed.

Prediction of probability and frequency of failure due to external interference

Failure models for damaged pipelines

The original work carried out to develop a failure model for damaged pipelines was carried out by Hopkins and Cairns for British Gas [7]. This model, known as the BG dent-gouge model, is a two-dimensional fracture-mechanics' model, which assumes that steel structures containing defects can fail due to a combination of plastic collapse and brittle fracture – see Annexe A. Details of the basic model (the 'Dugdale' model) are well-documented and are published in recognized standards [for example, 15], and the BG dent-gouge model has been adopted in API 579 [16]. The BG model is semi-empirical, in that the basic formulation is theoretical, but the actual equations are fitted to empirical data. The model was validated against empirical data comprising pipe-ring and vessel burst tests, and the recorded failure data were used to calibrate the model. Because the model is semi-empirical, its application is constrained by the limits of the data used in its calibration. It is intrinsically conservative, in that it is two-dimensional, and represents the failure of an infinitely-long, part-wall defect.

This BG model and its application have been critically reviewed by experts and are well-understood [17, 18, 19]. More-recent comparisons with empirical data are reported [20, 21], and confirm the model performs reasonably well. Updates to this model are being developed in accordance with more-recent fracture-mechanics' modelling principles [22]. Such updates have involved adding parameters such as micro-cracks, residual-stress, and plasticity functions. Currently, *ad hoc* empirical data are not available to validate models including these parameters. This work is on-going [23] and will be reported in 2009; consequently, the original BG dent-gouge fracture-mechanics' model is used in the current study.

Leak-rupture failure modes

As stated above, the BG dent-gouge model is two dimensional, and is used to study and predict the behaviour of part-wall damage. The failure mode of through-wall damage will be either a leak or a rupture. In the case of a leak, the through-wall defect is stable, whereas in the case of a rupture, the through-wall defect is unstable and extends during failure, resulting in a much greater release of product. The difference in the leak-rupture failure mode depends upon whether the pipeline contains a gas or a liquid.

For pipelines containing gas, if the axial length of a through-wall defect exceeds the critical length at which the defect will be unstable (which is dependent upon the pressure and the pipe properties), ductile propagation driven by the energy released by the decompressing gas will occur. This will result in a rupture, in which the fracture runs along the axis and then subsequently propagates and creates – in effect – two open pipe ends. This behaviour is observed in research studies and real incidents. For pipelines containing liquids, decompression occurs quickly and the energy released is insufficient to drive defect extension. In such cases, rupture may be defined as a release equivalent to the pipe diameter or greater, but in reality the failure mode of liquid pipelines is a leak of some size.

The principles of the analysis of part- and through-wall defects used in the predictive methodology are summarized in Annexe A.

Probability of failure of damaged pipelines

In order to apply the dent-gouge fracture-mechanics' model to the prediction of probability of failure of failure of a damaged pipeline, the likelihood of occurrence of dent and gouge damage in a specific pipeline population is required. British Gas developed a methodology for the prediction of the probability of failure of damaged pipelines using theoretical models for leak and rupture failure relating the defect size to pipeline geometry, material properties, and operating conditions [9, 24]. These were combined with Weibull probability distributions fitted to measured damage data.

The UKOPA pipeline fault and failure database [14] contains records of the dimensions of dent and gouge damage as well as the through-wall damage resulting in product loss by leak or rupture for all UK MAHPs. Weibull probability functions based on statistical analysis of the gouge length and depth and dent depth data recorded in the UKOPA database have been derived, and the methodology published by British Gas [8, 9] has been reconstructed.

Prediction of pipeline-failure frequency

The probability that a given pipeline will fail following an external interference incident is multiplied by an incident frequency in order to obtain the pipeline-failure frequency.

The incident frequency is the number of external-interference events which have caused dent and gouge damage in the total pipeline population, and is generally given as the number of events per 1000 km years (kmy).

Prediction of probability of failure due to external interference

In order to apply failure models to the prediction of the probability of failure of a specific pipeline and operating condition, the likelihood of dent-gouge damage caused by – and the frequency (or incident rate) of – external interference is required. A detailed assessment of the external interference damage and failure data recorded in the UKOPA database was therefore carried out.

UKOPA pipeline-damage data

The UKOPA fault database contains external interference fault records dating back to the 1960s. The database contains a total of 1257 records which describe external interference damage ranging from that classed as superficial to severe, where severe damage includes incidents of product loss. All data – such as pipe details and defect dimensions on the pipelines involved in the incidents – are recorded [14]. The database contains records of varying quality and detail, so it was necessary to review, evaluate and filter the data, and this process is summarized as follows.

The base external-interference data contains records which, on review of the associated investigation information, require re-categorization. A number of records categorized as external interference are detailed as damage due to construction, or mill damage. The base external-interference records also include incidents which were caused by external activity, but do not relate to dent or gouge damage; for example, hot tap/drilling in error, and damage to above-ground installations. Finally, external-interference records include someincidents detailed as coating/wrap damage only.

Parameter	a	b (mm)
Gouge length Weibull	0.6	120.851
Gouge depth Weibull	0.889	1.442
Dent depth Weibull	0.69	6.202

Table 1. UKOPA damage records.

In summary, records relating to the following types of incident were removed from the working dataset:

damage due to construction activities
incorrectly assigned damage (such as external corrosion, mill damage)
incorrect drilling operations
damage due to severing of small connections from larger diameter pipes
damage to above-ground installations
coating/wrap damage.

The remaining records relate to gouge and dent damage, and these were assessed and interpreted for use in deriving Weilbull probability distributions for gouge length, gouge depth, and dent depth. The data were further filtered at this stage to remove a number of superficial damage records (usually referred to as scratches or scrapes, with no/negligible recorded depth or width dimension), so that the probability distributions were not skewed to small-dimension trivial damage. The results of the above filtering are shown in Table 1, and the Weibull probability distribution parameters are given in Table 2.

The aim of the filtering process was to produce a working data set. In many cases, the base data contains multiple records for the same damage event, representing adjacent faults caused in the same damage incident. In such cases, all data were used, and where dent and gouge damage was recorded in the same incident, all recorded gouges were assumed to be associated with the dent unless the record stated otherwise. The filtering process is summarized as follows:

- The 854 data categorized as gouge and dent comprises 744 gouges and 110 dents.
- Of the 110 dents, 15 were recorded as dents only, and 95 were associated with 151 gouges, i.e. approximately 20% of the damage was dent and gouge damage.
- The final filtered data representing the significant incidents comprised 556 total incidents.
- These data were used to develop the Weibull probability distributions for the gouge length, gouge depth and dent depth.

Parameter	a	b (mm)
Gouge length Weibull	0.6	120.851
Gouge depth Weibull	0.889	1.442
Dent depth Weibull	0.69	6.202

Table 2. Weibull fit parameters.

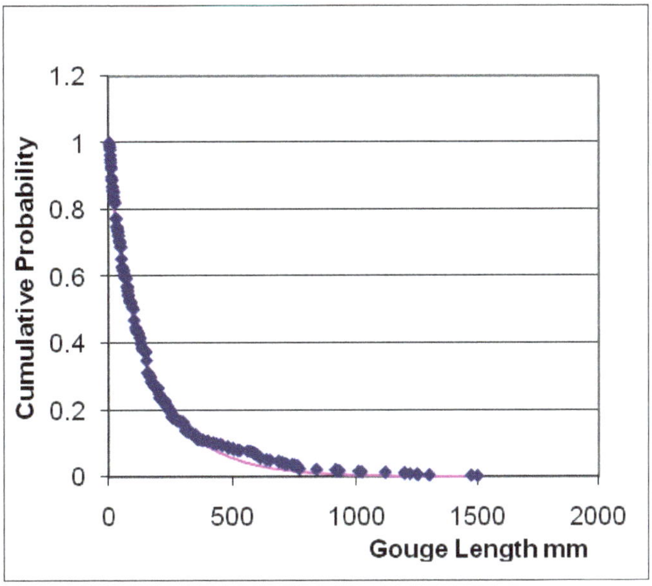

Fig. 1. Cumulative probability of gouge length 2c or greater.

The parameters for the Weibull curves fitted to the filtered data are given in Table 2.

The Weibull cumulative-probability curves, which give the probability of occurrence of a specified size of damage or greater, are plotted for gouge length, gouge depth, and dent depth in Figs 1-3, respectively. These curves represent a conservative interpretation of damage occurrence in which zero and low damage dimensions have been omitted to avoid weighting the distribution for insignificant damage.

UKOPA damage-incidence rate

The total failure frequency of a pipeline is calculated by multiplying the probability of through-wall failure of a damaged pipeline by the damage incidence rate, or the 'hit rate', which occurs in a given population of pipelines. The number of damage incidents in the UKOPA database are summarized in Table 1. In this study, the probability of damage parameters were derived from a dataset which excluded low values of damage, i.e. gouge depths and widths recorded as less than 0.4 mm. This approach was applied so that the damage-parameter probability distributions were not weighted to small, insignificant damage. For this reason the damage incidence rate was calculated assuming 556 incidents had occurred over the operational exposure of the UKOPA MAHP population. The operational exposure relating to the damage data used is 654,732 kmy, so the incident rate is calculated as:

$556/654732 = 8.49 \times 10^{-4}$ per kmy

Likelihood methodology

The method for the calculation of the likelihood of occurrence of the dent-gouge damage which results in failure for specified pipeline conditions using the above cumulative probability curves for gouge length (Fig.1), gouge depth (Fig.2), and dent depth (Fig.3), and its use in conjunction with a dent-gouge failure model in the prediction of pipeline failure frequencies, is briefly summarized in Annexe B. As previously stated, this methodology is reconstructed from the original work undertaken by the British Gas Engineering Research Station [7, 8, 9, 10].

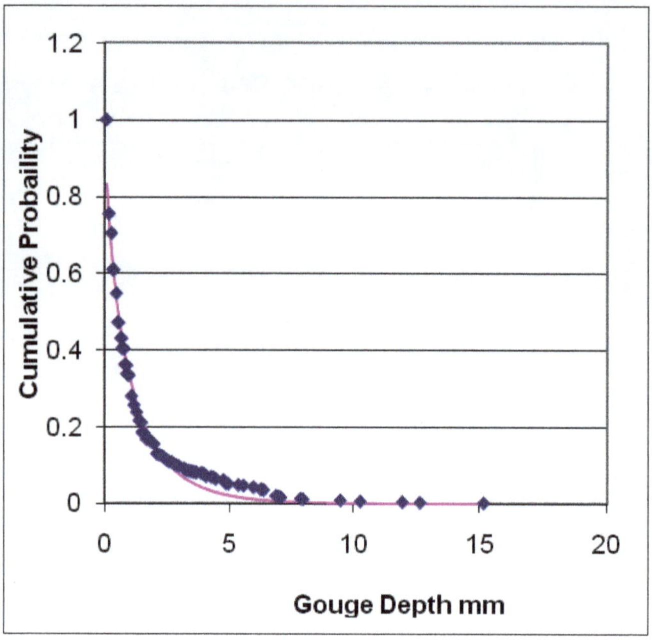

Fig.2. Cumulative probability of gouge depth d or greater.

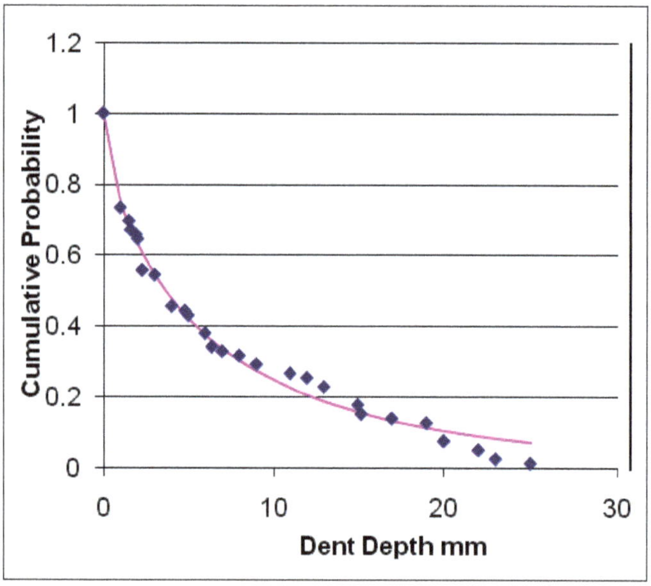

Fig,3. Cumulative probability of dent depth D or greater.

Failure-frequency predictions and comparisons

An important part of the UKOPA studies was the comparison of failure frequencies predicted using the methodology described above to failure frequencies predicted using models currently in use in the pipeline industry. Comparisons of predictions obtained using the model and methodology summarized in Annexes A and B with the damage probability distributions given above with FFREQ [12, 13] predictions for a number of pipeline cases were performed.

The initial study considered 21 pipeline cases arbitrarily selected from a database containing failure-frequency predictions for UK gas pipelines (confidentially provided by the National Grid, UK) calculated using the FFREQ model [11, 12, 13]. The pipeline case details are given in Table

Pressur (bar)	Dia (mm)	WT (mm)	Grd	Design factor	FF Predictions per 1000 kmy	
					Model	FFREQ
70	219	6.4	X42	0.44	0.041	0.056
69	273	6.4	X46	0.49	0.057	0.064
70	324	7.1	X46	0.53	0.058	0.058
70	324	7.9	X52	0.42	0.048	0.034
70	356	7.9	X46	0.52	0.051	0.043
32	406	9.5	X56	0.19	0.011	0.013
70	457	9.5	X52	0.50	0.044	0.024
70	508	11.1	X46	0.53	0.030	0.011
75	610	9.5	X52	0.71	0.070	0.031
75	610	9.5	X60	0.61	0.079	0.038
75	610	11.9	X52	0.57	0.038	0.010
75	762	11.9	X52	0.71	0.054	0.011
75	762	11.9	X65	0.56	0.061	0.010
75	762	11.9	X60	0.61	0.059	0.014
70	762	12.7	X60	0.54	0.043	0.008
70	914	12.7	X60	0.64	0.060	0.010
75	914	12.7	X65	0.63	0.068	0.010
75	914	12.7	X60	0.69	0.064	0.011
85	914	12.7	X65	0.72	0.081	0.013
85	914	12.7	X60	0.78	0.083	0.014
85	914	19.1	X60	0.52	0.016	0.002

Table 3. Pipe cases for comparison of failure-frequency predictions.

3 and the comparisons of predicted failure frequency (FF) values with FFREQ results are shown in Fig.4. These cases cover typical variations in diameter, wall thickness, material grade, and pressure.

Figure 4 shows good comparison between predictions obtained using reconstructed failure frequency prediction methodology and the established industry model FFREQ. Based on this, it was concluded that the methodology had been constructed, and damage data interpreted, in accordance with the original work developed by Hopkins [7] and Corder [8, 9] for British Gas.

The pipeline probability of failure is a function of a number of parameters, including pressure, diameter, wall thickness, material grade, and material toughness. The influence of different parameters has been studied using the dent-gouge failure model in a separate study for UKOPA [25, 26]. The results of this study confirmed that wall thickness and design factor have a primary influence on the probability of failure, while the influence of diameter and material properties is secondary. These cumulative variations of the various parameters in the pipe cases in Table 3 result in the non-uniform trends shown in Fig.4.

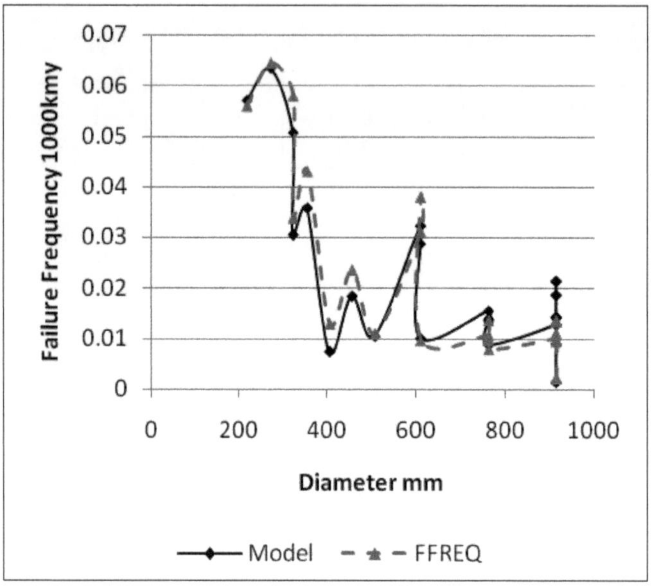

Fig.4. Comparison of failure-frequency predictions with FFREQ.

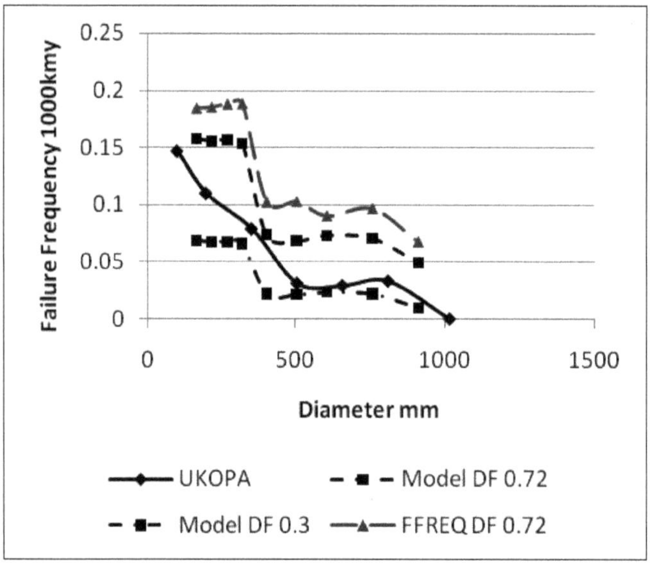

Fig.5. Comparison of predicted failure frequencies with operational data.

The trends indicated by these results were considered in detail, and more recent work carried out in relation to the development of the code supplements to IGE/TD/1 and PD 8010 Part 1 has involved failure-frequency predictions for pipe cases selected to provide a more-structured representation the range of pipelines in the UKOPA database. The pipe cases used in this study are given in Table 4. Failure-frequency predictions for these pipeline cases operating at design factors of 0.3 and 0.72 are compared in Fig.5 with UKOPA data for operational failures, where failures are defined as product losses. The operational failure data are sparse, and so it is approximate in that the failure frequencies are derived from groups of data which include ranges of diameter, wall thickness, grade, and pressure.

Results for the pipe cases listed in Table 4 were generated for design factors 0.2, 0.3, 0.4. 0.5, 0.6, and 0.72.

The UKOPA pipe cases given Table 4 represent a typical range of pipe diameters and material

Table 4. UKOPA pipe cases.

Diameter (mm)	WT (mm)	Grade
168.3	5.6	X42
219.1	5.6	X46
273	5.6	X52
323.9	5.6	X52
406.4	7.9	X52
508	7.9	X52
609	7.9	X60
762	7.9	X60
914	9.5	X65

Table 5. Pipeline geometries represented by constant R/t ratios.

Diameter (mm)	WT(mm)	
	R/t = 36	R/t = 34
219	3.04	4.56
324	4.5	6.75
457	6.35	9.52
610	8.47	12.71
762	10.58	15.88
914	12.69	19.04

grades, and a range of lower-bound wall thicknesses relating to the diameters. The UKOPA operational data are sparse and have therefore been smoothed (i.e. failure data have been related to a range of pipeline diameter and wall thickness values), but the failure frequency versus diameter relationship is non-linear for the reasons discussed above.

The predicted values show clearly the influence of (i) wall thickness (5.6 mm between diameters 168 - 324 mm, 7.9 mm between diameters 406 - 609 mm, and 9.5 mm at diameter 914 mm) in reducing the failure frequency in an almost stepwise fashion, and (ii) the design factor.

The results described above show the effects of diameter, wall thickness, and design factor variations, but are difficult to apply to specific pipelines. Generic predictions are therefore presented in terms of constant pipeline geometry, design factor, and material properties. Pipeline conditions are considered in terms of:

constant *R/t* ratios, in which the shell stiffness of the pipe is maintained as constant through a constant radius to wall thickness ratio; and

the design factor is considered at the design code limits of 0.3 and 0.72, and the material grade is considered for a typical range from X42 to X65.

The parameters selected are shown in Table 5, and represent a range of typical pipeline cases. The failure-frequency curves shown in Figs 6-8 provide sufficient data to enable the failure frequency for a typical pipeline to be estimated.

Figure 6 shows a generic failure frequency curve for an *R/t* ratio of 36, design factor of 0.72 and 0.3, and material grade X42 and X65. The figure indicates that the total failure-frequency values

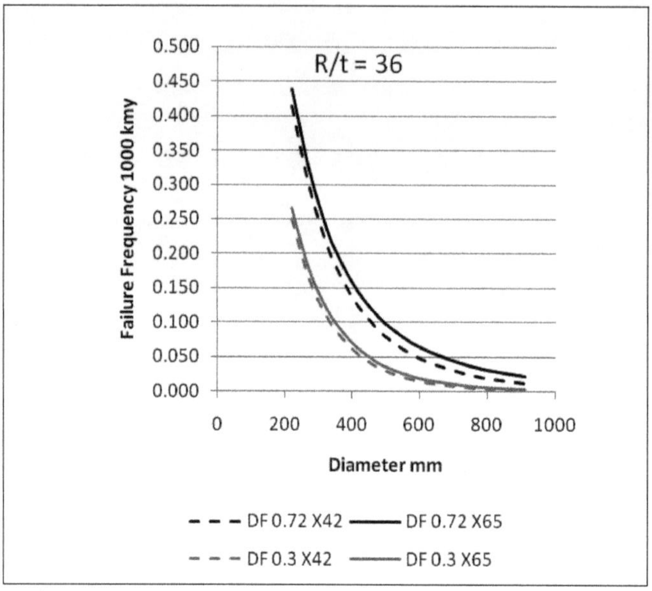

Fig.6. Generic failure-frequency curve for R/t ratio = 36.

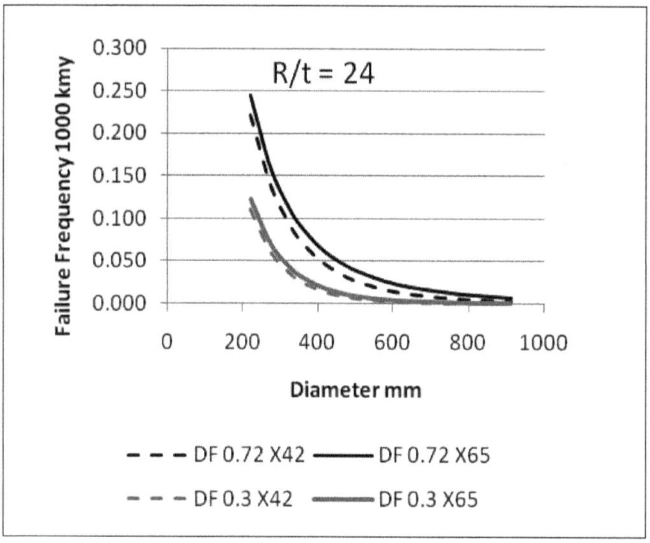

Fig.7. Generic failure-frequency curve for R/t ratio = 24.

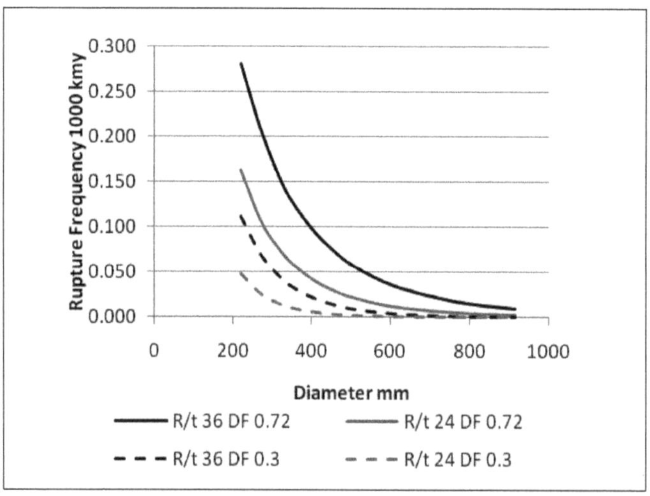

Fig.8. Rupture-frequency curves for R/t ratios = 36 and 24 at design factors of 0.72 and 0.3.

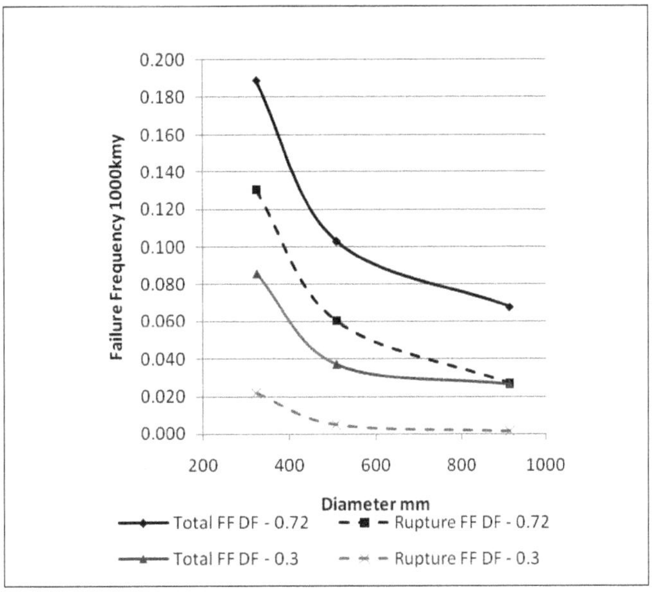

Fig.9. FFREQ results with respect to diameter and design factor.

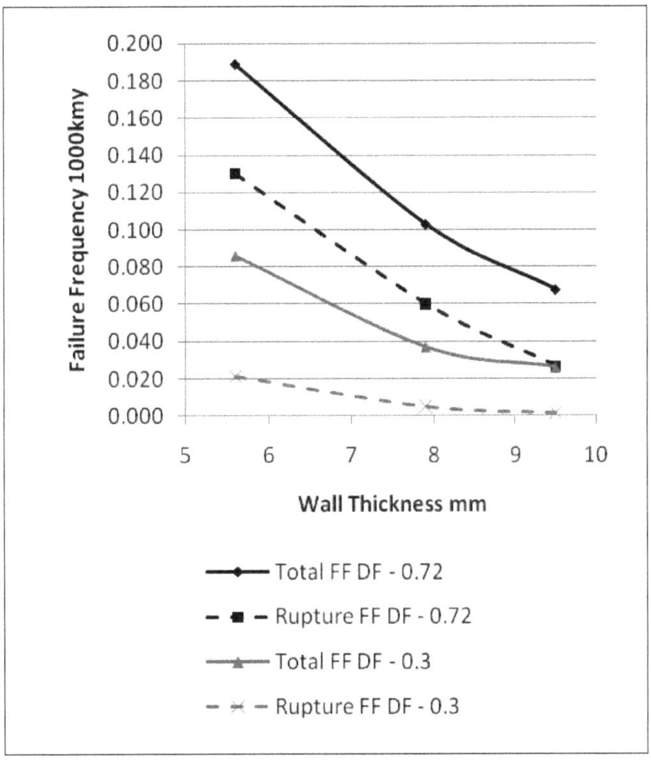

Fig.10. FFREQ results with respect to wall thickness.

are highest for the lowest-diameter pipelines, and then reduce as the pipe diameter is increased. The failure frequencies range from 0.4 for pipes of diameter 219.1 mm to less than 0.025 for pipes of 914 mm diameter. Figure 6 also shows that the effect of material grade is small, for both *R/t* ratios the failure frequency for X65 material is slightly higher, as the wall thickness in this case will be the lower.

Figure 7 shows a generic failure frequency curve for an *R/t* ratio of 24, design factor of 0.72 and 0.3, and material grade X42 and X65. This figure shows a similar trend to the *R/t* = 36 curve, but

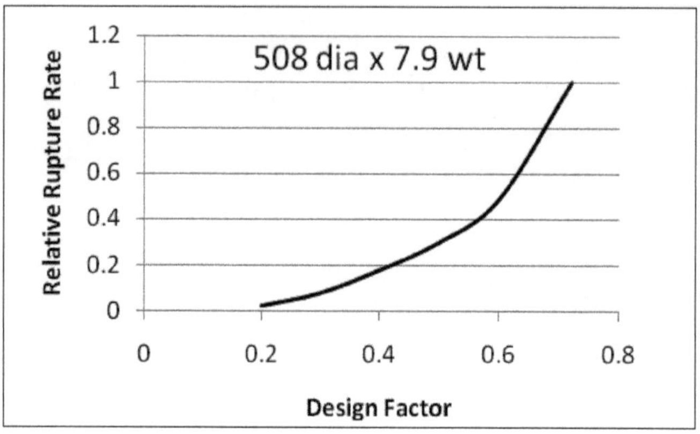

Fig. 11. Rupture rate vs design factor calculated from FFREQ results (508 mm diameter, 7.7 mm wall thickness).

with the failure frequencies being less than half the R/t = 36 values due to the greater wall thickness. Figure 7 also confirms that the effect of material grade is small.

As previously stated, the risk due to ruptures is significant for high-pressure gas pipelines. Generic rupture-frequency curves for R/t ratios of 36 and 24 at design factors of 0.72 and 0.3 are shown in Fig. 8. As Figs 6 and 7 show that the effect of material grade is small, the curves in Figure 8 have been generated for a material grade of X65, which results in slightly higher failure frequencies.

Following detailed review and consideration of the results of studies carried out using the reconstructed British Gas methodology, UKOPA concluded that the methodology was logical and understandable, was justifiable in terms of modelling of structural parameters, and robust in terms of comparison with operational data. UKOPA has therefore recommended the established methodology FFREQ as the preferred methodology for the prediction of pipeline-failure frequencies due to external interference.

FFREQ predictions and use

As previously described, the FFREQ methodology is based on an approach which combines fracture-mechanics' models for predicting defect behaviour with recorded damage data, which include the prediction of failure due to dent and gouge damage as described in this paper. FFREQ also includes the prediction of other types of damage caused by third parties which do not result in dents or gouges, and are classed as external interference, such as punctures, flange leaks, and damage to 'branches and flanges' and above-ground installations [9]. FFREQ uses historical data to estimate the probability of failure, and hence failure frequency, due to punctures and damage to 'branches and flanges'. In addition, the software includes a number of other refinements not discussed in this paper, such as factors (based on historical data) to account for location or area class, depth of cover, and pipeline protection [8, 9].

Following UKOPA's decision to recommend FFREQ as the preferred industry methodology for predicting pipeline-failure frequency due to external interference, Advantica provided FFREQ predictions for inclusion in the code supplements. These results are summarized below.

Figure 9 shows the FFREQ results interpreted with respect to diameter and design factor, and Fig.10 with respect to wall thickness.

Corder [9] published illustrative curves showing the variation of the rupture rate with pipeline-operating conditions, and presented results indicating the sensitivity of predictions to wall

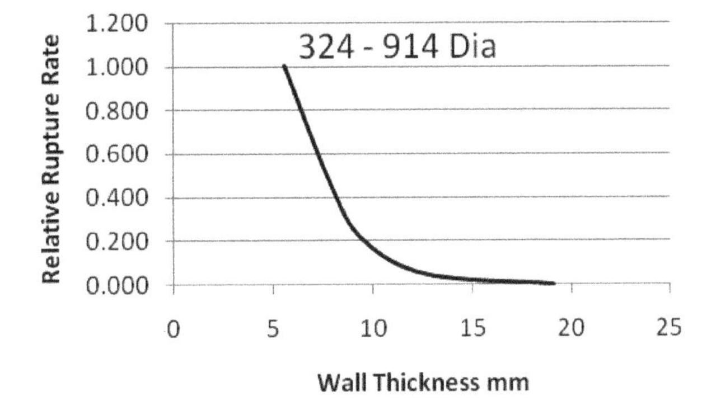

Fig. 12. Rupture rate vs wall thickness calculated from FFREQ results (324-914 mm diameter).

thickness and design factor. The FFREQ results provided for inclusion in the code supplements have been interpreted in a similar way in Figs 11 and 12.

Conclusions

QRA is used in the UK on major accident hazard pipelines. Supplements to the UK's pipeline design standard (BSI PD 8010) and recommendations (IGE/TD/1) will detail the methodologies that can be used in the QRAs, and give general guidance.

British Gas developed early pipeline QRA in the UK. Accordingly, UKOPA has reconstructed the original pipeline failure and prediction of failure frequency methodology due to external interference developed by British Gas. This methodology is encompassed in the FFREQ software.

The reconstructed model has been used to investigate the effect of pipeline parameters on failure frequency due to external interference. Based on an evaluation of the results of studies carried out using the reconstructed methodology, UKOPA has concluded that the methodology is logical and understandable, is justifiable in terms of modelling of structural parameters, and is robust in terms of comparison with operational data.

UKOPA has therefore recommended the FFREQ methodology as the preferred methodology for the prediction of pipeline failure frequencies due to external interference. Failure-frequency predictions using the reconstructed methodology and FFREQ for specific pipe cases have been reported in this paper.

Acknowledgements

The authors wish to acknowledge and thank UKOPA for support of this work, access to confidential operational data, and permission to publish the paper at this conference.

References

1. Anon., 1966. Pipelines Safety Regulations. SI 825. ISBN 0110543734.
2. Health and Safety Executive, 2007. Hazardous Installation Division: HID's approach to 'As Low As Reasonably Practicable' (ALARP) decisions. London: Health and Safety Executive.
3. Anon., 2004. Code of Practice for Pipelines - Part 1: Steel pipelines on land. PD 8010 - 1: 2004, British Standards Institution, London.
4. Anon., 2001. Steel Pipelines for High Pressure Gas Transmission, IGE/TD/1 Edition 4: 2000,

Recommendations on transmission and distribution practice. Institute of Gas Engineers, Communication 1670.
5. G.D.Goodfellow and J.V.Haswell, 2006. A comparison of inherent risk levels in ASME B31.8 and UK gas pipeline design codes. Proc. International Pipeline Conference, ASME, Calgary.
6. Health and Safety Executive, 2001. Reducing risks, protecting people – HSE's decision-making process. London: HSE Books, ISBN 0-7176-2151-0.
7. P.Hopkins and A.Cairns, 1981. A fracture mechanics model to predict the failure of defects in dented linepipe. British Gas Engineering Research Station Report R2382, Dec. (confidential).
8. I.Corder, 1995. The application of risk techniques to the design and operation of pipelines. Paper C502/016/95, Proc. International Conference on Pressure Systems: Operation and Risk Management, Institution of Mechanical Engineers, London, pp113-125.
9. I.Corder, 1995. The application of risk techniques to the design and operation of pipelines. Conference on Ageing Pipelines, Institution of Mechanical Engineers, London, September, C50-2/016/95.
10. I.Corder, G.D.Fearnehough, and R.N.Knott, 1992. Pipeline design using risk based criteria. Institute of Gas Engineers 129th Annual General Meeting and Spring Conference, Communication 1492, Eastbourne, UK.
11. H.F.Hopkins, S.E.Lewis, and A.D.Ramage, 1993. The development and application of the British Gas TRANSPIRE pipeline risk assessment package. Institute of Gas Engineers, Midland Section Meeting, Loughborough, UK.
12. M.R.Acton, T.R.Baldwin, P.J.Baldwin, and E.E.R.Jager, 1998. The development of the PIPESAFE risk assessment package for gas transmission pipelines. Proc. International Pipeline Conference, ASME, Calgary.
13. M.R.Acton *et al.*, 2002. Recent developments in the design and application of the PIPESAFE risk assessment package for gas transmission pipelines. Proc. International Pipeline Conference, ASME, Calgary.
14. D.Browne and R.Hicks, 2005. UKOPA pipeline fault database, pipeline product loss incidents (1962-2004). 4th Report of the UKOPA Fault Database Management Group prepared by Advantica for FDMG, UKOPA, UK.
15. Anon., 2000. Guidance on methods for assessing the acceptability of flaws in structures. BSI 7910, British Standards Institution, London.
16. Anon., 2007. Fitness-for-service. API 579-1 / ASME FFS-1, Second Edition, American Petroleum Institute.
17. A.Cosham and P.Hopkins, 2002. The pipeline defect assessment manual. Proc. International Pipeline Conference, ASME, Calgary.
18. I.Corder and P.Chatain, 1995. EPRG recommendations for the assessment of the resistance of pipelines to external damage. Proc. EPRG/PRC 10th Biennial Joint Technical Meeting on Line Pipe Research, Cambridge, UK.
19. P.Roovers, R.Bood, M.Galli, U.Marewski, M.Steiner, and M.Zarea, 2000. EPRG methods for assessing the tolerance and resistance of pipelines to external damage. Pipeline Technology, Volume II, Proc.3rd International Pipeline Technology Conference, Bruges, Belgium, R. Denys, Ed., Elsevier Science, pp 405-425.
20. A.Cosham and P.Hopkins, 2004. An overview of the pipeline defect assessment manual. Vol. 3, Proc. 4th International Pipeline Technology Conference, Scientific Surveys Ltd, R. Denys, Ed., Ostend, Belgium, pp1487-1502.
21. A.Cosham and P.Hopkins, 2004. The effect of dents in pipelines – guidance in the pipeline defect assessment manual. *Int. J. of Pressure Vessels and Piping*, **81**, pp127-139.
22. Anon., 2001. Assessment of the integrity of structures containing defects. British Energy, R6 Revision 4.
23. C.Jandu, R.Francini, M.Taylor, and A.Francis, 2008. Towards a new limit state function for determining the failure pressure of a pipeline containing mechanical damage. Proc. International Pipeline Conference, ASME, Calgary.
24. N.A.Townsend and G.D.Fearnehough, 1986. Controlling risk from UK gas transmission pipelines. Paper 3-1, 7th Symposium on Line Pipe Research, American Gas Association, Catalog No. L51495, USA.
25. C.Lyons and J.V.Haswell, 2005. The influence of pipe design factor and geometry on the failure of pipelines subject to third party damage. Report for UKOPA Pipeline Integrity Engineers, Report No.PIE/2005/R104, Issue 1.0, October.

26. A.Cosham, J.V.Haswell, and N.Jackson, 2008. Reduction factors for estimating the probability of failure of pipelines due to external interference. Proc. International Pipeline Conference, ASME, Calgary.

NOMENCLATURE

d	gouge depth (mm)
2c	gouge length (mm)
D	dent depth
Cv	Charpy Energy (J)
Dia	outside diameter of pipe (mm)
R	pipe radius (mm)
E	elastic modulus (207,000 Nmm^{-2})
L	gouge length (mm)
M	Folias factor
R	outside radius of pipe (mm)
t	wall thickness (mm)
Y_1	compliance function
Y_2	compliance function
α	shape parameter in probability density function
β	scale parameter in probability density function
$\bar{\sigma}$	flow stress (Nmm^{-2})
$\tilde{\sigma}$	plastic collapse stress of an infinitely long part-wall metal loss defect (Nmm^{-2})
σ_f	failure stress (Nmm^{-2})
σ_{SMYS}	SMYS (Nmm^{-2})
EPRG	European Pipeline Research Group
SMYS	specified minimum yield strength

Annexe A – overview of dent-gouge failure model

The original work to develop a method for the prediction of failure frequencies due to external interference was carried out for British Gas (BG) at the Engineering Research Station, Killingworth, UK, in the mid-1980s. This section details the fracture-mechanics' equations used in the modelling of the failure state of a two-dimensional (infinitely long) dent-gouge damage in a pipeline[1].

The depth of gouge required to cause failure for a particular pipeline geometry and known operating conditions can be obtained by rearranging the gouge failure equation:

$$\sigma_f = \bar{\sigma}(1-(d/t)/(1-[(d/t)(1/M)]) \qquad (1)$$

where:

[1] Note, the equations in this section are taken directly from the original British Gas references [7, 8,] and are given in imperial units.

d = defect depth
t = wall thickness
σ_f = failure stress
$\bar{\sigma}$ = flow stress (function of the specified minimum yield stress of pipeline material, e.g. 1.15 x SMYS (σ_{SMYS}))
M = Folias factor.

For the purposes of this study the Folias factor is defined as:

$$M = \sqrt{1 + 0.26\left(\frac{2c}{\sqrt{Rt}}\right)^2} \tag{2}$$

where:

2c = gouge length
R = pipeline radius

By defining a leak/rupture limit to the Folias factor:

$$M_{crit} = \bar{\sigma} / \sigma_f = 1.15\sigma_{SMYS} / \sigma_f \tag{3}$$

and substituting into the original Folias factor definition, the critical length of the gouge can be determined:

$$L_{crit} = \left[\left(1.3225\left[\frac{\sigma_{SMYS}}{\sigma_f}\right]^2 - 1\right) 3.846Rt\right]^{1/2} \tag{4}$$

Gouges of length L_{crit} or larger will rupture, shorter gouges will leak[2].

This is used to determine the differences between leak failure frequencies and rupture-failure frequencies.

It has been shown that the failure stress of a pipeline incorporating a dent/gouge combination of known geometry can be predicted from:

$$\frac{\sigma_f}{\sigma_{SMYS}} = \frac{2}{\pi}\cos^{-1}\left[\exp-\left(\frac{1.5\pi E}{\bar{\sigma}^2 Ad}\left[\begin{matrix} Y_1\left(1 - 1.8\left[\frac{D}{2R}\right]\right) + \\ Y_2\left(10.2\frac{R}{t}\left[\frac{D}{2R}\right]\right)\end{matrix}\right]^{-2} \exp\left[\frac{\ln(C_v) - 1.9}{0.57}\right]\right)\right] \tag{5}$$

where:

---

[1] Note: risk analysis consequence models require interpretation of critical gouge length in terms of hole size.

E	= elastic modulus of pipeline material
A	= 0.083
d	= gouge depth
D	= dent depth
C_v	= Charpy energy (measured using 2/3 specimen)

All other factors are as above.

$\bar{\sigma}$ is the flow stress, a measure of the resistance of the material to plastic collapse and is defined as:

$$\bar{\sigma} = 1.15\sigma_{SMYS}\left(1-\left(\frac{d}{t}\right)\right) \tag{6}$$

Y_1 and Y_2 are defined as follows:

$$Y_1 = 1.12 - 0.23\left(\frac{d}{t}\right) + 10.6\left(\frac{d}{t}\right)^2 - 21.7\left(\frac{d}{t}\right)^3 + 30.4\left(\frac{d}{t}\right)^4$$
$$Y_2 = 1.12 - 1.39\left(\frac{d}{t}\right) + 7.32\left(\frac{d}{t}\right)^2 - 13.1\left(\frac{d}{t}\right)^3 + 14.0\left(\frac{d}{t}\right)^4 \tag{7, 8}$$

The size of dent required to cause failure with a particular gouge can be obtained by re-arranging Equn 5:

$$D/2R = \frac{\left[\dfrac{\exp\left(\dfrac{\ln[C_v]-2.049}{0.534}\right)}{\ln\left(\sec\left[\dfrac{\pi\sigma_f}{2\bar{\sigma}}\right]\right)\left(\dfrac{\bar{\sigma}^2 Ad}{1.5\pi E}\right)Y_1^2}-1\right]^{1/2}}{10.2\left(\dfrac{Y_2}{Y_1}\right)\left(\dfrac{R}{t}\right)-1.8} \tag{9}$$

Equation 5 is semi-empirical based on multiple regression of the term (*ln*[C_v] - 1.9)/0.57. The subject of the equation has been changed from σ_f/σ_{SMYS} in the equation to *D/2R*, and hence it is necessary to perform a new regression for the new subject. This procedure results in the constants 1.9 and 0.57 being replaced by 2.049 and 0.534, respectively [7, 8]

Annexe B continues overleaf

Annexe B – predictive methodology

The method for the calculation of the likelihood of occurrence of the dent-gouge damage which results in failure for specified pipeline conditions using the above cumulative probability curves for gouge length (Fig.1), gouge depth (Fig.2), and dent depth (Fig.3), and its use in conjunction with a dent-gouge failure model as described in [8, 9] in the prediction of pipeline failure frequencies, is briefly summarized below.

1. For given pipeline parameters (diameter, wall thickness, pressure) use a defined (published) engineering equation for a dent-gouge model to calculate the critical defect length L_c for rupture.

2. Assume that gouges of length L ed L_{crit} will rupture, gouges of length $L < L_{crit}$ will leak.

3. Determine the probability of occurrence $P(L_{crit})$ of a gouge of length L_{crit} from Fig.1.

4. Obtain the probability of occurrence $P(d_{wt})$ a gouge of depth $d = wt$ from Fig.2, and calculate the probability of failure as:

PoF = $P(L_{crit}) * P(d_{wt})$

This value is the start of the PoF sum for leaks.

5. Divide the gouge length between 0 – L_{crit} into increments, L_{crit} / N_i

Calculate the mean length L_i and incremental probability $dP(L_i)$ for the current increment from Fig.2.

6. Calculate d_{crit} at L_i using the dent-gouge model.

7. Determine the probability of occurrence $P(d_{crit})$ of a gouge of depth d_{crit} from Fig.2, and calculate the probability of failure as:

PoF = $P(d_{crit}) * dP(L_i)$

Add this to the PoF sum for leaks.

8. Divide the gouge depth cumulative probability curve into a number, j, of gouge depths, d. For each gouge depth d_j, determine the probability of occurrence $dP(d_j)$ from the Fig.2 and calculate the depth of dent Dc_j using the dent-gouge model which would cause failure in combination with this gouge depth using a failure equation/limit state.

9. Determine the probability of occurrence PDc_j of dent depth Dc_j from Fig.3.

10. Calculate the probability of failure as:

PoF = $P(Dc_j) * dP(d_j) * dP(L_i)$

Add this to the PoF sum for leaks.

11. Repeat steps 3-10 for each gouge length increment up to L_{crit} and add all the PoF sums to obtain the leak probability.

12. To obtain the rupture probability, repeat steps 3-11 using gouge length increments between L_c and L_{max}.

13. Obtain the total probability of failure by adding the leak and rupture probabilities.

Evaluating damage to on- and offshore pipelines using data acquired using ILI

by Dr Chris Alexander

Stress Engineering Services, Inc, Houston, TX, USA

EVALUATING THE INTEGRITY of pipelines often involves assessing data acquired from an in-line inspection (ILI) run. ILI generates a range of data types, one of which is geometric data from a caliper tool. Once the data are collected, engineers are required to evaluate the relative severity of any indications that might have been found. With recent advances in storage capacity and instrumentation, the resolution of the acquired data is of sufficient magnitude to make relatively accurate assessments of the potential damage that might exist within a given pipeline system.

In this paper a case study is provided that used data collected during an in-line inspection run of a damaged pipeline. The assessments included the development of finite-element models constructed using the geometric ILI data. Integral to the assessments were integration of actual pressure history data that, when used in conjunction with a cumulative damage assessment model, determined the remaining life of the selected anomaly. Additionally, the assessment used prior full-scale experimental data to confirm the accuracy of the models. A systematic approach for evaluating damaged pipelines using ILI caliper tool data is described.

DENTS GENERATED IN onshore pipeline are typically the result of third-party damage, although rock dents are certainly a contributor for bottom-side defects. Damage to subsea pipelines typically occurs as the result of impact with an anchor. After the subsea incident occurs, ROVs (remotely-operated vehicles) are then deployed to survey the damage, followed by survey efforts to determine if the pipeline has been moved or laterally displaced. If it is believed that localized damage has been inflicted, it is essential that the profile of the dented region be determined, and in-line inspection is ideally-suited for collecting this data. From a geometry standpoint, the data collected includes points measuring radius, circumferential orientation, and longitudinal position (i.e. R-θ-Z coordinates).

Presented in this paper is a background section that discusses how to evaluate dents considering previous research efforts and experience, following which is a discussion on how raw ILI geometry data are converted into the mesh for evaluation using the finite-element (FEA) method. FEA is used to calculate the alternating stresses in the dented region; once the stresses due to cyclic pressure are calculated, a fatigue curve is used to estimate the remaining life for the given dents. Results are presented from previous research on fatigue testing of pipes having plain dents, and the final section of the paper provides recommendations for industry in using ILI data to estimate the remaining life of damaged pipelines, and integrating previous test data where appropriate for validation purposes.

Background

In the 1990s, a significant body of work on evaluating dented pipelines was performed under the direction of the Pipeline Research Council International, while other work was also performed on plain dents and related defects for the American Petroleum Institute. For the most part, this work focused on damage to pipelines involving plain dents and dents with gouges. Full-scale testing involving pipelines subjected to static and cyclic pressures were used to evaluate the effects of dents having varying degrees of severity on the integrity of pipelines, and interested readers are encouraged to consult the reference documents provided in this paper. The predominant conclusion from these research efforts is that to properly assess a defect's severity, one must appropriately categorize the defect. The major defect classifications that typically arise when assessing pipeline damage are:

plain dents
constrained dents
gouges
mechanical damage
wrinkles

The sections that follow discuss in detail experimental testing that has been conducted to address the several classes of dent listed previously by different research programmes around the world. Detailed in each section are the appropriate references, critical variables associated with the defect in question, and the effects of loading (static or cyclic) on failure behaviour.

Plain dents

Plain dents are defined as dents having no injurious defects – such as a gouge – and possessing a smooth profile (they are often classified as smooth dents). The critical variables relating to plain dents are:

dent depth (depth after rerounding due to pressure)
pipe geometry (relationship between diameter and wall thickness)
profile curvature of the dent profile
pressure at installation
applied cyclic pressure range.

While the effects of certain variables are not clearly understood, it is apparent that the denting process plays a critical role in determining the future behaviour of the dent. Early research recognized that dent depth was one of, if not the most important, variable of interest. The dent created initially changes as a function of applied pressure (statically or cyclically).

The following equation was developed Maxey [1] and correlates the relationship between initial dent depth and the residual dent depth as a function of applied pressure and yield strength.

$$D_o = \frac{D_R}{\left[-0.5066 \cdot \log\left(\frac{\hat{}}{\hat{}_y + 10{,}000}\right)\right]} \qquad (1)$$

where:

σ = hoop stress at instant of damage (psi)
σ_y = yield strength of pipe (psi)
D_o = dent depth at instant of damage (in)
D_R = residual dent depth after removal of damaging tool (in)

Sample number	Pipe geometry	Grade and yield strength	Charpy impact (ft-lbs)	Field dent depth (d/D%)	Failure stress (ksi)	Notes
BPU 2	36-in x 0.54-in	X60 (67.5 ksi)	44.2	3.4	67.2	Failed at 112% SMYS
BNO 2	36-in x 0.50-in	X60 (60.8 ksi)	19.1	4.5	67.7	Failed at 113% SMYS
BIE 1	24-in x 0.38-in	X52 (53.1 ksi)	14.0	5.4	24.9	Failed at 48% SMYS
BLV 1 (1)	30-in x 0.31-in	X52 (52.7 ksi)	19.2	3.5	71.1	(see note 2)
EUY 1	36-in x 0.66-in	X65 (68.9 ksi)	31.7	4.8	26.5	Failed at 41% SMYS
FJB 1 (1)	30-in x 0.48-in	X52 (58.8 ksi)	22.8	3.2	18.9	Failed at 36% SMYS
FJB 1 (1)	30-in x 0.48-in	X52 (58.8 ksi)	22.8	4.9	12.6	Failed at 24% SMYS

Table 1. Burst pressures for plain dents.
Note: (1) cracks detected on inside seam weld of the sample;
(2) sample yielded but did not break.

A review of the preceding equation by Hopkins [2] revealed some levels of unconservatism because the above formulation is lower-bound and ignores the elastic spring-back of the dent at zero internal pressure. Later work by Rosenfeld [3] indicates that some degree of progressive rerounding occurs with pressure cycles. It is these changes in dent depth, and associated changes in dent profile, that determine the eventual long-term behaviour of the dent. When considering pipes with relatively-high diameter to wall thickness ratios, a significant level of rerounding occurs on pressurisation. Work conducted for the American Petroleum Institute (API) [4] showed that for 12.75-in x 0.188-in X52 pipes, it was not possible to achieve dent depths greater than 3% of the pipe diameter when the pipe was pressurised to the maximum allowable operating pressure, even though initial dent depths as great as 18% were initially established. As will be discussed later in this paper, this rerounding reduces the severity of the dent.

The behaviour of plain dents in static and cyclic pressure environments differ. The sections that follow provide insights on these differences.

Response of plain dents to static pressure loading

The response of plain dents to static pressure loads deals primarily with the effects of the damage on the burst strength of the pipe. In addition to concerns relating to dent depth and profile, the mechanical properties of the damaged pipe material are also important. Work was reported in the 1980s that correlates burst pressure with dent depth and material properties for pipes with different geometries and grades [5]. The tests involved pipe ring samples that were dented prior to pressure testing; Table 1 provides a summary of the test results.

The definitive conclusion based on all available research is that plain dents do not pose a threat to the structural integrity of a pipeline other than the potential for reduced collapse/buckling capacity associated with the induced ovality. A discussion on the subject matter will follow in a

Sample number	Pipe geometry and grade	Initial dent depth (d/D, %)	Final dent depth (d/D, %)	Cycles to failure
US6A-2	12.75-in x 0.188-in, Grade X52	6	1.3	1,307,223
UD12A-3	12.75-in x 0.188-in, Grade X52	12	2.5	684,903
UD18A'-28	12.75-in x 0.188-in, Grade X52	18	0.7	101,056

Table 2. Cyclic pressure tests on plain dents.
Note: (1) no pressure in pipe sample during indentation.
(2) residual dent measured with no pressure in pipe after sample was pressurised to a 65% SMYS stress level.
(3) cycles to failure listed based upon Miner's Rule in combining results from two applied pressure ranges (36% and 72% SMYS).
(4) sample did not fail. Testing terminated due to excessive number of applied pressure cycles.

later section of this paper. However, the classification of a plain dent assumes that no cracks, gouges, or material imperfections are present in the vicinity of the dent. Interaction of plain dents with weld seams, especially girth welds and submerged arc welds (SAW), can significantly reduce the burst strength of the damaged pipeline [4]. The primary cause of the reduction is crack development at the toe of the welds during pressurizing the pipe and associated rerounding of the dent.

Response of plain dents to cyclic pressure loading

While plain dents do not pose a threat to pipeline integrity in a static environment, cyclic pressure applications can reduce the life of a pipeline. A survey of several gas and liquid transmission companies revealed the number of applied pressure cycles that can be expected for the respective fuel types [6]. A gas transmission line can be expected to see 60 cycles per year with a pressure differential of 200psi; however, the same pressure differential can occur over 1,800 times on a liquid pipeline in the course of a year. For this reason, liquid pipeline operators are considerably more concerned with fatigue than gas pipeline operators.

The impact that a plain dent has on the fatigue life of a pipeline is directly related to two factors, the first of which concerns the dent geometry in terms of shape and depth. Dents that are deeper and possess greater levels of local curvature reduce fatigue lives of pipes more than dents that are shallow with relatively-smooth contours. Work conducted for the American Gas Association [6], American Petroleum Institute [2], and by EPRG [5] all validate this position. The second factor determining the severity of plain dents is the range of applied pressures. In general, a fourth-order relationship can be assumed between the applied stress range and fatigue life: in other words, a dented pipeline subjected to a pressure differential of 200psi will have a fatigue life that is 16 times greater than if a pressure differential of 400psi were applied. Barring the effects of rerounding (which change the local stress in the dent), the fatigue lives of plain dents are reduced to a greater degree when increased pressure differentials are assumed.

Table 2 provides several data points extracted from the API research programme showing the effects of dent depth on fatigue life. As noted in the data, the 6% dent never failed and had a fatigue life that exceeded the fatigue life for the 18% dent by one order of magnitude.

Sample number	Pipe geometry and grade	Initial dent depth (d/D, %)	Burst pressure (psi)	Percentage SMYS
B1-1N	5	5	2,165	141
B1-3N	10	5	1,985	120
B1-6N	10	10	1,479	96
B1-7N	15	15	820	53
B1-8N	10	12	1,517	99
B1-11N	5	15	775	51

Table 3. Burst tests for dents with gouges.
Note: (1) dents installed with an internal pressure of 920 psi. Dents permitted to reround after pressurisation.
(2) material properties: 53.6ksi yield strength; 72.1ksi UTS; 51 ft-lbs CVN.

In assessing the overall impact that plain dents have on pipelines subjected to cyclic service, one must consider both the applied pressure range and geometry of the dent. A given dent may not be serious in gas service, but could pose a detriment to fatigue life when considering the service requirements of liquid transmission pipelines.

Dents with gouges

While plain dents may be regarded as rather benign in terms of their impact on structural integrity, dents with gouges are a major concern for pipeline companies. The leading cause of pipeline failures is mechanical damage, which often occurs during excavation of pipelines, and the United States Department of Transportation (US DOT) has specific criteria for reporting outside incidents. The rate of reportable incidents for gas pipelines from 1970 to June 1984 was 3.1 x 10^{-4}/km-yr, while the rate was approximately 6.8 x 10^{-5}/km-yr for the period from July 1984 to 1992. A more-conservative estimate assumes that the actual incident rate may be as high as 10^{-3}/km-yr due to unreported incidences. Regardless of the assumed incident rate, world-wide efforts have focused on the need for mechanical damage research. In the United States, most of the experimental work has been conducted by Battelle Memorial Institute and Stress Engineering Services, Inc, and has been funded by the American Gas Association and the American Petroleum Institute. In Europe, testing has been conducted primarily by British Gas and Gaz de France with funding from the European Pipeline Research Group.

The severity of mechanical damage is rooted in the presence of microcracks that develop at the base of the gouge during the process of dent rerounding due to pressure (and to some extent elastic rebound). As with plain dents, dents with gouges respond differently to static and cyclic pressure loading. The discussions that follow provide greater details regarding the associated responses.

Response of dents with gouges to static pressure loading

Unlike plain dents that do not severely affect the pressure-carrying capacity of pipelines, the deleterious nature of dents with gouges requires careful investigation. The failure patterns of dents with gouges that are subjected to static pressure overload involve the outward movement of the dent region, while development and propagation of microcracks at the base of the gouge occur with increasing pressure levels. Hopkins *et al.* [5] conducted numerous ring tests to address the failure pattern of dents combined with gouges and concluded that the failure mechanism was ductile tearing within an unstable structure.

Testing was conducted by Kiefner & Associates, Inc/Stress Engineering Services, Inc [4] for determining the burst pressure of dents containing gouges. All testing was conducted using 12-in NPS X52 pipes. Machined V-notches were made at various depths in the pipe samples, which were pressurised to 920psi (60% SMYS) and then dented with a 1-in wide bar. Table 3 lists six of the test samples and the pressures at which they failed. As noted in the table, dent and gouge combinations that exceed 10% of the pipe diameter and wall thicknesses (respectively) are likely to have burst pressures that are less than the pressure corresponding to SMYS. The pipes used in testing had relatively-good ductility and toughness (32% elongation and Charpy V-notch impact energy of 51ft-lbs at room temperature); however, pipes without such material qualifications will fail at lower pressures. Work conducted by the Snowy Mountains Engineering Corporation in Australia) validates the importance of having sufficient ductility and toughness in reducing the potential for low failure pressures.

Based upon a review of the data and the experience of the author in experimental testing, it is difficult to envision a closed-form solution for predicting the failure pressure due to static overload of dents containing gouges. Although attempts have been made to do so, a paper written by Eiber and Leis [7] shows that the current models (developed for the PRCI and EPRG) do not satisfactorily predict burst pressures. Several of the primary reasons for the complexities in predicting burst pressure of dents with gouges are as follows:

- material properties (especially ductility and toughness)
- sharpness and depth of gouge
- pressures at indentation and during rerounding
- dent profile and depth as well as resulting plastic deformation of pipe
- local work-hardening and variations in through-wall properties due to denting

The key to future experimental testing is only to address one variable while holding all others constant. The above list represents a satisfactory starting point for such investigations.

Response of dents with gouges to cyclic pressure loading

Initial efforts in the pipeline research community focused on static burst testing of mechanical damage, but once a basic level of understanding of the fracture mechanisms were developed, efforts focused on fatigue testing. Cyclic pressure tests have been conducted on pipe specimens with a variety of defect combinations [4, 5, 6]; the research efforts conducted for the EPRG, AGA, and PRCI indicate that if the fatigue life for plain dents is on the order of 105 cycles, then the presence of gouges (in dents) reduces this value to be of the order of 103. Table 4 summarises data from the research conducted for the EPRG on ring-test specimens for relating plain dents and dents with gouges subjected to cyclic pressure service [5]. As noted, the presence of a gouge significantly reduces the fatigue life of a plain dent, although a gouge by itself is non-threatening (an observation validated by Fowler *et al.*, [6]).

Response of dents in welds to cyclic pressure loading

In addition to considering interaction of dents with gouges, efforts to assess the interaction of welds with dents have been conducted. Testing on submerged and double-submerged arc welds indicated that the dents in seam welds could significantly reduce the burst pressures and fatigue lives of the affected pipelines. The recommendation by Hopkins *et al.* [5] is that these defects should be treated with extreme caution and immediate repair considered.

Research efforts funded by AGA and API indicate that when dents are installed in ERW seams

Residual dent depth (percent pipe diameter)	Gouge depth (percent pipe wall thickness)	Fatigue life
None	20%	Greater than 145,500 cycles
4 %	None	Less than 6,930 cycles
4 % (in pipe weld)	None	Less than 789 cycles
4 %	20 %	Less than 199 cycles

Table 4. Fatigue life for gouges, plain dents, and dents with gouges

the fatigue resistance is on the same order as plain dents [6, 8]. This assumes that good-quality seam welds are present in the pipe material. The presence of girth welds was shown to reduce the fatigue life of dents to a level less than ERW seams, but more than SAW seams. As an example, consider that the research programme for API tested a dent in a SAW weld seam that failed after 21,603 cycles, while the same dent in a girth weld failed after 108,164 cycles [8].

Experimental study of strains in dented pipes

While numerous studies have addressed the failure patterns of plain dents and dents with gouges, less effort has been made to evaluate the strains in dented pipes. Obviously, the complex nature of dent mechanics is a contributing factor; also, the use of finite-element analysis (FEA) permits engineers to accurately understand the stress/strain distribution in dents as will be discussed later in this paper.

Lancaster *et al.* has conducted numerous tests directed at developing an understanding of strains caused by pressurization of pipes with dents, employing the use of both strain gages and photoelastic coatings. His work provides several useful findings,

- During the process of rerounding the dents with internal pressure, approximately 60% of the dent had been recovered at a pressure equal to 70% of the yield pressure. There was evidence of creep at pressures above yield.

- The locations having the highest strains are on the rim of the dent. Interestingly, this location was consistent with the failure location for unconstrained dome dents in the API research programme that resulted in longitudinally-oriented cracks that developed on the exterior of the pipe [8].

- The highest strain measured on the rim of the dent was 7000$\mu\varepsilon$, and the maximum hoop stress concentration (SCF) was calculated to be 10.0. In comparing this SCF with those generated by finite-element methods (FEM) for the API research programme, the maximum FEM SCF was calculated to be 7.2 for an unconstrained dome dent having a residual dent depth of 10% [8].

In addition to the work conducted by Lancaster, Rosenfeld [3] developed a theoretical model that describes the structural behaviour of plain dents under pressure. His efforts also involved dent rerounding tests for validation purposes.

Wrinkle bends

Wrinkle bends are associated with the bending of pipe that results in creating local indentations

Fig. 1. 36-in diameter pipe with 2% wrinkles.

that may be regularly or irregularly spaced, along the length of the affected area. Wrinkle bends are not considered favourably by the pipeline codes and most operators. As a point of reference, ASME B31.8 841.231(g) states that wrinkle bends are permitted only on systems that operating at hoop stress levels less than 30% of the specified minimum yield strength.

As part of the American Petroleum Institute study [8], experimental efforts were undertaken to assess the effects of wrinkle bends on the fatigue life of pipelines. Three 36-in x 0.281-in pipes were fitted with wrinkle bends having nominal depths of 2%, 4%, and 6% (wrinkle depth percentage calculated by dividing wrinkle depth by the nominal diameter of the pipe). Figure 1 shows the pipe sample with 2% wrinkles, while Fig.2 shows the corresponding profiles for the three wrinkles that were tested.

Pressure-cycle testing was performed where the samples were pressure cycled to 100% of the operating pressure. The following fatigue results were obtained:

2% wrinkle - no failure after 44,541 cycles
4% wrinkle - failure after 2,791 cycles
6% wrinkle - failure after 1,086 cycles

The above results were a significant find for the API research programme. The critical observations is that although depth of damage is important (wrinkle or dent), the more important factor is the profile shape of the damage. The change in radius of curvature along the length of the line is directly related to bending strains. As noted in the fatigue data, a wrinkle having a depth of 6% poses a significant threat to the integrity of the pipeline. Although intentional wrinkle bends are unlikely to occur offshore, the authors observed several anchor impact zones that clearly resembled the damage profile associated with wrinkle bends. For this reason, any damage in an onshore or offshore pipeline that resembles a wrinkle bend (i.e. defect having a sharp curvature, as in a kink) should be removed as soon as is prudent.

Summary of experimental work

The information presented in this paper indicates that a significant level of research has been conducted world-wide in an effort to characterize and assess the severity of plain dents and dents with gouges. It can be concluded that a certain hierarchy exists in terms of defect severity, although unquestionable scatter is present in both the static and fatigue data. Empirical models and semi-empirical models have been able to predict with some success the failure pressure for dents with

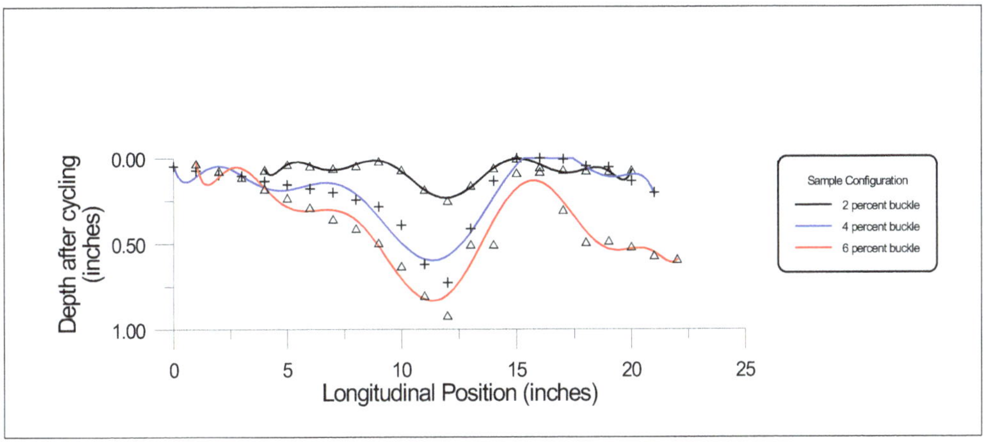

Fig.2. Wrinkle profile for the three test samples.

Circumferential position (every 12 degrees)

Axial position

Data shown (other than first column) are radial coordinates.

391300.1426	196.1399	199.0881	199.5950	201.6023	204.6078	207.6003	209.8907	211.0764
391300.1459	196.1445	199.0792	199.5974	201.6105	204.6081	207.5990	209.8935	211.0715
391300.1491	196.1445	199.0838	199.6020	201.6066	204.6069	207.6073	209.8920	211.0837
391300.1524	196.1445	199.0884	199.6066	201.6026	204.6057	207.6155	209.8904	211.0959
391300.1557	196.1469	199.0876	199.6119	201.6034	204.6089	207.6123	209.8949	211.0951
391300.1590	196.1494	199.0868	199.6172	201.6042	204.6122	207.6090	209.8994	211.0943
391300.1623	196.1518	199.0859	199.6225	201.6050	204.6154	207.6057	209.9039	211.0935
391300.1655	196.1494	199.0920	199.6131	201.6026	204.6171	207.6025	209.9008	211.0968
391300.1688	196.1469	199.0981	199.6037	201.6001	204.6187	207.5992	209.8978	211.1000
391300.1721	196.1445	[illegible]	[illegible]	[illegible]	[illegible]	[illegible]	209.8947	211.1033
[illegible]	196.1506	[illegible]	[illegible]	[illegible]	[illegible]	[illegible]	209.8981	211.1057
[illegible]	196.1567	[illegible]	[illegible]	[illegible]	[illegible]	[illegible]	209.9014	211.1082
391300.1819	196.1606	199.1311	199.5983	201.6018	204.6338	207.5974	209.8984	211.1114
391300.1852	196.1644	199.1299	199.6089	201.5985	204.6283	207.6013	209.8953	211.1147
391300.1885	196.1683	199.1287	199.6194	201.5953	204.6228	207.6051	209.8923	211.1179
391300.1918	196.1753	199.1271	199.6203	201.6001	204.6252	207.6039	209.8959	211.1130
391300.1951	196.1823	199.1256	199.6213	201.6050	204.6277	207.6027	209.8996	211.1082
391300.1984	196.1772	199.1266	199.6162	201.6050	204.6283	207.5994	209.8927	211.1171
391300.2016	196.1721	199.1277	199.6111	201.6050	204.6289	207.5962	209.8858	211.1261
391300.2049	196.1671	199.1287	199.6060	201.6050	204.6295	207.5929	209.8788	211.1350
391300.2082	196.1720	199.1381	199.6142	201.6148	204.6307	207.5978	209.8779	211.1262
391300.2115	196.1768	199.1476	199.6225	201.6246	204.6319	207.6027	209.8770	211.1173
391300.2148	196.1768	199.1541	199.6225	201.6205	204.6328	207.5954	209.8823	211.1167

Fig.3. Raw in-line inspection data in cylindrical coordinates.

gouges; however, the large number of variables has so far precluded the development of a general model that can accurately forecast the burst and fatigue behaviour of all possible types of mechanical damage. Any evaluation involving numerical modelling based on ILI geometry data should be validated by referencing previous experimental work.

Analysis of dents

The primary focus of this paper is to specifically address the use of ILI data in evaluating dent severity, and the approach presented can be used for both on- and offshore pipelines. The presentation includes a discussion on converting raw ILI data into a format useful for generating a finite-element mesh, actually performing the analysis using FEM, and interpreting the data in terms of estimating future performance.

Fig.4. Global view of dent in finite-element model.

Converting raw ILI data

The ILI data that are typically measured by an in-line inspection tool is presented in cylindrical coordinates (i.e. R-θ-Z). Figure 3 provides a portion of an example data set taken from an ILI tool run: as can be seen, radial coordinates are provided as functions of circumferential and axial positions. In this particular data set the circumferential positions are provided every 12°, or approximately every 1.75in for the given pipe diameter. To generate accurate analysis results, this spacing is too large, and therefore an algorithm was developed to increase the mesh density and generate a more-refined mesh for the FEM based on a fast Fourier transform (FFT) routine. As a point of reference, where the raw data had 30 points circumferentially resulting in nodal spacing of 1.75in, the FFT-modified procedure produces 177 points circumferentially spaced at approximately 0.50in. The number of data points in the axial direction is adjusted to match the circumferential spacing so that the two are approximately equal (an element aspect ratio of 1:1).

Finite-element analysis

Once the required level of mesh refinement has been made, the finite element model is generated, for which the R-θ-Z coordinates serve as the nodes. A Fortran code was developed to read the reduced data and generate an *Abaqus* input file. The coordinates for each node were developed using the relationships shown below.

$$X = (r + t/2) * \sin\theta$$

$$Y = (r + t/2) * \cos\theta$$

$$Z = Z$$

In these relationships, r is the inside radius from the ILI data, θ is the circumferential position relative to the pipe axis measured clockwise from the top of the pipe. The thickness of the pipe, t, is taken based on the pipe's nominal wall thickness. The axis of the pipe was taken as the global z-axis. Figure 4 shows an overall view of a dent model, while Fig.5 shows an enlarged view of the region where the mesh density can be seen. The "S4" type shell elements were specified in *Abaqus*, and symmetry boundary conditions were specified at each end of the pipe model. For each analysis, a linear elastic analysis was performed where the internal pressure was the yield pressure of the pipe using the specified minimum yield strength (SMYS) of the respective pipe grade (for example, X52 has an SMYS of 52,000psi). A typical finite-element model has of the order of 25,000 elements.

Once the model pre-processing was completed, stresses were calculated based on the internal

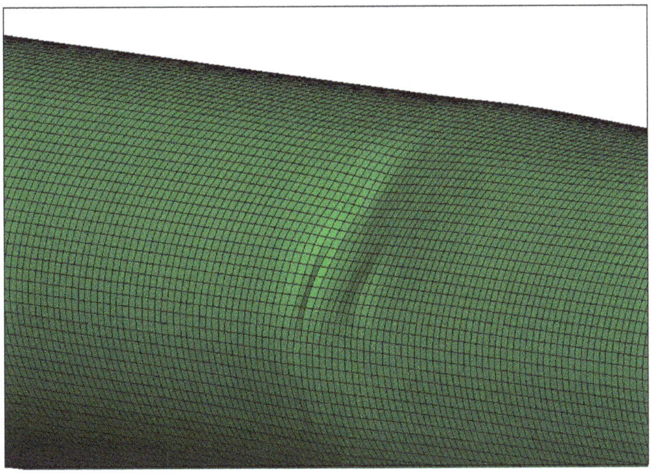

Fig.5. Close-up view of dent in finite-element model.

pressure loading. Although plastic strains are induced in any dented pipeline, experience has shown that after several pressure cycles a shakedown to elastic action occurs and the alternating stresses are typically within the elastic regime. Therefore, it is appropriate to elastically model cyclic stresses in dents. From the finite-element model, the principal stresses in the dented region of the model are calculated. From this stress state a stress concentration factor (SCF) is calculated by dividing the maximum principal stress by the nominal hoop stress. Figure 6 provides a contour plot showing the maximum principal stresses in a dent that resulted in a maximum SCF of 3.58. It is noted in this figure that the maximum stress occurred on the outside surface of the model: these results are consistent with previous findings from experimental studies where fractures in plain dents subjected to cyclic pressures initiated on the outside surface of the pipe.

Interpretation of data

Once the FEA model results are calculated and a representative SCF has been determined, the next step involves estimating remaining life. It should be noted that, for this particular discussion, the focus is on plain dents where failure due to static pressure overload is unlikely. If plain dents do fail, they are most likely to do so in the presence of cyclic pressures. Even if a large number of

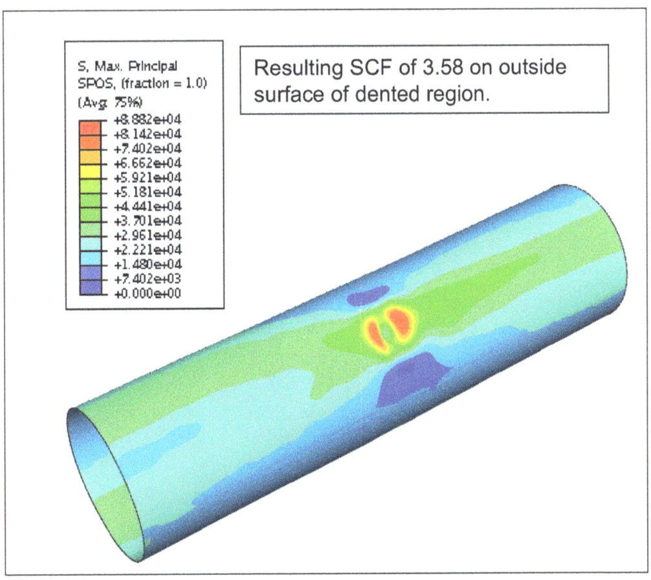

Fig.6. Maximum principal stresses on outside surface of FEA model.

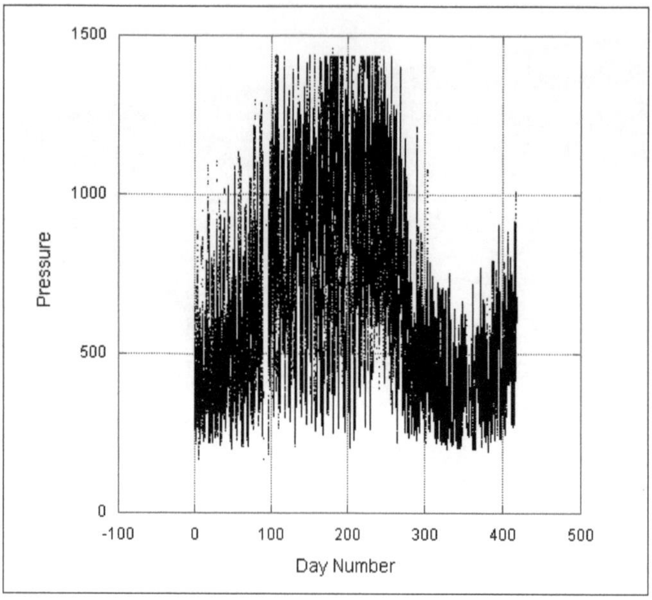

Fig.7. Historical pressure cycle data from an operating pipeline (pressure in psi).

cyclic pressures is not likely, the process of calculating SCFs provides operators with a means for evaluating the relative severity among competing dents.

From the author's experience, the API X' fatigue curve from API RP2A, *Planning, designing, and constructing fixed offshore platforms*, reasonably predicts the fatigue behaviour of plain dents subjected to cyclic pressure conditions. Provided below is the equation for the API X' curve where *Ds* represents the stress range in units of psi.

$$N = 2.978 \times 10^{21} \, Ds^{-3.74} \qquad (2)$$

As an example, consider the previously-presented dent analysis with the SCF of 3.58 (cf. Fig.6). If one assumes a cyclic pressure range of 36% SMYS for an X52 pipe, the nominal hoop stress range is 18,720psi. Including the SCF, the corresponding stress range in the dented region is 67,000psi. Using the API X' curve, the resulting fatigue life is 2,657 cycles.

While the above presentation is certainly useful, for most operators an important unanswered question remains: how many years of useful service remain? In the absence of actual historical operating data, the 2,657 cycle number is not entirely useful. Therefore, to complete the analysis one must consider actual operating history. Listed below are the steps involved in evaluating the remaining life of a dented pipeline considering the ILI-based stress concentration factor used in conjunction with actual operating pressure cycle data.

1. Obtain pressure history plot similar to one shown in Fig.7.

2. Use rainflow counting to develop a pressure cycle histogram similar to one shown in Fig.8.

3. Use histogram to determine a single equivalent cycle count such as 100 cycles at ΔP = 36% SMYS.

4. Divide the calculated fatigue life by the annual cycle count to determine the remaining life in years.

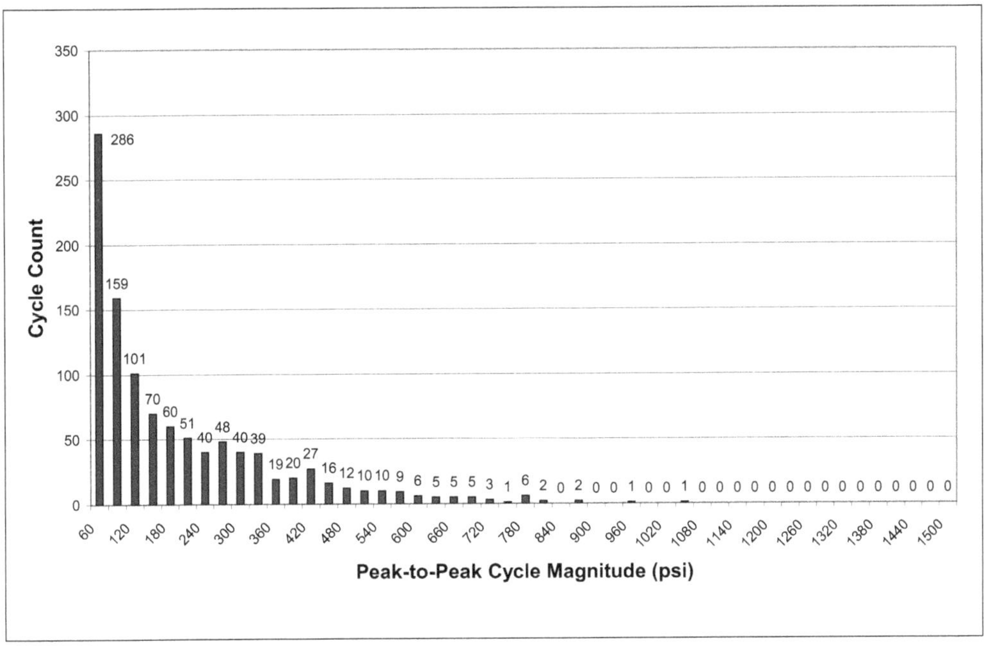

Fig.8. Pressure cycle histogram showing stress range cycle count.

Referring once again to the previous example, we determined that for a stress range of 36% SMYS the fatigue life was 2,657 cycles. If a given pipeline annually experienced 100 cycles at ΔP = 36% SMYS, the remaining life in years would be 26.5 years.

Discussion

The integrity of dents is related to not only the severity of the dent itself, but also to the possibility that the dent can interact with other features such as seam and girth welds. The author's company was the principal investigator in a study conducted for the American Petroleum Institute to evaluate the severity of plain and constrained rock dents. Included in this study were evaluating the effects of seam and girth welds that interacted with dents.

Listed below are the major dent groupings extracted from the dataset from this API study, and related data for these test samples are included in Table 5. Within these samples are groups based on a number of common characteristics. These groups are important as they serve as the basis for some of the assumptions regarding dent performance. As an example, the test results associated with girth welds in dents provides information regarding the expected performance of plain dents versus those dents containing girth welds. Unless noted, all dents are unconstrained.

plain dents - samples 1, 3, and 28
constrained dents - samples 15, 26, and 27
dents with welds - samples 16 and 20
dents with welds subjected to hydrotest - samples 30 and 31
double dents - sample 32

As noted in Equn 2 for the API X' RP2A S-N curve, there is a numerical relationship of 3.74 between design cycles and applied stress range. This exponent will be used in developing empirical stress concentration factors for specific pipeline imperfections.

Sample	Description	Initial Dent (% pipe OD)	Rebound Dent (% pipe OD)	Final Dent (% pipe OD)	N (DP=50% MAOP)
1	Plain dent, unconstrained	6	4.9	2.7	1,307,223
3	Plain dent, unconstrained	12	6.8	2.5	684,903
15	Constrained dent	12	N/A	N/A	426,585
16	ERW, Plain dent, unconstrained	12	7.7	1.4	22,375
20	GW, dent, unconstrained	12	7.6	1.4	2,020
21	GW 2" offset from dent, unconstrained	12	6.8	1.5	38,972
26	Constrained dent	24	N/A	N/A	98,483
27	Constrained dent	18	N/A	N/A	235,008
28	Plain dent, unconstrained	18	11.3	0.7	101,056
30	ERW, Plain dent, unconstrained, hydrotest	12	5.9	0.7	277,396
31	GW, dent, unconstrained, hydrotest	12	6.0	1.0	213,876
22	Double dent unconstrained (dents 3.5 inches apart)	12	5.2 5.6	0.8 1.2	217,976
69	Plain dent, unconstrained (4-inch dome indenter)	6	3.3	0.7	359,350
70	Plain dent, unconstrained (4-inch dome indenter)	12	7.1	2.3	263,910
71	Plain dent, unconstrained (4-inch dome indenter)	18	15.8	4.9	204,246
72	Plain dent, unconstrained (4-inch dome indenter)	24	15.9	5.0	234,934

Table 5. Test results for dents subjected to cyclic pressure fatigue testing.
Notes: (1) sample 1 (unconstrained 6% plain dent) and sample 15 (constrained 12% plain dent) did not fail even after extensive pressure cycling.
(2) the final dent depth was measured after all phases of testing were completed.
(3) observed failure pattern for unconstrained dents was an OD-initiated longitudinal flaw.
(4) observed failure pattern for constrained dents was an ID-initiated circumferential flaw.
(5) the tested cycles to failure, N, presented above assumed an applied pressure range of 50% MAOP (36% SMYS). For the 12.75-in x 0.188-in X52 pipe used in the testing the 50% MAOP value corresponds to 550psi.

One of the objectives of this study was to evaluate how the fatigue life of plain dents is reduced when considering features such as girth welds, seam welds, and double dents. The data presented in Table 5 are used to provide numerical correlation among these dents, as presented below.

Stress concentration factor for dents interacting with ERW seam welds

Sample 16 (unconstrained dent with ERW) – 22,375 cycles
Sample 3 (unconstrained dent) – 684,903 cycles

A stress concentration factor is calculated using the above cycles to failure using a 3.74 order relationship between stress and cycle life.

$$SCF = \left(\frac{22{,}375 \text{ cycles}}{684{,}903 \text{ cycles}}\right)^{\frac{-1}{3.74}} = 2.49 \qquad (3)$$

Stress concentration factor for dents interacting with girth welds

Sample 16 (unconstrained dent with ERW) – 20,220 cycles
Sample 3 (unconstrained dent) – 684,903 cycles

A stress concentration factor is calculated using the above cycles to failure using a 3.74 order relationship between stress and cycle life.

$$SCF = \left(\frac{20{,}220 \text{ cycles}}{684{,}903 \text{ cycles}}\right)^{\frac{-1}{3.74}} = 2.56 \qquad (4)$$

Damage type	SCF	FRF
Dent with ERW weld seam	2.49	0.033
Dent with girth weld	2.56	0.030
Double dent	1.36	0.318

Table 6. Fatigue life reduction factors.

Stress concentration factor for double dents

Sample 16 (unconstrained dent with ERW) - 217,976 cycles
Sample 3 (unconstrained dent) - 684,903 cycles

A stress concentration factor is calculated using the above cycles to failure using a 3.74 order relationship between stress and cycle life.

$$SCF = \left(\frac{217{,}976 \text{ cycles}}{684{,}903 \text{ cycles}}\right)^{\frac{-1}{3.74}} = 1.36 \tag{5}$$

Using the calculated stress concentration factors, it is possible to develop a fatigue reduction factor, FRF, for each respective imperfection type. This value can then be used to estimate the effect that a particular anomaly has on the fatigue life of a plain dent. Several example calculations are provided. The FRF is calculated using the following equation, with results for the three anomalies tabulated in Table 6.

$$FRF = (SCF)^{-3.74} \tag{6}$$

A final comment concerns two factors that were not considered in the analysis efforts discussed here. The first concerns the presence of corrosion: if corrosion is expected, one can assume that the remaining life of the dent will be reduced relative to the non-corroded case. Secondly, no consideration of tool tolerance was included in the geometry of the finite-element models. On this second issue, readers are encouraged to interface with tool vendors regarding tolerances and what, if any, effect they would have on the resulting dent geometry.

Conclusions

This paper has discussed methods for using ILI data to evaluate the severity of dents in pipeline systems. The most powerful feature of this technique is the ability for an operator to compare the relative severity of multiple dent-like defects in an effort to make decisions regarding which ones require immediate attention. In a world of unlimited resources, operators could evaluate and repair all defects; however, in the real world such options do not exist, and operators must prioritize their responses based on the best available sources of information.

From the author's perspective there is no standardized method for evaluating the severity of dents. It is hoped that the methods presented here can serve as a means for opening lines of communication between ILI companies, pipeline operators, and industry experts in formalizing a more systematic approach for evaluating dents. There is certainly ample evidence to suggest that a reasonable understanding of dent behaviour exists among subject matter experts. When this knowledge is coupled with a standardized analysis approach, the pipeline community at large will be well-served.

References and bibliography

1. W.A.Maxey, 1986. Outside force defect behaviour. NG-18 Report 162, AGA Catalog no. L51518.
2. P.Hopkins, 1991. The significance of mechanical damage in gas transmission pipelines. Paper 25, EPRG/PRC 8th Biennial Joint Technical Meeting on Line Pipe Research, Paris, May 14-17.
3. M.J.Rosenfeld, 1998. Investigations of dent rerounding behaviour. Proc. Int. Pipeline Conference, **1**, pp299-307, Calgary, Canada.
4. C.R.Alexander, J.F.Kiefner, and J. R. Fowler, 1997. Repair of dents combined with gouges considering cyclic pressure loading. 8th Annual International Energy Week Conference and Exhibition, –Houston, Texas, January.
5. P.Hopkins, D.G.Jones, and A.J.Clyne, 1989. Significance of dents and defects in transmission pipelines. Proc. Int. Conf. on Pipework Engineering and Operations, London, February 21-22.
6. J.R.Fowler, C. R.Alexander, P.J.Kovach, and L.M.Connelly, 1994. Cyclic pressure fatigue life of pipelines with plain dents, dents with gouges, and dents with welds. Prepared by Stress Engineering Services for the Offshore and Onshore Applications Supervisory Committee of the Pipeline Research Committee, PR-201-9324, June.
7. R.J.Eiber and B. N.Leis, 1995. Line pipe resistance to outside force. Paper 14, EPRG/PRC 10th Biennial Joint Technical Meeting on Line Pipe Research, Cambridge, April 18-21.
8. C.R.Alexander and J.F.Kiefner, 1997, 1999. Effects of smooth and rock dents on liquid petroleum pipelines, Phases 1 and 2. API Publication 1156, May, and October, respectively.

C.R. Alexander, 2006. Assessing the effects of external damage on subsea pipelines. Paper No. IOPF2006-014, Proceedings of the ASME International Offshore Pipeline Forum, October 24-25, 2006, Houston, Texas.

C.R.Alexander, J.R.Fowler, and K. Leewis, 1997. Analysis of composite repair methods for pipeline mechanical damage subjected to cyclic pressure loads. 8th Annual International Energy Week Conference and Exhibition, Houston, Texas, January.

C.R.Alexander and L. M.Connelly, 1998. Analytical recreation of a dent profile considering varied soil, operating and boundary conditions. Energy Sources Technology Conference & Exhibition, Sheraton Astrodome Hotel, Houston, Texas, February 2-4.

C.R.Alexander, 1999. Analysis of dented pipeline considering constrained and unconstrained dent configurations. Energy Sources Technology Conference & Exhibition, Sheraton Astrodome Hotel, Houston, Texas, February 1-3.

American Society of Mechanical Engineers, 1991. Manual for determining the remaining strength of corroded pipelines. ASME B31G-1991, New York.

American Society of Mechanical Engineers, 1992. Liquid transportation system for hydrocarbons, liquid petroleum gas, anhydrous ammonia and alcohols. ASME B31.4, New York.

American Society of Mechanical Engineers, 1995. Gas transmission and distribution piping systems. ASME B31.8, New York.

I.Corder and P. Corbin, 1991. The resistance of buried pressurised pipelines to outside force damage. Paper24, EPRG/PRC 8th Biennial Joint Technical Meeting on Line Pipe Research, Paris, France, May 14-17.

D.G.Jones and P. Hopkins, 1983. Influence of mechanical damage on transmission pipeline integrity. Proc. Int. Gas Research Conf., London, June 13-16.

P.B.Keating and R. L.Hoffman, 1997. Fatigue behavior of dented petroleum pipelines (Task 4), Office to the Office of Pipeline Safety, US Department of Transportation, Texas A&M University, May.

J.F.Kiefner, W.A.Bruce, and D.R.Stephens, 1994. Pipeline repair manual. Prepared for the Line Pipe Research Supervisory Committee of the Pipeline Research Committee.

J.F.Kiefner, C.R.Alexander, and J.R.Fowler, 1996. Repair of dents containing minor scratches. Proc. 9th Symposium on Pipeline Research, Houston, Texas, October.

Effects of inline inspection sizing uncertainties on the accuracy of the largest features and corrosion rate statistics

by Dr Luc Huyse and Albert van Roodselaar

Chevron ETC, Houston, TX, USA

WITH THE INCREASED acceptance of the use of probabilistic fitness-for-service methods, considerable effort has been dedicated to the estimation of the corrosion-rate distribution parameters. The corrosion rate is typically computed from the difference in anomaly size over a specific time interval. The anomaly sizes are measured through either in-line inspection or direct assessment. Sizing accuracies for inline inspection methods are reasonably well established and in many cases the sizing uncertainty is non-negligible.

In many approaches that are proposed in the literature the time-averaged corrosion rates are computed without explicitly considering the effect of the sizing uncertainties and, as a result, considerable interpretation and engineering judgment is required when estimating corrosion rates. This paper highlights some of the effects of the sizing uncertainties and the resulting biases that occur in the subsequent reliability calculations. These assessments are used to determine the most appropriate course of action: repair, replacement, or time of next inspection.

The cost for repair or replacement of subsea pipelines is much higher than for onshore pipelines. For subsea applications, it is therefore paramount that the risk calculations, and therefore the corrosion-rate estimates, be as accurate as possible. In subsea applications, the opportunity to repair individual defects is often limited due to practical constraints, and there is merit in an approach that focuses on entire spools or pipeline segments. The proposed statistical analysis method is ideally suited to this application although the principles behind the analysis apply equally well to onshore lines subject to either internal or external corrosion threats.

IN ORDER TO ASSESS the risk of pipeline failure due to a leak or burst, information about the current state of the pipeline must be combined with a corrosion rate that models how quickly the anomalies grow. Information about the current state of the pipeline can be inferred from inspections and is a critical ingredient in the integrity-management decision-making process. In-line inspection (ILI) results are subject to various sources of uncertainty. This paper specifically addresses the effects of sizing uncertainties on integrity decisions. The analysis in this paper is based on rigorous application of the principles behind mathematical statistics. Traditionally, each feature reported by ILI is treated as a stand-alone measurement and is subject to uncertainty. The uncertainty distribution is often identical for all features. This paper advocates looking at the ensemble of all data points and making maximum use of the additional information this brings about.

Aside from the current state of the pipeline, the corrosion rate is another critical component for integrity management. Corrosion rates can be estimated from standards and industry guidelines, correlation and regression models applied to similar service conditions, coupon losses, indirect measurements, or a comparison of the results of multiple ILIs; this paper discusses accurate estimation of corrosion rates from the results of the latter of these options.

The discussion in this paper is limited to the effects of the sizing uncertainty only, although in addition to sizing uncertainty, several other sources of uncertainty exist. Defects may go undetected (probability of detection, or PoD), be misidentified (probability of identification, or PoI) or phantom defects may be called (probability of false calls, or PoFC). It is reasonable to assume that PoD effects are small for significant corrosion features. False calls represent an inherent conservatism and are therefore sometimes overlooked; however this practice is not without consequence because it may trigger a considerable amount of unnecessary repairs. Although this false call practice may be sensible for onshore lines where excavation costs are reasonable, these costs rapidly increase for subsea pipelines. However, to keep the discussion contained the PoD, PoI, and PoFC effects are not included in the analysis. The paper focuses on the following topics: effects of sizing uncertainties on the measured values – and more specifically – on the largest features and the effects of sizing uncertainties on the corrosion rate estimates.

Nomenclature

α	= relative increase of average feature size between two inspections
ρ	= correlation coefficient
d	= true feature size (depth, length or width)
e	= sizing uncertainty (error)
i.i.d.	= independent and identically distributed
m	= measured feature size (reported by ILI tool)
pdf	= probability density function
Covar(...)	= covariance of two variables
E(...)	= expected value of a random variable
ILI	= inline inspection
Var(...)	= variance of a random variable

Sizing-uncertainty models

Sizing-accuracy data are typically obtained from inspection runs in test loops with machined defects. In this case the true size is known and the sizing error is computed as the difference between the measured and true size: $m = d + e$, where m is the measured size, d is the true size, and e is the sizing error. If the error distribution e has a zero mean, the mean value of the distribution of measured values m for a specific feature of size d will be equal to d, i.e. $E(m)$ is an unbiased estimator for the exact feature size d.

If the sizing error e is assumed to be independent of d, a single random variable can be used to describe the sizing error over the entire sizing range. It is important to recognize that, when the sizing error e is independent of d, the measured value m and the sizing error e are not statistically independent of each other [1]. This well-known statistical result is illustrated in Fig.1 but seems to be often overlooked in practical applications where m and e are treated as independent random variables. Figure 1 shows that although the sizing error is independent of the true or actual feature size, there is a clear bias in the measurement error as function of the reported feature size.

The spread in the measured values is larger than the spread in the actual true feature size distribution. If d and e are assumed independent, then $Var(m) = Var(d) + Var(e)$. This equation is

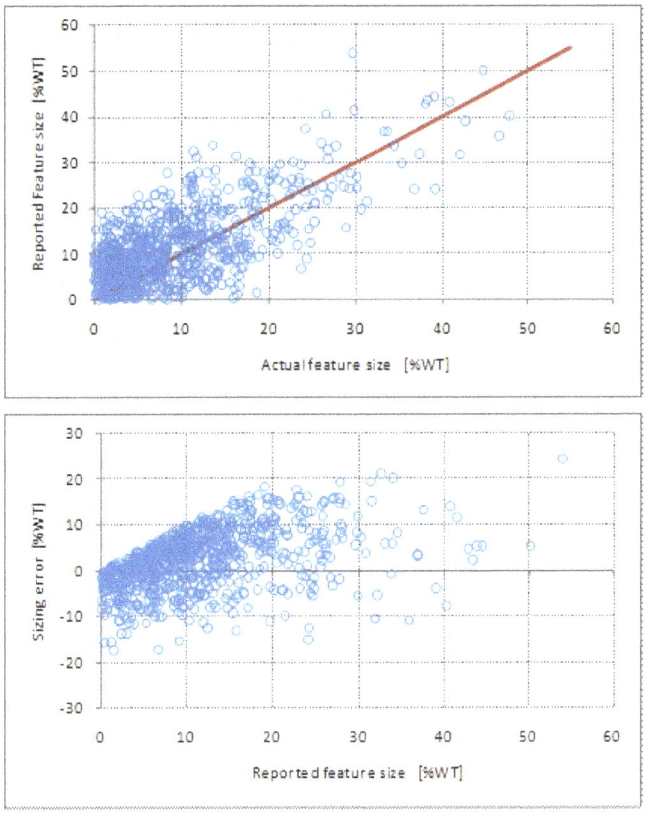

Fig. 1. Illustration of the dependence of the sizing error on reported feature size; even in cases where sizing error is independent of actual feature size.

distribution independent and reflects the additional uncertainty that is introduced due to sizing inaccuracies.

Sizing uncertainties are quantified in statistical terms. The document *Specifications and requirements for intelligent pig inspection of pipelines* [2] requires the specification of the depth at PoD = 90% as well as the sizing accuracy at both 80 and 90% confidence for depth, width, and length for general metal loss, and pitting, axial, and circumferential grooving. Separate specifications apply to longitudinally welded or seamless pipe and near the girth weld or in the heat-affected zone.

Inspection service vendors are obviously free to report additional information about the sizing accuracies. However, it is important to recognize that the document does not require specification of the entire sizing-uncertainty distribution. Such data are typically obtained from inspection runs in test loops with machined defects and are proprietary.

The *ith* order statistic of a sample is defined as the *ith*-smallest value. For a data set of size *n*, the nth order statistic is equal to the maximum value and the *n-1th* order statistic is equal to the second largest value, and so on. Consequently, the highest-order statistics are of primary interest in pipeline integrity. To investigate the effect of the sizing inaccuracy on the bias and distribution of order statistics, several candidate depth accuracy distributions – which all meet the ± 10% WT with 80% confidence specification – are considered:

- normal distribution with a zero mean and a standard deviation equal to 7.8% WT independent of the feature size (red bounds in Fig.2);

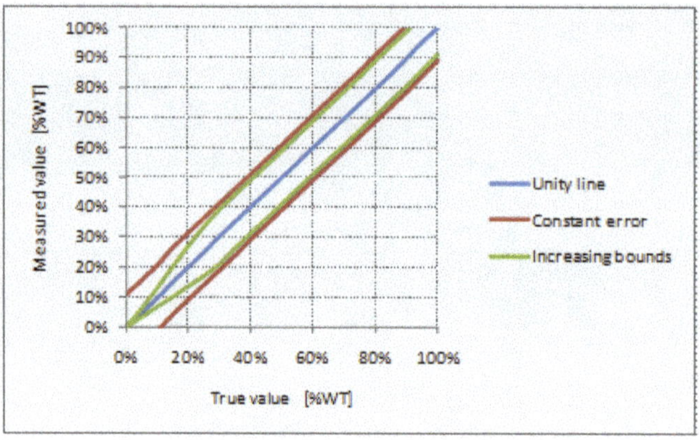

Fig.2. 80% confidence bounds for a normally distributed sizing uncertainty with constant or gradually increasing standard deviation.

- normal distribution with a zero mean and a standard deviation gradually increasing from zero to 7.8% WT for a 30% WT feature (green bounds in Fig.2);
- Beta distribution, which mimics the normal distribution for sizes near 50% WT but becomes increasingly skewed for true values near 0 and 100% (see Fig.3).

The effect of the sizing-uncertainty distribution assumptions on simulated ILI results is shown in Fig.4. In this figure the dots represent the true feature sizes (data set simulated from a Weibull distribution) and the measured values that could be reported by an ILI inspection with a normally distributed sizing error within ± 10%WT with 80% confidence. The green dots in each figure indicate the top 25 reported feature sizes. The effect of using a constant or gradually increasing sizing error is clearly visible: the smaller features tend to be much closer to the unity line for the gradually increasing sizing uncertainty model (Fig.4b). The most appropriate sizing uncertainty model for a particular inspection is tool-dependent, and should be determined in collaboration with the ILI vendor. The cumulative distribution function of the exact and measured size as well as the sizing error is shown on a normal probability scale in Fig.5.

Effect on ILI reported sizes

Figure 4 shows the measured defect size as function of the true feature size for a particular but randomly simulated set of features and assumed sizing error model. Such a plot can only be determined when the true feature size is known. In practice, it is the inverse problem of inferring

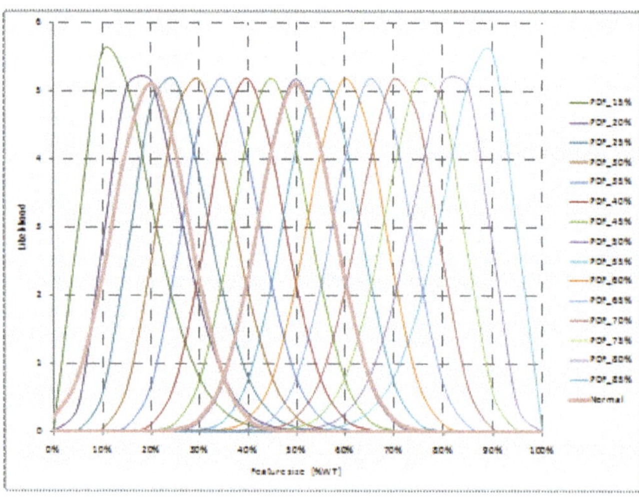

Fig.3. Beta-distribution sizing uncertainty model as function of true feature size. For feature sizes around 50%WT the beta distribution is virtually indistinguishable from the normal distribution, but considerable differences exist for small and large features. The figure shows the difference between the normal and Beta distribution model for a 20%WT and 50%WT feature.

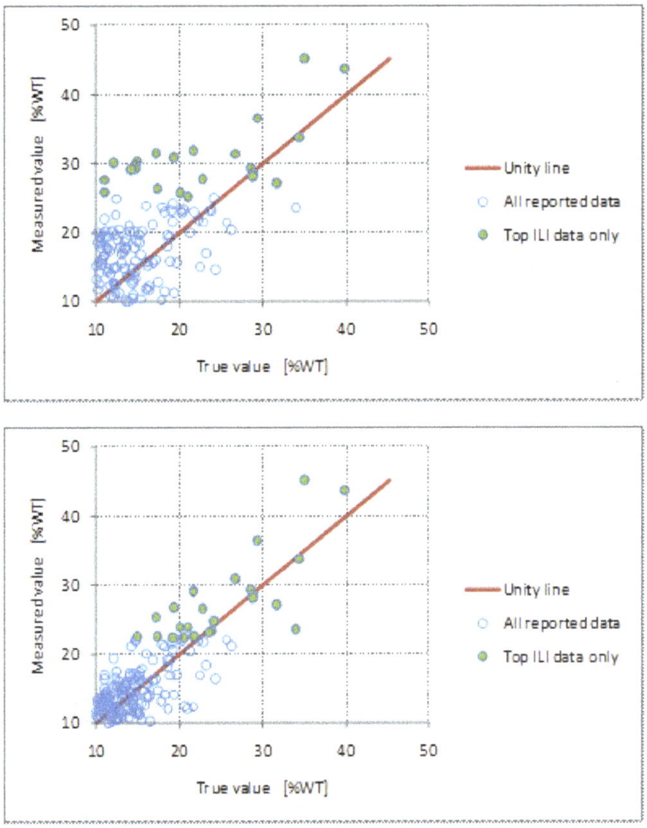

Fig.4. Illustration of positive bias in the largest ILI measurements. A normally distributed sizing error within ± 10%WT with 80% confidence is applied: results are shown for (a - top) constant standard deviation, and (b - bottom) gradually increasing standard deviation.

the true feature size '*d*' from a reported ILI size '*m*' that is most interest. Figure 4 shows a simulation result of the measured and true feature sizes, assuming a normally distributed random error; the figure suggests that overall the measurement errors for the most severe measurements are positively biased, irrespective of the sizing-uncertainty model assumed. A large measured value can be the result of (1) an accurately sized deep defect with minimal to moderate statistical bias (i.e. data evenly scattered above and below the red unity line in Fig.4); or (2) a moderate to shallow defect with significant sizing error (for example, the green dots toward the left edge of Fig.4 show significant overestimations).

Which scenario is most likely depends on the magnitude of the sizing uncertainty and the shape of the (unknown) exact feature-size distribution.

It can easily be shown (see Fig.6) that the positive bias that appears in Fig.4 is independent of the error-distribution type, and that for any zero mean error distribution, the mean value of the maximum measurement is not an unbiased estimator of the true maximum feature size: $E(m_{max})$ 'd $E(d_{max})$.

Consider a data set of *n* measurements and the features are sorted in decreasing order d_{max} ed d_{max-1} ed ...ed d_1 (Fig.6). If the sizing errors e_i are given by zero mean distributions, then the distribution of the measured value m_1 of the defect is centred on the true value d_{max} and is an unbiased estimator for d_{max}. Likewise, the distribution for m_{i+1} is centred at the true value d_{max-i}. However, because it is possible that either m_2, m_3, or any measured value m_{i+1} exceeds m_1, the distribution of the maximum measured value $m_{max} = max(m_1, m_2, ..., m_n)$ is no longer centred around d_{max}. The extent to which this happens obviously depends on the relative magnitude of the sizing uncertainty and the difference

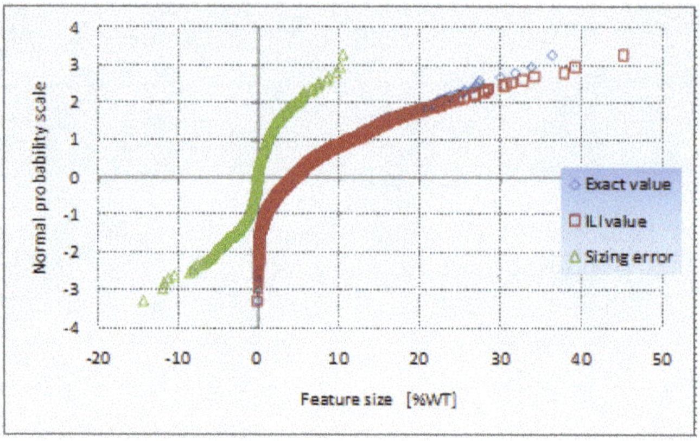

Fig.5. Distribution function of exact and ILI reported value as well as the sizing error for the data in Fig.4b.

between the true feature sizes d_{max} and $d_{max\text{-}i}$. Therefore m_{max} is a positively biased estimate for d_{max}. Mathematically speaking, this inequality between the expected maximum measured and exact size immediately follows from the non-linear nature of the maximization operator. A similar, yet opposite, argument can be made for the minimum reported values. Consequently, the highest-order statistics of the measured values tend to be overestimates, whereas the lower-order statistics tend to be underestimates. In practice, only the highest-order statistics are of interest to integrity management.

Effect on maximum feature size

For a leak-controlled pipeline (such as an oil line or a low-pressure gas line) the difference between the maximum reported feature depths and true feature depths is of practical concern. It should be noted that the largest measured value *mmax* may not occur at the largest feature d_{max}. An example can be found in Fig.4 where the maximum true depth is 40% (but reported as 43%) and the maximum reported feature size is 45% (with 35% true depth).

This effect has ramifications for pipeline repair: subsea pipelines are often repaired with clamps which are only a few feet long. For onshore pipelines a much longer stretch of pipeline is exposed and all defects within this section are repaired. In this regard, the difference between the deepest-reported and true feature size within the exposed segment, i.e. the distribution of $m_{max} - d_{max}$ is of interest. Throughout this paper, this difference will be referred to as 'segment accuracy'.

However, when assessing the performance of the ILI tool, each feature reported by the ILI is compared with the 'true' size of the feature[1]. The difference between the reported and the true size of a particular feature is of interest when assessing tool performance, and this distribution is shown by the green dots in Fig.5. This will be referred to as 'feature accuracy'.

The previous section presented a proof that the maximum ILI-reported value represents a positively biased estimate of the true maximum, whereas the converse is true for the minimum reported value. Obviously, the magnitude of the bias and the spread in the statistics' distribution is of particular relevance for integrity management.

---

[1] Note that 'true' feature sizes cannot readily be obtained from excavation since 'in-the-ditch' or 'AUT' or any other type of measurement also has uncertainties associated with it. When assessing ILI performance using 'in-the-ditch' measurements, the effects of in the ditch errors must be incorporated. Although that assessment is conceptually similar to the one presented here, this is outside the scope of the paper and no results are given in this paper.

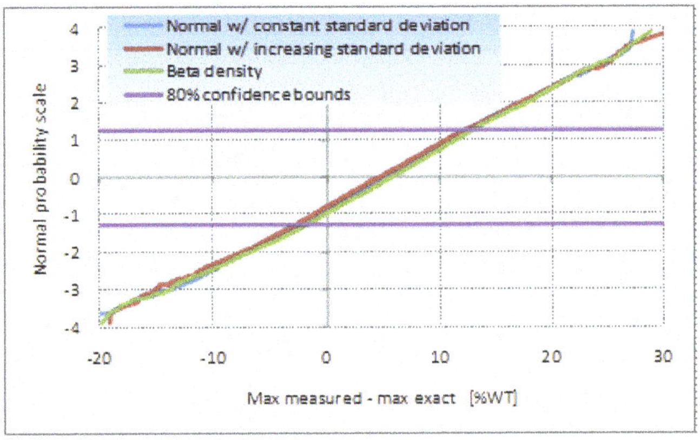

Fig.6. Illustration of positive bias in $m_{max} = max(m_1, m_2, \ldots, m_n)$.

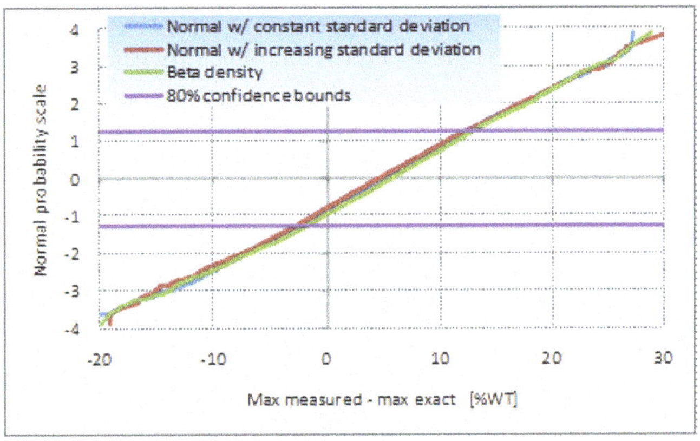

Fig.7. Effect of sizing uncertainty distribution on distribution of bias in largest measurement. All sizing error distributions fall within ± 10 WT with 80% confidence bounds for an individual defect. The figure shows the distribution of the 'segment accuracy'.

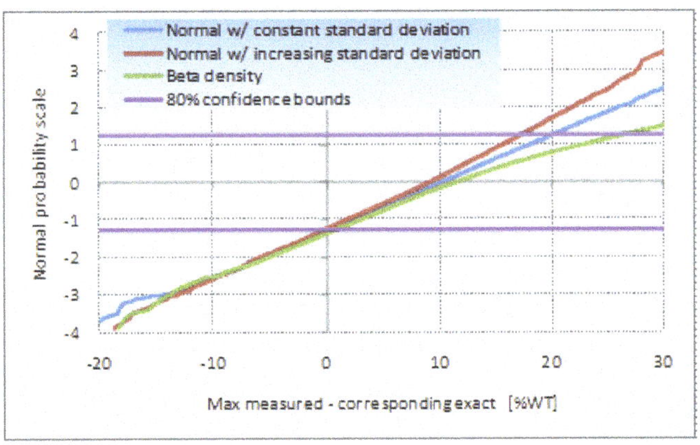

Fig.8. Effect of sizing uncertainty distribution on distribution of bias in largest measurement. All sizing error distributions fall within ± 10 WT with 80% confidence bounds for an individual defect. The figure shows the distribution of the 'feature accuracy'.

Reference 2 does not explicitly specify the distribution of the sizing errors. Sometimes, a zero-mean normal distribution is used to describe the sizing uncertainty. Although a normal distribution may seem sensible for many features, it becomes a bit more problematic for the really deep features which happen to pose the greatest integrity threat. For this reason it may be wiser to at least consider the possibility of using a bounded distribution (such as the beta distribution in Fig.3).

Figure 7 shows the effect of the sizing uncertainty distribution type on the distribution of the bias between the maximum measured and maximum true feature size. It can be concluded that for the feature distribution used in this analysis there is no sensitivity of the bias in the maximum reported feature size to the assumed uncertainty distribution shape. Figure 8 shows the effect of the sizing uncertainty distribution shape on the bias between the maximum reported feature size and the

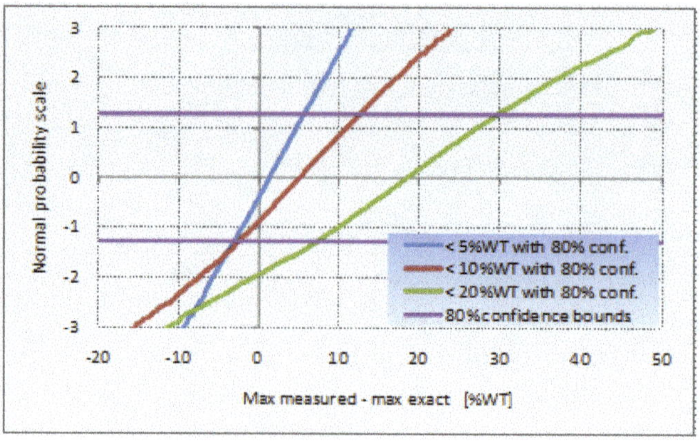

Fig.9. Effect of ILI tool accuracy on distribution of bias in largest measurement. The figure shows the distribution of the 'segment accuracy'. The sizing uncertainty is assumed to be constant and independent of actual feature size (see Fig.2).

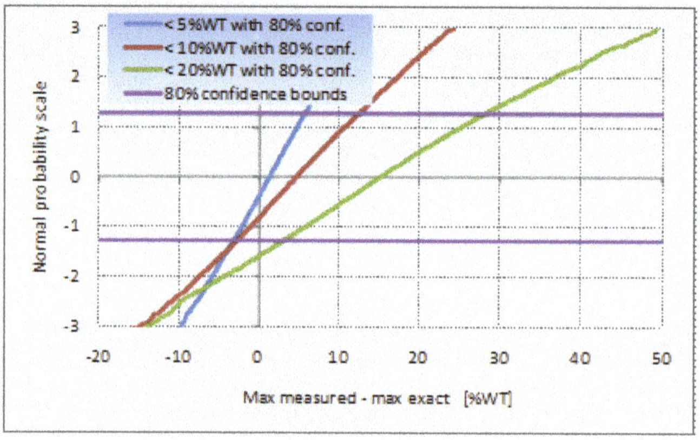

Fig.10. Effect of ILI tool accuracy on distribution of bias in largest measurement. The figure shows the distribution of the 'segment accuracy'. The sizing uncertainty is assumed to gradually increase (see Fig.2).

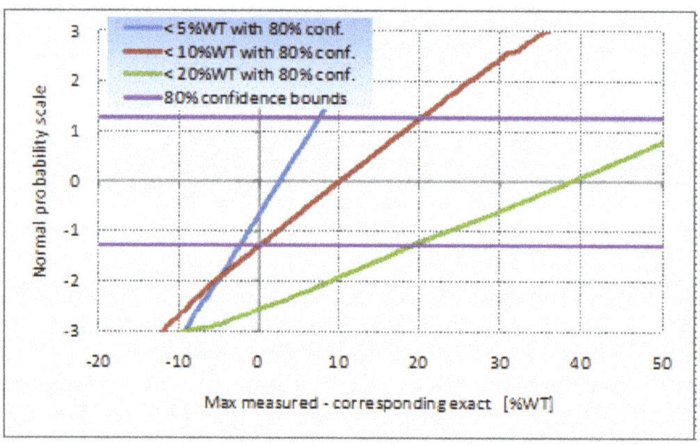

Fig.11. Effect of ILI tool accuracy on distribution of bias in largest measurement. The figure shows the distribution of the difference of the 'feature accuracy'. The sizing uncertainty is assumed to be constant and independent of actual feature size (see Fig.2).

true size of that specific feature for an inspection tool with 10% WT tolerance with 80% confidence. Although the upper limit of the 80% confidence bound is sensitive to the sizing-uncertainty distribution assumption, there is about 90% probability that the maximum reported feature will be oversized, independent of the assumed sizing-uncertainty distribution. This implies that the reported feature size actually represents the upper limit of the 80% confidence bounds of the largest feature: the 80% confidence interval for d_{max} is $[m_{max} - 18\%m_{max}]$

The effect of the amount of sizing uncertainty on the bias and spread of the maximum reported feature size is shown in Figs 9 through 12 for a sizing uncertainty with a normal distribution with various level of scatter. As expected, the bias of population-type comparisons of an entire segment (Figs 9 and 10) is consistently smaller than for defect-size comparisons (Figs 11 and 12). It can also

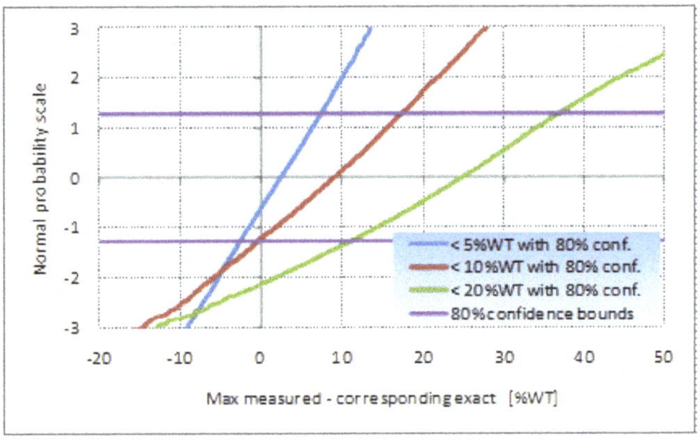

Fig.12. Effect of ILI tool accuracy on distribution of bias in largest measurement. The figure shows the distribution of the 'feature accuracy'. The sizing uncertainty is assumed to gradually increase (see Fig.2).

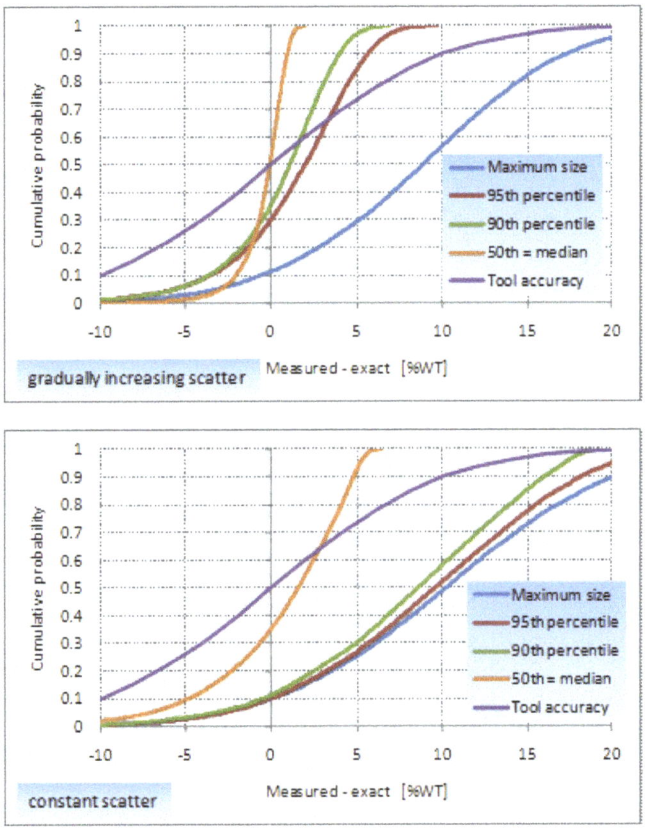

Fig.13. Effect of ILI tool accuracy (± 10%WT with 80% confidence) on order statistics percentiles of interest. The figure shows the distribution and 80% confidence bounds of the bias between measured (a) and exact (b) percentiles of the 'feature accuracy'.

be seen that the maximum measured value is typically an overestimate and that both the likelihood and average magnitude of the overestimation increase with increasing sizing uncertainty.

In conclusion, it can be stated that for the assumed sizing uncertainty models, the maximum reported feature size represents a positively biased estimate of the true maximum feature size. This bias does not result from a conservative bias (human factors) associated with a manual review of the deepest features, but follows from the mathematics of looking at all reported ILI features as a group rather than as individual measurements. The human factors are entirely separate from this issue. It is our belief that the mathematical and statistical effects that cause a positive bias in the estimates for the maximum feature size should be explicitly accounted for when performing either a deterministic or a probabilistic fitness-for-service assessment. In this regard, it is important to recognize that a different bias distribution applies to segment reliability, where the difference between two feature distributions is of interest (red and blue curves in Fig.5) than to 'in-the-ditch' verification of a specific feature (green curve in Fig.5).

Effect of sizing error on order statistics

The previous section indicated that the largest reported feature is likely oversized. Integrity-management decisions depend on more than just the depth of the largest feature, and it is therefore of interest to determine to what extent other large features are affected by bias and what their sizing spread is.

The effect of a zero-mean normally distributed sizing uncertainty with standard deviation of 7.8% WT (± 10% WT with 80% confidence) on different order statistics is shown in Fig.13 (compare with the red line in Fig.12 for reference which shows the effect on the maximum reported feature on a normal probability scale). It can be seen that the maximum exhibits the greatest bias. The amount of bias in other order statistics depends on the uncertainty model that was chosen: the model with gradually increasing sizing uncertainty (see Fig.2 for a definition) exhibits much smaller bias values (Fig.13a) than the model with constant sizing uncertainty throughout the entire defect range (Fig.13b). This is readily understood when one considers that – say the 90th percentile values – generally fall below 30%WT in the feature distribution (Fig.4). The median values are almost unbiased and any order statistic below the 50th percentile exhibits negative bias on average.

In addition to the bias, it is also important to consider the amount of scatter in the order statistics. The assumed tool accuracy of an individual feature is shown by the purple line in Fig.13. Broadly speaking, the distribution of the largest feature represents a shift of the entire distribution function (i.e. bias) relative to the individual tool accuracy. For lower-order statistics there is a significant compression of the distribution curve, i.e. reduction in the spread. For the model with gradually increasing sizing uncertainty, the median value is almost deterministic (Fig.13a); even for the model with constant sizing uncertainty the 80% confidence bounds for the median are only half as wide as for the tool accuracy itself (Fig.13b). In short, order statistics are often much less uncertain than the individual measurements themselves.

API 1163 Appendix E outlines a procedure to compare the individual verification measurements using the ILI tool performance characteristics. The approach outlined in this reference (provided the effects of a reporting threshold are ignored) is correct and applicable to 'a single, randomly selected' defect.

However, excavations and verification measurements are often undertaken for the most severe defects. Although it represents only a single simulation run, Fig.4 suggests that the sizing errors for the most severe measurements are positively biased. Figures 11 and 12 confirm that this trend is observed during repeated simulation, and these figures can be used to compute the probability that the maximum reported feature will fall within the tool confidence bounds. For instance for a tool with ± 10%WT at 80% confidence (red line), there really is only about 50% probability that the largest reported feature will fall within the ± 10%WT limits. For a tool with ± 20%WT at 80% confidence (green line), the probability that the largest reported feature will fall within the ± 20%WT limits is even less (as low as 10% it the sizing uncertainty model has gradually increasing confidence bounds, see Fig.2). In practice, not just the deepest feature is excavated and the actual likelihoods that other features will fall within the tool's stated 80% confidence bounds can be inferred from charts similar to Fig.13. The likelihood that a feature will fall within the tool's stated confidence bounds rapidly increases with the order statistic. Figure 13a indicates that for a tool with ± 10%WT limits at 80% confidence and gradually increasing sizing uncertainty there is 60% probability that the largest feature size will fall inside the ± 10%WT limits (as opposed to the 80% confidence for a generic feature), but there is 99% probability that the 95th percentile feature will fall within the ± 10%WT tool-accuracy limits.

In general, there is a different degree of likelihood that a specific feature will fall within the tool-accuracy limits due to the bias and spread associated with each order statistic. An accurate and appropriate verification criterion needs to take this information into consideration when judging whether the ILI results fall within the tool specifications. A more complete verification criterion would depend on the statistics of the sizing uncertainty model, the number of features identified in ILI, the number of features excavated, the shape of the distribution of the ILI reported features, and the order statistic of the excavated features (i.e. what percentile in the distribution the excavated feature corresponds to).

In this regard, the use of actual or 'run-specific' error distributions is preferred over the use of stated accuracy limits that are determined on the basis of machined defects in test loops. These 'in-the-field' distributions can either be derived from direct excavations of the features or from the distribution of the sizing differences for defects that are unlikely to have grown. Accurate classification of features as either 'mill flaw' or 'corrosion' is important in this context.

Impact of sizing error on corrosion-rate statistics

Accurate estimation of the corrosion rate is of primary importance to the integrity-management planning of a pipeline. When estimating corrosion rates from ILI data collected during successive ILI runs, two sources of error appear. A first source of error is attributed to an incorrect matching of feature pairs: this is mitigated by using only the paired features which are matched with a high degree of confidence. In practice this often requires relatively isolated features; it also requires consistent identification of features to the same class (for example, feature may be called 'corrosion' in one inspection and 'mill fault' in another). The problems associated with the lack of consistency have been reported by others [3].

A second source of error is due to sizing inaccuracies which increase the variance of the corrosion rate. Several factors contribute to sizing uncertainty and a good sizing-uncertainty model should incorporate the contribution of each of these constituent parts rather than model all sizing uncertainty as a single random variable. For this discussion it is assumed that the inspection is performed properly (appropriate magnetization and tool speeds are achieved during MFL run), and that the overall population bias is zero. Feature sizing is inherently an inverse problem that relies on several assumptions regarding the type of corrosion, and feature shape and aspect ratio. Therefore, for a given sizing algorithm, some feature configurations will tend to be overestimated whereas others will tend to be underestimated. Although some of these biases can be removed or minimized by a skilled and well-informed inspector and/or analyst, the total random scatter can be thought of as a sum between a feature-specific bias and a random sizing error: $e_{total} = e_{bias} + e_{random}$. If the bias and random contributions are assumed to be independent, then the total tool variance is equal to the sum of the variances of the bias and random components. In this paper, it is assumed that the bias and random components of the sizing error are equally important and are independent; they are independent and identically distributed (i.i.d.).

A time-averaged corrosion rate is given by the equation:

$$CR = \frac{d(t_2) - d(t_1)}{t_2 - t_1} \tag{1}$$

where CR stands for corrosion rate, d is the feature 'depth' or other dimension size, and t_1 and t_2 are the times of the first and second ILI, respectively. Because the computed corrosion rate really is a time-averaged value, its variance decreases with increasing length of time between the two inspections. The exact expression of the variance reduction function depends on the auto-correlation of the random process that describes the instantaneous corrosion rate [4].

An ILI inspection does not result in the true feature size but in a measured value which is an approximate indication thereof: $m = d + e = d + e_{bias} + e_{random}$. In this analysis, it will be assumed that the bias is identical during both ILI runs. Because feature-sizing models may have been updated since the first ILI, it may be necessary to resize the features of the first run using the most recent sizing models to achieve a consistent feature-specific bias. Under these conditions, the time-averaged corrosion rate, computed from the raw ILI data is (the 'random' subscript is dropped from the e-notation):

$$\begin{aligned} CR_{raw} &= \frac{m(t_2) - m(t_1)}{t_2 - t_1} = \frac{d(t_2) + e(t_2) - d(t_1) - e(t_1)}{t_2 - t_1} \\ &= CR_{true} + \frac{e(t_2) - e(t_1)}{t_2 - t_1} \end{aligned} \tag{2}$$

Not all features grow at the same rate and it therefore makes sense to compute the statistics of the observed corrosion rates in the matched feature pairs. The expected (or average) value of the raw ILI values is:

$$\begin{aligned} E[CR_{raw}] &= E\left[\frac{m(t_2) - m(t_1)}{t_2 - t_1}\right] \\ &= E[CR_{true}] + \frac{E[e(t_2)] - E[e(t_1)]}{t_2 - t_1} \end{aligned} \tag{3}$$

which indicates that the average corrosion rate obtained by the ILI measurements is unbiased (i.e. equal to the true average corrosion rate) as long as the sizing errors have the same average value during both inspections. Note that this expression applies to the complete feature distribution; in many cases only features that exceed a specified threshold are reported and this reporting threshold will introduce some bias in the average raw corrosion rate which must be corrected for.

The variance of the corrosion-rate distribution (variance is equal to the square of the standard deviation) is obtained from the following equation:

$$\begin{aligned} Var[CR_{raw}] &= Var\left[\frac{m(t_2) - m(t_1)}{t_2 - t_1}\right] \\ &= Var[CR_{true}] + Var\left[\frac{e(t_1)}{t_2 - t_1}\right] + Var\left[\frac{e(t_2)}{t_2 - t_1}\right] + 2Covar\left[CR_{true}, \frac{e(t_2)}{t_2 - t_1}\right] \\ &\quad - 2Covar\left[CR_{true}, \frac{e(t_1)}{t_2 - t_1}\right] - 2Covar\left[\frac{e(t_2)}{t_2 - t_1}, \frac{e(t_1)}{t_2 - t_1}\right] \end{aligned} \tag{4}$$

Since the covariance of the true corrosion rate and the random component of the measurement error is zero and – if the same tool is used – the variance of the first and second inspections are identical with independent random error components, this expression can in many practical cases be simplified to (again, the equations are only given for the case where the tool variance is independent of the actual feature size):

$$\begin{aligned} &Var\left[CR_{raw}\right] \approx Var\left[CR_{true}\right] + 2Var\left[\frac{e(t_1)}{t_2 - t_1}\right] \\ &or\, Var\left[CR_{true}\right] = Var\left[CR_{raw}\right] - 2Var\left[\frac{e(t)}{t_2 - t_1}\right] \end{aligned} \tag{5}$$

where the covariance between the first and second ILI error depends on the amount of feature-specific bias (which is consistent between the first and second inspection) relative to the amount of random scatter during either inspection (which are independent of each other). Note that this expression does not apply to sizing models with feature-size dependent uncertainties (such as the green curve in Fig.2). Appropriate correction terms can be derived for that case.

The variance equation indicates that the sizing uncertainty inflates the variability of the true corrosion rate: $Var[CR_{raw}]$ is greater than orequal to $Var[CR_{true}]$. This is readily understood: the measurement uncertainty adds noise to the actual corrosion growth which gets translated as additional scatter into the corrosion-rate statistics. Unless there is considerable feature growth between subsequent inspections, the noise terms in $Var[CR_{raw}]$ will often exceed the true variance.

The equations above allow computing accurate estimates for the mean and variance of the true corrosion rate from the raw ILI data and the ILI-performance specifications for tools where the sizing accuracy is independent of the actual feature size. Since the performance specifications have such a profound influence on the calculation of sizing-uncertainty-corrected corrosion-rate statistics, it is preferable to use the ILI-performance statistics 'as-run' and not 'as-specified'.

Mean value and variance are the first two moments of the growth-rate distribution. In addition, the statistical model needs to consider whether growth rates are dependent on feature size: are large features more or less likely to grow at larger than average rates than small features? There is no generally agreed upon consensus for an answer to this question because corrosion growth is intrinsically a time-dependent phenomenon that very much depends on the local micro-environment [5]. The covariance between the growth rate and the current feature size gives a first indication about statistical dependency between these two properties.

Previous studies have reported the lack of a significant correlation between the growth rate and feature depth [6, 7]. However, such studies calculated the correlation based on the reported ILI sizes. To this extent, it is instructive to determine the effect of sizing uncertainties on the correlation of ILI-reported growth rates and feature sizes.

If the total sizing uncertainty can be split into statistically equal contributions of feature-specific bias and random error, and if the bias is identical during both inspections, it can be shown that:

$$Covar\left[m_1, m_2 - m_1\right] = Covar\left[d_1, d_2 - d_1\right] - Var\left[e(t_1)\right] \tag{6}$$

This equation indicates that the covariance of the ILI-reported values is less than the original covariance. If the ILI-reported growth rates do not exhibit correlation, there likely was a correlation between the true feature size and true growth. Conversely, if the original covariance is very small, the random sizing error introduces a negative correlation in the ILI results! Let *á* denote the ratio between average feature growth $d(t_2) - d(t_1)$ and average feature size $d(t_1)$, and then the correlation coefficient ñ becomes:

$$\rho_{raw} = \frac{\rho_{exact}\alpha Var\left[d\right] - Var[e]}{\sqrt{\left(Var\left[d\right] + 2Var[e]\right)\left(Var\left[\alpha d\right] + 2Var[e]\right)}} \quad (7)$$

This expression indicates that the possible range of the correlation coefficient ñ$_{raw}$ (computed from ILI results) is no longer [-1, +1] but is in many cases restricted to a much-smaller interval due to the effect of sizing uncertainties. This is readily understood by considering that in many cases the random component to the sizing error will exceed the actual growth. An example is given in Fig.14 where strong correlation between actual growth and exact size is assumed (Fig.14a). Because the actual growth is less than the tool tolerance, there is almost complete lack of correlation in Fig.14b between observed growth and measured feature size.

Feature sizes typically do not follow a normal distribution. Although the covariance and correlation expressions are in principle distribution-free, statistical dependencies among non-normal variables are less intuitive. Consider the feature distributions used in Fig.4 and the uncertainty model shown by the green line in Fig.2. Correlation coefficients were computed on the ˜:marginally transformed equivalent normal distributions of the exact and ILI-reported feature size (simulation results). In that case, the correlation coefficients between the raw ILI size and growth scale varies over the reduced range [-ñ$_{max}$, ñ$_{max}$] instead of the range [-1, +1]: the correlation coefficient of the marginally transformed ILI data is equal to the product of the true correlation coefficient and a multiplier 'c' such that ñ$_{ILI}$ = cñ$_{exact}$. Figure 15 shows this multiplier on the raw

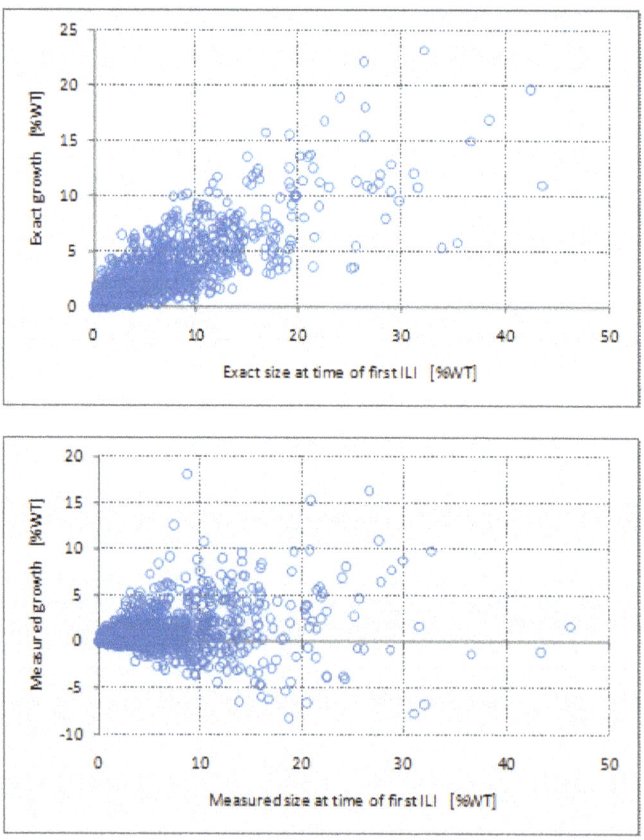

Fig.14. Effect of sizing uncertainty on correlation between growth and feature size at time of first inspection (ñ$_{exact}$ = 0.8. a = 0.2, tool accuracy ± 10%WT with 80% confidence).

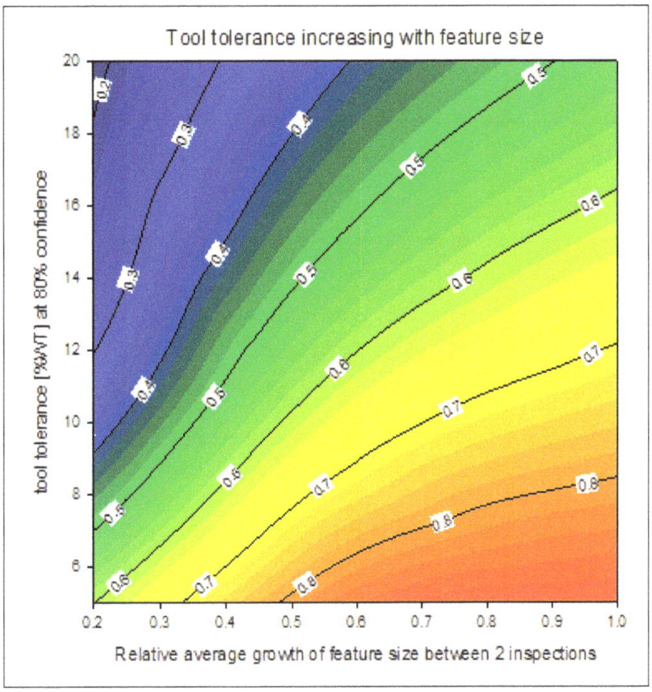

Fig.15. Contour plot of the correlation multiplier c as function of the relative average feature growth and tool tolerance.

correlation coefficients c as function of the relative average feature growth between ILI runs and tool tolerance. For standard accuracies (± 10%WT at 80% confidence), correlations are dramatically reduced even if the average feature size increases by a factor 1.4 between the successive ILI runs. This means that if a strong dependence between the actual growth and the exact size existed, it will often show up as a statistically insignificant dependency in the ILI results due to the sizing uncertainties. It must therefore be concluded that ILI tools currently do not have sufficient accuracy to directly estimate the extent of the dependence of future growth on the current feature size. If a sizing-uncertainty model with constant variance independent of the feature size is assumed, the correlations in the ILI results are even closer to zero.

Impact of sizing error on marginal corrosion-rate distributions

The effect of sizing uncertainties on first- and second-moment statistics has been determined. A complete reliability analysis also requires the derivation of the marginal probability density function of the corrosion growth rate for each feature dimension (depth, length, and width) as well as the statistical dependencies among these properties. The selection of the appropriate distribution is of great importance to probabilistic fitness-for-service calculations. It has been observed, that the empirical distributions of the raw ILI growth increments $m(t_2) - m(t_1)$ often closely resemble the tool accuracy distribution shapes (compare shape of Fig.17 to Fig.5). This is yet another indication that the measurement noise is often larger than the actual growth $d(t_2) - d(t_1)$.

The noise causes many differences $m(t_2) - m(t_1)$ to be negative. Some authors have proposed to account for these measurement uncertainties by adding more conservatism to the growth-rate distribution computed on the basis of the differences between the raw ILI data [8]. It is our belief that these negative growth rates are caused by measurement uncertainty and therefore not real. Based on the theoretical arguments explained above (see also Fig.16) as well as field observations,

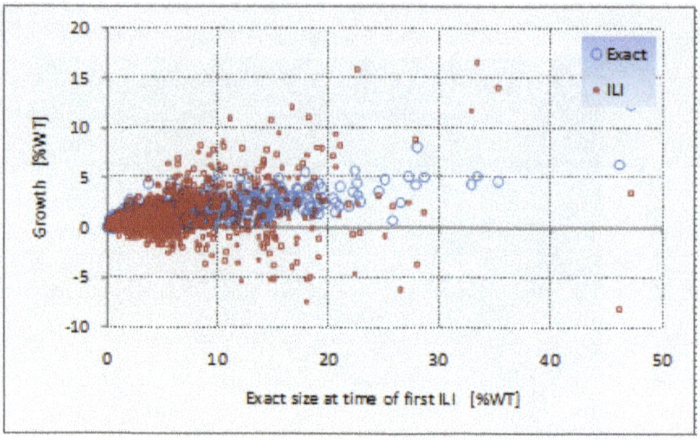

Fig.16. Cross plot of exact and ILI reported feature growth as function of exact feature size at time of the first ILI.

we think that adding conservatism on top of the already spurious sizing uncertainty-induced excess scatter (compare the distributions of the ILI-derived growth rates and true growth in Fig.17) is unwarranted and leads to excessively large corrosion rates. In addition, the corrosion-rate distributions created following the approach in Ref.8 are mathematically inconsistent with the results of the ILI runs.

Several others have advocated computing growth rates on the basis of only the deepest reported feature sizes. This needs to be done with care: a large difference $m(t_2) - m(t_1)$ may be due to significant growth or due to significant overestimation of $m(t_2)$ or under call of $m(t_1)$. If these aspects are not properly accounted for, it is our view that this approach may lead to excessively conservative corrosion rate values as well.

The probability density functions of the time-averaged growth rate can most accurately be obtained from a comparison of the probability densities of the matched pairs for the inert features (such as mill flaws, artificially induced or repaired defects) to determine tool-sizing consistency in each of the inspections, and the features that likely experienced growth between the times of the two inline inspections. In this manner, marginal growth-rate distributions can be determined for the depth, length, and width of all matched feature pairs in the ILI data sets.

Conclusions

This paper outlines some important effects of sizing uncertainty on inspection metrics that are relevant to pipeline-integrity management. The paper introduced a proof that, although individual defects may be unbiased, the maximum reported feature size is a biased estimator of the true maximum feature size. In addition to the obvious effects on fitness-for-service assessments, this statistical overestimation is also relevant when comparing ILI and verification dig results: excavations tend to be performed at the larger ILI calls.

The paper also introduced a practical method to filter out a lot of the spurious noise in the corrosion-rate statistics. This leads to much less-conservative corrosion-rate distributions.

Another key issue in the computation of probability of leak and or burst is the assumption regarding dependence of future growth on current feature size. Although a complete description of statistical dependencies is much more involved than a calculation of correlation coefficients, the paper presents some expressions to estimate the correlation coefficient of the measurements from the true correlation and the sizing error distributions as a first step.

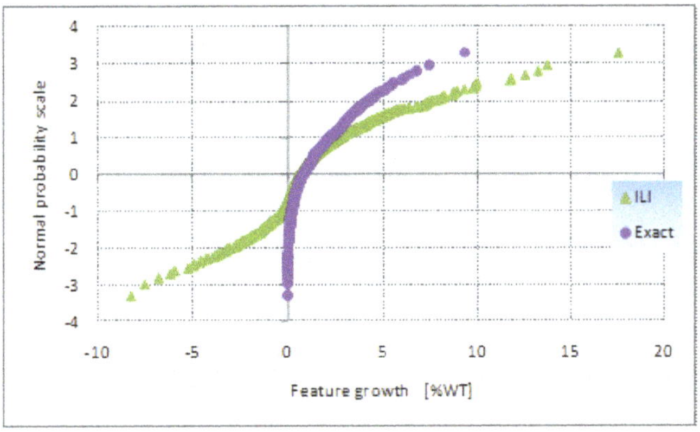

Fig. 17. Comparison of true feature growth distribution and raw ILI difference distribution.

Although the main results in this paper are independent of the actual sizing-error distributions, considerable improvements in pipeline-integrity decisions could be made if more-detailed information about actual tool performance was disclosed by ILI vendors. In that regard, the paper aims to illustrate some of the consequences of the current practical assumptions that are often used. The paper hopes to contribute to tighter integration and interaction between performing the actual inspection and post-inspection integrity assessments.

Acknowledgements

This work was funded through the Technology Development Program at Chevron ETC. The support from Richard Sweeney and the members of the Technical Leadership Team it the Facilities, Operations and Reliability Focus Area is gratefully acknowledged.

References

1. A.Gelman and J.Hill, 2007. Data analysis: using regression and multilevel/hierarchical models. Cambridge University Press, New York, NY, USA.
2. European Pipeline Operator Forum, 2005. Specifications and requirements for intelligent pig inspection of pipelines, Version 3.2, January.
3. G.G.J.Achterbosch and L.A. Grzelak, 2006. Determination of the corrosion rate of a MIC influenced pipeline using four consecutive pig runs. IPC 2006-10142, Proc. 6th International Pipeline Conference, Calgary, AB, Canada.
4. E.Vanmarcke, 1983. Random fields: analysis and synthesis. MIT Press, Cambridge MA, USA.
5. M.G.Fontana and N.D.Greene, 1986. Corrosion engineering, McGraw-Hill, 3rd Edn, New York, NY, USA.
6. L.Fenyvesi and S.Dumalski, 2005. Determining corrosion growth accurately and reliably. NACE Corrosion 2005 Paper 05154, NACE International, Houston, TX, USA.
7. S.J.Dawson, J.Wharf, and M.Nessim, 2008. Development of detailed procedures for comparing successive ILI runs to establish corrosion growth rates. PRCI Project EC 1-2.
8. M.Nessim, S.J.Dawson, R.Mora, and S.Hassanein, 2008. Obtaining corrosion growth rates from repeat in-line inspection runs and dealing with the measurement uncertainties. IPC 2008-64378, Proc. 7th International Pipeline Conference, Calgary, AB, Canada.

Bibliography

American Petroleum Institute, 2005. API 1163, In-line inspection systems qualification Standard, Washington, DC, USA.

ANSI/ASNT, 2005. In-line inspection personnel qualification and certification, ANSI/ASNT ILI-PQ-2005, Columbus, OH, USA.

W.H.Brown, 1999. Using ILI pigs to establish pipeline corrosion rates – case histories. Corrosion 1999, Paper 99523, NACE International, Houston, TX, USA.

G.Desjardins, 2001. Corrosion rate and severity results from in-line inspection data. Corrosion 2001, Paper 01624, NACE International, Houston, TX, USA.

A.K.Escoe, 2006. Piping and pipelines – assessment guide. Gulf Professional Publishing, Elsevier, Oxford, UK.

NACE, 2001. In-line nondestructive inspection of pipelines. TR 35100, NACE International, Houston, TX, USA.

NACE, 2002. Recommended practice: in-line inspection of pipelines. RP0102-2002, Houston, TX, USA.

J.M.Race, S.J.Dawson, L.Stanley, and S.Kariyawasam, 2006. Predicting corrosion rates for onshore oil and gas pipelines. IPC 2006-10261, Proc. 6th International Pipeline Conference, Calgary, AB, Canada.

S.W.Rust and E.R.Johnson, 2001. Statistical method for identifying active corrosion based on data from multiple in-line inspection runs. Corrosion 2001, Paper 01622, NACE International, Houston, TX, USA.

Section 5: Integrity management

Integrity management of a pipeline crossing the Andes

by Andrés Mendizábal and Fabián Sanchez

OCP Ecuador, Quito, Ecuador

THE OCP pipeline (Oleoducto de Crudos Pesados – heavy crude oil pipeline) in Ecuador crosses regions with very dynamic geology and which have unique characteristics. Along its route, the pipeline crosses the Andes mountains, reaching an altitude of 4,060 m above sea level. Within this regional geological context, OCP Ecuador emphasizes on the need to have a pipeline integrity-management (PIM) plan that accounts for and evaluates the areas that could be potentially vulnerable to certain geodynamic phenomena such as volcanic (12 volcanoes), seismic (28 geological faults), slope instability (landslides), etc., in order to define the monitoring and control measures that allows it to maintain the integrity of the pipeline.

This paper emphasizes how the PIM plan is executed for a pipeline subject to such specific conditions and threats such as those that need to be handled by this heavy crude oil pipeline company across the Andes.

ECUADOR'S OCP pipeline (Oleoducto de Crudos Pesados) transports heavy crude oil from the Amazon region to the Pacific Coast, extending from the Amazonas Terminal (kp 000) to the Marine Terminal (kp 485). The project's construction began in 2001, and pipeline operations were initiated at the end of 2003. The magnitude of the facilities, as well as the environment in which the project is situated, imposed enormous challenges. The pipeline route crosses the Amazon jungle lowlands, the Andes mountains, the central valley near Quito, the western Andes ridge, and the rolling lowlands leading to the Pacific Coast. The varied elevation of the pipeline starts at 300 m above sea level (masl) at the Amazonas Terminal, increases to 4,064 masl at the Andes mountains near kp 200, and then decreases to 205 masl at the Marine Terminal tank storage location near the Pacific Ocean coast. Figure 1 shows the pipeline's vertical profile.

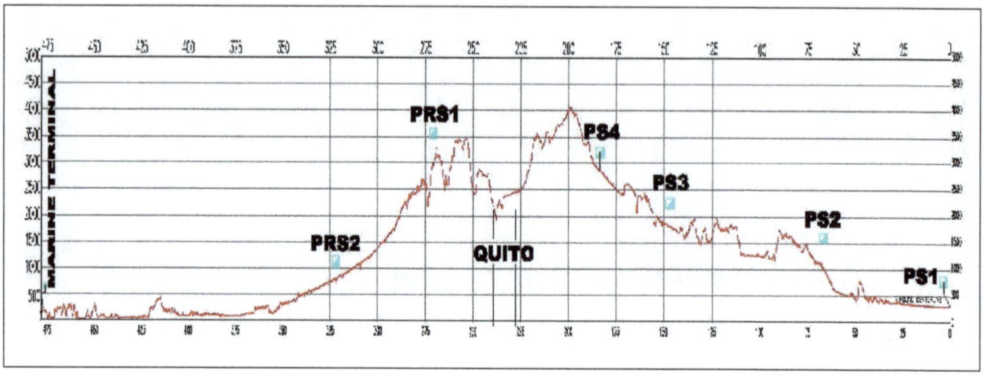

Fig. 1. Pipeline vertical profile.

OCP pipeline description

The OCP pipeline was designed to transport a blended heavy crude oil as a single product. Up to eight shippers can deliver crude oil into the pipeline, and its operational capacity is 450,000 bpd of crude oil with an API specific gravity of 18°. The design capacity is approximately 518,000 bpd.

The OCP pipeline system comprises one crude oil receiving terminal and pump station (the Amazonas Terminal PS1), three intermediate pump stations (Cayagama PS2, Sardinas PS3, and Paramo PS4), two pressure reduction stations (Chiquilpe PRS1 and Puerto Quito PRS2), one automatic block-valve station (ABS), and the Marine Terminal. The pipeline is constructed from high-pressure, DSAW manufactured, API Grade X-70 carbon steel coated with fusion-bonded epoxy. The diameters along the route vary between 24, 32, 34, and 36 in, with 15 different wall thicknesses, varying from 0.312 in to 1.062 in.

Special conditions along the route

Seismic faults

Description

Ecuador is located in a highly seismically active region. The region is controlled by the Oceanic Nazca, Continental South American, and Caribbean Plates. The Ecuadorian Andes mountains are directly affected by these fault systems, and there are 28 active faults which traverse the OCP pipeline.

Design and construction

To define the activity levels of each fault, different methods were used, including existing field information, experts' criteria based on field observations, and wave seismic analysis. In fault locations crossed by the OCP, the dynamic zone weight, orientation, and failure affected areas were identified.

Once the seismic sources were identified, probable displacements were calculated using the empiric relationships between the dimensions of probable future movements their associated displacements. Following this, soil and pipeline interaction analyses were performed using finite-

Fig.2. The Cascales geological fault crossing at kp 33+300.

element analysis. As a result, several changes were made in the original route alignment in order to minimize the effect of active faults on the pipeline.

Additionally, construction recommendations were issued for some crossings, including the use of supports for the Cascales fault crossing (Fig.2), and ditching and channelling for several other faults (including Lumbaqui, Sardinas, San José, and Sucus).

Monitoring and maintenance

In order to provide early warning of impending faults, allowing time for safe implementation of remedial actions, right-of-way (RoW) inspections are conducted following the company's established procedures that include:

- requirements for the RoW patrolling and routine inspection
- Guidelines for performing RoW inspections
- documentation and reports of RoW inspections
- RoW segment classification
- RoW inspection, engineering evaluation and maintenance frequency
- guidelines for evaluating and updating RoW inspections, engineering evaluation, and maintenance frequency
- guidelines for inspecting different RoW conditions such as river crossings, road crossings, slopes, third-party activity, etc.
- guidelines for performing engineering evaluations of stabilization and geotechnical structural works such as drain control, water management, erosion control, land-movement control, gabion walls, concrete walls, etc.

Seismic events

OCP has an agreement with the Ecuadorian Geophysical Institute (IG) such that if a seismic event occurs, the IG provides OCP with all the related information, including seismic category, magnitude, and epicentre. Immediately, OCP's RoW-response team activates inspections to the affected area to detect if there is any effect on the pipeline's integrity.

Ground displacements

Description

Given the terrain morphology, the soil characteristics, the slope drainage patterns, the evidences

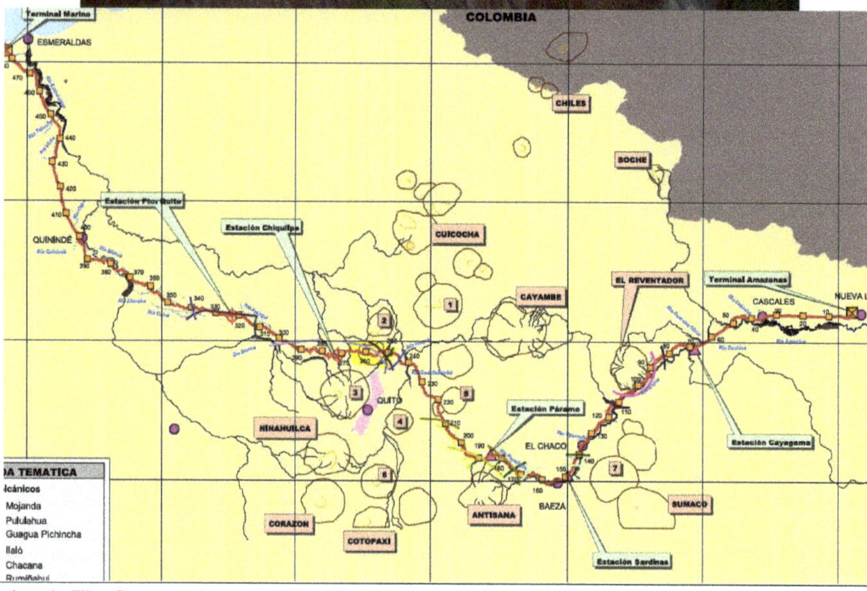

Fig.3 (top). The Reventador volcano, adjacent to kp 90.

Fig.4 (bottom). Volcanic area map.

of instability in certain zones, and the weather conditions, among other factors, the likelihood of ground movements along the OCP's route is very high. In several locations, the RoW is susceptible to ground motion such as cracks, landslides, tilting of trees, and below-ground damage.

Design and construction

Land-movement control measures were taken into account during the design and construction stages. Several engineering designs were issued to maintain the pipeline integrity as well as for stabilization works, and geotechnical structures were constructed or provided that included concrete walls, gabion walls, riprap, wooden barriers, sheet piling, and steel piling.

Fig.5. The Quininde aerial river crossing.

Fig.6. The Puchochoa river crossing.

In order to monitor ground movements and their effects on the pipeline's strain, inclinometers as well as strain gauges were installed during construction at specific locations.

Monitoring and maintenance

Ground movement and strains on the pipeline are monitored using instrumentation at an established frequency. Monitoring of ground displacement through inclinometers, topographical benchmarks, and tilting marks, together with strain-gauge reading of pipeline strain at the same locations and calculation of the consequent pipeline stress, are performed following established procedures.

OCP's RoW is periodically inspected to determine if instability processes are occurring, and if they might cause problems. Signals of instability at unstable areas – such as land movements, slumps, cracks, scars, settlements, and ground displacement – are evaluated to determine their root cause and possible consequences.

Volcanic risk

Description

Ecuador is located in an area called 'Cinturon de fuego del Pacifico' or the 'Pacific Ring of Fire', the main characteristic of which is the presence of several active volcanoes in the Andes mountains. Several studies were performed in order to identify the volcanic risks that could affect the OCP pipeline in a direct or indirect way. The OCP influence area includes 12 volcanoes: Soche, Reventador (Fig.3), Cayambe, Complejo Volcánico Chacana, Antisana, Sumaco, Cotopaxi, Ninahuilca, Guagua Pichincha, Pululahua, Quilotoa, and Cuicocha.

Design and construction

During volcanic activity periods, the areas of influence of volcanic products and eruptive material associated were identified in order to define the minimal construction requirements. Due to the distance of pipeline from the main volcanoes, their primary effect on the OCP is mud and rocks flowing over the RoW. In order to maintain the pipeline's integrity in some areas of volcanic influence, the depth of cover has been increased from the normal 0.90-1.00 m to between 8 and 14 m.

Monitoring and maintenance

As a result of studies performed prior to pipeline construction, drawings of the volcanic risk and its area of influence were issued (Fig.4). These drawings are used during the regular OCP pipeline monitoring.

Under the same agreement mentioned above, the IG provides OCP with all the information regarding volcanic activity that can affect the OCP pipeline. The IG has monitoring instrumentation installed in most of the active volcanoes which can influence the area traversed by the OCP pipeline, and for the ones without this instrumentation, portable instrumentation is available.

Immediately after receiving any information from the IG about volcanic activity, the OCP RoW team from the area makes detailed inspections to the RoW, rivers (water temperature changes), and adjacent areas to check if there is any effect and, if so, its magnitude. As soon as a volcano has initiated a period of activity, OCP receives a daily report including all the relevant information, which includes:

- number and type of event, such as rock fracture, seismicity level, and duration
- satellite photography, where possible;
- visual inspection, including rain level, vapour emissions, ash emissions, and lava speed and location;

To monitor the volcano condition, aerial inspections are performed periodically in co-ordination with the IG. During these inspections, aerial photography is obtained. Additionally, periodic evaluations are performed in which all the information available is analysed.

Fig.7 (top). River crossing stabilization works at kp 200+850.

Fig.8 (bottom). Pipeline installation at kp 278.

River crossings

Description

The OCP pipeline crosses 71 watercourses, of which 47 required a specific design approach. Four of the rivers were crossed with suspension bridges, the largest of which has a free span of 120 m. Additional aerial river crossings are the Quinindé (Fig.5), Puchochoa (Fig.6), Piedra Fina, and Quebrada Sin Nombre.

Extreme floods during the rainy season generally cause severe effects on river crossing stability, and in consequence stabilization works have been undertaken (Fig.7). To prevent any effect on river crossing stability, and to implement timely maintenance work, inspection and monitoring is performed with a high frequency.

Design and construction

Some of the rivers crossed by the OCP pipeline have special characteristics, and therefore are considered as major river crossings. During the pipeline design phase, specific designs for these crossings were made, based on one or more of the following characteristics:

- high flow and high velocities during the rainy seasons (flow peaks)
- mountainous streams with significantly steep riverbeds
- high design floods, over 100 m^3/s
- high banks subject to erosion, or low banks subject to overflowing at the crossing site
- streambeds or banks that exhibited challenging characteristics, to determine appropriate restoration methodology
- rivers with significant downstream population
- rivers exhibiting significant variation between average flow and peak flow
- rivers or streams potentially subject to avalanches, extreme floods, and lahar or debris flows.

The potential erosion/settlement factor for the river beds were calculated in order to define the crossing depth.

Monitoring and maintenance

To monitor the hydraulic behaviour of each river crossing, bathymetric inspections are performed annually at the major river crossings. The results are analysed in order to define the necessary actions to maintain the river-crossing stability and therefore the pipeline's integrity.

The intent of the periodical river-engineering assessments is to determine, on a river-engineering basis, if the designed bank- and bed-restoration measures are still in place and maintaining the stability of the streambed and banks. OCP has established river-crossing inspection routines and procedures that are a fundamental part of the pipeline integrity plan. The company's 'inspection and maintenance of major pipeline river crossings' procedure includes:

engineering evaluation requirements and considerations
guidelines for performing routine inspections at river crossings
river-crossing maintenance

Steep slopes

Description

The pipeline RoW traverses many steep slopes, and a minimum of 100 slopes required winching of equipment during construction. Extreme examples are the Quijos 2 slope (280 m long at 65°), the Chiquilpe slope (1,800 m at between 30° and 40°), and the El Castillo slope (120 m at 80°). The pipeline was routed wherever possible along mountain ridges to avoid hillside cuttings and to prevent erosion, landslides, and destabilizing embankments.

Monitoring and maintenance

Steep slopes are defined by OCP as areas requiring high frequency of inspection. This means that inspection and engineering monitoring have the highest level of frequency and maintenance jobs are considered a priority.

Inspections are carried out to determine if slope instability is occurring and its potential effect on the pipeline. All the RoW drainage and erosion-control measures are properly maintained, repaired, or replaced to ensure that all these measures are working correctly and efficiently, as well as the stabilization works and geotechnical structures (concrete walls, gabion walls, wooden barriers, steel piling, etc.).

One of the main threats to slope stability is the presence of cattle, which cause damage to the stabilization works (such as water drains) and may severely affect slope stability.

Protected areas

Description

The OCP route traverses six high sensibility protected areas with a total length of 20 km. Detailed environmental characterizations were performed for each area in order adequately to define the construction technology for each.

Design and construction

During design and construction, various restrictions were applied in order to avoid affecting the protected areas. As an example, at kp 278 the pipeline was installed in a RoW of only 9 m width using an aerial cable to transport the pipe and materials (Fig8).

At the Mindo-Nambillo protected area, the pipeline was designed with an oversized wall thickness and concrete cover, and installed with concrete anchor blocks. Specific stabilization works such as cement gabion walls were also used.

Monitoring and maintenance

Protected areas are defined by OCP as requiring a high frequency of inspection, and this means that inspection and engineering monitoring have the highest level of frequency, and maintenance jobs are considered a priority.

Pipeline integrity-management plan and risk analysis

Pipeline integrity-management programme

OCP has developed a PIM programme that best serves its unique operational needs, continuously improves the safety of the pipeline system and allocates the company's resources effectively. Considering the special characteristics along the route, it was necessary to implement certain key elements that form part of the programme, and which include:

- identification and characterization of the RoW segments
- definition of procedures and frequency of RoW inspections, focusing on those special areas that are considered critical such as major river crossings, slopes, protected areas, seismic areas, volcanic risk areas, etc.
- definition of adequate engineering evaluation methods
- implementation of an effective risk analysis methodology

Risk analysis

OCP has implemented risk analysis as a key element on managing pipeline integrity, in order to identify and prioritize the most significant risks so that the company's management can make informed decisions about integrity related issues and expenses.

Assessing risks to the integrity of the OCP pipeline is a continuously iterative process in order adequately to adjust the PIM programme. The company has implemented a risk-analysis assessment tool in order to perform the risk analysis, which is configured to the pipeline's specific conditions and operational requirements.

Conclusions

Along the OCP pipeline system there is a range of critical conditions such as major river crossings, steep slopes, volcanic risk areas, seismic areas, ground displacements areas, etc., that make the pipeline's integrity management very challenging.

To ensure the pipeline's integrity, OCP has developed specific procedures that address the inspection, evaluation, and maintenance of the pipeline and its unique characteristics.

To integrate the management of all the special conditions present along the pipeline route, it is necessary to apply an adequate, complete, and versatile PIM programme that includes risk management.

Legal issues in pipeline integrity programmes

by Chris Paul

Joyce & Paul PLLC, Tulsa, OK, USA

THIS PAPER BUILDS upon the presentations from the 2007 and 2008 Pipeline Pigging and Integrity Management conferences, where the discussions introduced legal issues involved in pipeline integrity programmes.

Pipeline integrity programmes carry with them inherent legal issues and exposures. A meaningful integrity programme will by its very nature be self-critical, and the processes involved in evaluating pipeline systems may not only result in the positive outcome of increasing pipeline safety, but also may result in creation of data and documentation that, if misused or viewed with the wisdom critics find in hindsight, could provide a roadmap for plaintiff attorneys or government investigators to question an operator's decisions in the event of an accident. These issues are all the more problematic when it is also recognized that there is a need for involving third parties in consulting arrangements and contracts for internal inspections, thus making data and documentation control more challenging. Also, management of documents that are provided to the government on integrity issues are subject to release to the public, raising security issues as well as putting information at increased risk of being used against the organization in enforcement or litigation proceedings.

The presentation will review the legal issues and the demands that pipeline integrity programmes place upon operators, that include data-integration and records'-retention requirements, including a discussion of how these issues and demands may result in misinterpretation and misuse of data and documents. The bases for management and company exposure will be discussed, as will the criteria used by the government for determining whether or not information within the knowledge of the company might result not only in simple liability, but also the possibility of criminal exposure.

The presentation will review solutions to the legal issues, including how to deal with improved ILI tools which provide tremendous amounts of data that must be captured and integrated with other information involving the operator's pipeline systems. It will be emphasized that while companies want to do the right thing, they need to understand the legal risks involved so that they can do the right thing in the right way. Companies that are legitimately and thoroughly trying to identify, qualify, quantify, and manage risks must understand how to handle documentation associated with their integrity programmes to minimize the potential for data and information to be taken out of context and used to imply deficiencies in programmes, whether this is done by government agencies or by private plaintiffs.

THIS PAPER WILL OUTLINE some of the legal issues in the context of the US' pipeline integrity management rules, and it will provide potential solutions on integrating legal concerns into the execution of effective pipeline-integrity programmes. Legal issues and the demands that pipeline-integrity programmes place upon operators will be reviewed, as will data-integration and records'-retention requirements, including a discussion of how these issues and demands may result in misinterpretation and misuse of data and documents. The bases for management and company exposure will be discussed, as will the criteria used by the government for determining whether or not information within the knowledge of the company might result not only in simple liability, but also the possibility of criminal exposure.

This paper builds upon the presentations from the 2007 and 2008 Pipeline Pigging and Integrity Management conferences. Much of the information presented at those conferences is repeated here for the convenience of the reader and to provide a comprehensive update. Additional information regarding legal issues is included in this paper.

Pipeline-integrity programmes carry with them inherent legal issues and exposures. A meaningful integrity programme will by its very nature be self-critical, and the processes involved in evaluating pipeline systems may not only result in the positive outcome of increasing pipeline safety, but also may result in creation of data and documentation that, if misused or viewed through the agendas and with the "wisdom" critics find in hindsight, could provide a roadmap for plaintiff attorneys or even government investigators to question an operatorNe:'s decisions in the event of an accident. These issues are all the more problematic when it is also recognized that there is a need for involving third parties in consulting arrangements and contracts for internal inspections, thus making data and documentation creation and control more challenging. Also, management of documents that are provided to the government on integrity issues are subject to release to the public, raising very serious security issues as well as putting information at increased risk of being misconstrued or taken out of context. While companies want to do the right thing, they need to understand the legal risks involved so that they can do the right thing in the right way. Companies that are legitimately and thoroughly trying to identify, qualify, quantify, and manage risks must understand how to handle the analyses and related documentation associated with their integrity programmes to minimize the potential for data and information to be taken out of context and used to imply deficiencies in programmes.

Consideration of legal issues in the context of integrity management (sometimes referred to as IM, or IMP when referring to integrity-management programmes) is appropriate because the legal implications of IM are broad and evolving. Some of the processes available to prudently and effectively manage a meaningful IMP can be discussed, even in the context of a brief paper and accompanying presentation, to show how best to address these legal implications.

First, it is necessary that a basic foundation be established regarding the potential legal liabilities that face parties involved in IMP – both operators and those performing IM work for operators, including internal line inspection (ILI) vendors. Better high-level educational institutions (the author is familiar with those in the United States) provide non-legal students (those in engineering, business and – most especially – medicine) some rudimentary classes in legal matters. This is necessary because the law, whether in the context of compliance or liability, has permeated the social fabric in the United States to the extent that businesses and business persons often complain that "the lawyers are running things." This author does not believe that this is the case, but does understand the frustrations experienced by businesses that constantly face the threat of lawsuits and the voices of lawyers who are too often good at identifying and making inflammatory claims about "risks" without qualifying the risk, without considering the benefits associated with the risk, and certainly without providing corresponding solutions. Many businesses have come to rely on lawyers to minimize exposure, maximize compliance, and generally achieve the best possible position to keep legal issues in perspective. It would be unfair to fail to note that while the legal implications are seen by many as a threat to their business, the rule of law has also allowed for stability in conducting business, boundaries to define what can and should be done (thus establishing standards which, if followed, can minimize, but not prevent, legal exposures), and provides a process, however flawed, for resolution of disputes and management of problems. Regulations, when consistently enforced, help provide for a level playing field as well as protect the public from excesses. In short, it is obvious that lawyers are both a threat to business conducted improperly and one of the primary tools for dealing with the threat. The goal is to avoid legal exposures, but if such exposures arise, to be in a position to prevail on the issue (understanding that "prevail" might not always be an outright win, but may be successful damage control).

The bottom line is that our society might despise lawyers, but at the same time celebrates the law whether in television programmes, the media or, when real problems arise, in seeking to ensure that some level of victory is the outcome. Even those who profess to hate lawyers will quickly file a lawsuit if they believe that they have suffered a wrong. Understanding where the liabilities may arise, then, is the first step in doing business within a society where disputes and litigation are inevitable. Once a basic level of understanding where legal exposures exist is met, then the tools to best position individuals and organizations to address potential liability can be considered and put into practice – as appropriate given the activity involved, the ability of the company to assess risk, and the appetite of the organization to accept such risk.

With the foregoing discussion providing a rather depressing background, the following is a brief review of the various types of liability that may face the pipeline operator and/or integrity services vendors, including those providing IM services.

Bases of exposure

To understand the legal issues associated with IM, it is necessary to briefly review the various bases of potential exposure to legal liabilities. This paper will discuss such liabilities as they exist between an operator and a third party (whether a private party or the government), as legal issues that may arise between the vendor and the operator should be fully addressed in the contract between the two parties (and later in this paper some of these contract issues will be discussed). This does not mean that the operator or vendor will not be pulled-in to a case involving a third-party proceeding against either the operator or the vendor (in fact, in most cases it would be expected that both the operator and vendor would be pulled-in to a case, either as a defendant or a witness).

It is important to remember that civil actions can be brought by both the government and by private individuals and entities. In civil actions brought by private plaintiffs, plaintiffs are seeking to address private wrongs or delineate private rights. The relief they seek is usually transfer of money or property from the defendant to the plaintiff.

Civil cases brought by the government generally allege noncompliance with a regulatory requirement, most often under environmental laws, but increasingly pursuant to transportation laws, and it is expected that security provisions will become cited in certain types of case. Civil cases brought by the government seek financial penalties and, for spills with environmental issues, injunctive relief (see below). Such cases are almost always brought only against the operator but, again, the ILI vendor may also become involved as a defendant or a witness.

Actions by the government may take the form of administrative or judicial proceedings. Most administrative enforcements are for smaller perceived violations, because penalties that could be obtained through the exercise of administrative proceedings are smaller than those that could be obtained through judicial proceedings.

Judicial enforcement will take place when the agency believes that a violation is serious enough that mechanisms provided for redress under administrative provisions are insufficient to penalize and further deter such conduct. In such an event, the agency will refer the matter to the

Department of Justice or the local United States Attorney (in federal cases) or, in state cases, to state or local prosecutors. As appropriate, the prosecuting body will file the necessary civil complaints and initiate a lawsuit, usually seeking significant penalties (criminal matters are handled elsewhere in this paper, but may also be processed through the same prosecuting body, often in conjunction with civil actions).

In addition, there is an area where civil enforcement between private parties and the government somewhat overlaps. These cases are generally pursued when a citizen's group perceives that the government is not adequately or aggressively enough pursuing its enforcement of the law. Congress therefore included in certain laws a provision allowing citizens to enforce the law when federal and state authorities fail to do so. These provisions, known as citizen suits, are common in environmental laws, and also are present in pipeline safety laws. Citizen suits provide private plaintiffs access to federal courts. A citizen's suit may result in injunctive relief against an ongoing violation of a statute and the plaintiff may recover its costs, including expert witness and attorney :'s fees. When a plaintiff is able to prove a violation of federal law, such violation may support the plaintiff's tort claim and enhance the plaintiff's position in proceeding with other private litigation (see negligence *per se*, following). If government authorities are diligently prosecuting the violator for the conduct at issue, a citizen's suit cannot proceed.

It is important to remember that even if a company is in compliance with regulations, there is still exposure because private citizens can file suit under common law. Further, the standards set in regulations are simply not determinative of liability. The fact is that performance of an operator or IM vendor will be measured subsequent to the event and meeting the letter of the law will not preclude liability, particularly if any type of injury (including serious environmental damage) results from an event. Simply, if a pipeline failure occurs, then some in the government (fortunately few), but many private plaintiff lawyers, will seek to persuade a jury that the failure itself is indicative of insufficient IM and penalties or damages are warranted. The real standard toward which pipelines need to strive is best practices, not simple compliance with the regulations.

Continuum of exposure

There are various bases for filing civil suits, but perhaps the most common is negligence. Negligence is conduct "which falls below the standard established by law for the protection of others against unreasonable risk of harm." In most jurisdictions, even conduct which falls below this standard will not give rise to liability unless it results in damage to persons or property.

There are other forms of liability, including strict liability, for companies that engage in abnormally-dangerous activities where there is a high degree of risk such that the ultimate duty of care is higher for those businesses that involve polluting activities or transportation of hazardous materials.

Many other forms of common law bases for pursuing claims against companies privately exist. These include nuisance, trespass, and other theories which competent attorneys will often pursue.

Finally, with respect to civil liability, it is important to understand the concept of joint and several liability. Where joint and several liability is the law, plaintiffs are not required to prove each defendant's contribution to any injury, and named defendants are liable to the plaintiff jointly for all of the damages caused. Judgment is imposed against the defendants as a group for the full amount of the damages. The plaintiff is then entitled to collect the entire amount from one or two (or any number) of the most-solvent and/or readily-attackable (where jurisdiction can be achieved

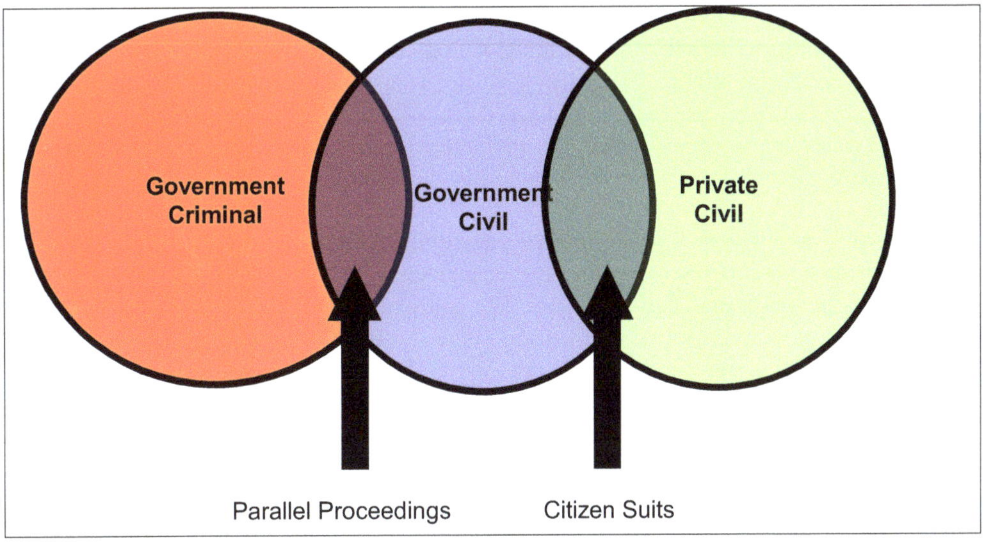

or perhaps the defendant can be subjected to adverse publicity) defendants. The paying defendants may then seek contribution from other defendants and they, not the plaintiff, bear the risk of non-recovery from others. This circumstance is particularly difficult in cases where defendants who may in fact be the most culpable are for one reason or another no longer in existence or otherwise are insolvent, and thus judgment-proof.

Not only for reasons associated with joint and several liability, plaintiffs will frequently sue every party they can possibly bring in to a case and hope not only that this allows them to have a larger pool from which to recover potential damages, but also may cause some of the defendants to begin pointing blame at each other, thus proving the plaintiffs' case with limited work from the plaintiffs' counsel. The expectation then, in the event of a pipeline failure, should be that both the operator and the IM vendor will become involved in the lawsuit.

As indicated previously, compliance with a regulation does not mean that liability is avoided. Again, the standard that will be applied is most often best practices. Failure to comply with a regulatory requirement, however, virtually means that civil liability is certain, because of the application of the doctrine of negligence *per se*. In brief, this doctrine means that liability is presumed if a law or regulation is broken. Therefore, if a failure is found in compliance with the organization's IMP in the aftermath of a failure or accident, then negligence on the part of the organization can readily be established. In practice, this doctrine does not provide absolute certainty of victory for the plaintiff, but it certainly puts the organization at a severe disadvantage. Therefore, it is critical in IMP implementation and maintenance that substantial compliance with the rules be achieved, and insubstantial non-compliances, which are very possible in the IM rules, be kept in context and perspective when evaluating programmes internally, or in responding to external (agency) evaluations or audits.

Criminal actions are designed to address perceived or actual wrongs to society. The criminal proceedings are brought only by government entities, but it is important to remember that investigations may result from private party complaints that generate interest on the part of investigative bodies. The relief in these cases may be a monetary penalty, imprisonment, and/or various forms of injunctive relief.

Injunctive relief can be applied by the government in civil and criminal cases. For pipelines, injunctive relief often includes extensive prescriptive measures in the IM realm, far beyond what the regulations would otherwise require. Furthermore, state and local environmental statutes commonly authorize criminal penalties for violations of certain laws, permits, or standards without any showing of intent.

There is an increasing tendency by the government to seek criminal liability, not only against the corporate entity, but also against individuals within the corporate entity.

Obviously, a person who actually commits a violation is liable. But the responsible corporate officer doctrine is used to find corporate officers, managers, and supervisors liable for the acts of their employees or acts under their control. The courts may find a corporate officer guilty of criminal violations if, by reason of the position in the corporation, the officer has responsibility and authority either to prevent or to promptly correct the violation complained of, and he/she fails to do so. Courts will determine if the individual had responsibility for compliance and the power commensurate with that responsibility to take measures necessary to ensure compliance. Inaction as well as improper acts may form the basis for liability where knowledge or control is proved.

Under this doctrine, a responsible corporate officer (RCO) may be held criminally liable even if he/she did not wilfully or negligently cause a violation. Instead, the wilfulness or negligence of the actor is imputed to the RCO by reason of the position of responsibility. What this means is that it is difficult, if not impossible, to delegate away certain responsibilities and thus exposures. To minimize the risk to management, programmes must be in place to address standards which help show management acted responsibly to try to identify and prevent violations.

What continues to be remarkable is that some organizations are still in denial regarding their potential liability under IMP, as well as under other regulatory programmes. The rules are real, and the expectations are becoming increasingly clear as the programme is developed (but see discussion following regarding the manner in which some changes to the rules have been made). Companies that fail to address their compliance responsibilities are taking a real and quantifiable risk that is unnecessary because a roadmap to compliance is readily available.

IM in the United States

Integrity management has been formalized in the United States. But before review of the formal IM regulations, it is important to mention that IM has existed within pipeline companies long before regulations were put in place. The IM "programmes" did not operate under a single umbrella, and were usually not even called integrity programmes, but rather were in place as corrosion programmes, aerial patrol, third-party damage prevention activities, leak detection, pigging, and in many cases smart-pigging consisting of ever-more-sophisticated in-line inspection (ILI). The distinction was that prior to formalization of the rules, integrity activities of companies were more variable and within a broader range of effort and effectiveness (as always, some companies had strong programmes, while others had "paper" programmes and really did next to nothing). It was and is in the best interests of companies to manage integrity, with the goal of preventing failures, to protect product, and to avoid the fallout from accidents, including legal liabilities such as those arising from impacts to the environment or injuries to persons. Some companies spent more money, and executed integrity activities better, and the regulations did help to level the playing field. Other companies had done more than even the current regulations require, and some continue to do more even with the regulations in place. Others did less, and continue to operate on the fringe of compliance.

The United States Department of Transportation (DOT), through the then-named Research and Special Programmes Administration (RSPA), announced the final rule for *Liquid pipeline integrity management for high consequence areas (for operators with more than 500 miles of lines)* in December, 2000. The rule took effect at the end of May, 2001 (the original March date was delayed); requirements for integrity-management programmes were extended to include operators with less than 500 miles of lines in February, 2002, and rules for gas pipelines became effective in September, 2002. The fact is that the rules are maturing and organizations are reasonably expected to have viable IM programmes in place. "Maturing" is purposely used rather than "mature" or "established" because PHMSA and operators see IM as a programme that will continually evolve and improve, whether this is driven by changes in technology, changes in the areas around the pipeline (revisions to HCAs), or changes related to data analysis.

RSPA's jurisdiction over pipelines has since been superseded by the creation of the Pipeline and Hazardous Materials Safety Administration (PHMSA), but for purposes of this paper, the DOT will be referred to as the governing agency since PHMSA is part of the DOT. The various integrity-management rules will be referred to as "programme" or "rule," sometimes plural and sometimes singular, without distinguishing between the various rules, because the legal issues are universal in application.

The reason for the rules deserves at least a brief mention. Several high-profile pipeline accidents (Bellingham and Carlsbad in particular) caused increased scrutiny from Congress, the General Accounting Office and, perhaps most-significantly, the National Transportation Safety Board, to be applied to the pipeline industry and the perceived level of effectiveness of the DOT in regulating the pipeline industry. The DOT was highly criticized, unfairly in the view of this author, but changes were nonetheless made, chief among them the development and implementation of the integrity rules as part of various pipeline safety acts. Ironically, while the DOT was forced to adopt the rules, the industry was supportive of the rule development, recognizing the need to have a metric to demonstrate to the public that the industry did place safety as the highest priority, and perhaps to help level the playing field between those companies that had rigorous programmes and those that relied upon luck and, in some cases, how close managers were to retirement.

Subsequent revisions and clarifications were made to the rules, such changes being made by the DOT both by formal rulemaking procedures, and, quite controversially, by revisions to the frequently-asked questions (FAQs). Changes are not unanticipated because the integrity rules were, according to DOT senior personnel, intended to evolve as the DOT and operators learned from programme implementation, and audits, how to improve the programmes. But the mechanics of the changes often create problems rather than provide clarity to operators. By way of example, the FAQs, which can be helpful, but have been used by the DOT to interpret the integrity rules, are issued and changed without going through normal rulemaking procedures, and they often present a moving target for operators who are seeking to stay in compliance.

The manner in which the changes are being made raise several legal issues that may ultimately be raised as defences in an IMP enforcement action. For example, the question is raised regarding whether the use of FAQs to modify the rules complies with the fair notice provisions under the Administrative Procedures Act. Further, it is inevitable that there will be inconsistencies in enforcement priorities as applied by different inspectors, although a defence based on such inconsistencies would be difficult to maintain because the agency can appropriately base enforcement on the criteria in the operator's own IMP manual.

Another "tool" available to the DOT, and operators, to measure compliance is the Integrity Management Inspection Protocols (Protocols). Like the FAQs, the Protocols have been unilaterally changed by the DOT, sometimes providing clarity, sometimes adding additional pieces to the "elements" against which operators are evaluated and sometimes creating confusion and changing the rules.

DOT has now also used Integrated Inspection Question Modules that cover IMP as well as other requirements. Operators know what the issues are and should be able to at least address all IM programme components, and the DOT can see just how difficult and complicated the execution of a vibrant IM programme may be and not only find problems with IM programmes, but provide help in finding solutions. DOT can bring to an audit not just questions and scrutiny, but also best practices that have been observed while auditing other operators, tempered with an understanding that IM programmes are not fungible but must be built, implemented, maintained, reviewed, and revised by each operator to fit its system and the threats to integrity that are identified in particular circumstances.

Operators can therefore fairly expect DOT to raise enforcement-proceedings' issues regarding risk model data and weighting, identification of HCAs and the potential effects on HCAs, baseline assessment plan assumptions, use of assessment and inspection data, issues involving proper use of ILI tool tolerances, the bases for preventative and mitigative measures taken, and the proper application of rules regarding continual evaluations and assessments.

Therefore, operators and DOT have both learned from the earliest rounds of IM audits. The initial round of audits focused on required programme elements and cited HCA identification and incomplete risk assessments as the most-common deficiencies. Later audits began to focus on threat identification, data integration, risk analysis, and a failure of many operators to justify reassessment intervals. The operators and the DOT were both faced with significant issues related to the baseline assessments. With inspections occurring in some cases for the first time, there were a large number of excavations to address anomalies that had been present since the construction of the pipeline. In some cases, operators were still trying to determine what the most appropriate assessment method would be for the risks to their pipelines that they were still identifying. Some of the greatest problems were related to tool performance, sometimes related to the inevitable reliability issues associated with complicated technology, and sometimes dealing again with tool tolerance issues and ultimately the process of validating the results of tool runs to gain confidence in the tool results.

Operators, in particular, found record keeping difficult, and were often challenged by developing performance measures that not only reflected input factors (number of pig runs?), but also outcome results (reduced number of releases?). The bottom line is that during the audit process, operators learned that integrity management was not just in-line inspection, hydrotesting, or direct assessment. Rather, integrity management had to be an integrated programme as envisioned by those in DOT and operators who worked with DOT in developing a workable IM regulatory framework.

Operators and the DOT have generally worked very well together to implement a complicated programme. The DOT and operators share the ultimate goals – keep the product in the pipe, protect the public and the environment, and allow sustained and uninterrupted operation. Industry has worked hard to meet the expectations of the DOT, sometimes struggling with the extensive record-keeping requirements in the rules while focusing on providing real safety benefits through integrity and other efforts to protect pipeline facilities. But accidents happen...

Measuring exposure

The government focuses on a variety of factors in determining whether to prosecute and, if prosecution proceeds and is successful, will apply guidelines that aggravate or reduce the severity of punishment.

Whether or not intent is an element of the offence – keep in mind that simple negligence may be enough for a criminal violation of certain laws – the government will generally look for some evidence of culpability. This may be less of a factor if the type of violation or the company presents an opportunity for a high-visibility prosecution that will provide enhanced industry-wide deterrence.

The level of co-operation with the government in addressing violations will be another factor in a decision as to whether prosecution is warranted, whether this co-operation is manifested through provisions of an audit disclosure programme or otherwise. "Co-operation" is sometimes difficult to define, and various DOJ guidance memos have implied that co-operation may be achieved only with collaboration or surrender.

The government will also look to harm or threat of harm to human health or the environment. Severe harm may trump all of the other factors.

Legal issues

Regulatory and compliance issues, i.e. legal issues, become increasingly important as pipeline-integrity rules evolve and are finalized under the new regulatory schemes. Operators are now confronted with data-integration and records'-retention requirements that can result in increased exposure, including the potential for misinterpretation and misuse of data. Companies are seeing the impact of the new rules at all levels, from increased government audit activity to aggressive enforcement and fines for alleged non-compliance. Potentially more-significant issues exist in the less-obvious exposures created by the rules, such as civil suits, and the impact that increased knowledge of the data from assessments and the obligation to understand what it means or implies can be imputed to management. This represents a significant shift in liability, potentially changing charges of negligence to allegations of wilful misconduct, with the possibility of criminal liability.

One example of the changing environment, where legal issues are increasingly important, involves the processes of risk assessment and ILI that are core to integrity-management programmes. The regulatory scheme calls for operators to capture and integrate all data involving their systems. This mandated activity creates its own set of issues, as the required critical self-analysis may result in generation of documents (meaning any record, including data compilations, electronic media, or photographs, in addition to traditionally prepared written reports) of a potentially-incriminatory nature that could be used against an operator in a future lawsuit by a regulator or by a plaintiff's attorney. Internal audits, incorrectly done, of the integrity-management programme carry the same risks. Companies want to do the right thing, but need to understand the legal risks involved so that they can do the right thing the right way. Information needs to be managed so that it cannot be taken out of context and used to imply deficiencies in programmes, or be used to create liabilities and exposures. This is especially true when the company is legitimately and thoroughly trying to identify, qualify, quantify, and then manage risks.

Companies also have to deal with the issue of improved ILI tools. These tools provide tremendous amounts of data, which may or may not be indicative of a system deficiency. In the hands of the uninformed public or lawyer, this data could be used to create the impression that an ILI-identified anomaly is equated with a defect that requires prompt or immediate repair, or perhaps even shutdown, of the system. Most operators know that valuable data can only be obtained by using multiple tools and methodologies. For example, combinations of MFL and UT tools are understood by many operators as providing necessary but different information that, when combined, can provide the best information for applying mitigative measures to ultimately reduce risks of operation. The tools are each sensitive to different types of anomaly, so tool data from multiple types of tool can be combined to provide clear advantages in seeing what is going on within the pipe. The disadvantage is that the operator is pressed with large amounts of data that must be dealt with, but failure to use multiple tools would be irresponsible given the advantages now known to be gained from a multi-dimensional IM programme.

Issues related to DA and hydrotests are beyond the scope of this paper, but the general rules of exposure and potential liability still apply. The biggest question that an operator may face is whether such methods are appropriate in lieu of pigging except where pigging is not possible.

The problem of terminology or nomenclature also presents significant problems. To a layperson, an anomaly is the equivalent of a defect, and a defect presents a danger. The rules make it somewhat clear that this is not the case, but for real clarity the industry needs to educate the public on the definitions set forth in API 1163.

Finally, vendors and operators need to ensure that the public and regulators are not misled by names applied to ILI tools, or specifications that may be misinterpreted. Crack tools do not find all cracks, and MFL tools cannot always find corrosion or predict growth rates.

What can go wrong?

Pipelines, and ILI vendors, must be advised of potential liabilities and guided to minimizing such liabilities.

The first step that companies sometimes undertake is a programme audit. This is a necessary and important activity but, as discussed previously, it needs to be conducted in a fashion that avoids the creation of unnecessary issues. Failure to conduct an audit may result in operational failures, as well as severe legal implications. As noted above, and discussed as part of the solutions outlined below, failure to actively look at systems to evaluate adequacy may itself be a negligent act subjecting the company to regulatory action or a civil lawsuit in the aftermath of an incident. Along with an audit, programmes need to be in place which provide mechanisms for actually addressing issues raised in audits, recognizing changes in operations on an ongoing basis, and training personnel to recognize, avoid, and address issues.

So what can go wrong? In brief, the problems generally flow from the following fact pattern:

If the operation fails in any way that is significant outside of the company, then outsiders will become involved. "Significant outside of the company" means anything from an adverse economic impact on a third party ("the pipeline went down because of a leak, resulting in a supply disruption"), to injury or death of any person (including an employee), to injury or damage to the environment, or a leak in a high-profile location.

The outsiders will look at the company and the failure, either because they have the public charter to do so (the DOT for safety and integrity of the pipeline, the FTC at supply disruption, OSHA at injuries or deaths, the environmental agencies, and NRDA trustee at environmental issues), or because they see an opportunity to make money (lawyers). The outsiders will look at operations with 20/20 hindsight and, depending on the incident, may look deep into records, policies, procedures, and decisions of the company.

Solutions

The key to solving many of these issues is found in review of the very guidance the government would use if a company were about to be prosecuted for violation of rules.

The best protection that management can provide to minimize liability is enactment of corporate policies and practices through an integrated programme that reduces the likelihood that problems will arise, and that rapidly handles problems that are discovered. If implemented prior to criminal conduct or an incident that results in some civil exposure, compliance programmes may be a useful tool in convincing prosecutors (or a jury) that the company and its management took all reasonable steps to prevent illegal or negligent conduct. If a company is convicted of a crime or found guilty of negligence, the absence of a compliance programme grounded in working policies and procedures virtually guarantees serious problems at sentencing or a larger jury verdict. Therefore, the viability and effectiveness of policies and procedures can best be measured by how well these would fare when the government makes decisions about how it would handle violations. The solutions therefore require the following:

1. A written corporate policy that addresses compliance with all applicable laws. Write policies and procedures so they are effective communications. Avoid technical and legal language whenever possible. Make sure the policy is workable and addresses various scenarios. Have you successfully budgeted for expenditures? Do you have a system for monitoring proposed regulatory changes? Do you handle compliance with new and changing regulations with a logical, systematic process? Publicize the policy. Ensure that it is sanctioned by senior management. Explain the policy to the people who must make it work. No matter how clear it is, some people will not read it or will claim not to understand it. Explain, train, and make records of training.

2. Delegation of responsibility for compliance to trained individuals, whose performance review includes this responsibility.

3. Endorsement of compliance policies by the highest levels of management, and communication of policies throughout the company, demonstrating strong institutional policy to comply with requirements.

4. Audits to measure compliance and effectiveness of systems, done with protections, to avoid having the audit become a problem rather than a useful tool.

5. Procedures for identifying potential problems, reporting them to the appropriate persons to correct them, and tracking issues to resolution, including a reporting system for employees to report criminal conduct by others within the organization without fear of retribution.

6. Commitment of adequate resources for compliance, including a programme to train employees.

7. Procedures for keeping the company aware of changes in regulations and trends in the law.

8. Records'-retention programmes (complying with applicable records'-maintenance requirements) showing that the company has acted thoroughly and promptly to assure compliance, and designed to preserve records (paper and electronic) should litigation be reasonably anticipated.

Contracting for IM services

When the IM regulations were first being discussed, many persons in the industry expressed the concern that vendors, specifically ILI vendors, did not have the capacity to provide the services that were necessary to comply with the rules. The concerns ran from the inability to obtain services to the potential that costs would be prohibitive. In short, there was a concern that not enough tools would be available.

The ILI industry responded by performing, making tools available, and continuing to improve the tools to address known and more-recently-discovered threats to integrity (SCC for example).

Whether an ILI or another type of vendor, it is important that vendors be given specific instructions on how to communicate the results of their efforts. With ILI results, the specifications for the tools leave a wide margin for interpretation, and such interpretation cannot be verified unless and until a visual inspection of the pipe is made. Combine this with the ability of ILI tools to find huge numbers of anomalies and a public that believes that any anomaly is equivalent to a defect that presents an integrity concern, and the problem becomes obvious. Add to this the fact that data is too often presented in reports without context and necessary qualification, and the circumstances are such that legal exposures are aggravated (in fact sometimes created) by poor documentation from vendors where a real problem may not even exist.

In some cases the contract itself can address this concern, with language addressing confidentiality obligations, report submission format, record-keeping requirements, and ownership of work product. Appropriate provisions depend on the type of work the vendor is to perform (i.e. sign the contract before work begins) and the latitude available in negotiations, but no contract should be accepted simply because it is presented as "always done this way." With the money invested in integrity activities, the investment in reviewing a proposed contract is obviously warranted.

Conclusion

The challenges with legal implications in IM are diverse and certainly have not been fully explored in this paper. Further, each company and each circumstance will be different. But the issues are real, and the issues are manageable. The issues are also more than a peripheral nuisance. In past papers the conclusion was that these issues are "not core to the business, but ignoring them can gore the business." Upon further reflection, these issues are core to the business as success in the pipeline business revolves around the ability to safely and reliably move materials through the pipe. Minimizing legal exposure is a fundamental measure of how well the safe and reliable factors are being met. An operator in compliance will avoid penalties for adverse audit findings, and while an operator in compliance may still suffer accidents or failures, the fallout from these will at least be manageable. Doing the right things in achieving compliance translates into business success when operators can demonstrate to the public, agencies, and their own employees that they conduct operations as best is as reasonably possible.

Author's note

The information obtained from these materials or this presentation is not, nor is it intended to be, legal advice. You should consult an attorney regarding your particular situation. We reserve the right to determine whether to accept any matters referred to us for representation. Until we have agreed to being hired by you in regard to any legal matter, we are not your lawyers. Never send confidential or sensitive information to us by e-mail without our permission. By sending such information, you may be waiving any potential attorney-client confidentiality privilege.

Acknowledgement

Much of this paper was first presented at the 19th and 20th International Pipeline Pigging & Integrity Management conferences held in February 2007 and 2008 in Houston, Texas. The substance of the paper, in various versions, was published in *Global Pipeline Monthly*, *The Journal of Pipeline Engineering*, *Oil, Gas & Energy Law Intelligence*, and the *Pipeline and Gas Journal*. Various government documents were referenced in preparing this paper, and the author appreciates all of those persons (especially S.Irwin, C.Foley, P.Vieth, and J.Godfrey) and organizations (DNV-CC Technologies, Keifner and Associates) who taught him about the technical aspects of IM and how to do it right.

How well do you know your pipeline?

by Paul Birkinshaw

Penspen Integrity, Newcastle upon Tyne, UK

PENSPEN INTEGRITY has been providing pipeline inspection or pigging support to pipeline operators for many years. With a focus on pipeline integrity, the efforts of the firm's pigging team have been centred on providing independent advice to operators to help them decide when to inspect their pipelines, which inspection technologies to choose, and then provide technical advice and support during the preparation and execution phases of the actual operations.

A significant part of this work has always involved assessing the piggability of pipelines to ensure that ILI pigging is feasible, and to help define the scope of the preparatory pigging (pipeline proving and cleaning) before ILI. This has generally been done in conjunction with the operator based on its existing records, and in conjunction with a nominated ILI contractor based on its particular requirements.

In recent times within Penspen, efforts have been concentrated on helping pipeline operators to inspect pipelines with little or no pigging history. This short paper describes some of the challenges faced and methods employed to ensure that safe and successful pigging campaigns are developed and executed.

Pigging of onshore gas supply pipelines serving power stations

Together with its colleagues GreyStar UK, which provides operations and maintenance (O&M) services to the UK's gas and liquids pipeline industry, the Penspen Integrity pigging team has recently been working with a number of electricity generators who operate gas-fired power stations with associated high-pressure pipelines connected to the UK's national transmission system (NTS).

The majority of these high pressure gas pipelines are aged between 5 and 15 years old, and have not been pigged at all since commissioning. Furthermore, the power-station operator's personnel often have little or no experience in carrying out pigging (or any of the associated pipeline operations necessary). In general the main aspects of pipeline operations are not considered a core activity by them, with their main pipeline O&M services being contracted out.

Common features for these pipelines include:

- owned by power station operator
- connected to the NTS (with or without pressure reduction)
- continuous operation
- often no alternative source of gas supply
- significant revenue streams dependent on the pipeline
- no operational pigging

- no permanent pigging facilities
- limited operator knowledge (not core business: O&M contracted out)
- doubts about the dependability of pipeline as-built records

Despite having many common features, these pipelines are all different and have their own unique set of challenges and issues.

Currently, UK industry practice (IGEM/TD/1-5) advocates that the frequency of internal inspection of high pressure gas transmission pipelines can be set in one of two ways: either a risk-based approach can be used, where appropriate data and records are available, or – if records are not available – then the maximum interval between internal condition monitoring should not exceed ten years. Against this background, many reluctant pipeline operators are now contemplating their first inspection operations.

The piggability study

The traditional approach within Penspen Integrity in providing pigging support has been to act as a consultant to the pipeline operator, carry out pigging-feasibility studies and provide subsequent support in executing an ILI operation. Increasingly however, through closer O&M ties with many of these customers, Penspen is being asked to deliver turnkey solutions covering all aspects of the pigging operations, including providing temporary pig traps and performing the necessary operations of the pipeline to load, launch, run, receive, and recover all preparatory and ILI pigs and carry out post-inspection integrity-assessment work.

This has brought into sharp focus the importance of the initial feasibility assessment and the important role it plays in identifying all the project requirements, highlighting the key challenges, and developing workable solutions. In the majority of cases for power-station operators, the continued operation of their generating equipment is entirely dependent on supply through a single pipeline. While there may be some limited flexibility in operating conditions, any interruptions in gas delivery and the resultant loss in generation can be measured in excess of £1.0M per day in revenue terms. Furthermore, when temporary pig traps, a dedicated team of operators and specialist subcontract services are all being provided for the execution of the site works, it is critical that the pigging operations are well thought out in advance and that appropriate tools and equipment are on hand so that all planned works can be completed in an efficient and controlled manner.

To ensure that a robust assessment is made and the pigging operations are properly planned, it is essential that all available pipeline data are gathered and assessed. In many cases, data for the pipeline can often be found and/or verified through a site survey and, in principle, the proposed operations might appear straightforward. However for the buried part of the pipeline system it can often be surprisingly difficult to verify that the available data and as-laid pipeline records are a true reflection of reality.

In recognition of this challenge, Penspen's approach is to carry out a comprehensive 'piggability' study from the outset, by conducting a thorough analysis of all available pipeline data to ensure that the company (or others taking on the responsibility of pigging operations) gets to know the pipeline intimately. To ensure all aspects of the pipeline and proposed pigging operations are properly considered, Penspen's approach is to carry out an initial site visit to gather pipeline data and conduct a site survey of the launch and receive facilities. This is subsequently followed by a second visit to determine any unknowns following an initial assessment, and to verify preliminary findings where appropriate. Experience has shown that it is important to challenge the pipeline operator to get as much reliable data as possible so as to eliminate doubts and clarify uncertainties wherever feasible.

It is important to note that the piggability study is not just an assessment of the practical aspects of pigging. It is also essential to consider the possible threats to the pipeline and what inspection tools and techniques should be employed to ensure that a proper condition assessment can be made.

Getting hold of the pipeline data

Getting hold of accurate pipeline data to support a pigging campaign (and any subsequent pipeline integrity assessment work) can sometimes be difficult. In the case of pipelines serving power stations, the available pipeline records are often incomplete and their provenance often uncertain. In the majority of cases, these pipelines have been constructed on an EPC (engineer, procure, and construct) basis, with the resulting pipeline documentation having been supplied by the pipeline contractor throughout the construction phase. Data are often unavailable from initial tender activity, design, procurement, pipe laying, and final commissioning phases.

In general, the data are held in paper form and are kept in archive or plant data rooms together with all similar records for the whole power station site. In some cases, pipeline records have been found to be held on more than one site or have over time been moved from one location to another. As a result, operators often do not entirely know what records they have and where they are kept.

The principle sources of pipeline information and as-built data that might generally be expected to be available include:

- as-built data:

  route information (route maps/drawings)
  site / AGI plans
  process and instrumentation drawings (P&IDs)
  isometric drawings (usually of AGI plant)
  pipebook / weld records or charts
  construction POs and procurement documentation

- construction/commissioning data including:

  construction reports
  commissioning records (including pigging reports)
  third-party incident reports
  repair and maintenance records

- operational data:

  O&M data (such as CP checks)
  current operating conditions
  historical operating conditions
  suspected or known issues (such as evidence of dust / sludge in filters)

Assessment of available pipeline data

Any available pipeline data gathered for a prospective pigging campaign needs to be carefully considered. Operators can sometimes retain huge volumes of records including numerous revisions of the same documentation. It is important to ensure that all the available documentation has been located, and then to invest time assessing it all. It is also essential to pay attention to each document's revision history to identify the latest version.

Additional information contained in construction reports can often help dispel worries regarding unusual pipeline geometry, especially at tie-in locations. Photographs from the time of construction in particular can prove to be an invaluable source of reference.

Commissioning data often include records of pigging that may have been carried out to clean, de-water, and dry the pipeline after hydro-test. This information can be invaluable in deciding what preparatory pigging may be required and in particular what level of initial pipeline proving may be considered necessary.

Operational data are usually relatively easy to obtain, with most operators recording the throughput routinely and on a frequent basis. Historical operating data and any records regarding the frequency of replacement of the plant inlet filters, together with reports on the condition of filter elements, can help to form judgements of the likelihood and potential quantities of debris or contaminants in the pipeline.

Suspected or known issues with a pipeline need to be considered but can, however, give rise to concern. Typical concerns expressed by operational personnel for power-station pipelines centre on the potential for significant quantities of dust (including pyrophoric dust), construction debris, and on occasions a possible build-up of liquid. Anecdotal reports of potential or suspected problems are often difficult to ignore, can be hard to disprove, and can also lead to over-conservatism in the approach to pigging.

The principal outputs of the piggability study are to:

- confirm pigging feasibility
- identify any areas of uncertainty for further investigation
- identify any necessary pipeline adaptations and modifications
- provide key technical data for pig selection and specification
- recommend appropriate preparatory pigging operations and related tasks
- identify the key requirements for ILI pigging (and the ILI service requirements' specification)
- identify any supplementary services (such as pig tracking)
- provide key data for the development of reliable operational procedures
- provide a basis for risk assessment and to develop mitigation measures and emergency-response plans
- provide relevant data to ILI pig vendors to facilitate data analysis

A more considered and thorough review approach in order to get to know a pipeline closely before embarking on a pigging campaign has been proven to yield many direct and indirect advantages. Examples of this can include:

- confirming the adequacy of all launch and receive facilities – pig-trap requirements, access issues, serviceability of valves

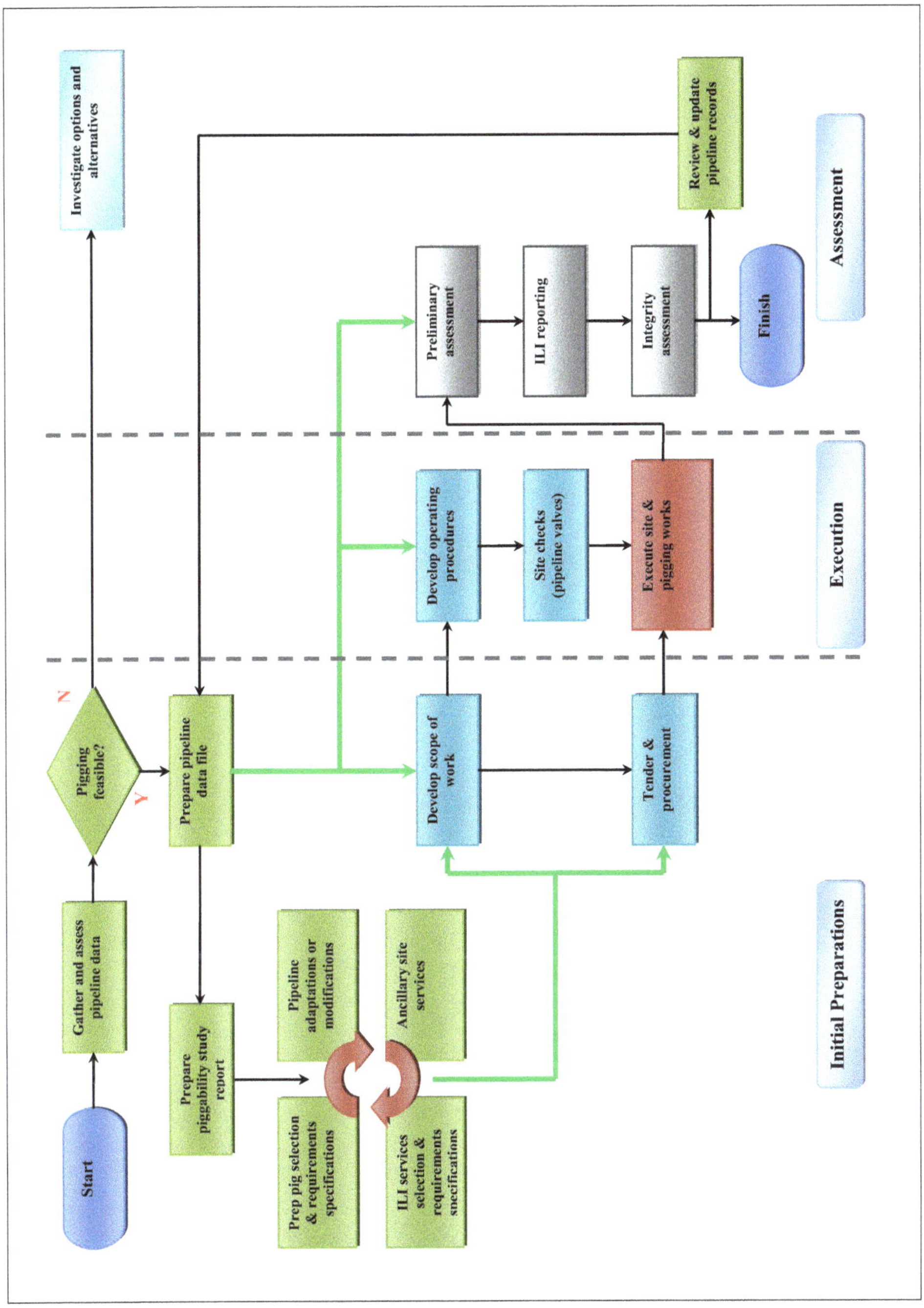

Fig. 1. Piggability study flow chart.

- confirming the arrangement and serviceability of the AGI pipework – for preparation of comprehensive pigging procedures
- quantifying the full range of pipe thickness and bores – for optimum sizing of pigs and sealing elements
- identifying the location and configuration of all major infrastructure crossings locations – for risk-management and emergency-response planning
- identification of significant geometric features including known minimum bend radii – for correct pig selection, pig configuration and sequencing of pig runs

- identification of potential debris sources and contaminants - for correct pig selection, evaluating risk to downstream plant, and for preparedness at receive during operations
- understanding the likely integrity threats to a pipeline and ensuring that the right inspection tools and techniques are selected and deployed.
- improving the quality of the inspection data analysis and reporting output and adding value to the subsequent integrity assessment work

In summary

When considered holistically, a thorough assessment of all the available pipeline data prior to a prospective pigging campaign through a comprehensive piggability study can be seen to provide significant benefits to both the operator and those taking on the responsibility for delivering pigging services, and the approach adopted by Penspen is summarized in the flow chart in Fig1.

Recent experience within Penspen has show that taking the time and effort to get to know a pipeline intimately makes it possible to significantly increase the effectiveness of a planned pigging campaign while at the same time reducing both overall risk and eliminating any unnecessary conservatism.

The piggability study therefore now forms a key part of Penspen's approach to delivering pigging services in this and other market sectors.

Advanced assessment of pipeline integrity using ILI data

by Dr Ted L Anderson

Quest Integrity Group, Boulder, CO, USA

IMPROVEMENTS IN in-line inspection (ILI) and computing technology, coupled with the emergence of fitness-for-service standards, have created an opportunity to advance the state-of-the-art in pipeline-integrity assessment. This paper describes novel approaches for assessing cracks, wall loss, and dents in pipelines using data from ILI tools.

Crack-detection ILI tools that rely on shear-wave UT have improved significantly in both detection probability and sizing accuracy. The Quest Integrity Group employs realistic fracture-mechanics' models that use 3-D elastic-plastic finite-element analysis. The combination of advanced modelling and reliable ILI provides a superior alternative to hydrostatic testing for ensuring pipeline integrity.

ILI tools that measure wall loss with compression-wave UT provide superior results compared to MFL tools. The former outputs a digital map of individual thickness readings, which is ideally suited to effective area assessment methods such as RSTRENG and the API 579 Level 2 remaining strength factor (RSF) calculation. Quest Integrity has developed software that can rapidly process large quantities of ILI wall-loss data and evaluate the maximum allowable operation pressure (MAOP) at discrete locations. The ranking of these MAOP values serves as a rational and rapid means for prioritizing the severity of corrosion throughout the line.

Dents that are introduced during fabrication, installation, or by a third party are the most common source of failure in pipelines. Traditional assessments are based on a simplistic characterization of the dent (such as the ratio of the dent depth to the pipe di:iameter), combined with a simple empirical equation. An advanced dent assessment that combines a detailed mapping of the dent from ILI data (either UT or a caliper pig) with 3-D elastic-plastic finite-element analysis is also described in the paper. A dimensionally-accurate 3-D model of the dented pipe is subjected to cyclic loading, and remaining life is computed through a proprietary low-cycle-fatigue damage model. This advanced methodology can be applied to interacting anomalies such as dent/gouge and dent/crack combinations.

ADVANCES IN in-line inspection (ILI) technology have led to enhancements in both the quality and quantity of pipeline inspection data. Corresponding improvements in fitness-for-service assessment methods and technology are necessary to take full advantage of inspection data with higher resolution and higher accuracy.

The fitness-for-service standard API 579-1/ASME FFS-1 [1] provides a comprehensive guideline for assessing various flaw types and damage mechanisms in all pressure equipment including pipelines. This standard incorporates three levels of assessment:

- Level 1. This is a basic assessment that can be performed by properly-trained inspectors or plant engineers. A Level 1 assessment may involve simple hand calculations.

- Level 2. This assessment level is more complex than Level 1, and should be performed only by engineers trained in the API/ASME FFS standard. Most Level 2 calculations can be performed with a spreadsheet.

- Level 3. This is the most advanced assessment level, which should be performed only by engineers with a high level of expertise and experience. A Level 3 assessment may include computer simulation, such as finite-element analysis (FEA) or computational fluid dynamics (CFD).

These three assessment levels represent a trade-off between simplicity and accuracy. The simplified assessment procedures are necessarily more conservative than more-sophisticated engineering analyses. With Level 1 assessments, the specified procedures must be followed exactly, and there is little or no room for interpretation. Level 2 procedures provide some latitude to exercise sound engineering judgment. For Level 3 assessments, the API/ASME standard provides a few overall guidelines, but the details of the assessment are left to the user. The lack of specificity in Level 3 is by design: there is no practical way to codify step-by-step procedures for advanced engineering analyses because every situation is different, and there a wide range of approaches that may be suitable for a given situation.

The combination of Level 3 fitness-for-service technology and high-fidelity ILI data makes accurate predictions of burst pressure and remaining life feasible. In certain instances, simplified assessments are not sufficient: in the case of crack assessments, for example, supposedly conservative analyses have led to unconservative predictions in some cases.

Quest Integrity Group (QIG) has recently developed advanced assessment techniques for cracks, wall loss, and dents. Level 3 assessments that incorporate elastic-plastic finite-element analysis are used for cracks and dents, and the Group has adapted the API/ASME Level 2 assessment for wall loss in order to process large quantities of ILI compression wave UT data. Each of these advanced assessments is described below.

Level 3 crack assessment as an alternative to hydrostatic testing

Traditional models for crack assessment are considered "conservative" because they tend to underestimate burst pressure and critical crack size. One such approach is the NG-18 method [2], which dates back to the early 1970s and is still widely used today. So-called conservative methods such as NG-18 can actually be unconservative in some instances, as described below.

Hydrostatic testing has traditionally been used to protect pipelines against unexpected failures from cracks or other planar flaws. The hydrostatic test is designed to "detect" critical flaws by causing leaks and ruptures under controlled conditions. In many cases, the NG-18 equation has been used to estimate the critical flaw dimensions at the test pressure. If the pipe passes the hydrostatic test, it is assumed that no flaws larger than the calculated critical dimensions are present. However, this assumption is not justified because the NG-18 equation and other simplified models typically underestimate the critical flaw size.

Figure 1 shows a bell curve that represents the population of crack-like flaws in a pipeline. If a hydrostatic test is performed on this line, cracks on the upper tail of the bell curve will be identified, as indicated by the area shaded in red. The NG-18 equation significantly under-

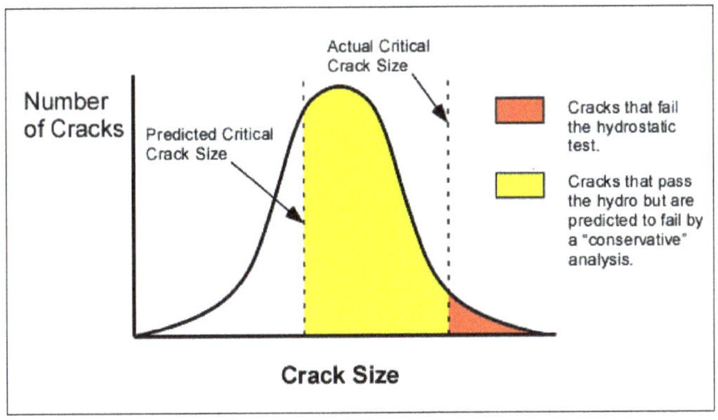

Fig.1. Schematic comparison of predicted and actual critical flaw size for a hydrostatic test. The "conservative" analysis under-predicts the maximum flaw sizes that survive the hydrostatic test.

predicts the critical crack size: the yellow shaded area in Fig.1 represents the population of flaws that were predicted to fail the test but did not. In other words, larger-than-predicted cracks are left in the pipe following a hydrostatic test. The scenario that is schematically illustrated in Fig.1 is demonstrated with actual data below.

A 16-in Schedule-10 pipeline, which was installed in 1955, has experienced hook cracks in ERW seams, and cracks have grown over time by fatigue due to pressure cycling. As a result of several in-service failures, the operator instituted a hydrostatic testing programme in 1991. The NG-18 equation was used to predict the critical flaw dimensions at the test pressure. A fatigue crack propagation analysis was then performed on the calculated critical flaw sizes in order to infer an appropriate retest interval. The most recent full-line hydrostatic test on this pipeline was performed in 1999, and the corresponding critical flaw calculation from the NG-18 equation is represented by the blue curve in Fig.2.

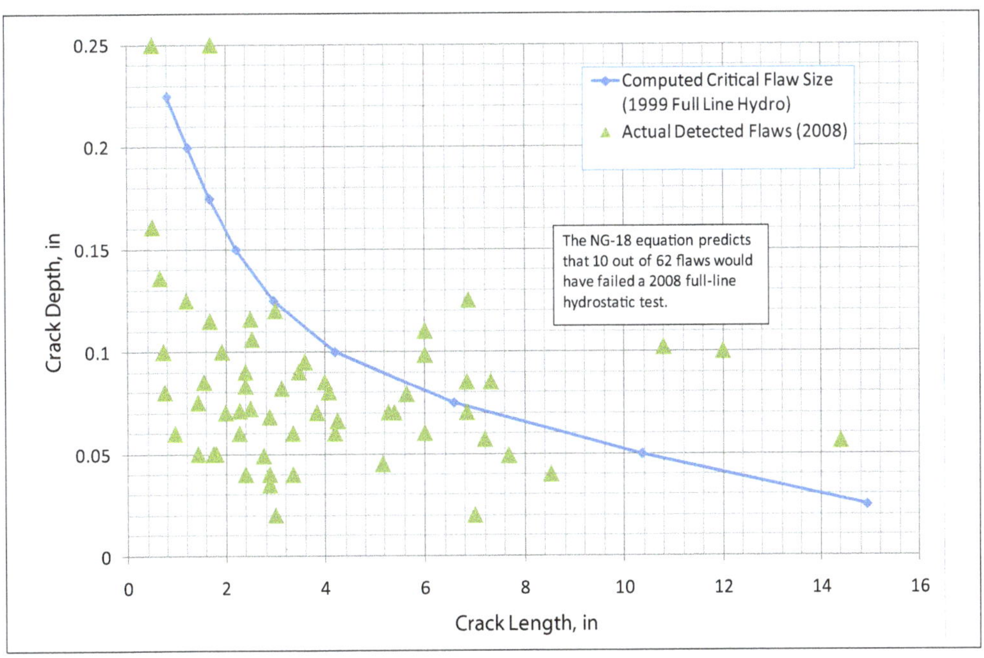

Fig.2. Comparison of predicted maximum flaw sizes that survived the 1999 hydrostatic test with actual measured flaws following a 2008 ILI tool run. The NG-18 equation was used for critical flaw predictions.

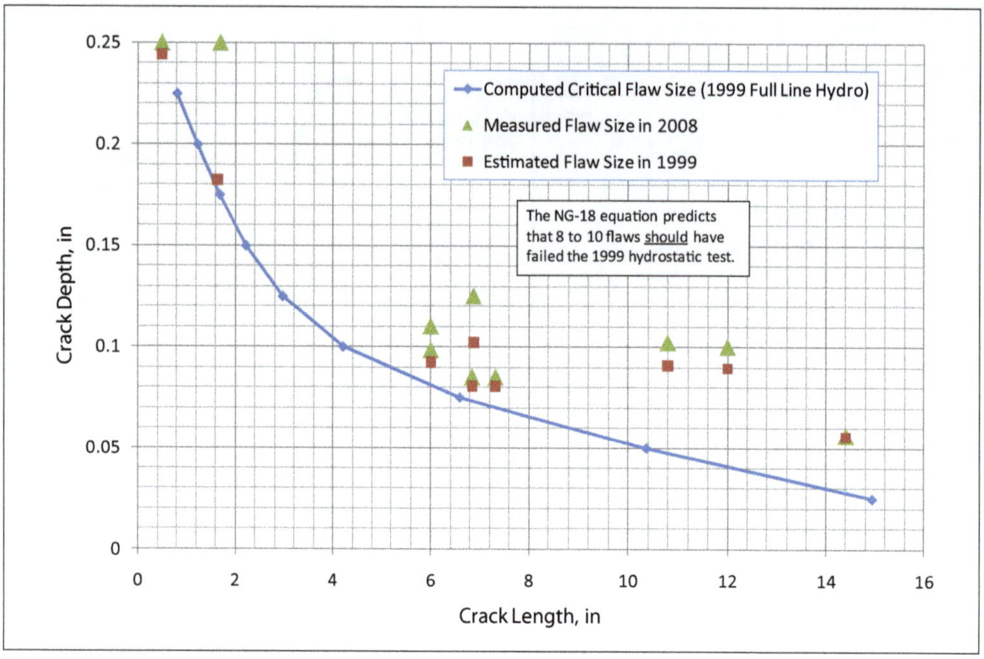

Fig.3. Comparison of predicted critical flaw size for the 1999 hydrostatic test with the calculated dimensions of the ten worst flaws in 1999.

This pipe was inspected by a shear wave UT ILI tool in 2008: 139 cracks were reported, 62 of which were sized by manual UT, and the measured crack dimensions for these 62 flaws are plotted in Fig.2. The NG-18 equation predicts that 10 of these 62 flaws would have failed a follow-up full-line hydrostatic test, had it been conducted at the time of the 2008 inspection. We performed a reverse fatigue analysis of these 10 flaws in order to estimate their dimensions at the time of the 1999 test, and the results of this exercise are plotted in Fig.3. Although the flaw dimensions were smaller in 1999 than in 2008 (red data points versus green data points), 8 out of 10 of the red data points lie above the critical flaw curve, as computed from the NG-18 relationship. The other two flaws fall on the curve. This analysis demonstrates that larger-than-predicted flaws survived the 1999 hydrostatic test, which is consistent with the schematic in Fig.1. Underestimating the critical flaw size for a hydrostatic test is potentially unconservative: large flaws grow faster than small flaws, so an underestimate of the maximum flaw sizes that survived the test can result in an overestimate of the safe operating interval between tests.

The 1970s–vintage NG-18 equation is incapable of accurate predictions of critical flaw size or burst pressure, and a state-of-the-art Level 3 crack analysis provides a much more accurate reflection of reality. Quest has applied a Level 3 assessment to the 16-in pipeline described above, and the assessment procedure contains the following features:

- Three-dimensional elastic-plastic finite element models of cracks in ERW seams.
- Fracture toughness inferred from laboratory tests on samples extracted from the pipe of interest.
- Weld residual stress computed from a finite-element simulation of the ERW process.

Figure 4 shows a typical 3-D model of a crack in an ERW seam: 35 such analyses were run for the 16-in ERW pipe, which encompassed a wide range of crack dimensions. Figure 5 is a repeat of the comparison between predicted and measured flaws in Fig.2, but with predictions based on the

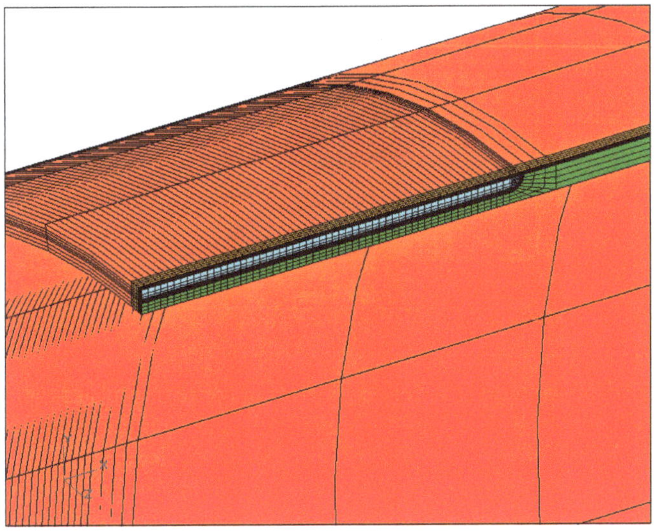

Fig.4. Finite-element model of a crack in an ERW seam. The model is ¼ symmetric.

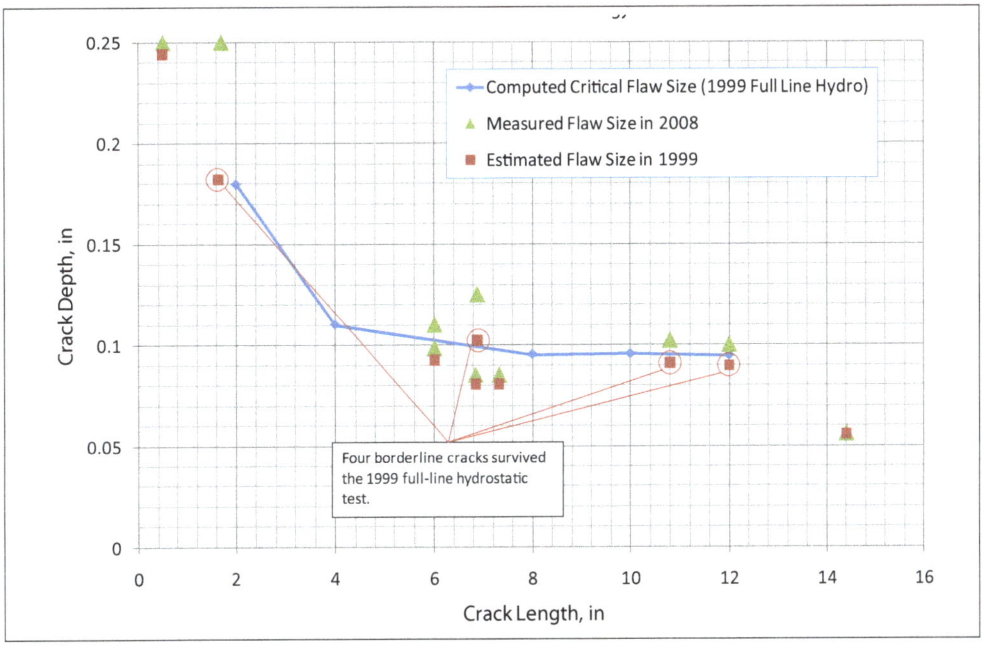

Fig.5. Repeat of Fig.3, but with critical flaw size predictions based on the QIG Level 3 assessment.

Level 3 assessment. This analysis indicates that four flaws were marginal at the time of the 1999 full-line hydrostatic test, that is, they barely survived the test and would almost certainly have failed a follow-up test. It is fortunate that these flaws did not lead to in-service failures in the nine-year period between the full-line hydro and the ILI tool run.

The 16-in line discussed here was due for a full-line hydrostatic test in September 2009, but the operator received a temporary deferment from the US Department of Transportation (DOT). Quest is working with the operator to validate an alternative to hydrostatic testing that is based on a combination of ILI and Level 3 crack assessment. Pending the results of this study, the DOT may permit the operator to permanently replace the existing hydrostatic testing program with the alternative strategy.

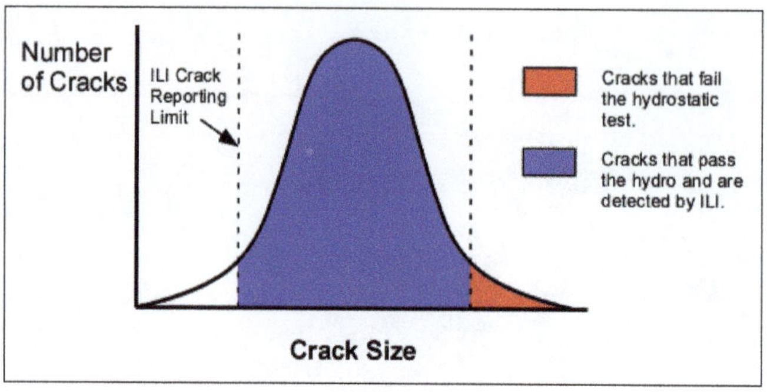

Fig.6. Comparison of ILI crack detection capabilities with the ability of hydrostatic testing to identify cracks.

Hydrostatic testing is a very expensive but ineffective means for identifying cracks and other planar flaws in pipelines. Figure 6 schematically compares the relative effectiveness of hydrostatic testing with ILI: the former identifies only the largest flaws, while the current generation of shear-wave ILI tools can detect very small flaws. For example, of the 139 reported cracks from the 2008 ILI of the 16-in pipe, only four or five would have failed a full-line hydrostatic test. Given the ILI data, a Level 3 analysis can be used to establish repair criteria and re-inspection intervals. This alternative strategy provides a greater degree of reliability at a significantly lower cost compared to the traditional hydrostatic testing approach.

The shear-wave UT ILI tool used to inspect the 16-in ERW pipe has a 90% probability of detection for cracks greater than 40mils (1mm) in depth. Thus, this tool is far more sensitive at detecting flaws compared to hydrostatic testing. However, there is still room for improvement on flaw sizing accuracy with shear-wave ILI data. In the case of the inspection on the 16-in pipe, flaw depths were reported in ranges: 40-80mils (1-2mm), 80-160mils (2-4mm), and > 160mils. While flaws shallower than 40mils (1mm) can be detected, such indications were not reported because it is difficult to distinguish cracks from extraneous reflections from the ERW seam.

Figures 7 and 8 are plots of the measured flaw depths for cracks reported in the 40-80 and 80-160mil ranges, respectively. For flaws reported in the 40-80mil range, the manual UT measurements exhibit a significantly wider range of crack depths compared to the reported range. Note that two 20-mil (0.5-mm) deep cracks were reported, which is an indication of the high sensitivity of the ILI tool. For the 80-160mil depth range, the measured flaw depths generally fall within the reported range. This indicates that sizing accuracy with ILI shear wave UT data is better for deeper cracks. Both populations of flaws (40-80 and 80-160mil reported ranges) follow Weibull statistical distributions. Given the uncertainty between the actual depth of a given flaw and the reported range from the ILI data, a probabilistic analysis is recommended.

Rapid assessment of metal loss with compression-wave UT ILI data

Metal loss in pipelines has traditionally been assessed with the ASME B31.G and RSTRENG [3] methods. Given an ILI dataset covering several hundred kilometres of pipe, a manual data analysis taking up to three months is typically performed prior to assessing the wall loss and applying acceptance criteria. A primary purpose of this initial analysis is to identify and size discrete corrosion flaws. In addition to the time and cost associated with this painstaking process, a major problem with this approach is that reality seldom conforms to the ideal of discrete areas of wall thinning surrounded by uncorroded metal. Instead, wall thickness in a corroded pipe varies continuously over the surface; obvious discrete flaws are the exception rather than the rule.

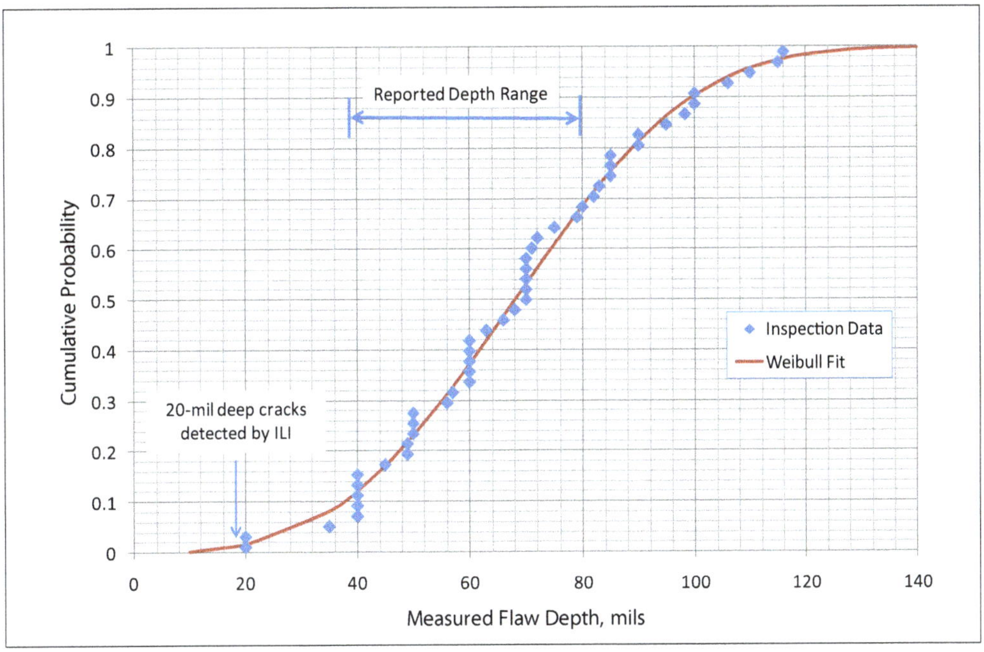

Fig.7. Measured depths (with manual UT) of flaws reported to be within the 40-80mil (1-2mm) range based on ILI UT data.

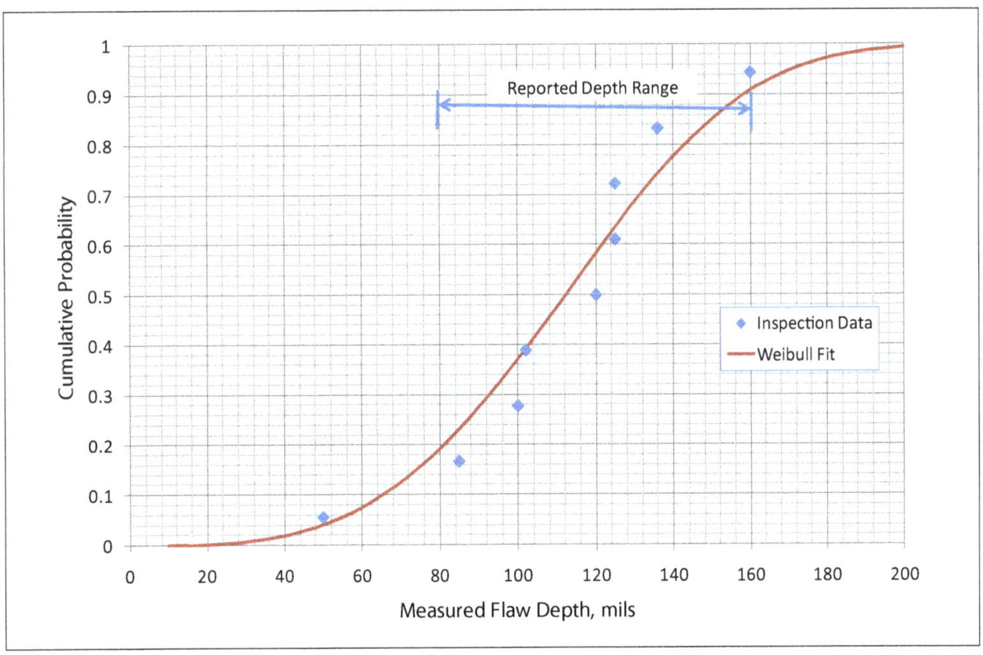

Fig.8. Measured depths (with manual UT) of flaws reported to be within the 80-160mil (2-4mm) range based on the ILI UT data.
(a) Idealized case with discrete flaws.
(b) Actual UT data. This is a 2-D "unwrapped" plot of wall thickness.

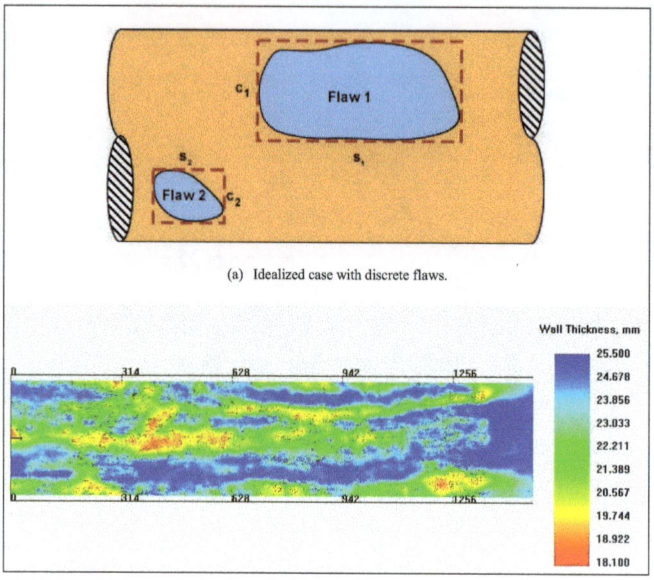

Fig.9. Comparison of actual UT wall loss data with the idealized case where discrete flaws are surrounded by uncorroded material.

This reality is evident in high-resolution compression-wave UT data which, unlike MFL data, can be displayed as a digital map of wall thickness. Figure 9 compares the ideal of discrete flaws with a colour map of actual UT wall thickness data: part of the UT data analyst's job is to take the non-ideal wall thickness data and force-fit it to the discrete flaw ideal. The process is often referred to as "flaw boxing", as the analyst defines the length and width of the "flaw" with a rectangle that contains the corresponding wall loss data. When applying the B31.G acceptance criteria, the only measurements that are used in the assessment are the length and width of the boxed flaw, along with the minimum measured wall within the box. In such cases, over 99% of the wall thickness data are discarded, and a key advantage of high-resolution UT data relative to MFL is lost.

The Level 2 assessment of metal loss in API 579-1/ASME FFS-1 2007 [1] is an effective-area method that is similar to RSTRENG [3]. Flaw boxing is not required with the API/ASME method, however. A "river-bottom" profile is constructed from the thickness data, and a remaining strength factor (RSF) is calculated, which can be used to compute a maximum allowable operating pressure (MAOP). These calculations can be performed over a short segment of pipe, or a single MAOP can be computed for an entire pipe section between girth welds. All valid wall thickness readings are considered with this assessment method. This approach is not only less labour intensive than flaw boxing, it is much less subjective, and results in a more technically-sound MAOP.

Quest has developed its *LifeQuest Pipeline* software to process and visualize data from high-resolution compression-wave UT ILI tools, including intelligent pigs [4]. The software (Fig.10) performs a Level 2 API/ASME wall-loss assessment over an entire ILI dataset, and computes the RSF and MAOP for each pipe section. The areas of highest corrosion damage can be quickly identified by ranking the calculated RSF and MAOP values.

Level 3 dent assessment

Pipe denting is a sufficiently complex phenomenon that Level 3 assessment technology is warranted. Significant plastic strain occurs when a dent first forms, and the pipe tends to re-round upon pressure cycling, such that the observed deformation understates the true damage that has

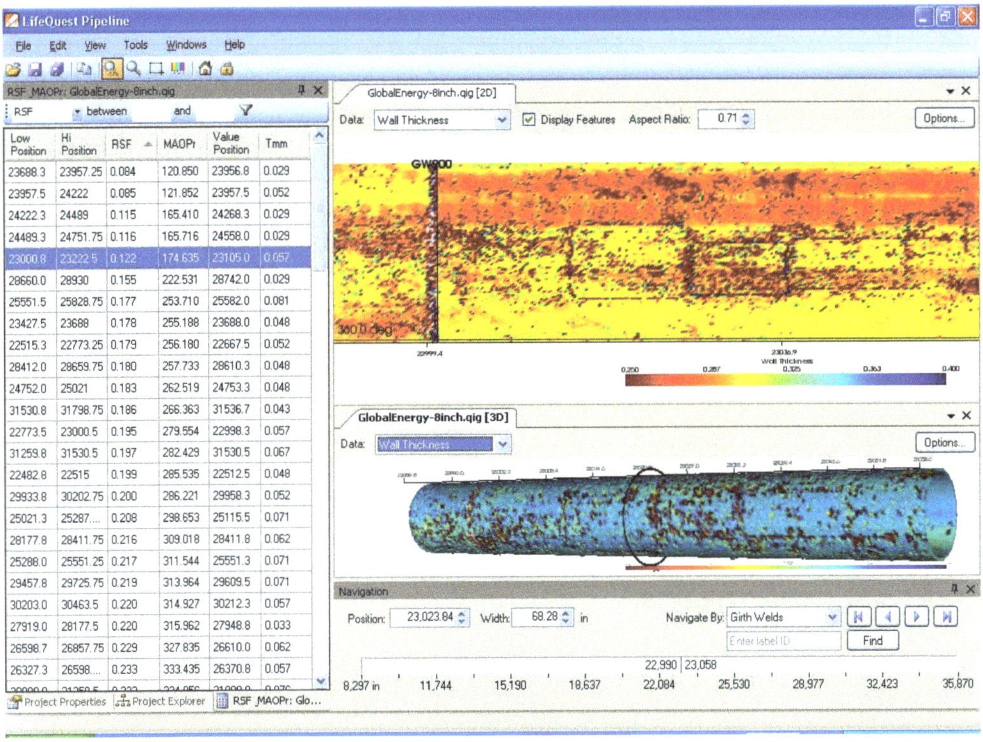

Fig. 10. The LifeQuest Pipeline *software.*
(a) Immediately after formation of the dent.
(b) Re-rounding after ten pressure cycles.

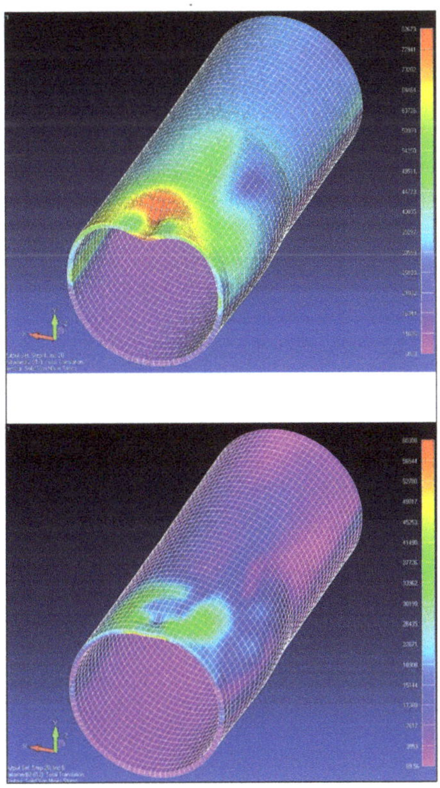

Fig. 11. Elastic-plastic finite-element simulation of dent formation and pressure cycling.

accumulated in the pipe. The size, shape, and location of the original dent affect the remaining life, as do external factors such as the constraint provided by the surrounding soil.

In order to handle the complexities associated with dents, a Level 3 assessment methodology has been developed that relies on elastic-plastic finite-element simulation, and in which the formation of the dent is simulated, along with the subsequent pressure cycling. The support of the surrounding soil is incorporated as appropriate. The remaining life is calculated through the use of a proprietary low-cycle fatigue damage model that has been incorporated into the elastic-plastic finite-element simulation. Dimensional data from ILI can be used to build 3-D finite-element models of dented pipes, although the prior damage created during the initial denting must be taken into account. Quest has performed parametric studies to infer the relationship between the current dimensions and the as-dented configuration. Elastic-plastic finite-element simulation can also be used to model interacting anomalies, such as a crack in a dent.

Figure 11a shows a typical 3-D finite-element model of a pipe after the formation of a dent, and Fig.11b shows the same model after ten pressure cycles. Note that the pipe has re-rounded.

Acknowledgements

Much of the work described in this paper was funded by Koch Pipeline. The author would like to acknowledge the contributions of his colleagues at Quest Integrity Group who have participated in the development of the advanced pipeline assessment technology described here, including Greg Brown, Devon Brendecke, Eric Scheibler, Dan Revelle, Jim Rowe, and Greg Thorwald.

References

1. APIand ASME, 2007. API 579-1/ASME FFS-1 Fitness-for-service. Jointly published by the American Petroleum Institute and the American Society for Mechanical Engineers, June.
2. J.F.Kiefner, W.A.Maxey, R.J.Eiber, and A.R.Duffy, 1973. Failure stress levels of flaws in pressurized cylinders. ASTM STP 536, American Society for Testing and Materials.
3. PRCI. A modified criterion for evaluating the remaining strength of corroded pipelines. PRCI/AGA, contract: PR-3-805, catalog no L51688.
4. S.Papenfuss, 2009. Pigging the 'unpiggable': new technology enables in-line inspection and analysis for non-traditional pipelines. 5th MENDT Conference, Bahrain, November.

Measuring the effectiveness of the US IM programme

by Terry Boss[1], David Johnson[2], Bernie Selig[3], and John Zurcher[3]

1 Interstate Natural Gas Association of America (INGAA), Chicago, IL, USA
2 Panhandle Energy (Chair of INGAA Pipeline Safety Committee), Houston, TX, USA
3 Process Performance Improvement Consultants, Bloomfield, CT, USA

THE REQUIREMENT to perform integrity-management (IM) programmes in the US was mandated by Congress at the end of 2002, and actual inspections began in 2004. The Interstate Natural Gas Association of America (INGAA) began a programme to measure the effectiveness of the IM programmes with some of its member companies, representing approximately 192,000 km of transmission pipeline. The US has 472,000 km of onshore gas transmission piping. This paper provides six years of gathered data on IM activities and compares them to PHMSA data.

The INGAA participating companies had inspected more than 80% of their high-consequence area (HCA) pipelines, while the total for all PHMSA miles was more than 90% by the end of 2009. The number of PHMSA reported 'immediate' and 'scheduled' repairs being made in HCAs is 0.17 repairs/mile (0.11 repairs/km) of the assessed HCA pipelines averaged over the six-year period. The total number of all repairs reported for the INGAA companies is an average of 0.11 repairs/mile (0.07 repairs/km) of HCA inspected. There were six reportable incidents in HCAs in 2009 for all onshore gas transmission piping, five of which were due to third-party caused damage.

Reassessments, re-inspection of pipe that already had a baseline inspection, are reported for the INGAA programme. For the calendar years 2007 through 2009, 641 HCA miles (1025 km) of pipeline have been reassessed. There were 19 repairs made in the reassessed pipe, equating to 0.03 repairs/mile (0.02 repairs/km), a 73% reduction in the number of repairs in reassessed pipeline.

THE PIPELINE Safety Committee of INGAA initiated a programme in 2003 to gather information about the conduct of integrity-management (IM) programmes by member gas-transmission pipeline companies. The goal of the programme is to determine the impact that IM may have on operations and to provide industry data for participating companies to utilize for benchmarking purposes.

Integrity-management programmes are required by the Pipeline Safety Improvement Act of 2002 and the US Department of Transportations' Pipeline and Hazardous Materials Administration (PHMSA) regulations in 49CFR192, Subpart O, of December 17th, 2003 [1]. As part of the IM programme regulation (192.945), operators are required to collect "the four overall performance measures" specified in ASME B31.8S section 9.4 [2] and the specific measures for each identified threat listed in B31.8S, Table 9. Operators must submit the four overall measures to PHMSA on an annual basis. The threat-specific measures of Table 9 of B31.8S must be collected by the operators but are not required to be submitted to PHMSA.

This paper compares six years of INGAA IM data with PHMSA data, and provides some of the results for the Table 9 data collected as part of this programme. In addition, this paper also presents data on incidents and leaks reported over the same period.

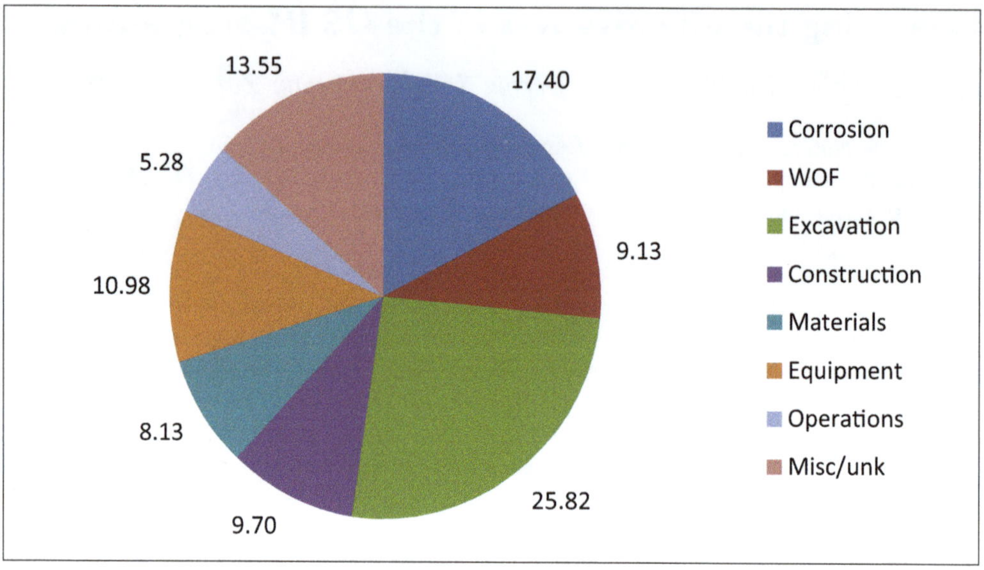

Fig. 1. Incident causes averaged during 2002-2009 by percent.

Prior to collecting specific data, the INGAA participants more clearly defined the data elements to be collected and some of these definitions are provided and discussed. The INGAA group also addressed reassessments and decided that for the "four overall measurements" the reassessments are to be reported separately, and those results are also included in this paper. The definitions can be found in Reference 3.

Reportable-incident data

Incidents reported to PHMSA for the years 2002 through 2009 show that the number reported each year has averaged 87.6 with a high of 106 and a low of 55[1]. The number was driven in some years by significant weather events in the Gulf Coast area. The trend overall is basically flat, and the number of gas-transmission miles averaged 296,022 for this period (473,635 km).

Three factors may be affecting this steady incident number. First, when the reporting requirements changed, beginning in 2002, the cost of gas was $2.50. In years with higher gas prices, the number of incidents may be inflated. Second, the number of incidents reported due to operator determination that the incident was significant - even though there were no fatalities or injuries and the cost did not exceed $50,000 - is included in the PHMSA tally. This fluctuation in reporting adds complexity to trending. Third, the cost of repairs has risen significantly since 2002. Adjusting the number of reportable incidents for gas cost and determination of a significant incident may allow a decrease in incidents to an average of 59 per year with a high of 70 and a low of 48. Overall, the trend is still basically flat. The incident rate was approximately 0.3 incidents per 1000 miles/year given the total reported incidents or 0.20 per 1000 miles/year based on the adjusted number of incidents.

The number of fatalities reported during this period was seven. Of these fatalities, six were due to third-party damage and one was due to external corrosion. Three involved company contractors,

1 A reportable incident is one where either a fatality, or injury requiring hospitalization and or has losses, including lost gas, in excess of $50,000.

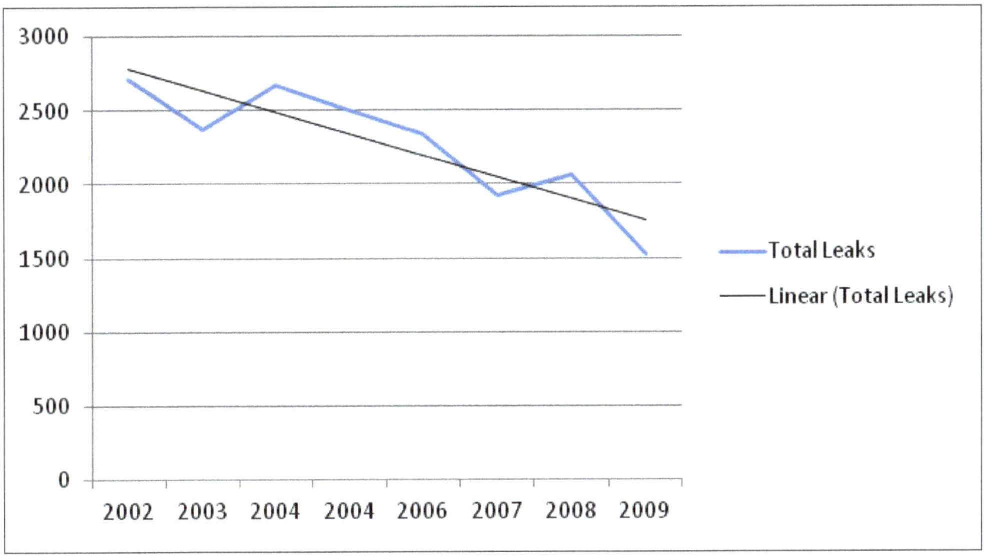

Fig.2. Number of leaks, 2002-2008.

one involved a company employee, and three involved the general public. Two of the three general public fatalities were due to third-party damage where the fatally injured person was the excavator; the other general public fatality was due to external corrosion.

The number of injuries reported during this period was 50. Of these, 17 were company employees, 17 were company contractors, and 16 were general public injuries.

The causes of these incidents shows excavation damage as the leading cause at 25.82%, with corrosion (external and internal) as the second leading cause at 17.40%. Equipment as the cause was third at 10.98%, while construction was fourth at 9.70% and weather-related causes were fifth at 9.13%.

Incidents in high-consequence areas (HCAs) totalled 50 for the reporting years of 2004 through 2009, of which 24 were due to third-party damage. The number of HCA miles for this period averaged 20,021 (32,034 km). The incident rate was approximately 0.4 incidents per 1000 miles/year, which is approximately 30% higher than the overall incident rate for all gas-transmission miles.

Reportable-leak data

Leaks reported to PHMSA for the years 2002 through 2009 show that the number reported each year has averaged 2264 with a high of 2675 and a low of 1521. The trend overall is downward. The number of gas transmission miles averaged 296,022 for this period.

Figure 2 shows the number of leaks per year for the years 2002-2009, and Table 2 shows leaks by cause for same period. The major contributor to the number of leaks was corrosion with an average of 990 per year, or 44%[2]. The second leading cause was material/weld with an average of 390 or 17%, while the third leading cause was equipment/operations with an average of 355 or 16%.

2 The corrosion category includes external and internal corrosion as well as SCC

	2002	2003	2004	2005	2006	2007	2008	2009	Average
Total incidents	55	81	83	106	105	91	92	88	87.6
Adjustment	7	5	15	5	12	9	18	16	28.6
Net incidents	48	60	50	63	56	70	63	62	59.0

Table 1. Incidents: 2002-2009.

Year	Corrosion	Natural force	Excavation	Outside force	Material weld	Equipment operations	Other
2002	1179	33	110	44	662	306	380
2003	1054	15	108	63	470	264	403
2004	1482	33	85	47	404	324	300
2005	893	62	79	44	421	311	691
2006	854	29	91	115	408	536	307
2007	980	45	66	58	265	270	236
2008	872	34	58	61	275	466	300
2009	608	35	51	27	214	362	224

Table 2. Leaks by cause, 2002-2009.

Review of the leak information by cause shows downward trends for corrosion, excavations, and for material/weld. The downward trend in corrosion may be attributable in part to the over-testing aspect of the IM programme. A significantly greater length of pipelines is being assessed than is required (up to 2009, 139,252 miles (222,803 km) of pipe had been assessed). This over-testing may also be contributing to the material/weld leaks declining. The downward trend for the excavation damage cause may be attributable in part to expanded damage-prevention programmes including the 811 One-Call number and implementation of the Common Ground Alliance's best practices.

Leaks in HCAs totalled 593 for the years 2004 through 2009. Of the 593 leaks reported, 325 (55.2%) were due to equipment leakage. The second leading cause of leaks in HCAs was due to corrosion with 124 reported, or 20.9%. The third leading cause was due to third-party damage with 44 leaks reported (7.4%); construction, and weather-related, caused leaks numbered 38 (6.4%) and 33 (5.6%), respectively.

The corrosion-leak category shows a basic downward trend with 29 in 2004, decreasing steadily to 16 in 2008 but up to 20 in 2009. This may be directly attributable to the requirement by the IM programme for corrosion assessments for all HCA areas by the end of 2012.

Reportable integrity-management data

Integrity-management data reported to PHMSA for the years 2004 through 2009 show that the HCA miles averaged 20,177 (32,283 km), representing approximately 6.8% of the average total gas-transmission mileage of 294,991 (471,986 km). For this period, the total length inspected was 139,252 miles (222,803 km), or 47.4% of the total US mileage. There were 19,989 miles

Year	System miles	System miles inspected	HCA miles	HCA miles inspected	Immediate repairs in HCAs	Scheduled repairs in HCAs
2004	298,207	31,273	21,764	3,997	104	599
2005	297,968	19,516	20,561	2,908	261	378
2006	293,696	20,250	19,949	3,500	169	342
2007	291,898	25,940	19,277	4,661	258	452
2008	295,779	20,258	19,568	2,454	146	213
2009	292,399	23,027	18,996	2,337	124	251

Table 3. IMP data, 2002-2008.

	2004	2005	2006	2007	2008	2009
Total miles of gas transmission piping reporting	122,881	107,952	116,757	120,318	120,000	142,020
Gas capacity reductions due solely to IMP activities - MMCF	16	7	10.5	13.4	5.9	N.C
Interstate high consequence (HCA) miles	4403	4344	5574	5493	5113	5946
Intrastate HCA miles	2594	1,180	1004	1104	1085	1093
Number of miles inspected by ILI		5,029	6183	9605	6514	6100
Number of miles Inspected by hydrostatic test		224	206	256	154	984
Number of miles inspected by direct assessment		331	152	303	332	1379
Non-HCA miles inspected	5456	5,128	5,733	9157	5759	6951
HCA miles inspected	820	457	808	1021	1241	707
Number of repairs made in non-HCA miles of pipe	537	501	1041	1237	1644	2088
Number of repairs made in HCAs	74	85	93	69	167	194
Pipe replaced in non-HCAs	10,000	15,391	25,294	66,955	52,599	20,057
Pipe replaced in HCAs	0	1,297	3,498	5491	9847	6146

Table 4. IMP activities 2004-2008 for INGAA members.

(31,982 km) of HCAs inspected during this period. The over-testing ratio is 6.96, meaning that for every mile of HCA inspected, 6.96 miles (11.14 km) of non-HCA miles were inspected.

For this period, there were 1,062 repairs made in HCAs that were classified as 'immediate' and 2235 repairs made that were classified as 'scheduled'. There were 0.17 repairs made per mile of HCA. Table 3 shows information reported to PHMSA for the years 2002 through 2009.

Incident and leak information in HCAs has been discussed previously in this paper. However, in addition to the incident and leak information, failures are also tracked. Failures are significant events that do not result in an incident or leak, but which mean that the facility was not operated

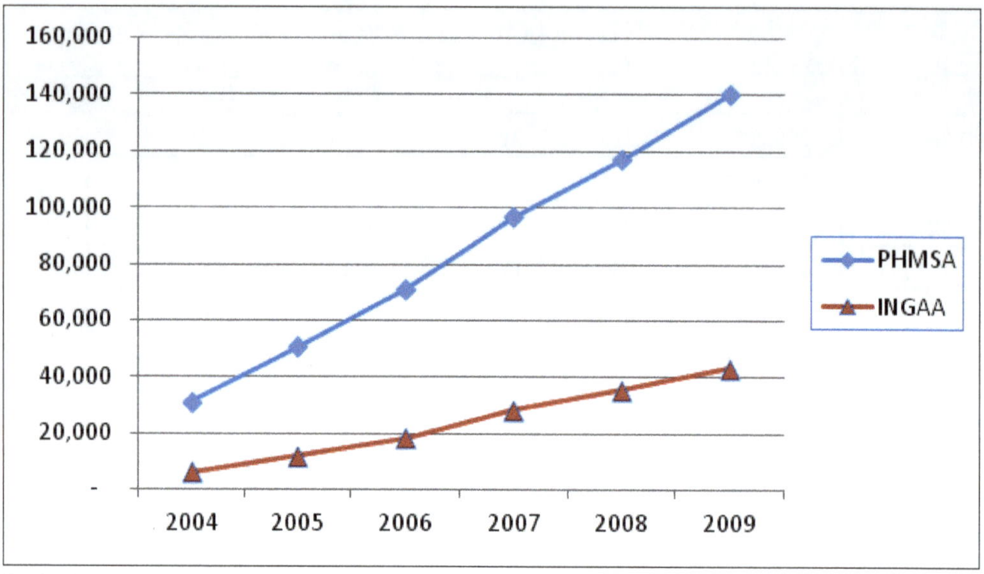

Fig.3. Cumulative length (miles) of pipe assessed.

as intended. Included in this category would be mechanical coupling failures and equipment failures.

There were 174 failures reported in HCAs. The largest category was equipment, with 61 (or 35.1%). Third-party damage failures were 42 (24.1%0, external corrosion failures were 35 (20.1%), and construction and incorrect operations accounted for 14 each, or 8.0%. There is no discernible trend in these data.

In addition to the baseline assessments, 1285 HCA miles (2056 km) were reassessed in 2008 and 2009. For the reassessments, 29 immediate repairs were made and 19 scheduled repairs were made. Of the immediate repairs made, seven were actually coating repairs; 17 of the immediate repairs were minor dents with minor corrosion metal loss, one was a plain dent, and four were corrosion on pipelines with a known corrosion history and an assessment frequency of five years or less. The overall repair rate for reassessed HCAs was 0.037 repairs/mile, a 78% reduction from the baseline repair rate of 0.17 repairs/mile.

Integrity measures: comparison of INGAA and PHMSA data

Six years of INGAA-reported data are shown in Table 4. One of the programme's objectives has been to determine the impact of IM on the pipelines. Initially, industry was concerned that the

Assessment method	Total miles	Percent
ILI	33,431	93.4
Pressure testing	984	2.7
Direct assessment	1379	3.9
Total	35,794	100.0

Table 5. Total length (miles) inspected by assessment method 2005-2008 for INGAA members.

Cause	2004	2005	2006	2007	2008
External corrosion	0.043	0.107	0.018	0.032	0.035
Internal corrosion	0.005	0	0	0	0
Stress corrosion cracking	0.005	0.011	0.001	0	0
Manufacturing	0	0	0	0	0
Construction	0.037	0.492	0.179	0.251	0.073
Equipment	0.006	0.004	0.002	0.001	0.007
Third-party damage	0.004	0.055	0.012	0.001	0.01
Incorrect operations	0	0.002	0	0.001	0
Weather/outside force	0	0.007	0	0.001	0

Table 6. Repairs/HCA mile inspected by cause 2002-2008 for INGAA members.

Cause	2004	2005	2006	2007	2008
External corrosion	0.109	0.1	0.125	0.096	0.21
Internal corrosion	0.01	0.014	0.008	0.002	0.003
Stress corrosion cracking	0.005	0.007	0.001	0.001	0.003
Manufacturing	0	0	0	0.0003	0.0003
Construction	0.023	0.13	0.028	0.136	0.089
Equipment	0.001	0.001	0.003	0.004	0.006
Third-party damage	0.008	0.009	0.001	0.0019	0.007
Incorrect operations	0.0004	0.001	0.0005	0.0003	0.002
Weather/outside force	0.0002	0.004	0.0002	0.0017	0.002

Table 7. Repairs/non-HCA miles by cause for INGAA members.

inspections, especially in-line inspection, could have a deleterious effect on pipeline shipping capacity. The capacity reductions made due to IM activities over the first five years indicates that this effect was minimal.

Table 5 shows the total miles inspected by each of the three assessment methods: in-line inspection (ILI); pressure testing; and direct assessment (DA). Over 93% of the INGAA miles have been inspected by ILI.

The IM programme metrics team agreed upon a number of definitions to be used during the programme (see Reference 3); the most significant of these is the definition of a repair. The 'total number of actionable anomalies repaired – non-HCA and HCA', is defined as: "the total number of actionable anomaly repairs made to pipelines as a consequence of the IMP inspections, whether within an HCA or outside HCAs. Only repairs physically made to the pipe are considered repairs. For this metric, coating repairs are not considered repairs. Each actionable anomaly repaired shall be counted when a repair method is used that repairs multiple anomalies in one repair." It is the ILI data analysis that determines whether an anomaly is immediate, scheduled, or monitored, and that result is used to determine the number of repairs. The term 'actionable anomaly' comes from the definition in API 1163 *In-line inspection systems qualification standard* [4].

	2004	2005	2006	2007	2008	Total
Number of audits/reviews	78	105	147	81	49	460
Number of findings -High	0	0	0	0	0	0
Number of findings - Medium	0	1	5	3	1	10
Number of findings - Low	77	116	68	1515	83	1859
Number of procedural changes due to findings	21	156	103	126	5	411

Table 8. Audit results.

Over 41 miles (71 km) of pipeline have been replaced as a consequence of the IM programme assessments. All of the actionable anomalies in those miles of pipe have been included in the number of repairs made. So, for example, if 100 ft of pipe was replaced because there were ten 'immediate', five 'scheduled', and five 'monitored' actionable anomalies in that 100-ft length, that has counted as 20 repairs, not one.

Tables 6 and 7 list the repairs/mile made for each of the nine threats by cause listed in B31.8S for both HCAs and non-HCAs. (The 2009 data for the INGAA companies had not been compiled as of the final date for submitting this paper.) These statistics and the number of leaks by cause, which can be found in the INGAA IM programme metrics report for 2008 [3], are useful for guidance in risk analysis and risk management. They provide clear guidance on which threats have the highest probabilities of occurrence.

Table 9 of ASME B31.8S also requires collecting data on the number of audits, both internal and external, that are conducted. Table 8 shows the data for the five-year period, in which there were no high-impact findings. (B31.8S requires that findings be listed by severity: the INGAA metrics team used high, medium, and low severities, and defined each of them. See Reference 3 for further details.)

The 460 audits conducted by the INGAA member companies resulted in 411 procedural changes/improvements to their IM programmes. These audit results and the changes they engendered are strong evidence of 'continuous improvement' by the member companies, a requirement of the IM regulations.

Conclusions

A number of conclusions can be reached from the presented data.

- The capacity reductions made to accommodate IMP activities were not large over a five-year period.
- The INGAA repairs per mile at 0.11, are 35% less than the total PHMSA result of 0.17 repairs per mile.
- The total number of incidents per year has not gone down over the six-year period. The number of incidents in HCAs is a very small number and the incident causes are not sufficiently impacted by IM activities.

- More than 50% of the incidents in HCAs were due to third-party damage and weather. With the increasing use of the 811 One-Call number, the CGA Best Practices, and the recent tighter requirements of the States on excavation practices, third-party incidents should decrease over time.

- The corrosion-leak category shows a steady downward trend in HCAs. This may be directly attributable to the IM programme which requires corrosion assessments for all HCAs by the end of 2012.

- Perhaps the most-effective near-term measure of the validity of the IM programme is that the repair rate for reassessed HCAs decreased by 78%.

- Construction and external corrosion are the leading causes for repairs in both HCAs and non-HCAs. Construction repairs included a large number of mechanical coupling replacements.

- For the INGAA companies, there have been over 450 IM audits conducted over the five-year period. There were no high-impact findings, and only ten medium-impact findings in this period.

- The audits resulted in 411 procedural changes over the five-year period, providing continuous improvement to O&M and IMP practices.

The data collected through the INGAA programme will permit us, at the appropriate time, to determine the approximate cost of the IMP, relative to the original cost/benefit analysis. The PHMSA analysis indicated that industry would have to spend $20 billion over a 20-year period to implement the IM programme.

References

1. Department of Transportation, 2003. PHMSA Regulation - 49CFR192, Sub-Part O, 17 December.
2. American Society of Mechanical Engineers, 2004. ASME Standard B31.8S: Managing the integrity of gas transmission pipelines.
3. INGAA, 2009. The impact of the integrity management program on gas transmission pipelines: summary of results 2004-2009.

Integrity management of offshore pipelines using risk-based inspection planning

Jens Erik Thygesen

DONG Energy E&P, Horsholm, Denmark

THE PROPOSED automatic-identification system (AIS) may provide a significant improvement in offshore pipeline operators' emergency response to possible mechanical damage. The continuous notification of vessel traffic above pipeline routes will add great value to the database for pipeline-integrity management and input for risk-based inspection planning. It should also become a valuable supplement for pipeline operators to mitigate damage to their pipeline networks, thereby minimizing the risk to personnel and the marine environment.

ONSHORE PIPELINES have been monitored for many years to avoid damage and associated risk to the surroundings. A similar monitoring of traffic across offshore gas and oil pipelines has been an aspiration for offshore pipeline operators for many years. One of the threats and major risks to offshore pipelines is the risk of mechanical damage, either by anchoring or by other impacts; the total failure statistics from the North Sea are shown in Fig. 1. Targeted inspection for mechanical damage is therefore of high importance when maximizing inspection and minimizing cost.

Following the legislation that required an AIS (automatic-identification system) to be installed on every vessel above 300 GT (gross tonnage), the offshore pipeline industry has now got a beneficial tool to monitor all offshore traffic in the area where their pipelines are situated as long as there is AIS coverage around them. This is the case in many areas, particular where the traffic is as dense as shown in Fig.2.

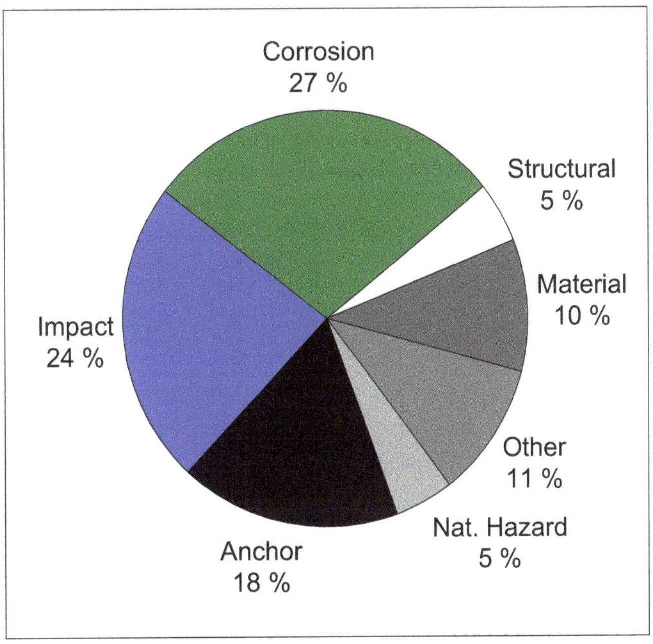

Fig. 1. Pipeline-incident statistics for the North Sea (incidents involving fittings are not included).

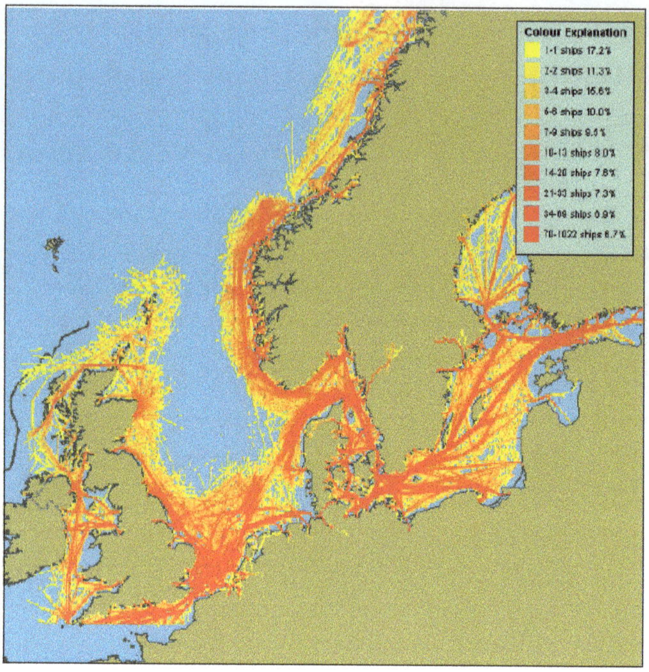

Fig.2. HELCOM, North Sea servers, 6000 targets, AIS.

What is AIS?

The AIS is a system that monitors all civil ship traffic, and is based on VHF communication. Satellite coverage might in the future improve the coverage of the system. The system exists in two versions: Class A and Class B. It is the Class A system which is relevant for offshore pipeline monitoring, as this is mandatory for vessels above 300 GT, which are the vessels that are the greatest threat to pipeline integrity. The system has been used for some years to monitor and control ship traffic around offshore platforms to avoid collisions, but has not yet been applied to offshore pipeline monitoring. The system gives information on the vessel's name and type, its course and speed over the ground, and its position at all times.

At the beginning of 2009 DONG Energy E&P started evaluating how the AIS could be used for monitoring all activities around oil and gas transmission pipelines in the Danish sector of the North Sea. The idea was to track abnormal behaviour of vessels crossing the pipelines or those stopping inside a defined area around a specific pipeline. The idea is illustrated in Fig.3.

A so-called 'watchdog zone' is placed around and along the pipeline. In DONG Energy E&P's case, this was defined as one nautical mile either side of the pipeline. The 'watchdog' observes abnormal behaviour of any ships passing through the zone and logs such events as 'watchdog events'. A watchdog event log will contain the following information:

- actual time at which the event was triggered
- actual time of registered entrance into the watchdog zone
- location of entrance into the watchdog zone
- expected exit of watchdog zone, time and location
- vessel identification, name, contact numbers, and standard AIS vessel information
- observed location of vessel within the watchdog zone at the time of the triggered watchdog event, coordinates of the vessel in system longitude and latitude and coordinates for the pipeline

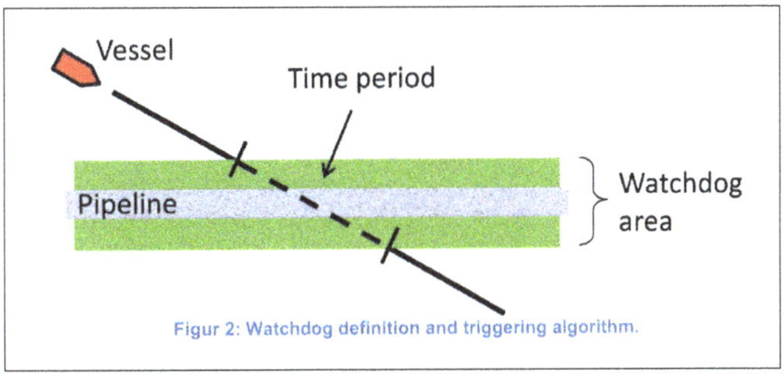

Fig.3. Watchdog definition and triggering algorithm.

- log of the specific vessel movements, and its route continuously monitored thereafter

The reason for the search for integrity improvements for pipeline monitoring is that over the 26 years of operations, DONG Energy E&P has become aware of abnormal traffic across its pipeline routes, and in some cases these pipelines have suffered severe mechanical damage from such traffic. A historical overview is provided in Fig.4.

The accepted policy for the detection of mechanical damage to buried pipelines has always been to perform a calliper inspection every second year. Mechanical damage by anchors to buried pipelines might not show visible signs on the seabed; the frequency of inspection is decided based on an arbitrary expectation that severe damage left undetected and exposed to the CP coverage in the marine environment could withstand two years' of operation without degradation and eventual pipeline rupture. A damaged metal surface in the sea environment which is only protected by a cathodic anode system might suffer from hydrogen penetration into the steel, making it brittle, thereby losing its pressure containing strength and finely leading to a rupture of the pipeline.

Over the years many different justifications have been used to determine the frequency of inspection, without success. Several years ago DONG Energy E&P implemented risk-based

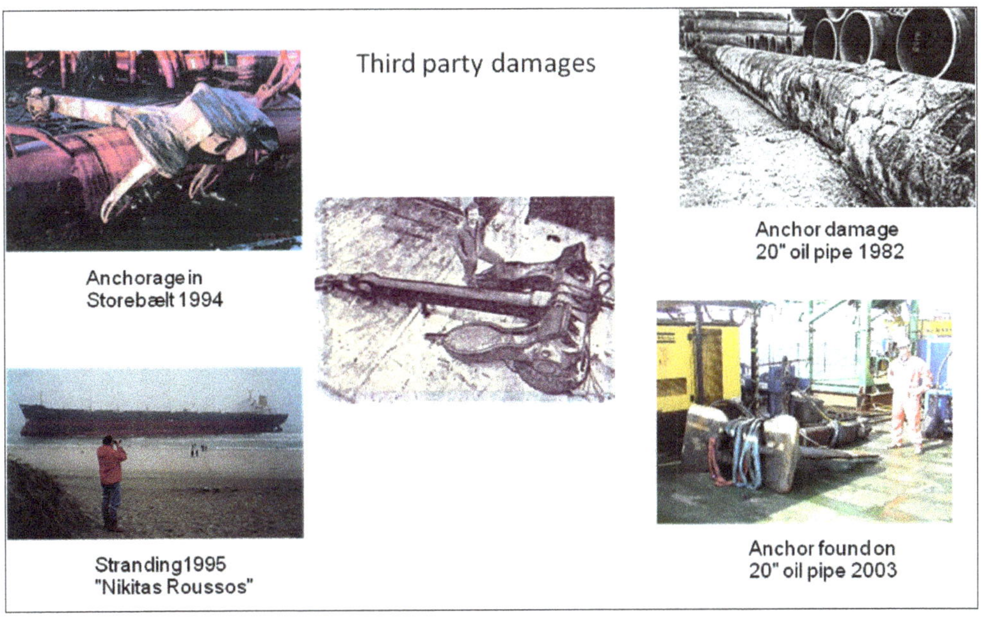

Fig.4. Overview of historical pipeline damage and near misses.

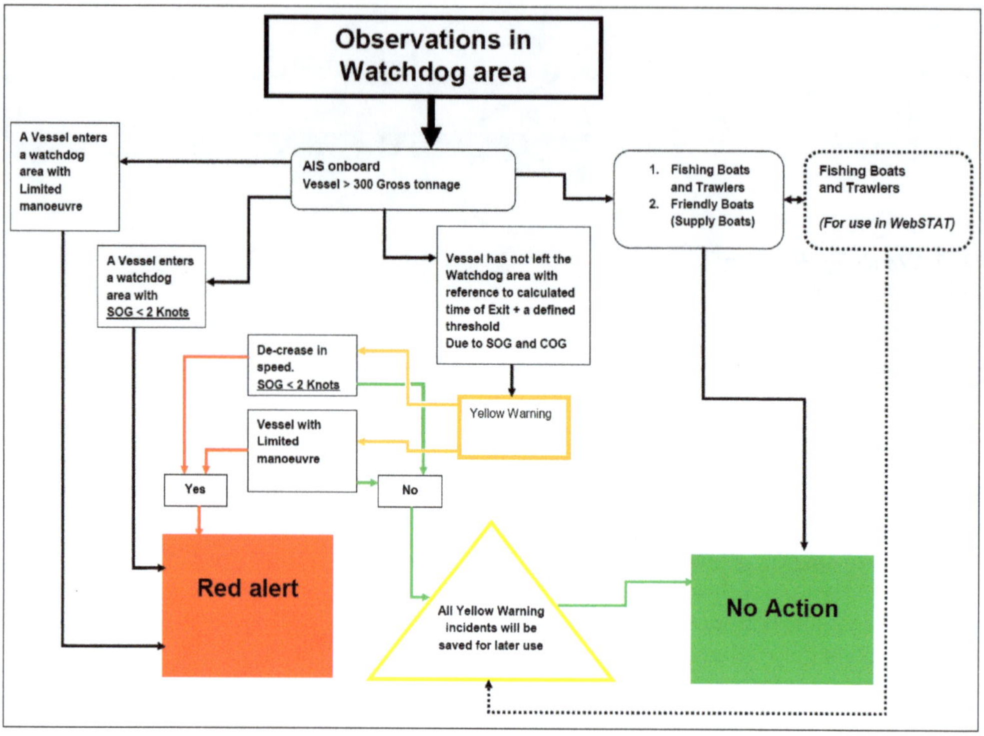

Fig.5. Warning criteria for 'watchdog'.

inspection and pipeline integrity-management systems based on the DNV *Orbit* system. Even with this system, DONG Energy E&P still needed to improve the information database to determine the inspection philosophy and frequency for mechanical damage, rather than relying on the two-year interval.

Based on damage suffered and analysis of near-miss situations, DONG Energy E&P started developing the criteria to be observed by an AIS (the watchdog) to track in real time shipping manoeuvres around pipelines which, in the worst case, could lead to mechanical damage, thereby threatening the security of supply. The criteria that were decided upon are shown in Fig.5.

In 2009 DONG Energy E&P contacted the Danish Coastguard and a Danish software company called GateHouse, who had been involved in developing ship-traffic monitoring and management for the Danish Coastguard. The principle of applying a detection zone around pipelines for

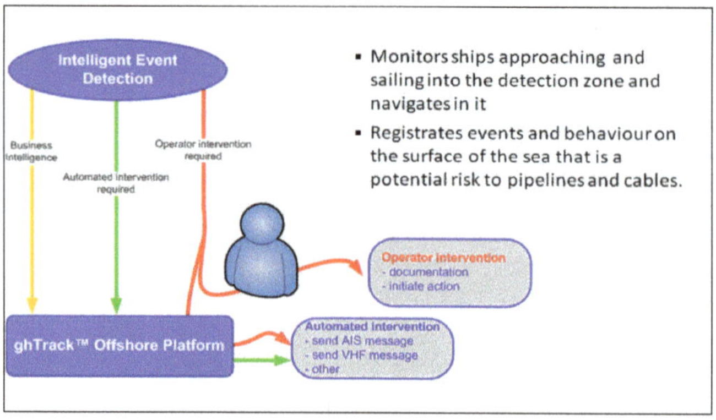

Fig.6. Intelligent event detection.

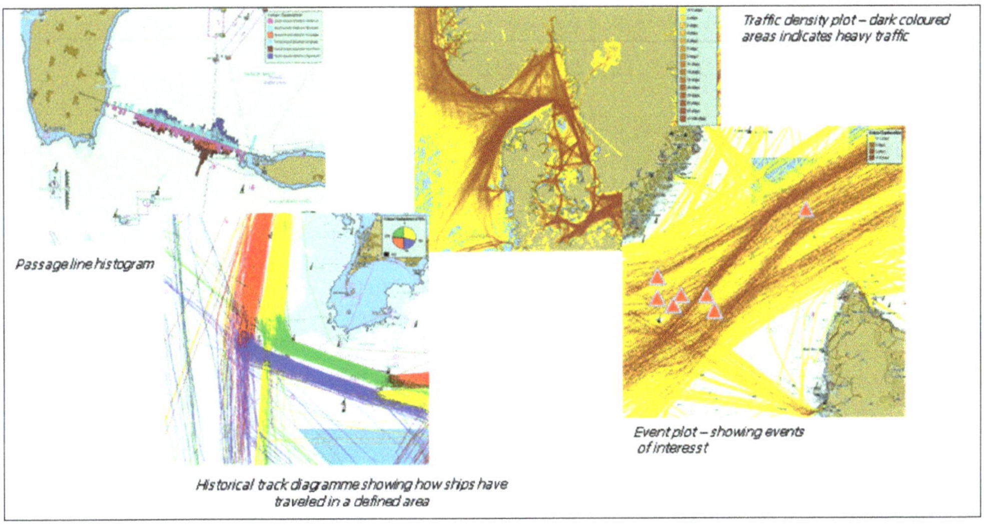

Fig.7. Historical data for ship traffic above pipelines.

detection of traffic was discussed, and the GateHouse software modified to cover the criteria selected. The principle for this system is shown in Fig.6.

At the beginning of 2010, DONG Energy E&P performed a pilot test on selected areas around its oil and gas pipeline network in the Danish sector to prove the concept. The pilot test was successful and showed that the principle was working.

How will such a system improve pipeline-integrity management?

The transport by pipeline of energy is extremely vital system which serves the energy needs of modern society. Offshore pipelines transport a major part of such energy, and it is therefore vital to secure such pipeline systems against mechanical damage. In cases where it is detected, it is imperative to act at an early stage before the damage leads to the interruption of the energy transport without any warning.

In extreme cases, the early detection of a critical 'Mayday' around an offshore pipeline can - through co-operation between pipeline operators and the rescue organizations -minimize escalating the risk to personnel and environment, in an already intense situation.

The sorting and storage of observations, as illustrated in Figs 2 and 5, can be used for planning of inspection for possible mechanical damage instead of choosing an arbitrary frequency. In this way the AIS data provide a better focus on the high-risk areas for inspection, thereby leading to an improvement in inspection and value for money.

The registration and storage of traffic intensity across and along the offshore pipelines provides the best statistical data for risk-based inspection planning (Fig.7).

Finally, DONG Energy E&P believes that the application of the AIS 'watchdog' principle around offshore pipelines will have a preventative effect on the risk potential for mechanical damage, once shipping traffic becomes aware that such an application is in place.

The use of AIS allows repairs to be performed as fast as possible

The AIS-based intelligent event-detection system will provide an alarm to the on-duty pipeline personnel within minutes and allow them to contact the particular vessel – and, in the case when the vessel is in distress, advise the rescue services – with the aim of reducing the risk potential of the situation.

A repair of a subsea pipeline which has suffered extreme mechanical damage is not an easy task and can take more than 1-2 months, depending on the complexity of the damage, pipeline operating conditions, and the specific water depth. If the damage has not lead to a rupture or leak, it is important to try to minimize the repair time and if possible minimize the influence on the pipeline's operation.

Planning of a repair is time-consuming and needs a lot of information so that the severity of the damage can be analysed, and the repair method to be applied to the pipeline can be confirmed, without a long service interruption. In order to reduce the time for repair and prevent escalation of damage severity, immediately detection is vital for planning and to perform a proper repair, without risk to personnel and environment.

A review of crack-detection ILI case studies

by Neil A Bates, David Lee, and Clifford J Maier

DNV Canada Ltd, Calgary, AB, Canada

THIS PAPER DESCRIBES case studies involving crack-detection ILI and fitness-for-service assessments that were performed based on the inspection data. The assessments were used to evaluate the immediate integrity of the pipeline based on the reported features and the long-term integrity of the pipeline based on excavation data and probabilistic SCC and fatigue-crack-growth simulations.

Two different case studies are analysed, which illustrate how the data from an ultrasonic crack tool inspection were used to assess threats such as low-frequency electrical-resistance-weld seam defects and stress-corrosion cracking. Specific issues, such as probability of detection/identification and the length/depth accuracy of the tool, were evaluated to determine the suitability of the tool to accurately classify and size different types of defect.

The long-term assessment is based on the Monte Carlo method [1], where the material properties, pipeline details, crack-growth parameters, and feature dimensions are randomly selected from certain specified probability distributions to determine the probability of failure versus time for the pipeline segment. The distributions of unreported crack-related features from the excavation programme are used to distribute unreported features along the pipeline.

Simulated crack growth by fatigue, SCC, or a combination of the two is performed until failure by either leak or rupture is predicted. The probability-of-failure calculation is performed through a number of crack-growth simulations for each of the reported and unreported features and tallying their respective remaining lives. The results of the probabilistic analysis were used to determine the most effective and economic means of remediation by identifying areas or crack mechanisms that contribute most to the probability of failure.

IN-LINE INSPECTION for detecting and sizing cracks and related features using ultrasonic technology is becoming increasingly common within the pipeline industry. This paper presents two case studies that show how data from the in-line inspections and other sources were used to assess the present condition of the pipelines and predict when the pipelines will require remediation and/or reinspection.

Analysis method

The analysis was performed in two parts. The first part is a short-term assessment, which involved evaluating the immediate integrity of the pipelines and developing a tool-validation programme (if a validation programme had not yet been completed). The second part is a long-term assessment that was used to evaluate the tool performance and determine the long-term integrity of the pipelines.

Short-term assessment

The reported features were assessed for their immediate impact on pipeline integrity. This process is similar to that outlined that for metal loss listed in standards such as CSA Z662-07 [2], but with criteria based on the limits for ultrasonic tools. Such criteria may include:

- features with a depth > 40% wall thickness;
- features with a predicted burst pressure less than a minimum value dependant on the type of product and class location of the pipeline;
- crack-related features associated with a deformation; and
- laminations that interact with a weld seam or girth weld.

Additionally, for cases where a validation programme had not yet been performed, this was developed. In order to develop a validation programme, sample-size calculations were performed and were used to determine the minimum number of features that should be excavated in order to evaluate the tool performance (i.e., how well the tool sized and classified features). The minimum sample size is considered statistically significant at a given confidence level. Statistical significance means that the observed trends are real and not a coincidence.

For developing the validation programme, a number of features were recommended for excavation and inspection, and these included the features identified as unacceptable using the above criteria. If these features alone did not satisfy the minimum statistical sample size, more features were added to the recommended list by determining the number of additional features required to meet the minimum sample size. The additional features may have been recommended based on severity (with preference to deeper features) and/or feature classification.

Long-term assessment

Following the validation programme and repair excavations, the field data were correlated with the tool-reported data. Where available, photographs were used to match the field observation with the tool data. Additionally, the photographs were used to verify crack lengths, particularly the longest interlinked length of SCC colonies. Correct matching of the field data with the tool data was critical for evaluating tool performance (probability of detection, probability of identification, and sizing accuracy).

Tool performance – POD/POI

The tool generally classified a feature as a crack field, crack-like, notch-like, or a weld anomaly. The tool performance was based on the tool (i) correctly detecting the presence of a feature at the reported location, and (ii) correctly identifying the type of feature at that location. Known as the probability of detection (POD) and probability of identification (POI), respectively, these parameters were calculated separately for each feature classification. The definitions below are consistent with the guidance given in section 7.2.3 of API 1163 [3].

The probability of detection is defined as:

$$POD = \frac{n_{rep}}{n_{rep} + n_{unrep}} \qquad (1)$$

where n_{rep} is the number of features reported by the tool and found in the field, and n_{unrep} is the number of features not reported by the tool but found in the field. If any defect found in the field can be correlated with a tool-reported feature, regardless of its classification, it is considered in the count of n_{rep}. Additionally, only unreported features with measurements exceeding the minimum tool detection threshold are considered for n_{unrep}. Whether a feature exceeds the minimum threshold depends on the length of the feature at the minimum detectable depth. Ideally, the length is measured after grinding to a depth equal to the tool's minimum detectable depth. The feature must satisfy both the specified length and depth thresholds to be considered detectable.

Similarly, the probability of identification is defined as:

$$POI = \frac{n_{corr}}{n_{corr} + n_{incorr}} \quad (2)$$

where n_{corr} is the number of features reported by the tool and found in the field with correct identification, and n_{incorr} is the number of features reported by the tool but found in the field with incorrect identification. The POI is calculated using only tool-reported features that correlated with field-observed features.

Correct identification is determined using the following criteria:

- The reported feature type is considered correct for SCC defects if it is reported as either crack field or crack-like.
- The reported feature type is considered correct for lack of fusion if it is reported as weld anomalies (if weld anomalies are not reported, then crack-like and notch-like are correct).
- The reported feature type is considered correct for scratches, gouges, scrapes, roller marks, grooves, and contact marks if it is reported as notch-like.
- ERW seam laps are considered correctly identified if the crack-detection tool associates them with a weld-anomaly classification.

Proper classification of correlated defects/features should be determined based on a review of field photographs to determine the likely cause of the crack-detection signal (for example, for light SCC coincident with a single substantial crack, the crack-detection tool likely reported the single substantial crack instead of the SCC colony).

Depth and length correlations

Sizing accuracy was evaluated by creating unity plots to compare the tool-reported dimensions with field measurements. Unity plots are useful for establishing trends in the data, which are then used to adjust the reported feature dimensions. The adjusted feature dimensions are then used to calculate predicted burst pressures, re-evaluate the immediate integrity of the pipeline, and simulate SCC and fatigue-crack growth.

Tool performance – achieved sizing accuracy

Performance specifications typically specify a tolerance and corresponding confidence level for sizing accuracy. For example, depth accuracy can be specified as ± 0.4 mm at 80% confidence, or ± 0.5 mm at 90% confidence. Similarly, length can be specified as ± 7.5 mm/7.5% at 80%

confidence or ± 10 mm/10% at 90% confidence. The achieved sizing accuracy was calculated by evaluating how many of the features (i.e. the achieved confidence level) were sized within the tolerances described above. When the tool depths are reported in percent wall thickness ranges, the upper and lower bounds of each range were converted into their respective millimetre equivalents based on the tool-reported wall thickness for the pipe joint.

Probabilistic crack-growth modelling and remaining-life assessment

The objective of the probabilistic assessment was to determine the cumulative probability of failure versus time for each pipeline section in the respective case studies. Each assessment takes into consideration the expected population of defects remaining in the pipeline comprised of tool-reported features and an estimated number of unreported features based on field observations.

The Monte Carlo method of statistical analysis was used to calculate the probability of failure versus time for the assessment. First, statistical distributions of all the parameters related to crack remaining life were created. These distributions were used to generate thousands of random samples for each assessed feature. The remaining life for each simulation was calculated and tallied to determine the probability of failure versus time for each feature. A cumulative-probability calculation was used to combine the individual feature probability of failures into a single probability of failure for the pipeline section.

The population of the assessed features is made up of both reported and unreported features. Reported features that were part of a past or upcoming planned excavation were not included in the assessment. A population of unreported features was incorporated in to the assessment based on trends of the various unreported features and feature types found in the field excavations. The trends found in the field excavations were extrapolated to determine the number and location of the remaining unreported features to be addressed in the assessment.

The parameters related to crack remaining life fell into one of four categories, namely pipe details, material properties, defect size, and crack-growth parameters.

The pipeline details encompassed the operating pressure, outer diameter, and wall thickness. The operating pressure applied to each simulation governed the feature's critical flaw size and was determined based on the expected future operations of the pipeline. Since ultrasonic crack-detection (UTCD) tools are able to measure wall thickness, a wall-thickness distribution was made based on a correlation between tool-reported and field-measured wall thickness for each joint that was excavated.

The material properties considered for the assessment included yield strength, ultimate tensile strength, and pipe toughness. Distributions were made for these properties using laboratory data, pipe mill test records, or historical values based on the pipe vintage. The distributions for yield and ultimate tensile strength were simulated together to ensure the resulting values for the yield to tensile strength ratio were realistic.

Defect sizes for the tool-reported features were simulated using either field-tool regressions or distributions of the field measurements created using excavation data. Field-tool regressions were used for the tool-reported lengths and in cases where the tool reported discrete depth values, but only when the resulting regression accurately represented the data. When the tool reports feature depths in range bins, a distribution was made for each bin based on field measurements of features in that particular bin. The regressions and distributions were made for specific tool-reported feature types. Sometimes, multiple feature types were combined if their respective regressions or distributions appeared similar or if there was insufficient field data for that feature type.

Tool-reported features that had a poor field-tool regression or distribution, or cases where the tool did not provide a length or depth for a specific feature type, were simulated using the same process as for the unreported features discussed below.

The unreported features were simulated based on the field-measured dimensions of the excavated features. All of the unreported features found in the field were grouped based on their type and/or severity. The dimensions of the features in each of these groups were plotted on a length and depth 'scatter plot', and length and depth distributions were created to mimic the field-found dimensions. The length and depth distributions may either be independent or dependent: dependent length and depths require an algorithm to adjust the independent length and depth results.

The simulated features were grown using an SCC growth mechanism and/or a fatigue-crack growth mechanism. Both the SCC and fatigue-crack growth mechanisms were considered for tool-reported features that correlated with field-found SCC colonies and field-found unreported SCC colonies. Feature types not correlated with field-found SCC were grown using the fatigue-crack growth mechanism only. Using one year increments, the faster mechanism was applied for that year. Certain excavated tool-reported features that were correlated with SCC in the field and were only recoated after the excavation may be included in the assessment and grown using the fatigue-crack growth mechanism.

For features subject to SCC growth, an 'at-site' SCC growth rate or growth rate distribution was used instead of a single SCC growth rate across the entire pipeline. The 'at-site' rates were calculated for liquids pipelines by establishing an 'at-site' pressure history for each location constructed from numerous hydraulic profiles based on provided pressure data and applying SCC growth rate correlations developed though prior research [4]. For gas pipelines, a distribution of time-averaged SCC growth rates was created based on the depths of the field found SCC colonies.

Fatigue crack growth was simulated using the Paris Law crack-growth method. Distributions for the Paris Law coefficient and exponent were created from either laboratory test data or a combination of historical laboratory results and industry recommended practices. A local pressure history was created for every feature location based on the historical discharge and suction pressure data. The discharge and suction pressure histories may be segmented or modified based on the expected future operation of the pipeline.

Changes to certain distributions were made based on engineering judgment and past experiences to ensure the results were realistic with some conservatism.

Using the above distributions and regressions, thousands of randomly generated samples were created for every assessed feature. A critical depth was calculated for every sample using the *CorLAS* fracture-mechanics' model. Samples where the critical depth was either less than the initial depth, or greater than half of the initial length (because of a limitation of *CorLAS*) were considered invalid and were removed from the assessment. All of the valid samples were grown to failure and the resulting remaining life was tallied in one-year increments. The probability of failure for each feature was calculated using the same one-year increments.

Long-term excavation and re-inspection programmes were developed based on the results of the probabilistic assessment and each client's particular requirements. The excavations were scheduled

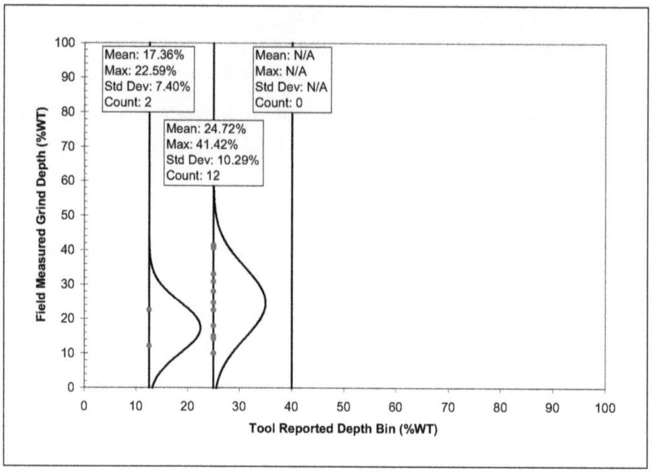

Fig. 1. Field-tool depth correlation for SCC features.

	Crack field	Crack like	Notch like	Weld anomaly
POD	100%	100%	100%	100%
POI	76%	60%	100%	100%
# Inspected	25	28	17	61

Table 1. POD and POI for case study 1.

such that the cumulative probability of failure would not exceed a specified threshold until completion of the next re-inspection and initial excavations.

Case studies

Case study 1

The pipeline in this study is 290 km long, was constructed in 1970 of 323.9-mm diameter by 4.8-mm wall-thickness Grade 359 linepipe. The licensed MOP is 8,205 kPa. The pipeline transports natural gas and has two compressor stations, one of which is not in operation.

Following a baseline MFL inspection of the entire pipeline in 2002, a validation programme was initiated, which included 36 excavations for metal loss, dents, and stress-corrosion cracking direct assessment (SCCDA). During the excavations, SCC was identified in several locations. As a result, a crack detection in-line inspection was performed in 2007. The inspection identified weld anomalies, crack-like features, and crack-field features. In the summer of 2007, a validation programme involving 15 excavations was performed. A probabilistic fitness-for-service assessment of this pipeline was performed to evaluate these validation excavations.

Through the validation digs, weld anomalies were confirmed as linear long-seam indications; these were deemed a low priority as they had survived the original commissioning hydrostatic test and were considered to be a low threat from fatigue growth. Additionally, crack-like features were found as mill scabs and mill slivers, which were also deemed low priority due to the successful commissioning hydrostatic test. The single crack field that was accessible and excavated was found as SCC. Based on this validation programme, a repair programme was executed.

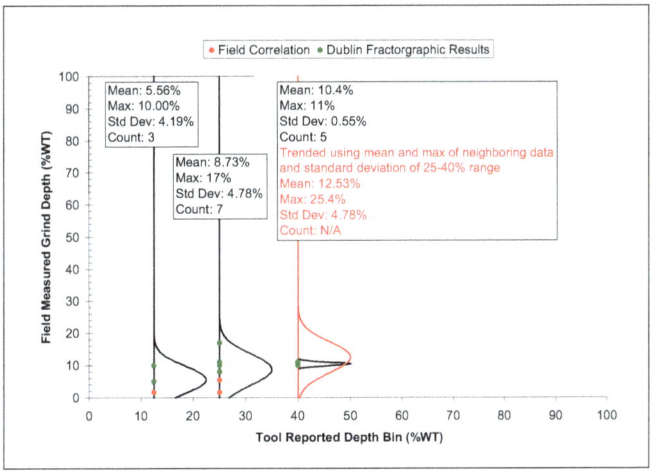

Fig.2. Field-tool depth correlation for non-SCC features.

The excavation programme included 15 crack-field, 18 crack-like, 15 notch-like, and 47 weld-anomaly features reported by the tool. These features were matched to 15 SCC colonies, 31 long-seam linear indications, six notches and scratches, two surface-breaking laminations, one non-descript internal feature, and 26 other features that were not completely documented. A total of 14 features were not found.

Tool performance: POD/POI

None of the unreported features had dimensions above the tool's minimum detection threshold, and consequently, the probability of detection was 100%, as shown in Table 1. With regard to the probability of identification, the only features that were misclassified were reported as crack-field and crack-like. Many of the incorrectly identified features were notches that did not contain cracking.

Depth correlation

A depth correlation of the SCC features was evaluated, which suggested some differentiation with respect to the range of actual depths measured for two of the tool-reported depth ranges (no features reported in other depth ranges were excavated). Figure 1 shows the field depths of the features measured by grinding or UT versus those predicted by the ILI. Normal distributions were plotted vertically for both depth ranges.

A depth correlation was also created for the non-SCC defects. This correlation, shown in Fig.2, shows that the distribution of actual depths for the various tool reported depth ranges are more similar and have less differentiation as compared to those for the SCC defects. In Fig.2, the green symbols are based on a laboratory fractographic analysis whereas the red symbols are based on measurements performed in the field. Given the small number of samples in the largest depth range, a normal distribution was fabricated by trending the distributions observed for the other depth ranges (as shown by the red distribution).

Length correlation

A comparison of the interlink length of each SCC colony found in the field to the crack-field interlink length reported by the tool was also performed. An RMA regression was performed using the upper-bound correlation data. There was a large variability in the field-measured interlink lengths versus those reported by the tool, as illustrated by Fig.3.

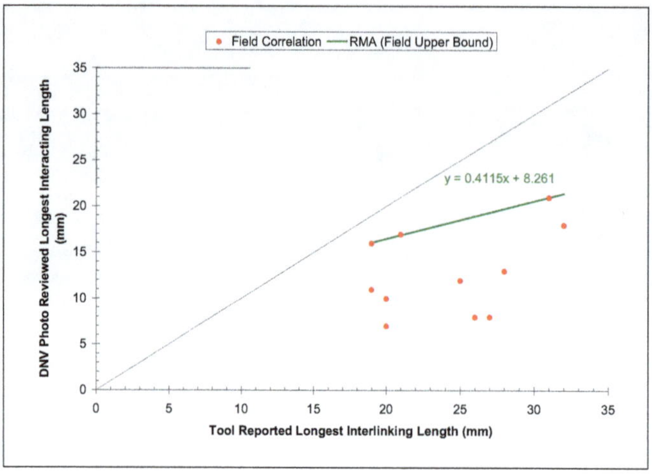

Fig.3. Field versus tool SCC interlink length.

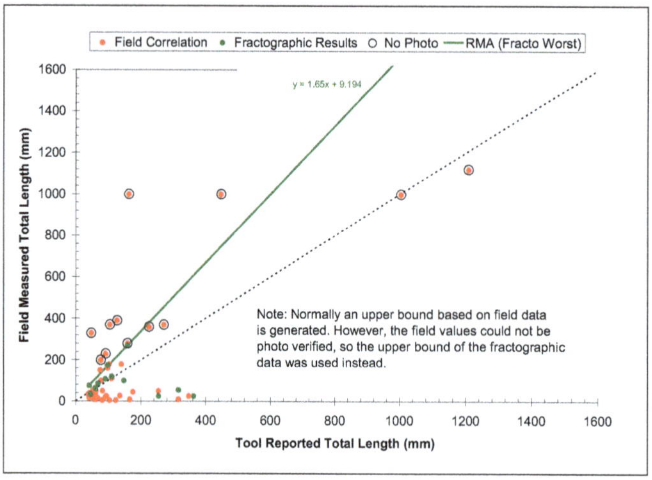

Fig.4. Field versus tool total length.

Figure 4 shows the correlation between the crack-like tool-reported length (interlink lengths were not reported for crack-like features) versus their field-measured interlink lengths. Again, large variability was observed.

Evaluation of weld anomalies

Pipe samples containing weld anomalies were cut out and sent for fractographic analysis which revealed that the tool was considerably overstating the depth of the weld anomalies, as shown in Fig.5 (one crack-like feature was included in the analysis, as indicated).

For the length regression, shown in Fig.6, tool lengths of up to 150 mm were well correlated but a single feature with a tool-reported length of 316 mm had a field-measured length of 55 mm. This resulted in a correlation with a negative slope and poor correlation coefficient. This was addressed by treating the longest weld anomaly as an outlier. Consequently, the regression calculated for the weld anomalies (except the longest) was used for subsequent calculations.

To further explore the measurement inaccuracies of the tool with respect to weld anomalies, the critical flaw sizes were compared with the dimensions of the most severe anomaly reported by the tool. Using the tool-reported dimensions, it is apparent that the tool-reported (original) dimensions of the feature are far too severe to have survived at the licensed MOP. Alternatively, when the

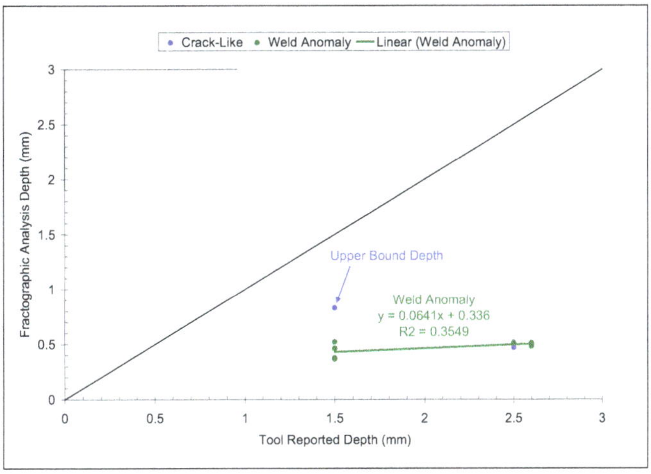

Fig.5. Depth correlation of fractographic results to tool-reported depth.

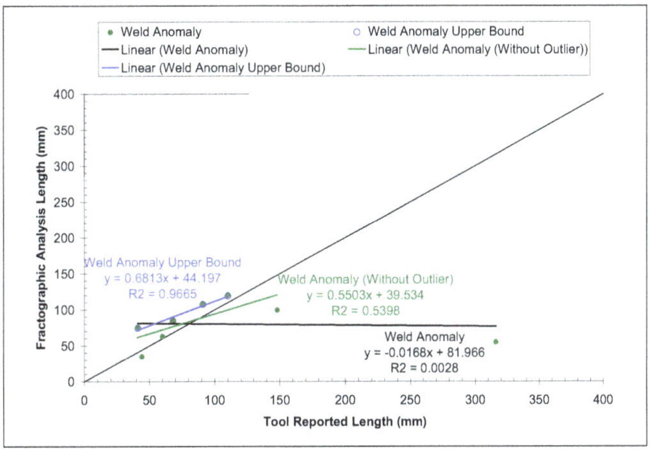

Fig.6. Length correlation of fractographic results to tool-reported length.

dimensions were adjusted based on the regressions in Figs 5 and 6, it is evident that the adjusted feature dimensions are well within the boundary of acceptable flaw dimensions at a pressure equivalent to 125% of the licensed MOP. Figure 7 shows these comparisons.

While the inspection identified a large number of weld anomalies, excavation results, fractographic analyses, and operating experience suggest that the weld anomalies are not subject to fatigue-crack growth. These observations were substantiated by fatigue-crack growth calculations, which indicate very long fatigue lives (>1,000 years).

Tool performance: achieved sizing accuracy

For this pipeline, the actual sizing accuracy achieved for depth was determined as follows:

Crack-field features:	±0.4 mm: 78.6%
	±0.5 mm: 85.7%
Crack-like features:	±0.4 mm: 33.3%
	±0.5 mm: 33.3%
Notch-like features:	±0.4 mm: 100%
	±0.5 mm: 100%
Weld-anomaly features:	±0.4 mm: 0%
	±0.5 mm: 0%

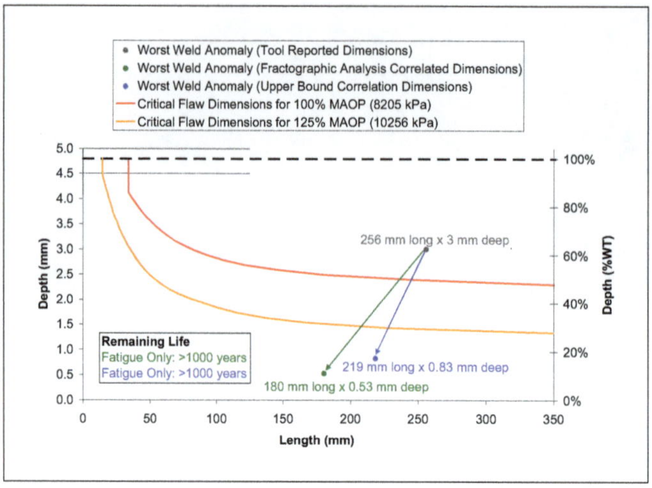

Fig.7. Critical flaw size curves and dimensions associated with the worst reported weld anomaly.

For this pipeline, the actual sizing accuracy achieved for length was determined as follows:

Crack-field features:	±7.5 mm/7.5%:	18.2%
	±10 mm/10%:	45.5%
Crack-like features:	±7.5 mm/7.5%:	12.5%
	±10 mm/10%:	12.5%
Notch-like features:	±7.5 mm/7.5%:	12.5%
	±10 mm/10%:	25.0%
Weld-anomaly features:	±7.5 mm/7.5%:	9.1%
	±10 mm/10%:	15.2%

Probabilistic crack-growth modelling and remaining-life assessment

Because this case involves a natural gas pipeline, the SCC growth rate correlations mentioned earlier could not be applied. The correlations were developed for liquids' pipelines and are not applicable to gas pipelines. Therefore, SCC growth rates were estimated based on time-averaged growth rates experienced with this pipeline system and industry-accepted values for pipe of similar diameter to this pipeline.

For the probabilistic crack-growth modelling, 50% of the SCC growth rates used in the simulations were equal to 0.06 mm/yr, 30% were equal to 0.15 mm/yr, and the remaining values were equal to 0.3 mm/yr.

The probabilistic assessment of the remaining features consisted of the 17 remaining crack-field features and 3,483 unreported features. The number of unreported features was calculated based on 15 unreported SCC colonies found in the 695.61 m of inspected pipe from the excavation programme. The resulting density of unreported SCC colonies for the pipeline was 0.0216 colonies per meter. The length of the tool run according to the in-line inspection tool was 162,161 m; removing the inspected pipe results in 161,501 m of uninspected pipe. The 3,483 unreported features were calculated by combining the length of uninspected pipe with the unreported SCC colony density.

The resulting probability of failure for this pipeline was calculated to reach 1% probability of failure towards the end of 2014, as shown in Fig.8. The probability of failure was also separated into tool-reported crack-field and unreported SCC colonies. It is apparent that the remaining

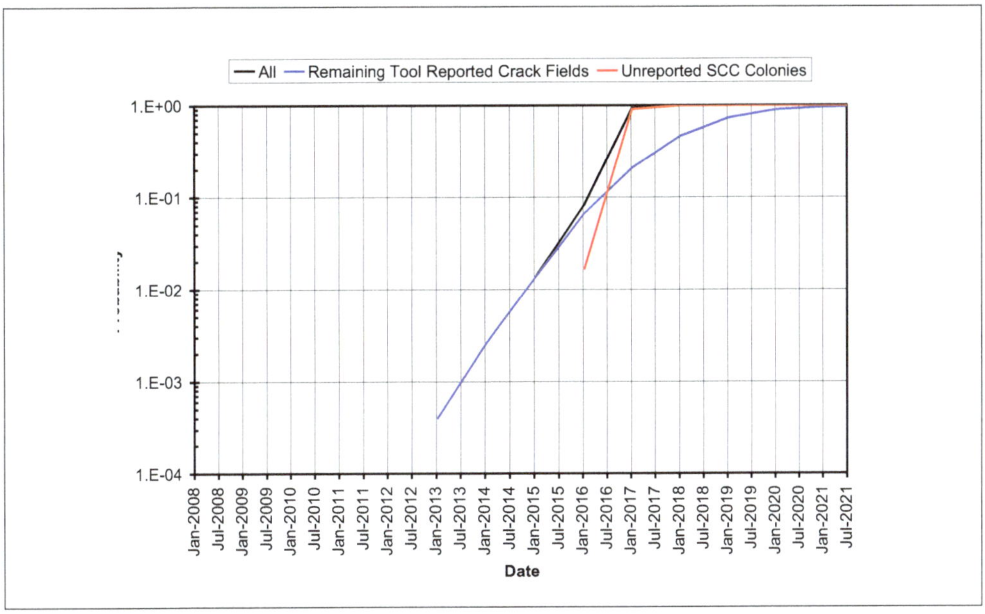

Fig.8. Calculated probability of failure vs time.

tool-reported crack-field features are the primary features driving the overall probability of failure with the unreported SCC colonies driving the overall probability of failure in mid-2016.

Conclusions

For this pipeline, it was concluded that:

1. only features reported as crack fields were found to be SCC and are considered a potential integrity threat, while other feature types were found to be associated with weld-seam or manufacturing defects and are not considered to be a significant integrity threat;
2. the tool generally performed well with respect to defect detection and identification;
3. the sizing accuracy of the tool was reasonably good for depths of crack field and notch-like features;
4. sizing accuracy of the tool was conservative but poor for depths of other feature types and reported lengths of crack-field features;
5. the sizing accuracy was non-conservative and poor for lengths of other feature types; and
6. the tool substantially overstated the depths of weld anomalies, resulting in an overstated severity.

Case study 2

The second pipeline in this study is 430 km long, 406.4 mm in diameter, and was constructed in 1966. It has two distinct operating regions: the first 85 km have licensed MOP of 9,930 kPa and the remainder of the pipeline has an MOP of 7,290 kPa. The former section is constructed of 7.14 or 7.92-mm wall thickness, API Grade X52 pipe, while the latter section is primarily constructed from 5.16-mm wall thickness Grade X52 pipe. The pipeline was used to transport synthetic crude and gas liquids in batches.

In 1997 the entire pipeline was hydrotested to 125% of the maximum operating pressure (MOP) to verify the integrity of the system and increase the maximum licensed operating pressures

	Crack field	Crack like	Notch like	Weld anomaly
POD	99%	100%	100%	100%
POI	96%	69%	44%	77%
# Inspected	106	96	35	22

Table 2. POD and POI for case study 2.

(MLOP). In addition, the licensed service was upgraded from low vapour pressure (LVP) to high vapour pressure (HVP). During the hydrotest, only one section of the pipeline experienced a rupture caused by a weak ERW long-seam weld. No failures were experienced from SCC.

From 1997 to 1999, the pipeline was expanded from three to seven pump stations. This involved construction of six new auxiliary pump stations and expansion of one existing pump station. The new pump stations were added to increase the maximum throughput of the pipeline; however, this changed the hydraulic profile of the system.

In 137 excavations conducted between 1995 and 2003 only four SCC colonies were found, but in 2004 a rupture due to near-neutral pH SCC occurred 6 km downstream of a pump station in the 5.16-mm wall thickness section. In 2008, a second failure, also due to near-neutral pH SCC, occurred 8 km downstream of the same pump station.

After the 2004 failure, the pipeline was inspected with an ultrasonic crack-detection tool (UTCD) to locate and size SCC defects. This tool was chosen to inspect this line because it was considered to be the most precise and cost-effective method for the detection of SCC. However, due to the length of the pipeline, two tool runs within the same liquid product batch were required. A total of 344 crack-related features were reported, and all of these features that were not located in a river crossing were excavated and repaired. Those within the heavy wall thickness river crossings were not considered a threat because of their long remaining lives with respect to fatigue and SCC.

A second UTCD inspection was done in 2007, with 339 crack-related features being reported (75 of these were excavated and sleeved or recoated after the 2004 inspection). Although only 32 features failed the short-term assessment, because of the 2008 failure a decision was made again to excavate and repair any accessible crack-related features.

The 2008 failure feature was reported as a crack field by the 2007 inspection but the reported dimensions did not fail any of the short-term assessment criteria. This feature was classified as an inclusion by the 2004 inspection.

During the excavation programme, 106 crack-field, 96 crack-like, 35 notch-like, and 22 weld-anomaly features reported by the tool were excavated. These features were matched to 128 SCC colonies, 61 lack of fusion defects, and 70 mill or construction defects. No defects were found at three of the crack-field feature locations. It is important to note that since the 2004 failure, SCC has only been found in the 5.16-mm wall thickness sections of pipe.

In addition to the reported features 2,923 SCC colonies, 144 lack-of-fusion defects, and 57 mill or construction defects not reported by the tool were found.

After the second failure, a pressure reduction was imposed on the pipeline until a fitness-for-service assessment was completed and remedial actions could be taken to prove that the pipeline could be operated safely at its original operating pressure.

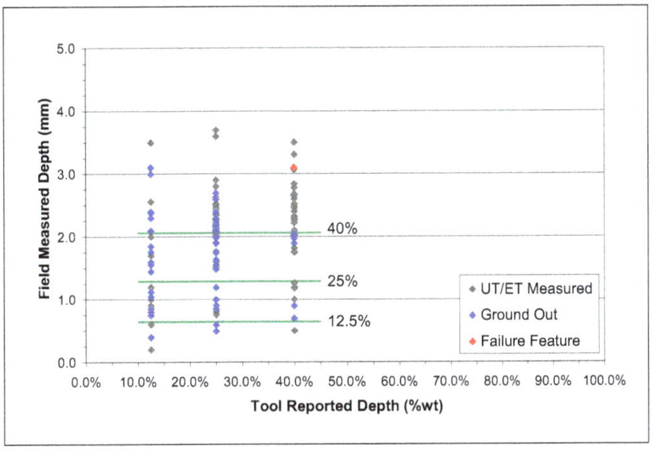

Fig.9. Field-tool depth correlation for crack-related features (5.16-mm wall thickness section).

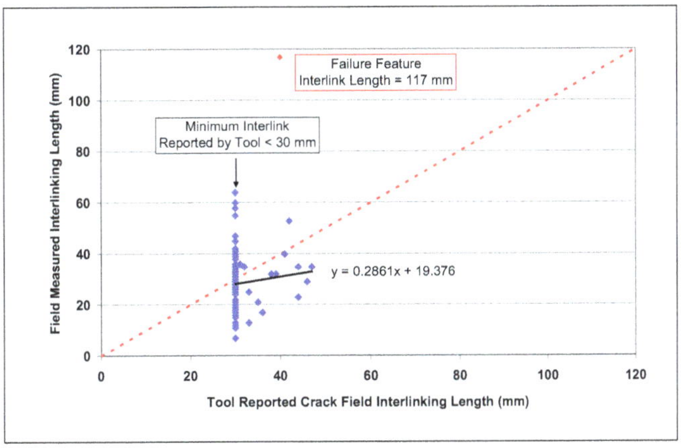

Fig.10. Field vs tool SCC interlink length.

In addition to the reported features from the crack tool, pipe-stress levels, soil characteristics, excavation data, MFL data, and low-level anomalies not normally reported by the inspection company were used in the fitness-for-service assessment to predict future areas of SCC susceptibility and growth for a long-term probabilistic assessment.

Tool performance: POD/POI

Only one of the 3,124 (0.03%) unreported features found during the field excavations was above the tool reporting threshold. However this feature had a remaining life of over nine years.

As shown in Table 2, the probability of detection was not significantly impacted. The table also shows the success of the tool in correctly classifying SCC as crack-field features, whereas the probability of identification was lower for the other three feature classifications. Many of the incorrectly identified features were raised caps on the ERW welds, laminations, or other mill defects. SCC was not found to correspond to notch-like and weld anomaly tool calls.

Depth correlation

As additional features were excavated, a trend of the depth of the crack-related features (SCC and lack-of-fusion) being undersized by the tool was observed. Figure 9 shows the field depths of the features measured by grinding or UT versus those predicted by the ILI. The failure feature (shown in red) was one of the deepest features measured in the field.

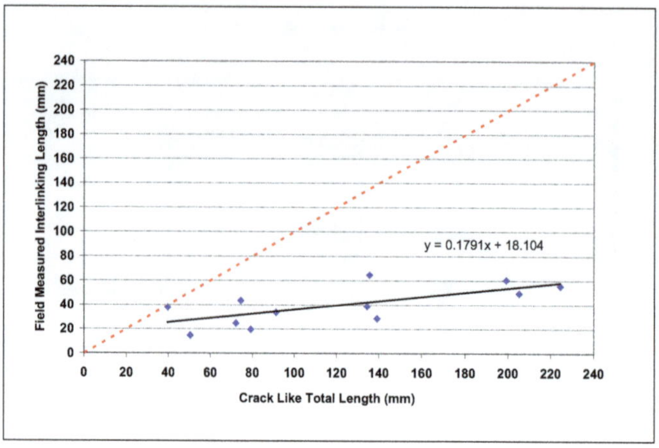

Fig.11. Crack-like tool length vs SCC interlink length.

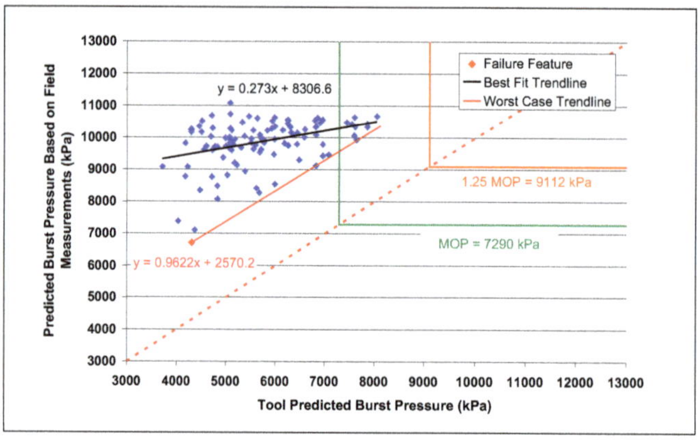

Fig.12. Field vs tool-predicted burst pressure for crack-related features.

It should be noted that the UT/ET measurements in Fig.9 were adjusted according to a correlation of both UT/ET and grind depth measurements of other SCC features for the same field crew.

Length correlation

The interlink length of each SCC colony was compared to the crack-field interlink reported by the tool. As Fig.10 shows, there was a large variability in the field-measured interlink lengths versus those reported by the tool. However, the failure feature appears to be an outlier compared to the rest of the data.

Figure 11 shows the correlation between the crack-like tool-reported length (interlink lengths were not reported for crack-like features) versus their field-measured interlink length, which indicates the tool was extremely conservative.

Predicted burst pressure correlation

The length correlations for crack-field and crack-like features were deemed unreliable for predicting the interlink length of the unexcavated features. Hence, an approach of comparing the predicted burst pressures from field and tool dimensions was used to predict the burst pressures of these features.

Similar to the approach for case study 1, burst pressures were calculated by *CorLAS* using the field-measured depth and interlink lengths versus the tool-reported depth and its overall length. The results are shown in Fig.12, which demonstrates that the predicted burst pressure from the field-measured depths and lengths were substantially higher than those predicted by the tool.

A worst-case scenario line (shown in red) was used to adjust the predicted burst pressures of the unexcavated crack-field and crack-like features and prioritize the features for excavation.

Tool performance: achieved sizing accuracy

The actual sizing accuracy achieved for this pipeline was not determined. After comparing the field measurements of the defects with the tool-reported measurements, it was apparent that the specified sizing accuracy was not achieved by the inspection, even in the absence of confirmation calculations. The inaccuracy of the tool-reported dimensions was taken into account by using scatter plots instead of the field-tool regressions for length and depth. Scatter plots illustrate the actual length and depth associated with the features found in the field; bounds of these data are defined and subsequently used to restrict the length and depth combinations that are generated in the probabilistic assessment. Also, the density of the field data with respect to length and depth combinations is reproduced in the probabilistic assessment.

Metal loss and SCC

In addition to the reported features, the vendor also included a list of 3,587 'metal-loss' features. Only relative distance, orientation, and length for these features were reported; depth was not. These features were aligned with features from excavations, and 85 of the 115 (74%) of the features were correlated to unreported SCC colonies below the reporting threshold of the tool. Some, but not all, of these colonies were associated with corrosion. This case illustrates the potential that metal-loss features reported by the crack-detection tool could potentially be SCC, particularly if the features were not previously reported by an MFL inspection. Consequently, UTCD-reported metal-loss features that did not correspond to previous MFL indications were included in the probabilistic crack-growth assessment.

It is important to note that not all in-line inspection vendors report metal loss for crack-detection inspections.

Average stress versus SCC severity

The pressure profile of the pipeline was calculated as outlined in the analysis method section of this paper. When the SCC severity (burst pressure expressed as a percentage of the licensed MOP) was plotted against the average stress at the SCC location (Fig.13) it was observed that the minimum at-site average stress for SCC with a burst pressure less than 125% of the licensed MOP was 43.6% SMYS. As a result, an average 'at-site' stress of 40% SMYS was used as a threshold to determine which features would be included in the probabilistic crack-growth assessment.

Probabilistic crack-growth modelling and remaining-life assessment

This assessment was divided into eight individual segments based on the seven pump station locations and two MOP operating regions. By assessing the pipeline in separate sections, it was possible to evaluate the effect of applying different integrity actions to different sections. This assessment was also performed using two different pressure histories, one based on the licensed MOP and the other again based on the reduced MOP. Performing the assessment using different discharge and suction pressure histories changes the MOP, SCC growth rate, and pressure history for each location along the pipeline, all of which have a great impact on the overall results.

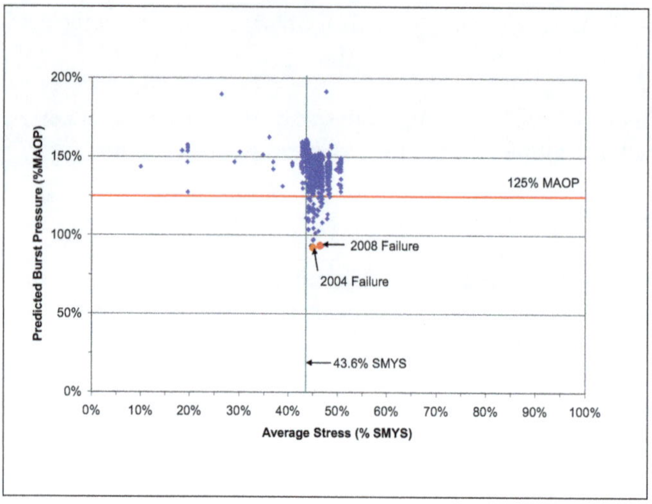

Fig.13. At-site average stress vs SCC severity.

The assessment at licensed MOP was used to determine what integrity actions were needed to return the pipeline to its licensed MOP. The first section calculated to exceed the failure rate threshold of 0.001 failures per km-year is Section 5, as shown in Fig.14. Based on this analysis, excavations and/or a re-inspection are required before July, 2010, in order for the pipeline to be returned to licensed MOP. Although the pipeline's expected failure rate was not calculated to exceed the threshold until July, 2012, integrity activities are scheduled two years earlier to allow time for a tool run and subsequent initial excavations to be completed. Since Section 5 has a higher expected failure rate if integrity activities were directed to that section, the re-inspection for the entire pipeline could be delayed for over one year.

Evaluating the pipeline sections at the reduced MOP established the current integrity of the pipeline with respect to cracking and determined whether any immediate integrity-related actions were required. Figure 15 shows that none of the pipeline sections are calculated to exceed the threshold prior to July, 2018, and in July, 2012, when the pipeline was calculated to exceed the threshold based on licensed MOP, the calculated expected failure rate is significantly lower.

Conclusions

For this pipeline, it was concluded that:

1. only features reported as crack-field and crack-like were found to be SCC;
2. the tool generally performed well with respect to defect detection, but misclassified some manufacturing defects as crack-like or notch-like;
3. the sizing accuracy of the tool with respect to depth and length was poor; instead of regressions, scatter plots of actual field data were used to model the remaining reported and unreported features;
4. analysis of the SCC colonies found to date show a link between their severity/numbers and their at-site average stress level;
5. the failure feature's interlink length was an outlier compared to the other correlated SCC features, but its depth was within the range of measured depths of other SCC colonies found in the field; and
6. since a return to the original operating pressure regime is not immediately required by the operator, the results of this study indicate that the pipeline is safe to operate until a re-inspection is planned.

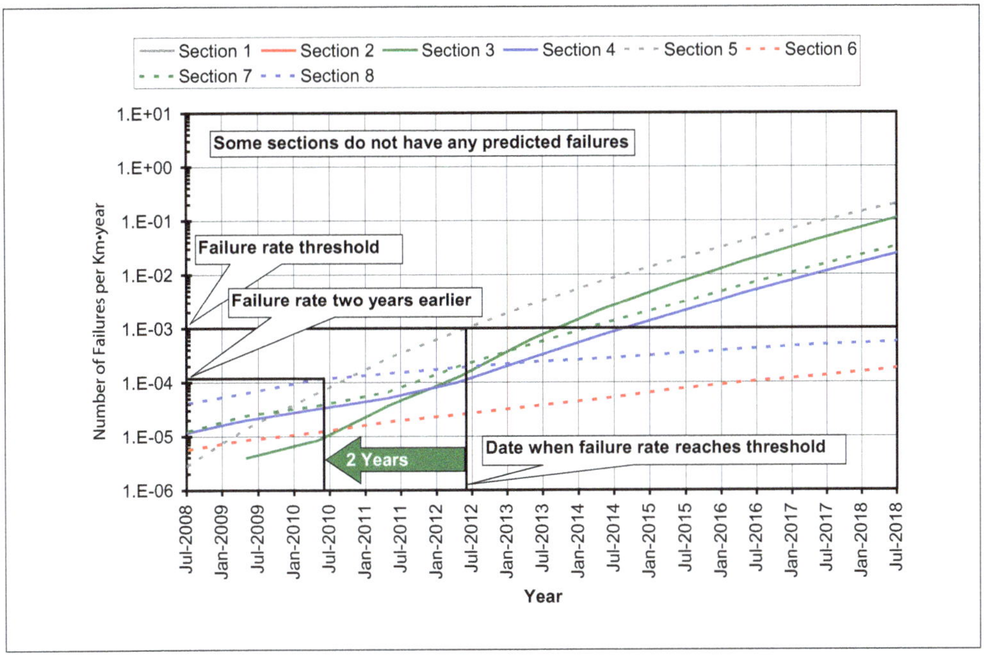

Fig.14. Calculated expected failure rate vs time based on licensed MOP operation.

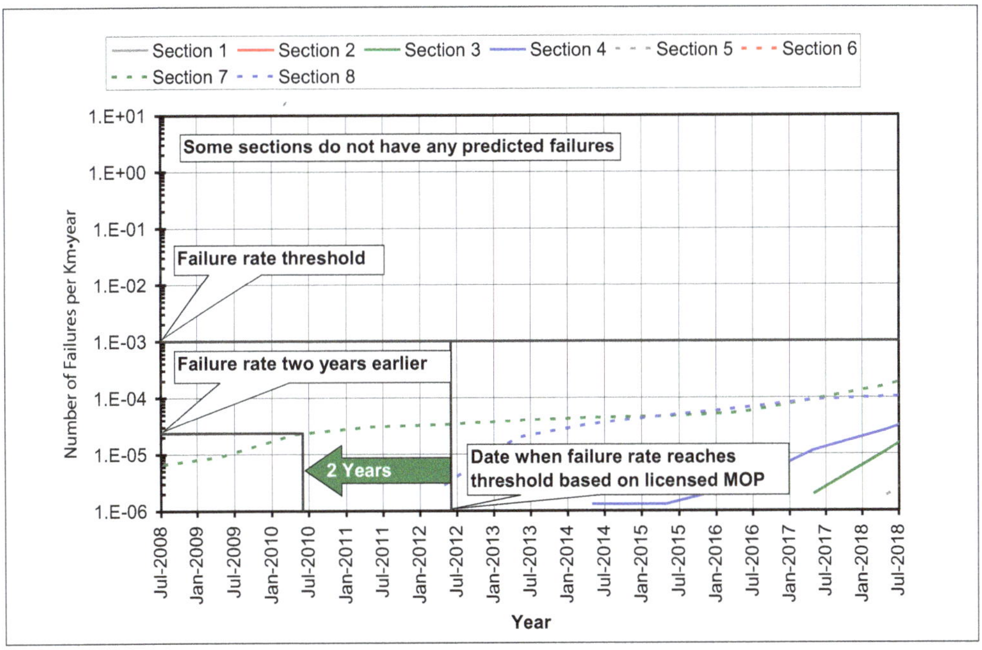

Fig.15. Calculated expected failure rate vs time based on reduced MOP operation.

General conclusions

Ultrasonic in-line inspection tools have provided operators with a method of detecting critical crack-related integrity threats.

While probability of detection was excellent in both case studies, increased clarification ability would likely result in a better probability of identification (i.e. notches being called as crack-like instead of notch-like).

In-line inspection data should be correlated with field data in order to evaluate tool performance and provide feedback to the in-line inspection vendor. Scrutiny of both the tool and field data also improves confidence in correlations that are made. From the case studies provided, it is clear that prediction errors from the field-tool regressions can be exaserpated by inaccurate field data. Not only are grind depths considered more reliable than those measured by ultrasonics, but there can be significant variability in the field-measurement accuracy between different NDT personnel.

Additionally, it is recognized that in-line inspection technology is continuously evolving and inspection capabilities continue to improve.

When possible, reported features from the tool should be aligned and compared to pipe-manufacturing data, pipe-stress levels, soil-survey data, and other pipeline information in order to find areas where integrity activities need to be focused.

Excavation defects should also be correlated to metal-loss or not-decidable defects reported by the tool vendor. In the second case study, many of these defects were actually SCC colonies below the reporting threshold of the tool.

The probabilistic assessment provided critical insight into the integrity of the pipeline beyond the information reported by the in-line inspection tools. The assessment allowed for a safe re-inspection interval to be established for each pipeline.

Acknowledgements

The authors gratefully acknowledge the co-operation of the respective pipeline owners in preparing this paper and the permission to present the inspection and assessment findings.

References

1. P.H.Vieth, C.J.Maier, and C.E.Jaske, 2004. Pressure cycle fatigue – a statistical assessment approach. Paper IPC04-0556, International Pipeline Conference, Calgary, ASME International.
2. CSA, 2007. Z662-07, Oil and gas pipeline systems. Canadian Standards Association, Mississauga, Ontario, June.
3. API, 2005. 1163, In-line inspection systems qualification standard. 1st Edn, American Petroleum Institute, Washington, DC, August.
4. J.A.Beavers, C.J.Maier, C.E.Jaske, and R.Worthingham, 2007. Methodology for ranking SCC susceptibility of pipeline segments based on pressure cycle history. Corrosion/2007, NACE International, Paper 07128.

Optimizing magnetic-flux leakage inspection sizing model performance using high-resolution non-destructive examination data

by Scott Miller and Stuart Clouston

Baker Hughes, Calgary, AB, Canada

MAGNETIC FLUX LEAKAGE (MFL) inspection tools have been used successfully for many years to estimate the dimension and severity of corrosion features in transmission and distribution pipelines. MFL is an indirect measurement system and a mathematical model or algorithm is used to translate MFL signals recorded by the tool into estimations of pipeline corrosion feature depth, length, and width, respectively. The derivation of these mathematical models can be anything from a simple calibration process of a representative sample of manufactured features in a pull rig, to an in-depth development process of highly complex algorithms.

One of the challenges to MFL technology is that the signal response, and hence sizing performance, is directly related to the shape of the corrosion. More importantly, since": the MFL measurement technique is indirect and models are 'trained', in some cases when the geometries of real corrosion differ significantly from those used to develop sizing algorithms, higher than expected sizing error can occur. This situation is of course of most importance when corrosion is aggressive and can lead rapidly to deep, potentially injurious, defects.

This paper describes a process which uses a large volume of statistically significant high-resolution non-destructive examination (NDE) data as a primary means to train and optimize MFL sizing models when defect geometry is a major contributor to poor MFL inspection-sizing performance. The practical application of the method to a Canadian oil pipeline is discussed in detail along with the approach used to achieve greater than 90% sizing confidence on field verified automatic UT data.

THE PRINCIPLES of magnetic-flux leakage (MFL) tools have been well understood by the pipeline industry for a number of years and, without doubt, the technology has been by far the most successful and most commonly used by pipeline operators to ensure the integrity of their pipelines. Even though MFL is an indirect measurement technique, the benefits that the technology provides have kept the technology in the pole position in terms of total length of inspections performed on a global basis. These benefits include the tool's being able to run at higher speeds (thereby not reducing production during inspection), the ability to operate in less than clean pipe, effectiveness in liquids and gases and in the vast majority of cases, and manageable data volumes for analysis.

Similar methods have been used by vendors to develop sizing models for magnetic-flux based pipeline-inspection tools. This generally involves a process of:

- establishing a representative sample set of manufactured metal loss defects in test pipe;
- collecting MFL signal data from the test pipe, usually by performing pull tests;
- developing a sizing algorithm to provide the mathematical transfer function of the signal response at a defect to an actual width, depth and length;
- algorithm refinement through additional data collected from inspection runs.

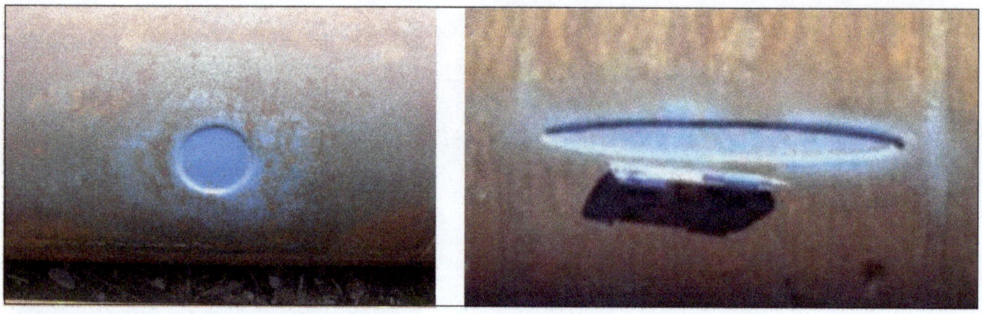

Fig. 1. Electrochemically etched defects used for sizing algorithm development.

Whilst vendors may have differing techniques to mathematically generate and manage the sizing algorithms and, indeed, different levels of sophistication in terms of the analysis and sizing process, the technology is well established. Experienced vendors should be able to consistently meet their specifications for simple metal-loss features given rigorous sizing model development and validation of those sizing models and analysis techniques through customer feedback and dig verification of 'real corrosion'.

Sizing model generation and performance

Figure 1 shows an example of typical pull-test defects used as a basis for sizing algorithm development. This particular set was created through an electrochemical machining process; alternatively, training sets can be created with a milling or drilling process. As will be discussed later, the manufacturing method used to create defects or assumptions in defect geometries that 'train' algorithms can be important to the overall success of the analysis and sizing performance of an inspection.

Figure 2 shows a standard unity plot which represents how well the sizing algorithm reproduces the actual defect sizes relative to a manufactured defect set. It is worth noting that during algorithm development it is not necessarily the case that if a sizing model achieves confidence levels approaching 100% on manufactured defects that the same model will perform well on real corrosion. In fact, quite the opposite, as it may mean it is over-tuned to artificial defects. Ensuring that a sizing model is robust and stable in the real world will often mean a compromise on pull-test data. This therefore emphasizes how critical it is to acquire large volumes of accurate data from the field before you can be sure that a sizing model is reliable and at least meeting the defined specification. Figure 3 shows the same sizing performance when the algorithm used in Fig.2 is applied to field collected data.

In the case of MFL technology, all vendors tend to provide a sizing specification at a given confidence level. There are a number of influencers/situations that can lead to out-of-tolerance sizing. Some of the most common of these include, but are not limited to:

- feature width and/or length being below specification;
- tool over speed;
- interacting anomalies or 'complex' corrosion, such as pit in pit;
- analyst bias or error;
- insufficient or poor algorithm training or calibration;
- pipe wall thickness too great for tool magnetic strength (poor saturation);
- defect profile/geometry.

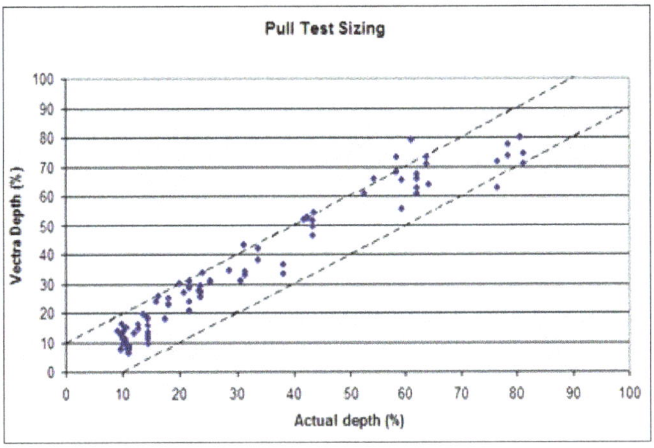

Fig.2. Unity plot of pull-data of manufactured defects, showing > 80% confidence with slight general over-sizing.

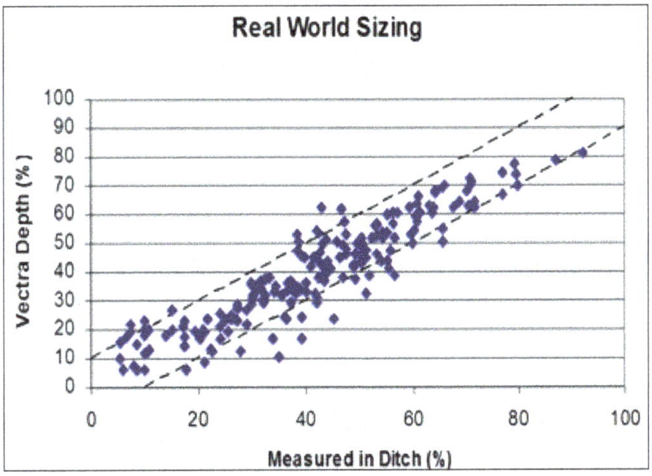

Fig.3. Unity plot of field-verified 'real' corrosion showing > 80% confidence with no over-sizing.

In some cases, such as tool over-speed or insufficient magnetization, it is relatively easy to determine why sizing accuracy may have been impaired; however, often it is not so simple and it is easy to jump to the conclusion that the analysis is the root cause. In the past, data provided back from the field was often no more than the deepest point of an anomaly or cluster of corrosion. When presented with such limited information, it is hard to truly identify why the discrepancy has occurred and, importantly, rectify the issue. Faced with significant discrepancies from reported to field-measured data, field data can and are sometimes used to re-calibrate an established sizing model. If this approach is used, caution should be taken that the method used to re-calibrate what was a previously robust sizing model still works generally well on existing data sets and that the process used is not simply shifting data to provide better confidence levels on very few field data points.

Over the last few years there has been a consistent progression in the quality of data that are being collected from the field. This is two-fold: firstly, more detailed information is being more consistently documented by the technicians or engineers in the ditch for review by the ILI vendors. Secondly, new technologies such as automatic UT and laser-based measurement techniques are providing much greater insight into the actual pipeline condition though collection of very-high-resolution data. These detailed data have enabled Baker Hughes to establish a more-rigorous technique for comparing very statistically significant numbers of field data measurements and to then better train and optimize sizing algorithms to deal with the harder-to-detect, and resolve defect-geometry-related sizing issues.

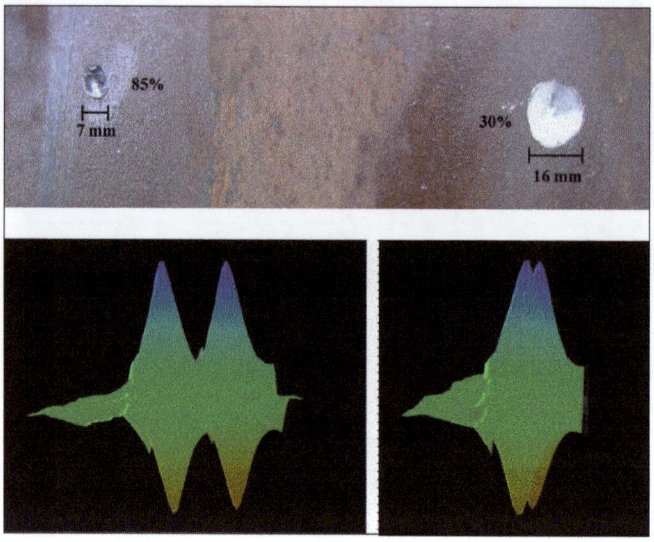

Fig.4. Dramatically different metal-loss geometries producing near-identical MFL signal responses.

The impact of defect geometry on sizing

A sizing model predicts depth based upon certain assumptions about the shape or profile of a feature. Typical pull-test features have a close to elliptical or parabolic shape regardless of the method used to create them. In general, this assumption works well when compared with the excavation data received from the field – but there are exceptions. A sizing model may be optimized to reproduce virtually any feature profile; however, the model cannot reproduce all profiles at once. The issue is highlighted in Fig.4 where a 0.28-in x 85% wall thickness depth pinhole and an 0.63-in x 30% wall thickness depth pit both exhibit near-identical MFL signal responses. Ideally, a rigorous algorithm creation process should be designed so that in such instances the algorithm estimates the most likely physical characteristics based on the MFL signals to arrive at an overall robust solution which is accurate across many defect profiles.

The effects of varying defect geometry can also be seen in Fig.5, which shows the theoretical impact of two different defect profiles and the impact it has on signal response. The first two images show two different defect shapes created using finite-element modelling; the third image shows the change to the metal loss signal response between Type 1 to Type 2. As this effect may be additional to the normal accuracy error associated with sizing, it can be seen how sizing error can be detrimentally affected by different defect geometries.

New-generation high-resolution NDE data are providing field-verification results which demonstrate the profile of features to a higher degree of accuracy. The more these profiles vary from those used to develop the algorithm, the more likely that sizing accuracy will be affected. Generally this is accommodated well by a model, but in some cases can become significant as will be discussed in more detail.

Managing and utilizing high-resolution corrosion-verification data

With many operators now regularly using techniques that provide high-resolution scans of verified corrosion sites on their pipelines, there is an increasing need for ILI vendors to be able to handle and interpret the large volumes of data that they produce. Traditionally, field-data comparison was

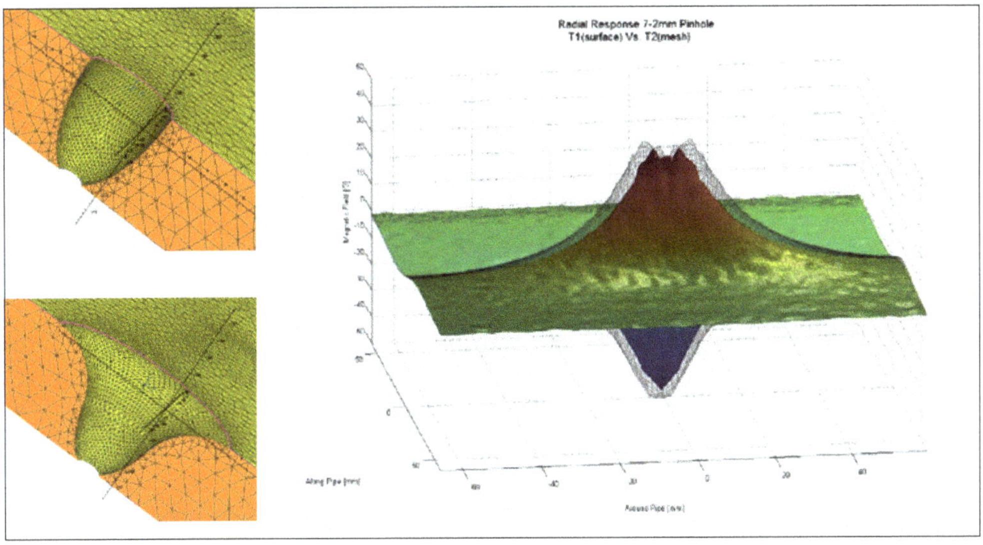

Fig.5. Finite-element model showing impact of defect profile on MFL signal response.

generally a localized look at a specific feature which, given a few reference points, was easy to do. The data now being provided to the ILI vendors for review are long scans or full joints (many thousands or millions of data points) often containing high numbers of interacting corrosion. Without some specific tools to read, accurately compare, and make sense of how the MFL signals relate to the NDE data, there is a higher risk than ever of creating errors in matching. This can have a dramatic effect on the apparent performance of the inspection tool when below-specification anomalies are incorrectly matched and compared, or when match errors go unnoticed. When mismatches occur, additional errors are then often unknowingly propagated along the joint. Without a detailed understanding of the MFL signals - providing the ability to correctly interpret the validity of data being compared - the correct matching of the large numbers of defects that these NDE techniques deliver is a challenging prospect.

In response to this, Baker Hughes has developed a proprietary software tool to read and compare 'raw' high-resolution NDE data types in multiple formats. The software has the ability to align and overlay the NDE data with MFL features and make positive correlations which are used in further analysis. A number of tools are available to review and compare sizing performance, defect geometries, and burst pressures directly between the two data sets. Figure 6 shows several screen captures of the software, showing features as boxes, correlated feature matches in green, and clusters as dashed outlines. It is also possible to view the data in 3D to review the specific profile of the geometry of a metal loss.

One of the key benefits of high-resolution NDE data is that, when properly matched and aligned, the accuracy of the data allows us to effectively treat the measurements as having minimal measurement error and therefore take advantage of the large number of real data points we can reference to the analysed MFL data. In effect, this means that we can support pull-test data with larger numbers of real data from the field than before, as a means to construct more-robust and accurate sizing algorithms. As an example, just a few joints of laser-scanned pipe can provide thousands of correlation and reference points for sizing algorithm refinement - more than initially used in pull-test data. These data can be highly statistically significant and will likely span the full depth spectrum needed to truly verify sizing models. In the past, and generally, verification data are available in the deeper depth ranges, such as >50% wall thickness, but it is much rarer to receive feedback on features in the 10-25% ranges.

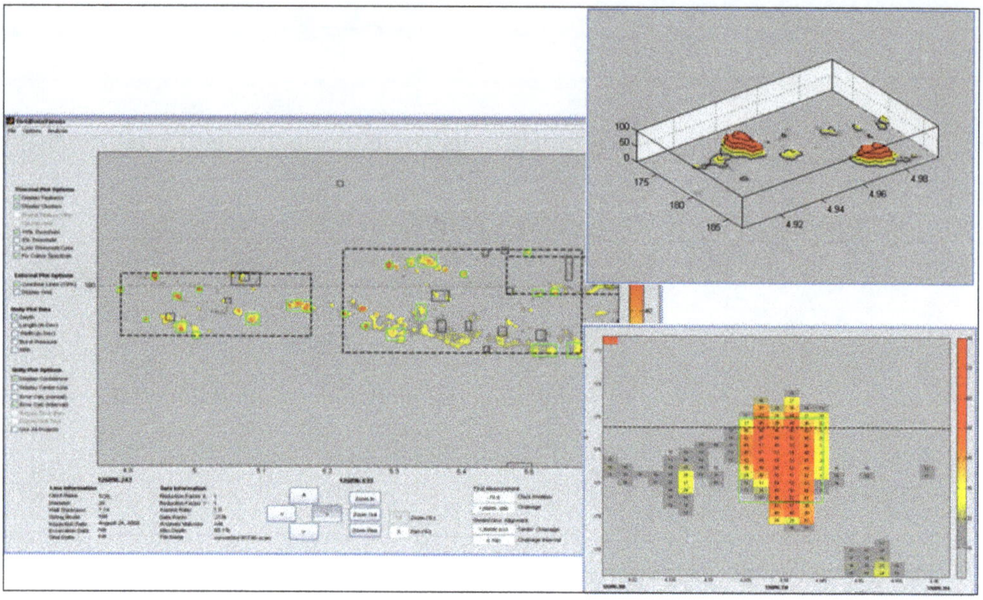

Fig.6. Baker Hughes' software for matching, correlating, and reviewing high-resolution NDE data.

Case study: sizing optimization using the *LaserView* process on a Canadian oil pipeline

Perhaps the best way to appreciate the benefits offered by the process of optimizing sizing models based on high-resolution NDE data is through a case study of a project performed by Baker Hughes on a Canadian oil pipeline. The line was known to exhibit areas of corrosion with sudden sharp or steep sided profiles. The specific nature of the corrosion was very small (below normal MFL sizing specification), and deep internal pinholes inside pits or areas of pits seemingly preferentially corroding at a much higher rate. Figure 7 shows an example of a pipeline exhibiting this type of corrosion.

After performing an initial MFL inspection with a vendor, the pipeline operator observed significant under-sizing issues (± 18% at 80% confidence overall) but – critically – the largest errors were routinely occurring on the deepest corrosions. This overall result is not unexpected with corrosion that exhibits locations of preferential pinhole corrosion.

Given the results, the operator asked the vendor to perform a re-inspection of the line to determine if a second data set could be used to enhance the results. This could be of benefit in the event that the poor accuracy was not due to sizing algorithm or analysis error but purely due to the corrosion being too small for the true signal amplitudes to be recorded by the tool's sensors (i.e. the tool was unable to detect the full amplitude of the signal, thereby leading to under-sizing). Additional runs may improve the chances of collecting higher amplitudes on some anomalies, but will not resolve inherent analysis or algorithm shortfalls.

Given the significant under-sizing of critical anomalies and the extent of the problem in this pipeline, the operator elected to contract Baker Hughes to run its *Vectra* MFL technology as an independent check on pipeline condition.

An inspection of the pipeline was performed by Baker Hughes and the results were consistent with the previous vendor's inspection results. Again, systematic under-sizing was providing a major

Fig.7. Typical area of corrosion exhibiting sharp or steep-walled corrosion geometry profile.

challenge to knowing, with an adequate level of confidence, the immediate integrity threats to the pipeline.

To effectively understand the sizing discrepancies being exhibited in this line, the operator used high-resolution automatic UT on a cut-out joint as the basis for the sizing comparison. The data were provided in raw format for import directly into Baker Hughes' comparison software, providing depth at a resolution of ± 0.004in on an 0.08-in x 0.12-in grid. Using the toolset available within the software to accurately correlate the reported internal anomalies with the field data, it was clear that there was a similar under-sizing on anomalies greater than 40% of wall thickness. There were also two other interesting findings as a result of the comparison of the Baker Hughes' data to the raw NDE data:

- of the 81 features compared, nine mismatches were identified from the original feedback provided by the operator;
- the UT data repeatability may not be insignificant as was evident in one particular area which was scanned twice.

A unity plot for the initial Baker Hughes results is shown in Fig.8. The confidence level at ± 10%

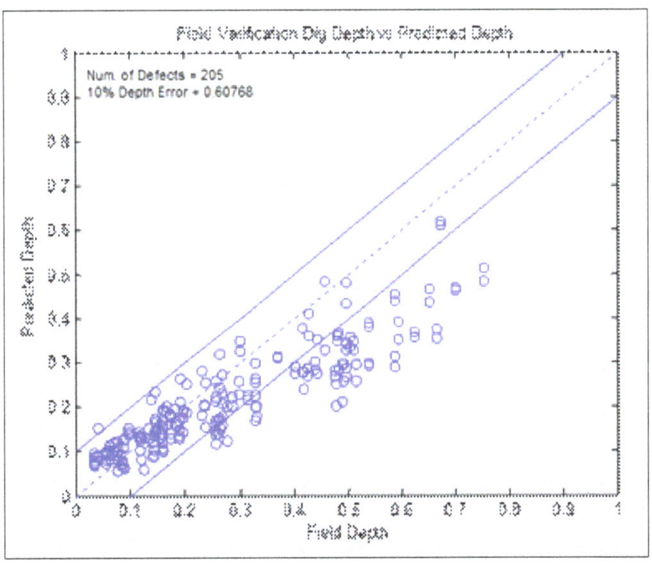

Fig.8. Unity plot showing initial Baker Hughes' sizing performance after inspection of the Canadian crude oil pipeline.

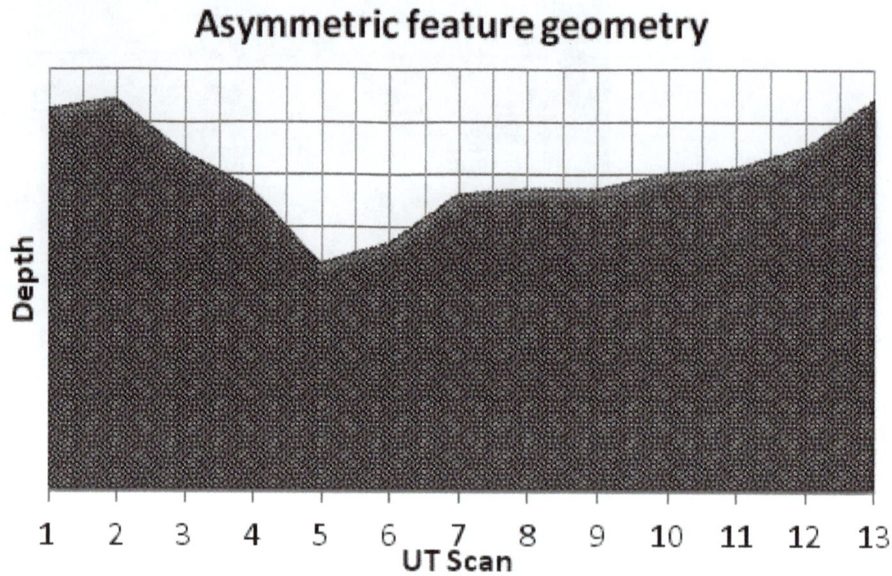

7.200	7.100	6.400	6.000	6.100	5.900	5.800	6.000	6.100	6.500	7.100	7.300
7.400	7.100	5.900	6.000	5.700	6.000	5.700	5.800	5.900	7.400	7.300	7.400
6.700	6.700	5.700	5.800	5.600	5.600	5.700	5.700	5.900	7.500	7.300	7.200
7.400	5.900	5.600	5.700	5.100	5.600	5.600	5.800	5.900	7.000	7.200	7.300
7.100	6.500	N/A	5.000	4.500	5.500	5.600	5.700	6.200	6.500	6.800	7.400
N/A	N/A	4.500	4.200	4.500	5.500	5.700	5.700	6.000	6.200	6.400	7.400
7.400	6.400	5.700	4.300	4.700	5.600	5.700	5.700	6.000	6.100	6.500	7.400
6.800	5.700	N/A	4.600	5.100	5.600	5.600	5.700	6.200	6.400	6.600	7.400
6.800	6.700	N/A	N/A	5.500	5.500	5.800	5.700	5.700	6.600	N/A	7.400
7.100	6.800	6.500	5.800	5.800	5.500	5.700	5.900	6.100	6.400	6.500	7.500
7.000	7.100	7.100	5.900	5.900	5.500	5.900	6.200	6.100	6.100	6.400	7.500
7.200	7.100	7.200	6.400	5.900	5.600	5.800	5.800	5.900	6.100	6.400	7.400
7.300	7.200	7.100	7.600	6.000	5.800	5.700	5.700	5.800	6.000	6.200	7.400
7.300	7.100	7.300	6.900	6.400	6.000	5.700	5.700	5.800	6.100	7.100	7.400
7.300	7.200	7.300	7.000	7.300	6.100	5.900	5.900	5.600	5.700	7.400	7.300
7.300	7.200	7.300	7.100	7.100	6.400	6.600	6.100	6.300	5.700	7.300	7.300

Fig.9. Irregular steep sided defect profile determined using automatic-UT measurement.

of wall thickness is 61% which was well below expectation. As previously stated, there is a systematic under-sizing of metal loss at depths greater than 40%.

In order to evaluate the error, Baker Hughes first manually verified all sizing on the outliers to ensure that analyst bias was not the cause of error. On detailed review of the high-resolution data where the largest sizing issues occurred there were obvious common characteristics to the shape and profile of anomalies where steep-sided wedge-shaped anomalies, or where small deep pits within the defect profile, existed. In many cases, these abrupt changes in profile occurred over less than 0.1in, which is below the physical limit in resolution of MFL technology. Figure 9 shows an example of a typical outlier's depth profile and the associated readings from the auto-UT scan.

Given the regular occurrence of defects exhibiting areas of small and sudden increases in depth, there was a possibility that the observed error may have been as result of tool repeatability which could also lead to under-sizing. To investigate whether tool repeatability was playing a significant role, Baker Hughes performed three more inspections back-to-back in the pipeline and matched all defects for comparison between each of the runs. The overall repeatability between the runs

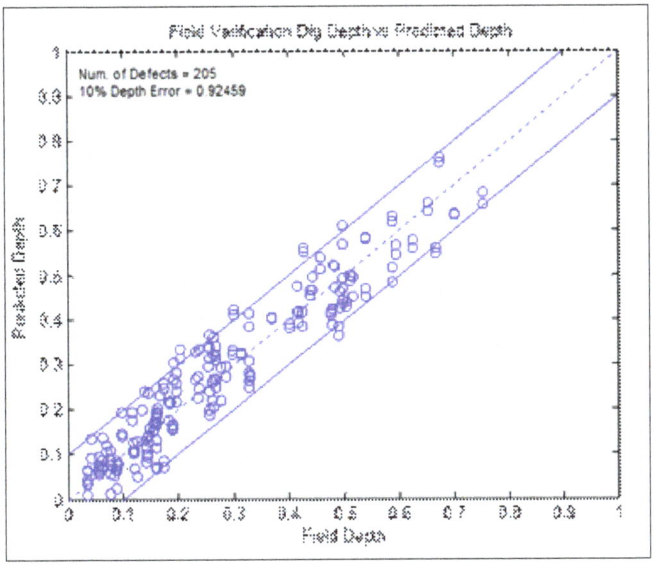

Fig. 10. 92% confidence at ± 10% wall thickness after sizing-algorithm optimization.

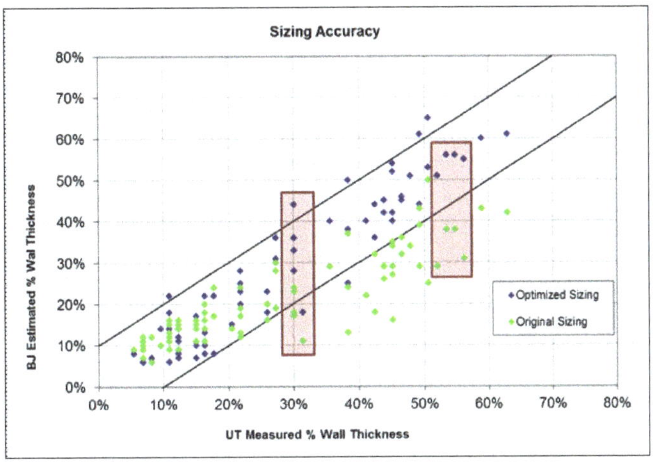

Fig. 11. Change-in-depth estimation before and after sizing-algorithm optimization.

was concluded to be reasonable and it was believed that this was not likely to be driving the systematic under-sizing of defects.

With this information, Baker Hughes focused on utilizing the accurately matched NDE data to establish a sizing algorithm that would produce increased sizing performance on this specific pipeline, and in particular dramatically improve confidence and accuracy on the likely more-critical anomalies above 40% of wall thickness.

Using Baker Hughes' proprietary techniques for sizing-model development, the NDE data were first used to train and then optimize the sizing algorithm as previously discussed. Figure 10 shows the results of this advanced process when the depths estimated by the new, optimized, algorithm are compared to the original high-resolution NDE data. As can be seen, there is a dramatic improvement with a 92% confidence level being achieved at an accuracy of ± 10% wall thickness – considerably above normal tool specification. Furthermore, it can be seen by looking at the two highlighted areas in Fig.11 that this is not a simple re-calibration exercise as the relative displacements of anomalies in the unity plot are different. This demonstrates quite clearly that the algorithm has been re-designed based on the supporting NDE data to provide superior sizing performance.

The highly effective optimization of the MFL sizing model and resulting accuracy improvements allowed the operator to go from an unacceptable level to a high degree of confidence that the depths of potentially critical defects were being estimated correctly.

Conclusions

There are many factors that affect the accuracy of the data provided from an MFL inspection. When sizing does not meet expectation, there are a number of possible reasons, though often these issues are quickly put down to poor analysis or sizing models. Often the cause is simply below-specification features, but when this is not the case, and systematic sizing discrepancies occur, it is highly possible that it is due to the inherent differences between the geometry of the real, randomly occurring, corrosion in the pipeline section and those used by ILI vendors during the inspection tool sizing model development process to calibrate or train sizing algorithms.

It has been shown that a combination newer, higher-resolution, NDE data from dig verifications, accurate comparison tools, and sophisticated mathematical techniques can be used to not only overcome the challenges that specific defect geometries can present but to exceed normal MFL sizing-accuracy specifications.

Furthermore, when pipelines are experiencing extensive, critical corrosion, this advanced process introduced by Baker Hughes has been shown to consistently improve sizing confidence to greater than 90% – providing the mechanism to reduce assumed tolerances in probability of exceedance (PoE) calculations.

Predicting future pipeline integrity in landslides using ILI mapping data

by Aaron Lockey and Andy Young

Penspen Integrity, Newcastle, UK

PIPELINES ROUTED THROUGH mountainous areas susceptible to landslides are often inspected using inertial mapping tools to determine position and strain. Viewed in isolation, data from a single inspection only give an indication of the pipeline integrity at a single point in time. Multiple inspections over a period of time can be used to estimate positional change. To extend the capability of these approaches, a method is required reliably to predict the future development of pipeline integrity based on trends in the mapping data from multiple inspections.

This paper presents a novel method developed by Penspen to predict the future integrity of a pipeline subject to landslide loading. The technique takes inertial mapping data from multiple inspections and calculates future strains in the pipeline using finite-element analysis. Unlike methods based on interpreting inspection data alone, the finite-element model includes the effects of soil-pipe interaction and axial pipeline stress to provide a more complete assessment of pipeline integrity. A case study of a large diameter oil pipeline is described to demonstrate the method.

The paper illustrates how the maximum benefit can be derived from existing data, reducing the need for additional inspections. The method may also be used to optimize future inspection strategy, provide timescales for planning and implementation of remedial works, and make a cost-effective contribution to an integrity-management system.

Background

Pipelines routed through mountainous areas can be susceptible to damage by ground movement caused by landslides. The presence of landslides along a pipeline route can be difficult to identify at the design stage, and routeing through these sites is sometimes unavoidable. When a landslide does affect a pipeline, it is necessary to assess its effect on pipeline integrity as part of an integrity-management programme.

A reliable assessment of current pipeline integrity and a prediction of the remaining period of safe operation would bring significant benefits to a pipeline operator. It could inform decisions on remedial works and help derive maximum value from the operator's investment in in-line inspections.

In areas of ground movement, and for landslides in particular, in-line inspection mapping tools are often used to monitor the displacement and curvature of a pipeline. A single mapping inspection gives an indication of a pipeline's position and curvature at a single point in time. However, this includes the effect of all bends in the pipeline: field bends, and installation geometry due to unevenness of the trench, as well as curvature due to ground movement.

After a second mapping inspection has been carried out, taking the difference between the inspection results filters out features that have not changed. This can be used to show how pipeline

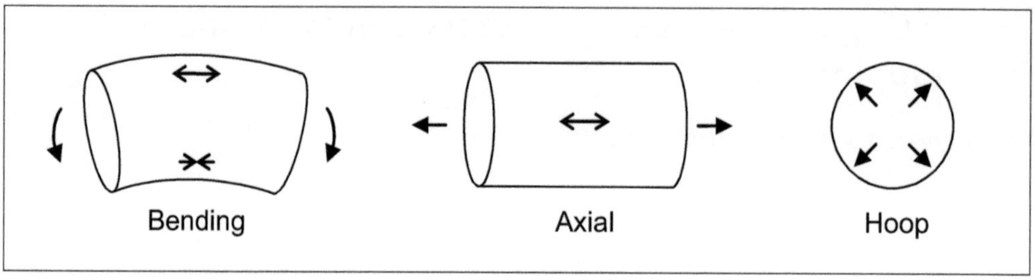

Fig. 1. Strain components acting on a pipeline subject to landslide loading.

position and curvature have changed over time, giving an indication of the profile and rate of landslide movement. For small landslide movements, a simple assessment of the pipeline's integrity at the time of the second inspection can then be carried out. In limited circumstances, it may also be possible to project the position and curvature changes forward to predict future pipeline integrity.

A method is required reliably to carry out an assessment of pipeline integrity for any amount of landslide movement, and to predict the future development of the pipeline's integrity. This will aid planning of further inspections or remedial works as part of an integrity-management programme. Penspen has developed a novel methodology for carrying out this type of assessment, which is described in this paper.

Strain-based assessment

A buried pipeline passing through a landslide generally follows the profile of the displaced ground fairly closely. This is, therefore, a displacement-controlled situation where strain-based assessment methods of pipeline integrity can be applied successfully.

The possible failure modes are fracture of girth welds due to tensile strain and local buckling (also known as wrinkling) due to compressive strain. Before carrying out an assessment, appropriate tensile and compressive strain limits should be determined to represent ongoing safe operation of the pipeline. Penspen generally uses guidance provided by PRCI for this purpose [1].

There are three significant components of strain that combine to give the total strain state in the pipe wall for pipelines operating at ambient temperatures, illustrated in Fig.1:

- Bending strain

  This is a longitudinal strain caused by bending of the pipeline. It is equally tensile on the outside of a bend and compressive on the inside. In-line inspection mapping tools measure pipeline curvature, which is directly proportional to bending strain at all times.

- Axial strain

  When landslide movement occurs, an initially straight pipeline trench effectively becomes longer, causing a tensile force to develop in the pipeline. This causes a corresponding strain which is constant around the pipe ring. The extension and strain are non-linear with respect to landslide movement: they increase more quickly when landslide movement is larger. The magnitude of extension is also dependent on the landslide profile. Landslides with narrow transition sections between the stable and moving ground will lead to higher axial strains.

- Hoop strain

  Internal pressure of the pipeline product causes a tensile strain in the pipe wall in the hoop direction and a corresponding tensile strain in the longitudinal direction due to the Poisson effect. These strains affect the tensile and compressive material yield points in the longitudinal direction, so must be taken account of in a full assessment of pipeline integrity.

A simple assessment based on bending strain alone is only reliable when landslide movement is small, such that axial strain is negligible and the material yield point is not approached.

Modelling approach

In order to take proper account of all factors contributing significantly to the strain in the pipe wall, a finite-element model of a buried pipeline has been developed, including both geometrical and material non-linearity. In this model, a pipe-soil interaction relationship is used to simulate the application of a landslide movement profile to the pipeline. The pipe-soil interaction is modelled as a force-displacement function calculated according to standard formulations [2] from experimentally determined soils data.

The landslide-movement profile is determined from two or more sets of in-line inspection mapping data, supported by site surveys if these are available. The aim is to determine a profile that, when applied to the finite-element model, gives bending-strain change results that match the measurements from the in-line inspections. Completing this loop by showing that the finite-element model correctly predicts the known measurements gives confidence in its predictions when further landslide movement is applied to represent future development.

In most cases, the absolute accuracy of the *xyz* positional data reported by the inspections is not sufficient to reliably determine a pipeline movement profile, particularly where small measurements of the order of tens of millimetres are important.

A better approach is to determine the change in pipeline curvature between two sets of inspection results. This can then be converted to a pipeline movement profile by integration. The same method is applied as is used by the inspection vendors to produce positional data from curvature measurements.

The ground movement in the landslide may be different from the pipe movement, and can be determined by inverting the pipe-soil interaction relationship. The calculated landslide-movement profile is now guaranteed to give the measured bending strain when applied to the finite-element model, since it has been determined by effectively reversing the finite-element calculation.

With only two inspections, it is generally assumed that the landslide movement speed is constant and the shape of the movement profile remains the same. If more inspection results are available, it is possible to determine a more-detailed model for past and future changes.

Calculation example

An example of a 42-in diameter crude oil pipeline will be used to help illustrate the method; the details are shown in Table 1. The buried pipeline crosses a landslide perpendicularly, as shown schematically in Fig.2. Two in-line mapping inspections have been carried out at an interval of two years. For safe operation of this pipeline, the tensile and compressive strain limits are 1.7% and 0.5%, respectively.

The difference between the two measured horizontal longitudinal bending strain profiles for the example pipeline is shown in Fig.3. The resulting landslide movement profile and its development over time since construction of the pipeline are shown in Fig. 4.

The predicted peaks of each strain component throughout the whole landslide area resulting from applying the ground-movement profile to the finite-element model are shown in Fig.5. This includes the total tensile and compressive strains, and the separated components of bending and axial strain.

The bending-strain component increases in a gentle non-linear trend with increasing landslide movement. The axial strain component increases slowly at first, but more quickly as the landslide movement becomes larger. The tensile and compressive strains represent the actual strains in the pipe wall; it is these that are checked against the strain limits for safe operation. The tensile and compressive strains diverge from the bending strain as the axial strain increases, since tensile strain is the sum of the bending and axial components, and compressive strain is the difference.

A similar form of results could be calculated for all pipeline and landslide geometries. However, the magnitude of the axial strain component and the landslide movement that causes the tensile and compressive strain results to diverge would vary.

Evaluation of methodology

It has been shown that for larger landslide movements, axial strain has a significant effect on the total tensile and compressive strains in the pipe wall. An assessment based only on checking the bending strain component against strain limits could be non-conservative.

Compared to an assessment based only on bending strain, the tensile strain limit is reached after lower landslide movement and the compressive limit is reached after greater landslide movement.

Whether the tensile or compressive strain limit is reached first depends on the pipeline geometry (diameter to wall-thickness ratio) and the nature of the loading on the pipeline. This corresponds to different failure modes:

- Local buckling failure mode

  For larger-diameter, thin-wall pipe, such as the example pipeline, local buckling is the first failure mode to occur and the compressive strain limit is reached first. Since compressive strain is predicted to develop more slowly than bending strain, the full strain analysis predicts that the pipeline can operate safely at larger landslide movements.

  An assessment of pipeline integrity based on full strain analysis would therefore be beneficial in terms of extending safe operating life compared to an assessment based only

Table 1. Parameters for the example pipeline.

Diameter	1066.8mm (42in)
Wall thickness	12.5mm (0.5in)
Material grade	API 5L X60
Product	crude oil
Burial depth	1.2m

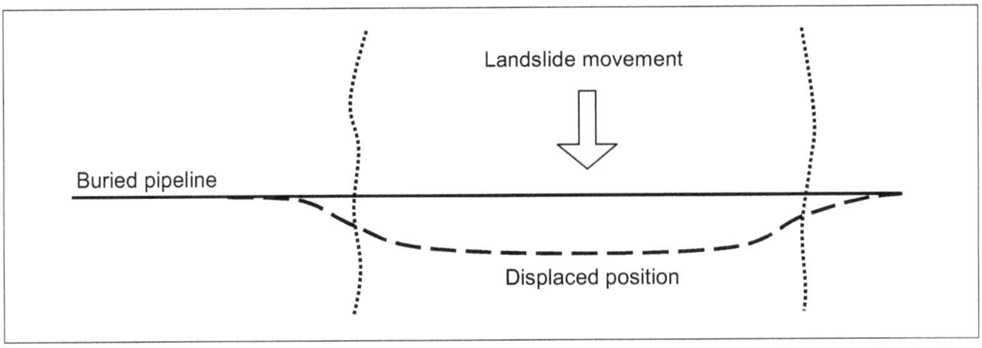

Fig.2. Schematic drawing showing the effect of landslide movement on the example pipeline.

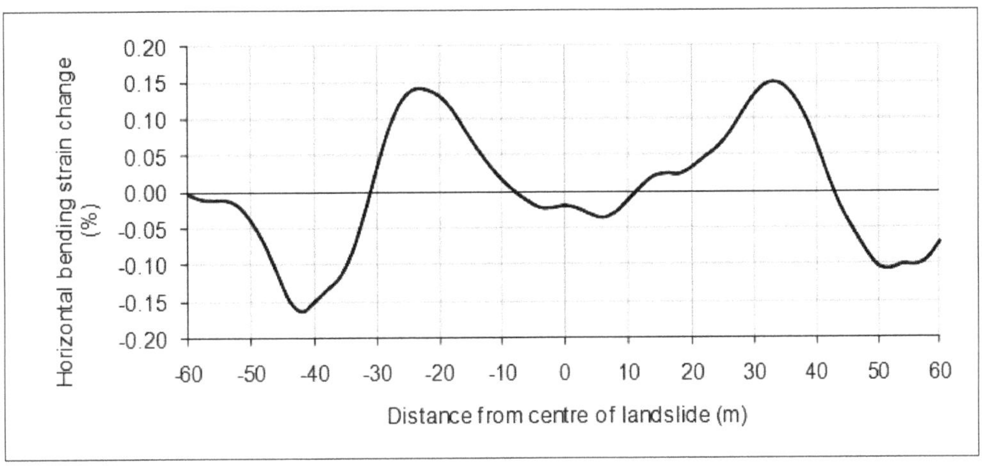

Fig.3. Smoothed bending strain change between inspections.

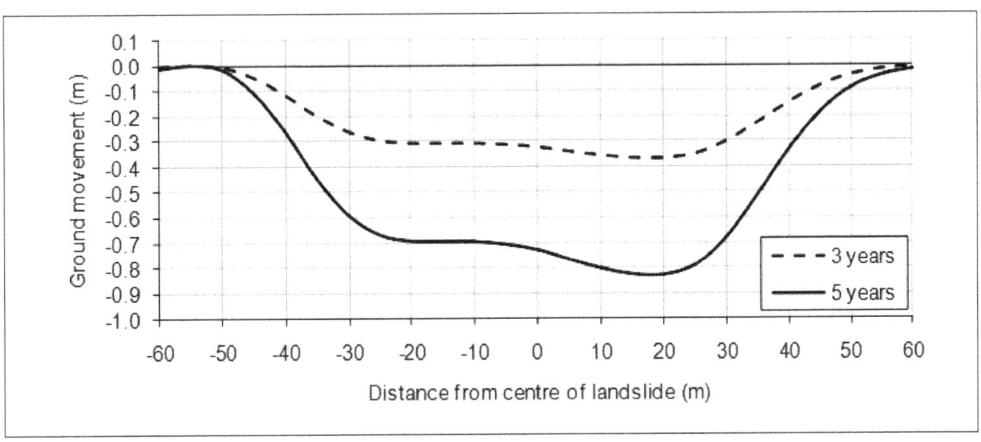

Fig.4. Ground-movement profile since construction, calculated from two inspections.

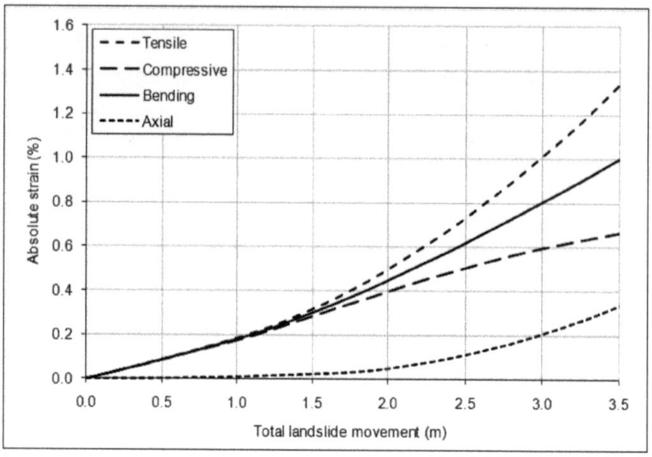

Fig.5. The development of each peak-strain component as landslide movement increases.

on bending strain. It would increase the predicted remaining safe operation life with regard to compressive failure when landslide movements are large.

- Girth-weld fracture failure mode

For smaller-diameter, thick-wall pipe, girth-weld fracture is the first failure mode to occur, so the tensile strain limit is reached first. Since tensile strain is predicted to develop more quickly than bending strain, the full strain analysis predicts that the pipeline can only operate safely at smaller landslide movements.

An assessment of pipeline integrity considering only bending strain may therefore be significantly non-conservative with regard to tensile failure when landslide movements are large.

Benefits to a pipeline operator

An assessment of pipeline integrity based on full strain analysis gives many advantages to a pipeline operator, in addition to the improved assessment reliability explained above. As such it forms an important part of an integrity-management programme.

By making reliable predictions for the remaining safe operating life of a pipeline subjected to landslide loading, planning for remedial works can be carried out with greater certainty. In some cases, it may be possible to show that no site work is required at all, saving considerable costs. Appropriate remedial works can include slope stabilization[1], stress relief of the pipeline[2] or re-routing, depending on the particular situation. By taking full account of the current and future effect of a landslide on pipeline integrity, the results of a full-strain analysis can be used to help determine the most cost-effective option in both the short and long terms.

Knowledge of the landslide movement required to cause a pipeline to approach safe operation limits can assist an operator in scheduling further in-line inspections. These inspections can be used to check on and refine the predictions made by a full-strain analysis, and to prove that the

1 For example drainage, slope re-profiling, or construction of retaining walls.

2 This involves uncovering the pipeline to allow stresses to relax out, then re-covering.

pipeline remains safe to operate. The schedule can be optimized to minimize the number of additional inspections required.

Due to the flexibility of the finite-element modelling approach, further analysis can be carried out to assist the operator's decision making. For example, Penspen has carried out sophisticated analyses of both stress-relief works and special trench designs[3]. These demonstrated the direct benefit of stress relieving a heavily loaded pipeline and determined the amount of further landslide movement the pipeline could withstand whilst remaining safe to operate. In both cases, being able to estimate the additional safe operational time 'bought' by the cost of remedial works helped the operator quantify the value of carrying out the works, compared to other potential schemes.

All of this is possible using the same in-line inspection data that would need to be collected for a simpler assessment based only on bending strain, and which are often collected in the course of conventional metal-loss or other inspections. The operator therefore derives the maximum value from its in-line inspection budget and investment.

References

1. D.G.Honegger and D.J.Nyman, 2004. Guidelines for the seismic design and assessment of natural gas and liquid hydrocarbon pipelines. Pipeline Research Council International, L51927.
2. American Society of Civil Engineers, 1984. . Guidelines for the seismic design of oil and gas pipeline systems. V.A.Reston: Committee on Gas and Liquid Fuel Lifelines (CGL), ASCE Technical Council on Lifeline Earthquake Engineering.

3 These use special trench profiles and fill materials to minimize load transfer onto the pipeline.

Section 6: New technology

A case study of the crack sizing performance of the GE ultrasonic phased-array inspection tool on the Centennial pipeline

by T Hrncir[1], S Turner[1], S J Polaski[2], P Vieth[2], D Allen[3], I Lachtchouk[3], P Senf[3], and G Foreman[3]

1 Marathon Pipe Line, LLC, Houston, TX, USA
2 DNV Columbus, Columbus, OH, USA
3 GE Oil & Gas, PII Pipeline Solutions, Houston, TX, USA

GE PERFORMED an ultrasonic phase-array (USCD DUO) in-line inspection (ILI) survey of a 24-in and 26-in products pipeline. The primary purpose of this ILI survey was to detect and characterize stress corrosion cracking (SCC). A dig verification was subsequently performed in 2008 in order to establish a higher level of confidence in the detection and depth-sizing capabilities of this technology. An overview of the USCD technology and experience is presented here, along with the method used for validating the ILI survey results, enhancements to the ILI data analysis, and the impact on managing the integrity of the subject line section.

GE INTRODUCED ITS first phased-array inspection tool to the oil and gas pipeline inspection market in 2005. Since its introduction, the inspection tool has inspected 4700 km of pipeline: a portion of this work has been conducted in crack-detection mode only, another in a combined ultrasonic wall thickness measurement (UTWM) and ultrasonic crack detection (*DUO*) mode. This paper focuses on the ultrasonic crack detection (*DUO*) results.

The case study presented here involves the ILI survey of a 1086-km long products pipeline system that was assessed for SCC. Upon review of the ILI survey results, 76 crack-like features were identified and subsequently excavated. Since all anomalies were located on the pipeline's external

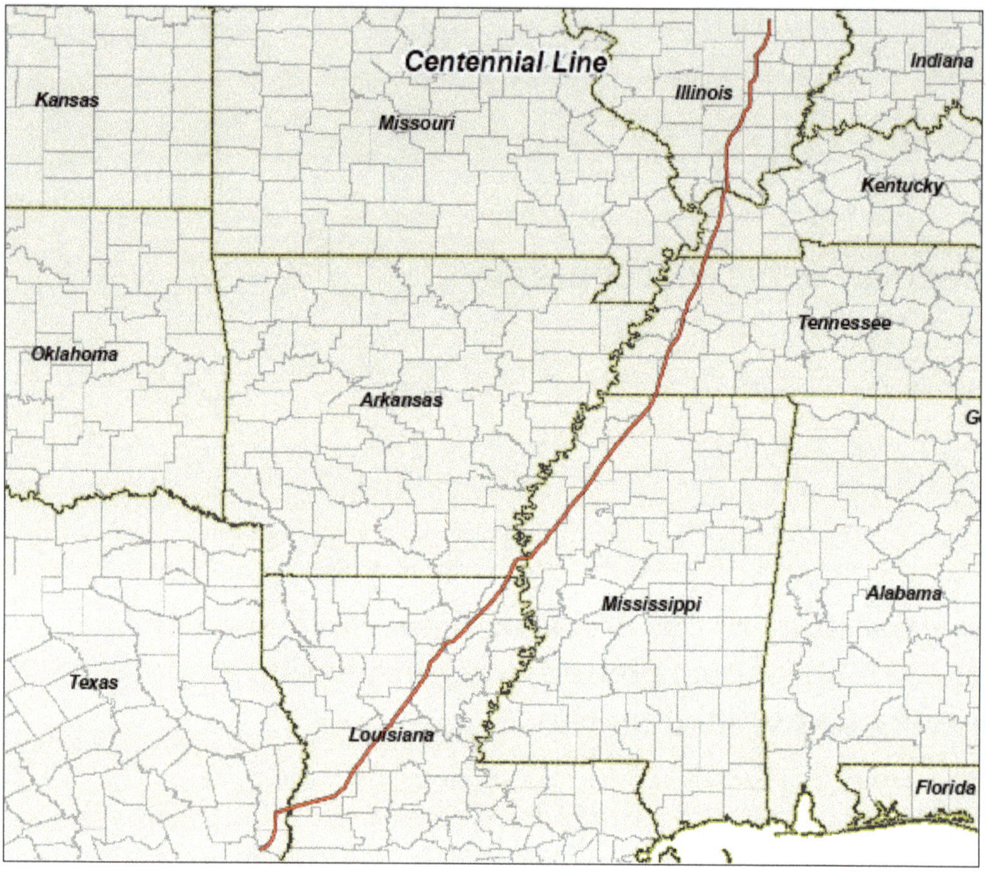

The Centennial pipeline route.

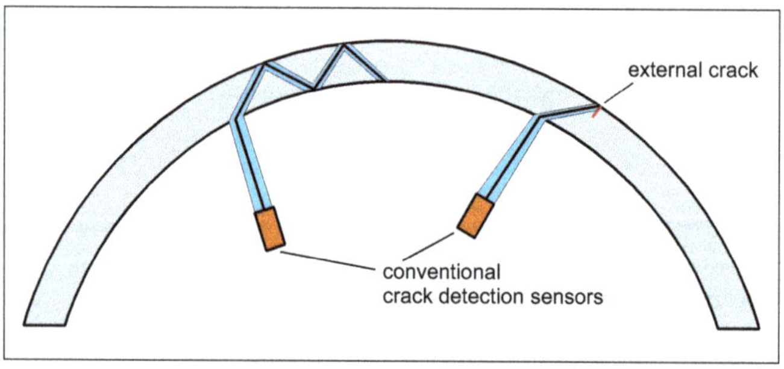

Fig. 1. Principle of ultrasonic crack detection: sound path of the ultrasonic pulse in the pipe wall (left); sound path of an ultrasonic pulse with a crack reflecting the sound (right).

surface, the defect-sizing capability could be confirmed through an accurate method involving incrementally grinding-out the defects. The evaluations were necessary to support the development of an improved sizing algorithm thereby increasing the confidence in reported depths and lengths required for integrity-management decisions.

Overview of the Centennial pipeline system

The Centennial Pipeline System is a 1213-km long liquid products pipeline operated by Marathon Pipe Line LLC (MPL), which is jointly owned by Marathon Petroleum Co LLC and Enterprise Products Partners LP. The pipeline originates in eastern Texas and delivers into product tanks in southern Illinois with an additional segment of the system continuing to the north. The first 119

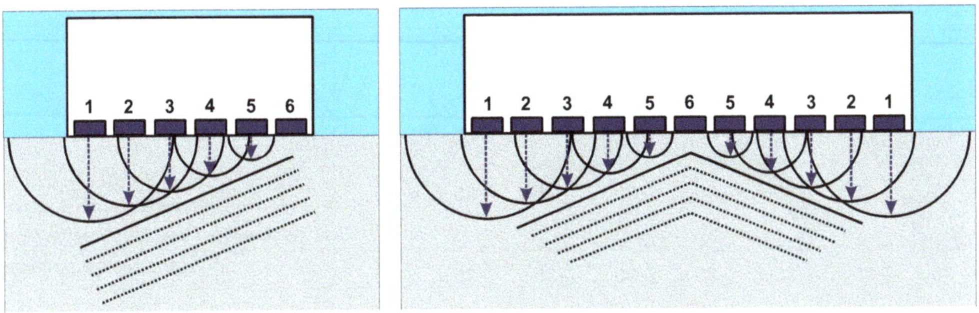

Fig.2. Steering the ultrasonic pulse by delaying the excitation between neighbouring elements.

km of the system is comprised of 24-in (609.6-mm) diameter by 6.35-mm wall-thickness, API 5L X52 linepipe constructed in 2001. This section was not inspected using the phased-array inspection tool.

The Centennial pipeline segment between Louisiana and Illinois was originally constructed and commissioned in 1951 for natural gas service. In 2001 this section was converted, and in 2002 commissioned, to liquid product service. The phased-array inspection tool inspected 1087 km in three sections which are predominately comprised of 26-in diameter by 7.92-mm wall-thickness, API 5L X52 double-submerged-arc welded (DSAW) linepipe.

Ultrasound crack-detection refresher

Conventional ultrasound crack detection tools use single crystal oscillator transducers, oriented at an angle to the pipe wall surface and at a defined distance from the surface. A portion of the ultrasonic pulse penetrates into the pipe wall with a refracted angle, and 'skips' between the internal and external surface (see left sensor in Fig.1). If a surface-breaking longitudinal crack appears within the sound path (see right sensor in Fig.1), a part of the pulse will be reflected by the crack and return on the same path back to the sensor. The reflected sound wave is detected by the sensor and converted into an electrical signal, which is further processed and stored in memory banks on the tool.

Phased-array refresher

Instead of a single crystal oscillator (of 13 mm approximate diameter), a phased array is comprised of many narrow stripe-like elements. Several neighbouring elements (width approx. 0.4 mm) are electronically grouped together to form a 'virtual' sensor. By varying the timing sequence, various elements of the 'virtual' sensor are excited (on the order of nanoseconds) and produce an ultrasonic pulse that travels away from the sensor with an angle (see Fig.2, left) or with a specific beam shape (such as focused, see Fig.2, right). The sequencing determines the direction and the angle of the ultrasonic pulse. By delaying the excitation of the elements in the centre of the virtual sensor, the pulse can be focused (for example, for a wall-thickness measurement).

Because the grouping of elements is performed electronically, the grouped elements can be easily and quickly modified. Each element can also be grouped into more than one virtual sensor, where the same element can serve multiple purposes. For example, one virtual sensor can first generate a sound wave in the clockwise direction, then in the counter clockwise direction, and finally

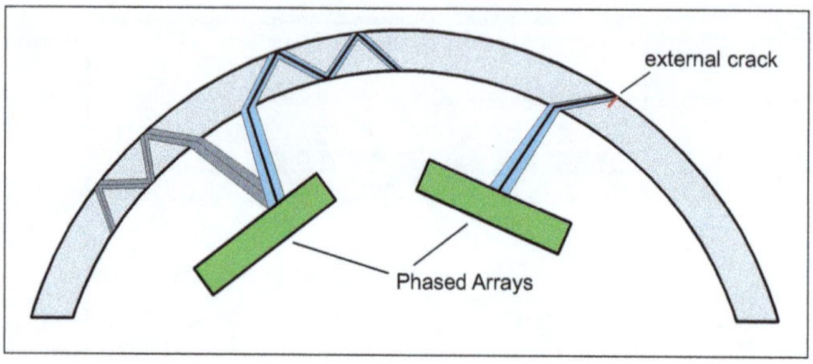

Fig.3. Same elements used for clockwise and counter clockwise shots (left); reflection from a crack (right).

perpendicular to the pipe wall. Since two neighbouring virtual sensors have an overlap, the same elements will also contribute to each of these two virtual sensors.

GE's ultrasonic phased-array inspection tool

As with other ILI tools, the phased-array tool consists of battery modules, electronic firing and data storage modules, and sensor carriers. The pipeline product acting against the polyurethane drive cups mounted on the leading module of the tool provides the driving force for the tool in the pipeline (see Fig.4).

The sensor carrier consists of three separate sensor rings, each oriented at a rotated angle from each other to provide 360° sensor coverage of the pipe wall circumference. Each sensor contains an array of elements (see Fig.5) and, depending on the measurement mode selected, contains as many as 44 virtual (grouped) sensors.

Run record

Since first introduced in 2005, the phased-array tool has commercially inspected 4700 km of pipeline (as of March, 2009), predominately operating in crack-detection mode only.

MPL's feature requirements for assessment purposes

In order to manage pipeline integrity as reliably and cost-effectively as possible, pipeline operators depend on the quality of the data provided by ILI reports. The most crucial criteria for establishing a quality inspection include:

- complete detection of the defect according to tool specification;
- correct classification of the defect regarding feature type; and
- accurate sizing of the defect within the tool specification.

The results of the above criteria for this particular ILI tool run and rehabilitation project are listed below.

Defect detection

Defect-detection capability for an ILI tool is quantified by its POD (probability of detection). This value states a run-independent probability that the tool is capable of detecting a defined defect size (for example, the minimum defect size). The calculation of the POD involves a consideration of

Fig.4. Receiving GE's UltraScan DUO ultrasound phased-array inspection tool.

Fig.5. Phased-array sensor carrier. Staggered arrangement of three rings (left); rear view of the sensor carrier pulled into a pipe (right).

all existing defects examined in a pipeline, both those which may or may not have been detected. To evaluate the tool's performance against its specified POD, it is necessary to identify defects not detected by the tool. Since it is not practical to expose the entire length of the pipeline, the POD value is commonly calculated using the results of pipe-loop tests, which contain defects of various sizes, both above and below the tool's specification, and are supplemented by the results from field examination.

Typically, during field-verification activities, pipe sections are uncovered on either side of the location containing the feature of interest. The fully exposed pipe length is then inspected using non-destructive examination (NDE) and all defects are identified, recorded and compared to the ILI survey results. This additional information is used in estimating the performance of the tool against its stated specification.

The POD value for the phased-array inspection tool was established through extensive loop testing. GE claims that a crack with a length of 25 mm and a depth of 1 mm can be reliably detected with a POD of 90% according to API 1163 methodology.

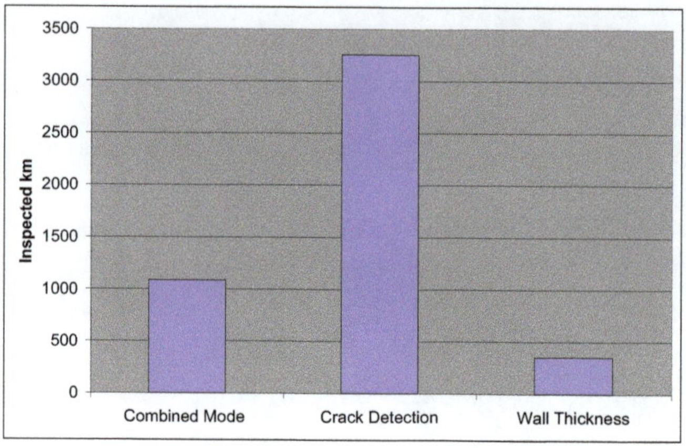

Fig.6. Run record.

Defect classification

Defect classification capability is the ability to distinguish between certain defect types that may exist in the pipeline. If an ILI tool has difficulty distinguishing between defect types (for example, cracks and mid-wall laminations), the value of an inspection can be significantly reduced. Additional field-investigation activity based on defect mis-classification leads to significant and unnecessary costs.

A reliable integrity-management programme is also affected by incorrectly classified features. The discriminatory capability is quantified by the POI (probability of identification) value. In contrast to the POD value, the POI value can be evaluated based on field verifications. With a sufficient number of 'digs', the POI can be calculated for a single inspection.

A POI value for the discrimination capability of cracks of the phased-array inspection tool was calculated based upon dig verifications performed as part of this programme. GE claims that for each inspection run a POI of 90% could be exceeded using the methods of API 1163.

Sizing of defects

The sizing accuracy of a tool has a significant impact on the integrity-management programme for a specific pipeline. The advantages of higher accuracies are:

- increased confidence in failure pressure predictions for prioritization
- improved selection of the most critical features
- reduction of non-essential excavations
- ˜potentially longer inspection intervals

The sizing accuracy is defined by a tolerance and an associated certainty. The length of a crack, for example, can be stated as ± 0.4 in (± 10 mm) with 90% certainty. These values are determined initially from loop test results and later validated against dig results, both having specific advantages. Dig-verification results are based on actual defects with variations in shape and orientation, and produces a broad data sample.

Centennial inspection

GE's phased-array tool inspected three 26-in diameter pipeline segments with a total length of 1086 km in the *DUO* mode (simultaneous crack-detection and wall-thickness measurement, or

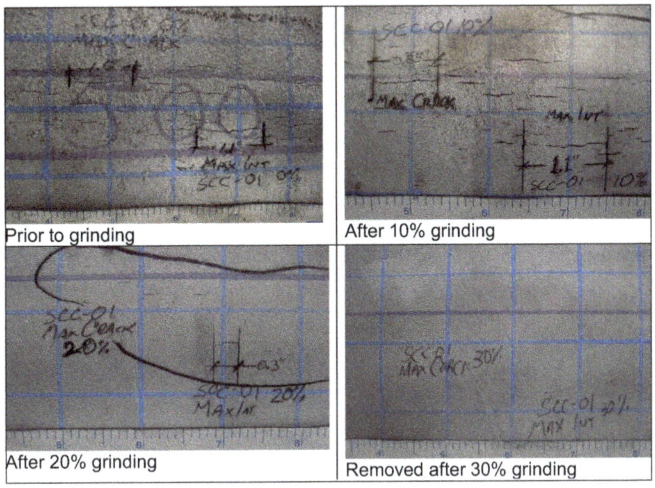

Fig.7. Defects ground in 10% steps:

(top, left) prior to grinding
(top, right) after 10% grinding
(bottom, left) after 20% grinding
(bottom, right) removed after 30% grinding

metal-loss inspection). The majority of crack-type anomalies reported by the tool on this system were crack fields; further investigation determined that the crack fields were primarily high-pH SCC that had formed when the system was in natural gas service (i.e. due to latent SCC).

Report and verification process

After receipt of the initial report, MPL proceeded with verification digs and began implementing its ILI response plan. During many of the subsequent excavations, it was discovered that grinding up to 40% of the wall thickness did not remove all cracks. Many of the indications had ILI reported depths of 12.5-25% WT and 25-40% WT, indicating that the depth of the cracks was undersized by the phase-array tool. To collect more accurate field data for better analytical correlation, an improved grinding procedure was established to better characterize the SCC in the field.

Experience has shown that the method of grinding defects in incremental steps leads to more-reliable measurements. The grinding procedure included measuring the wall thickness in proximity to the defect using an ultrasonic wall-thickness measurement device. Then, the pipe wall was ground in incremental steps of 10% of the pipe wall thickness and the defect was measured. This was done until the deepest portion of the defect was completely removed or a maximum grind depth has been reached. By documenting the results of each step, a profile of the crack could be generated for both the maximum individual crack and the maximum interlinking crack (using CEPA guidelines).

Improvements to sizing algorithms

Based upon the preliminary results, MPL, DNV, and GE developed and carried out a process to improve the accuracy of the phased-array tool calls to establish a better correlation between the depths predicted by the tool and those depths measured in the field. This required revising the sizing algorithms used by GE, and relied upon accurate and reliable field data.

In order to identify locations for more-detailed examination, DNV calculated the predicted failure pressures (using *CorLAS*) for all of the features reported based on the total axial length and predicted maximum depth range. Twenty crack-type features were identified, and GE applied a revised depth-estimate algorithm to the selected features and features in close proximity to the target feature. This served as a blind test to the revised algorithm.

Rev. 0 Feature Classification \ Rev. 2 Feature Classification	Crack Field	Crack-Like	Not decidable	Notch-Like
Crack Field	929	1		
Crack-Like	511	223	1	
Not decidable	1	27	12	
Notch-Like				287

1451	Same
541	Different
1992	Total

Fig.8. Feature classification changes for one section in Centennial.

The blind test included the detailed grinding procedure for crack-type anomalies. DNV supervised the dig-verification process including the analysis of grinding and crack measurements produced in the field. At periodic reviews, MPL, DNV, and GE compared the field results to the revised sizing algorithm for the purpose of determining if there was sufficient improvement in the revised algorithm to justify using it as the basis for re-grading all of the features identified. If there was insufficient evidence, the next excavations were selected from the 20 identified. When there was increased confidence in the improvement of the revised algorithm, any anomalies remaining from the original 20 locations would be re-evaluated after the re-grade was fully implemented.

During the process described above, GE also developed and implemented several iterations for an improved algorithm to identify and measure the longest interacting crack length based on the data received from the field. As the process continued, MPL, DNV, and GE jointly agreed that the results showed improved confidence in the revised sizing algorithm (both depth and length sizing). Therefore, MPL opted to discontinue the blind test validation programme and proceeded with the full re-grade. Once it was determined that the revised algorithm would be the basis for a re-grade, GE quantified the confidence in sizing by determining a tolerance around the discrete depth estimate instead of tolerances around depth bins (as was provided in the original ILI report).

The following three sections discuss in more detail the results of the blind test as well as incorporating the results from the re-grade using the revised sizing algorithm.

Defect detection

As stated earlier, GE performed loop testing and claimed that a crack with a length of 25 mm and depth of 1 mm (approx. 12.6% of the wall thickness for the Centennial pipeline) can be reliably detected with a POD of 90%. However, real defects exhibit variations in shape and orientation, whereas loop testing defects are often machined into the test loop and have very controlled dimensions.

During the blind-test programme, a total of 22 SCC features were located that were not reported by the *DUO* tool; these features are listed in Table 1. Of the 22 features, none had a maximum

DNV ID	Maximum individual length (in)	Maximum interlinking length (in)	Maximum grind depth (in)	Grinding removed cracks?
01.08.06	0.80	2.20	0.107	Y
02.38.64	0.50	1.20	*	**
03.34.20	0.40	0.60	*	**
04.38.90	0.30	0.50	*	**
05.03.75	0.60	1.00	0.062	Y
06.38.25	0.30	0.50	0.033	Y
07.15.95	0.45	0.80	0.076	Y
08.14.98	0.25	0.35	0.057	Y
09.21.15	0.25	0.45	0.058	Y
10.03.45	0.30	0.20	0.095	Y
11.01.97	0.40	0.50	0.090	Y
12.26.05	0.35	0.70	0.099	Y
13.31.91	0.35	0.50	0.072	Y
14.12.92	0.20	0.25	**	**
15.28.05	0.20	0.60	**	**
16.35.29	0.25	0.50	**	**
17.37.89	0.08	0.10	**	**
18.39.80	0.15	0.30	**	**
19.31.96	0.25	1.80	*	*
20.32.52	0.13	0.25	*	*
21.38.61	0.60	0.50	*	*
22.39.06	0.35	0.60	*	*

Table 1. SCC features identified in the field but not reported by the DUO tool.

** This indication was not ground in the field*
*** This indication was not ground in the field due to proximity to the DSAW seam weld*

individual crack length greater than 1.0 in, although three of the features not identified by the tool had maximum interlinking lengths greater than 1.0 inch. Of the features in Table 1, all but one were of depths greater than 1 mm (0.0394 in).

Defect classification

Between the initial dig-verification programme and the blind-test programme, both crack-like and crack-field features were identified in the field to be SCC. None of the notch-like or not-decidable features excavated were identified as SCC in the field. During the sizing-algorithm modifications, GE also revised the anomaly classification algorithms to better reflect these results. Figure 8 demonstrates how the feature classification changed for one section of Centennial in order to better represent the excavation findings: as shown, the vast majority of the 541 reclassified features were originally classified as crack-like features and were re-classified as crack-field features.

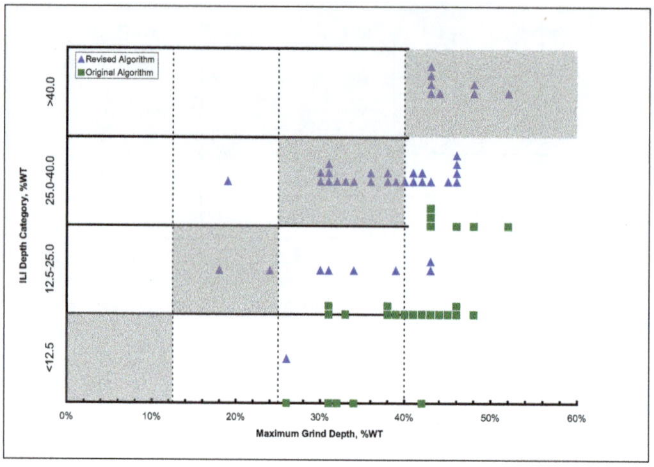

Fig.9. Comparison of depth-sizing algorithms with respect to maximum grind depth.

Crack sizing

For SCC, the maximum depth, the length of the crack field, and the length of the largest interlinked crack are reported for each crack field identified by the phased-array survey. In order to improve defect sizing, the first dig results were used to calibrate GE's crack-sizing algorithms. The blind test was then used to validate the revised algorithms prior to MPL requesting a re-grade.

Figure 9 shows the effect of the revised algorithm on the reported depth. It should be noted that the original depths were reported in bins (< 12.5%, 12.5% to 25%, etc.), whereas actual depth estimates were produced by the revised algorithm.

As shown in Fig.9, both algorithms showed the same general trend of increasing maximum grind depth as the reported depth increased. However, the original algorithm consistently under-called the maximum grind depth. The revised algorithm, on the other hand, shows an improvement in the number of features with correctly categorized depths.

Figures 10 and 11 show further validation of the revised sizing algorithms (both depth and length) developed by GE. After the crack anomalies were re-analysed using the revised crack algorithms, 64 of 76 (84%) reported depths were within the ±0.039-in (±1-mm) band indicated by the red lines, and 36 of 53 (68%) verified lengths of interlinked cracks were within the +1.57-in/-0.78-in (+40/-20-mm) range indicated by the red lines. This demonstrates that the depth measurement reported by the phased-array tool approaches the 90% certainty statement of the tool specification.

The certainty of the length measurement however, while it improved, did not approach 90% as well as the depth prediction, given due consideration to differences between tool call and field measurement of length. There are however, outliers, and Fig.11 indicates that the general prediction trend is still to overcall the interlinked lengths. There is one field interlinking length reported near 19.6 in (500 mm): this particular data point is inconsistent with the results of the other excavations.

Summary and path forward

The analysis of the performance of the phased-array technology on the *UltraScan DUO* inspection tool from this case study indicates that the revised algorithm developed for phased array meets or

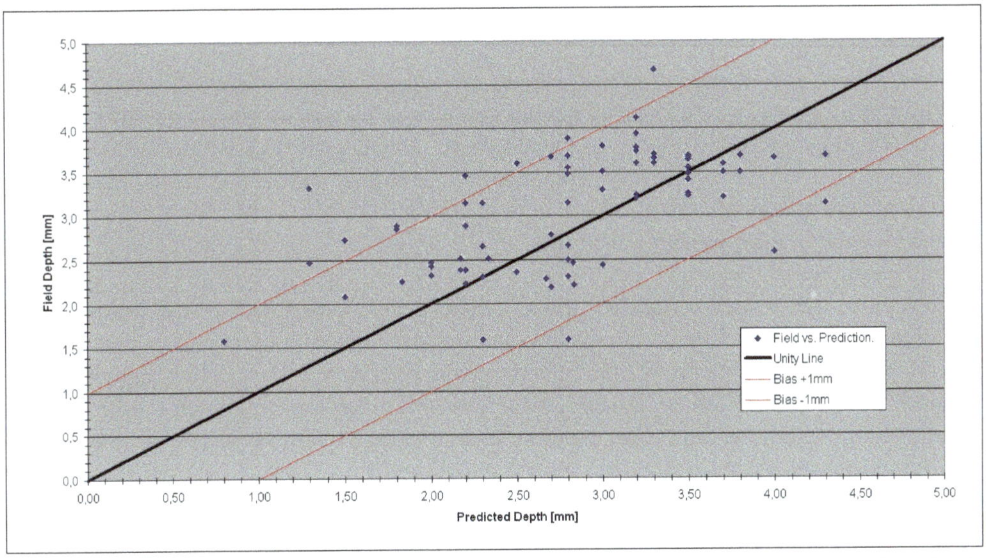

Fig.10. Unity plot predicted depth vs field depth.

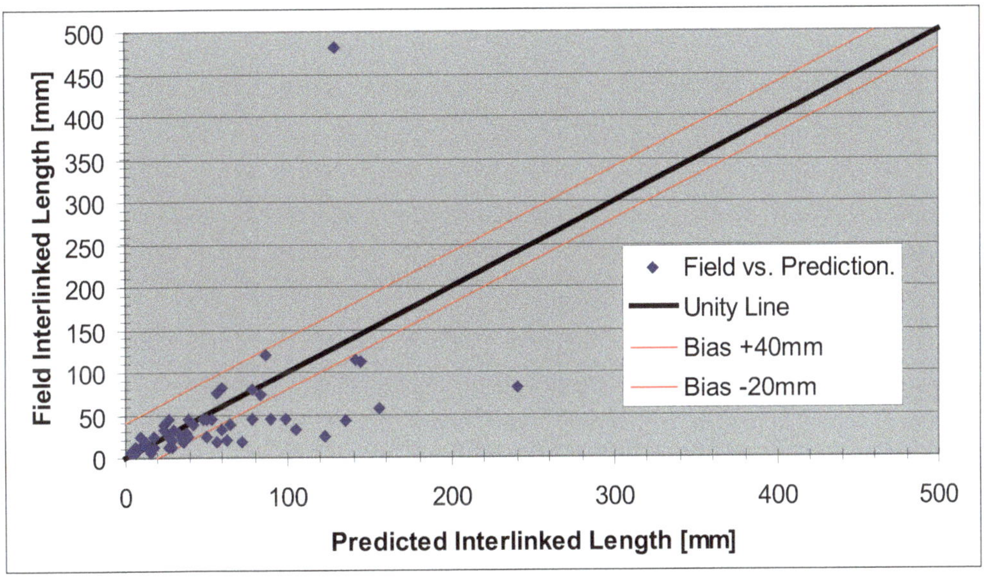

Fig.11. Unity plot predicted interlinked length vs field inter-linked length.

exceeds specifications provided for USCD tools that rely upon single crystal oscillator (piezo) transducers.

The next step for the phased-array technology is to take advantage of this flexibility to bring more value to the pipeline operator through enhanced sizing accuracy. Projects underway in this area include pitch-and-catch studies, paint brush, and varying firing angles during an inspection to deliver the highest reflected signal amplitude.

Further improvement of defect detection and depth sizing will also be subject of the next steps of improvement in crack detection: besides shooting at a spot with only one angle, two different angles could be applied, and instead of one sensor shooting and listening, one virtual sensor can shoot and another can listen.

Conclusions

The analysis of the performance of the phased-array technology on the USCD *DUO* inspection tool from this case study indicates that the phased-array technology approached a 90% certainty predicted depth with a given tolerance of ±0.039 in (±1 mm) at a 95% confidence level (as per the API 1163 guidelines) for the Centennial pipeline's SCC integrity-management plan. The certainty of the length measurement has also been improved, when applying the CEPA interaction rule, with field and tool measurement tolerances.

By moving to the revised sizing algorithms developed during this study, MPL has improved confidence in the reported feature depths and lengths and predicted failure pressures. Prioritization of features is important to ensuring the integrity of any pipeline system. In order to prioritize the features, MPL and DNV are integrating the re-graded ILI data and validation results with the pressure history, elevation, and pipe design to estimate a probability of failure for each feature.

Recent innovations in pipeline seam-weld integrity assessment

by Dr Ted Anderson

Quest Integrity Group, Boulder, CO, USA

THE INTEGRITY OF pipelines with longitudinal seam welds has received renewed interest by operators and regulators, due primarily to a number of high-profile incidents. Most operators and pipeline-integrity consultants have assessed seam weld flaws with methodologies that have changed very little over the past 30 years. However, the status quo is no longer viable, given the heightened public scrutiny and regulatory pressure.

This paper presents a number of recent innovations in assessment technology that can lead to improved reliability and a more optimal use of finite integrity budgets.

THERE HAVE BEEN a number of catastrophic pipeline incidents in recent years, the most notable of which was the 2010 explosion of a Pacific Gas & Electric (PG&E) pipeline in San Bruno, California. The belief among the general public is that pipeline failures are more frequent than in the past. It is debatable whether this belief has a factual basis (i.e. more frequent failures are the result of the aging pipeline infrastructure), or whether the Internet and the 24-hr news cycle cause an inflated sense of the actual threat[1]. Nevertheless, perception is reality in politics, so both Congress and PHMSA are instituting tighter regulations on the pipeline industry. There is increasing pressure on operators to demonstrate that they are taking steps to improve the integrity of their pipelines. Simply adhering to the *status quo* in the form of existing integrity plans is no longer an option.

Governmental bodies are paying particular attention to seam-welded pipes because several prominent releases, including the PG&E explosion, occurred at longitudinal seams. In the past year, there has been much discussion of the seam-weld issue by various parties, including state and local government agencies, pipeline operators, industry organizations, and consultants. Some have advocated for a large influx of research funding to address the perceived gaps in technology. In a number of cases, however, the necessary technology already exists, so further R&D might result in reinventing the wheel.

For example, the pipeline industry currently relies on flaw-assessment methods that are over 30 years old, but improved models are available. There have been significant advances in fracture mechanics, fitness-for-service assessment, and remaining-life models in the past 30 years. The pipeline industry can benefit by adopting methodologies that have been successfully applied in other industries, including oil and gas production, refinery, chemical, petrochemical, and power generation.

This paper presents a sample of innovative technology that can be applied to the integrity management of seam-welded pipe. The focus of this article is on cracks and other planar flaws, but innovative approaches for other anomaly types are also available.

1 Historical data from PHMSA shows a decreasing rate of serious pipeline incidents overall, but there were an unusually high number of incidents in 2010.

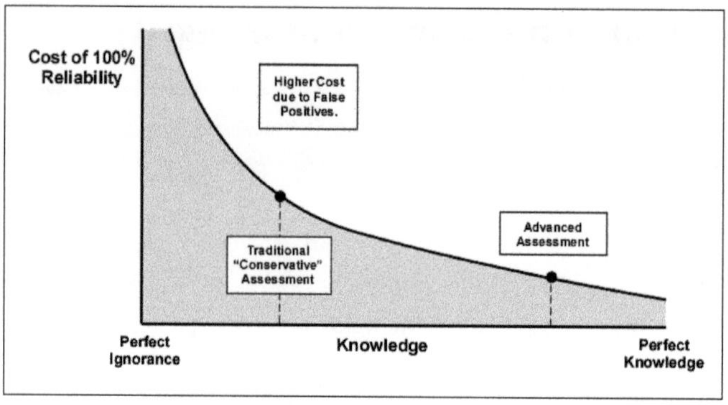

Fig. 1. The relationship between the cost of achieving 100% and knowledge about the condition of the pipeline.

Can a 'conservative' approach be unsafe?

Although many pipeline operators are open to innovations in integrity management, some adopt the attitude of "if it ain't broke, don't fix it." One of the most common arguments against using advanced flaw-assessment methods is that the traditional approaches are 'conservative', in that they tend to underestimate burst pressure and critical flaw size. There are at least two counter arguments to this point of view:

- When a 'conservative' failure model is used in conjunction with a hydrostatic test, the simplified model underestimates the maximum flaw size that could have survived the test. As a result, larger-than-expected flaws are often left in the pipe after a hydrostatic test. Since large cracks grow faster than small cracks, the 'conservative' approach can overestimate remaining life. Using a supposedly conservative model in reverse is analogous to looking through the wrong end of a telescope.

- When a 'conservative' flaw-assessment model is used make decisions on digs and repairs, a large number of anomalies are remediated unnecessarily. This would not be a problem if integrity budgets were infinite. However, funds spent on unnecessary repairs are not available to address real areas of concern.

The first point was addressed in a 2010 PPIM paper [1]. The second argument is explored in more detail below.

Given a pipeline that contains a number of anomalies, there are four possible outcomes for each anomaly[2]:

- true positive – an anomaly that poses a risk is remediated
- true negative – action on an anomaly that doesn't pose an immediate risk is deferred
- false positive – an anomaly that doesn't pose an immediate risk is remediated
- false negative – no action is taken on an anomaly that poses a risk, either because it is not detected by ILI or because inaction is a conscious decision

In an ideal world, only true positives and true negatives occur. False positives result in unnecessary expenditures and false negatives result in higher risk.

2 These terms are traditionally used with respect to flaw detection, but the present meaning is different. In present case, the terminology of true positive, false positive, etc., pertains to the decision on whether or not to remediate a particular anomaly.

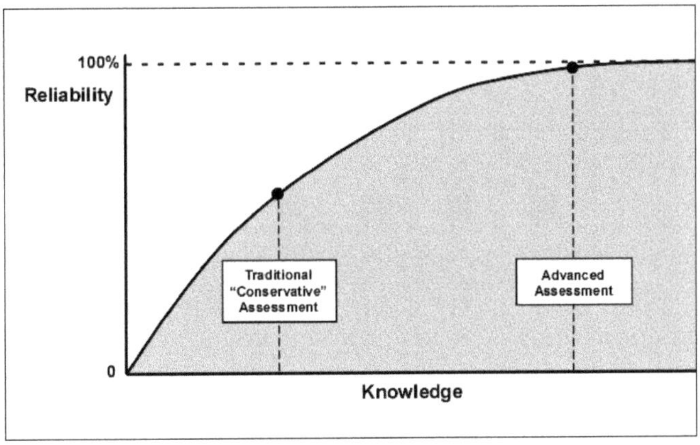

Fig.2. Reliability of a pipeline (or a system of lines) versus knowledge, given a fixed integrity budget.

Figure 1 illustrates the effect of knowledge of the pipeline condition on the cost of integrity. Consider two theoretical extremes: *perfect ignorance* and *perfect knowledge*. The former corresponds to the situation where *nothing* is known about the condition of the pipe, and digs and repairs are made randomly. Perfect knowledge means that the operator has advance knowledge of the exact timing and location of failures, which enables just-in-time action to prevent incidents. Real pipelines, of course, operate between these two extremes, and the cost of 100% integrity decreases with knowledge about the presence of flaws and their associated risk because remediating false positives costs money. Advanced-assessment methods improve the state of knowledge about the risk that various flaws pose, which reduces the cost of achieving 100% reliability.

Figure 2 illustrates the case where the integrity budget is fixed. Given a finite budget, a 'conservative' assessment can result in less reliability compared to what could be achieved with an advanced assessment. The reason for the diminished reliability is that false positives consume the integrity budget, so fewer resources are available to inspect and assess other areas that may contain dangerous flaws. In other words, false positives can lead to false negatives, as described below.

Consider the hypothetical scenario of an operator who owns six similar pipelines, and has a total integrity budget of $6 million. Assume that the ILI cost is $0.5 million per line. Figure 3 illustrates the case where a 'conservative' assessment is applied. A large number of false positives cause unnecessary digs and repairs, which results in the budget being consumed without inspecting Lines 5 and 6. Figure 4 illustrates how advanced assessment can result in an optimum use of the integrity budget. The advanced assessment costs slightly more than the traditional approach, but a significant cost saving results from reducing the number of digs and repairs in each line. Consequently, sufficient budget is available to ensure reliable operation of all six lines.

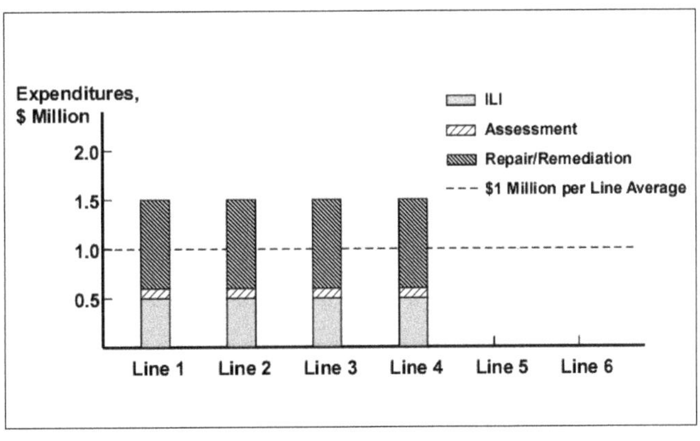

Fig.3. Allocation of resources when anomalies are assessed by a 'conservative' methodology. Repairs and remediation of false positives result in the integrity budget being consumed without inspecting Lines 5 and 6.

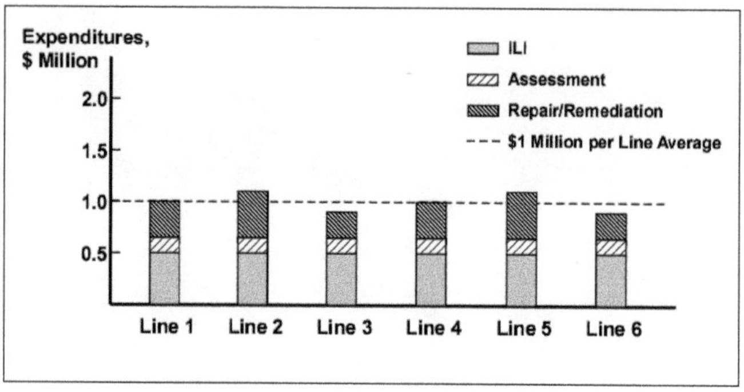

Fig.4. Allocation of resources when an advanced assessment is applied. Reduction or elimination of false positives results in an optimum use of resources.

Failure models for cracks

The assessment of cracks and other planar flaws is a perfect illustration of new technology offering a distinct advantage over traditional pipeline-centric models. A comparison old and new approaches is given below.

The pipeline industry has traditionally used the NG-18 equation to estimate burst pressure and critical flaw size. This approach, which is also known as the ln-sec model, was developed in the early 1970s [2] and is a semi-empirical equation that was calibrated to burst-test data. This equation contains a known glitch, in that it is overly conservative for long, shallow flaws˜. Most of the flaws in the original burst test dataset were less than 6 in long, but a few burst tests on pipes with longer flaws were outliers in the empirical correlation. The problem with this model can be seen more directly when a plot of burst pressure versus flaw length is generated: if the flaw depth is set to zero, the calculated burst pressure decreases with flaw length, which obviously does not comport with reality.

Recently, Keifner [3] has published a modified version of the ln-sec equation. This modified model does not reflect the significant advances in the field of fracture mechanics that have occurred since the 1970s. Rather it merely incorporates a correction factor that eliminates the non-physical trend for zero-depth flaws. The modified ln-sec model represents an improvement over the original method, but more rigorous and accurate approaches are available.

The American Petroleum Institute (API) and the American Society for Mechanical Engineers (ASME) have jointly published a standard that covers fitness-for-service assessment of pressure equipment, including pressure vessels, storage tanks, piping, and pipelines [4]. This standard, informally known as API 579, includes assessment procedures for crack-like flaws. A variety of analysis options are available in API 579, ranging from simplified methods that can be implemented in a spreadsheet, to sophisticated computer simulations. The most-accurate predictions of burst pressure and critical crack size are obtained from 3D finite-element analyses (FEA); Fig.5 shows a typical FEA model of a crack in a longitudinal seam weld.

Figure 6 compares a critical-crack-size curve inferred from 3D FEA with curves computed from the original and modified ln-sec equations. Curves of this type are used to infer the maximum flaw sizes that survive a hydrostatic test: cracks that fall below the critical curve are expected to survive the test, while flaws above the curve are expected to result in a leak or rupture. The three curves agree reasonably well for cracks less than 4 in long in this case, but there is a significant difference for longer flaws. This trend is expected, since the original ln-sec equation was calibrated to burst-test data for mostly shorter cracks; the ln-sec method has serious shortcomings for longer cracks, as previously discussed. Note that the original ln-sec model predicts burst for a 14-in flaw with zero

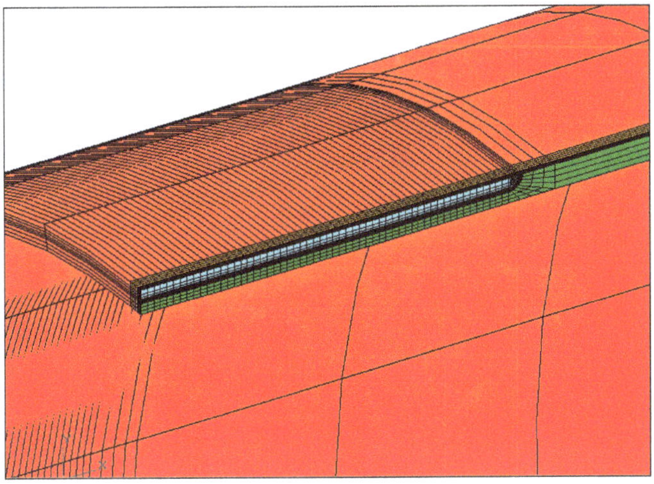

Fig.5. Finite-element model of an OD crack in an ERW seam. The model is ¼ symmetric.

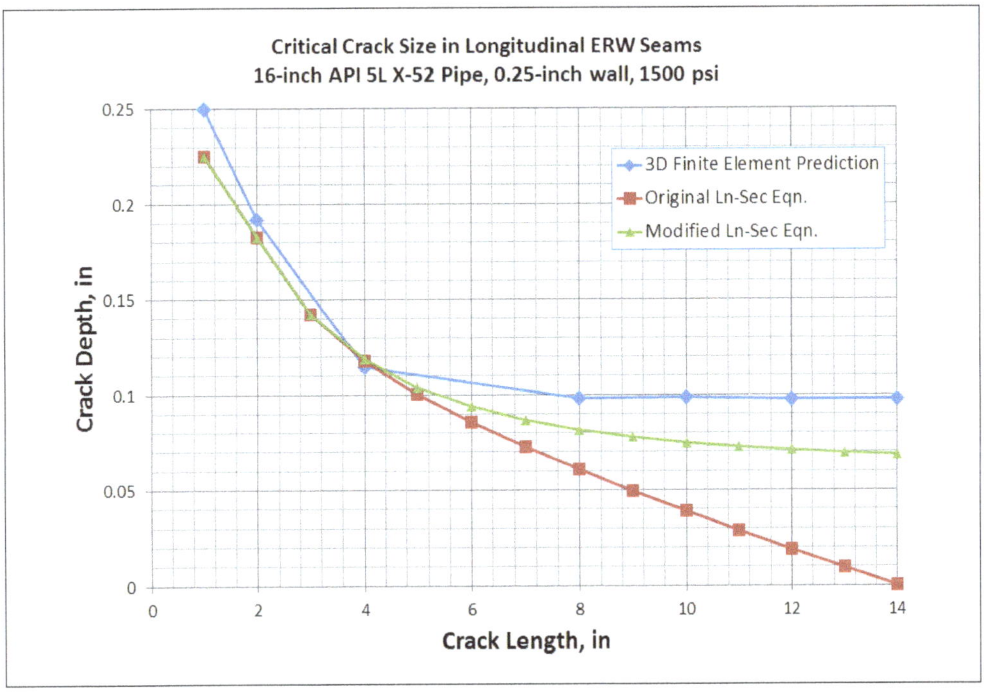

Fig.6. Critical flaw curves for three failure models.

depth: in other words, a superficial scratch 14-in long should fail the hydrostatic test, according to the original ln-sec model. To put this in perspective, a 1500-psi test pressure in a 16-in X52 pipe with 0.25-in wall thickness corresponds to 92% of SMYS, so the original ln-sec model is obviously incorrect. The modified ln-sec model gives improved predictions for long flaws, but it still underestimates the critical crack depth for flaws greater than 4 in long in this case.

Recently, PRCI completed a research project whose aim was to develop an improved failure model for cracks in longitudinal seam welds [5]. This project consisted of a 3D finite-element parametric study, where a range of crack sizes, pipe dimensions, and material properties were analysed. The FEA results were then fit to a series of equations. Thus the new PRCI crack-assessment model should approximately match the FEA-based critical flaw curve in Fig.6.

Fig.7. Laboratory specimens for measuring material toughness.

(top) Charpy V-notch specimen;
(bottom) fracture-mechanics' specimen.

Quantifying toughness of pipeline steels

Both the original and modified ln-sec equations use Charpy impact energy to characterize the toughness of the pipeline steel. Since this model was first published, more sophisticated material tests based on the principles of fracture mechanics have been developed and standardized. Figure 7 shows photographs of the Charpy V-notch and fracture-mechanics' specimens: a key difference between the two specimen types is that fracture-mechanics' specimens contain sharp fatigue cracks. This distinction is particularly important when testing ERW seams. The photograph in Fig.8 is a close-up of a Charpy notch at an ERW bond line: the notch radius is significantly larger than the width of the bond line, and consequently the measured toughness reflects an average for the various microstructures in the vicinity of the bond line rather than the material at the bond line. The sharp fatigue crack in the fracture-mechanics' specimen can be precisely located in the relevant microstructure, so it is better able to discriminate the variations in material properties from the bond line to the parent metal.

Real-time pressure cycle fatigue analysis

Seam-welded pipelines that are in cyclic service can experience fatigue failure if not properly managed. Planar flaws that are introduced at manufacture can grow over time due to pressure cycling, and eventually a growing crack will lead to a leak or rupture if it is not remediated.

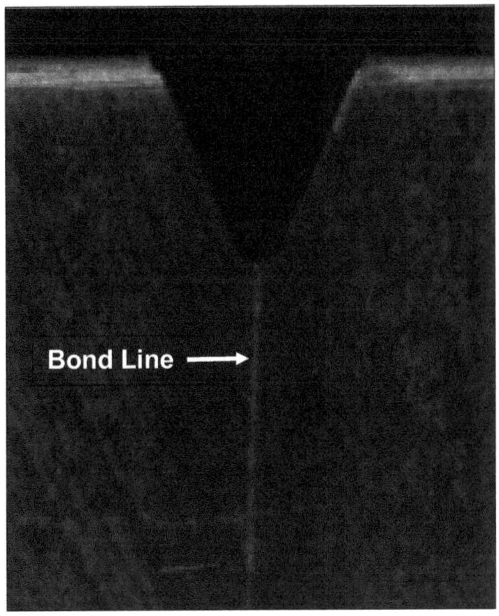

Fig.8. Close-up of a Charpy notch at an ERW bond line.

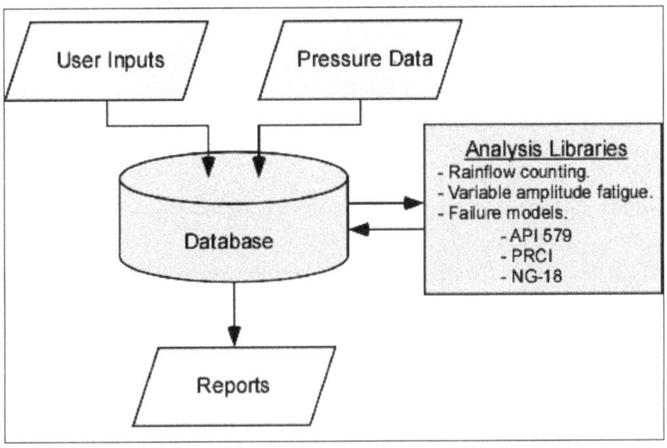

Fig.9. Overall architecture of Quest Integrity's automated PCFA system.

Pressure-cycle-fatigue analysis (PCFA) is a technique that has been used by the pipeline industry to manage the risk associated with seam-weld flaws that may grow in service. Pressure data are typically collected at pumping stations (in liquid lines) and stored in a PI data historian or similar system. Periodically, pressure readings at discrete time intervals are exported to a CSV file or spreadsheet. These data are processed through a rain-flow cycle-counting algorithm, which quantifies the number and magnitude of pressure cycles in the form of a histogram. The histogram is then input into a fracture-mechanics' model to predict the growth of actual or postulated flaws in the pipeline. The PCFA is used to make decisions on the retest interval or re-inspection interval in cases where the integrity-management plan calls for hydrostatic testing or ILI, respectively.

The PCFA process is fairly time consuming and labour intensive. In a typical case, a pipeline operator sends pressure data to a consultant, who then submits a report to the operator two or three months later. A PCFA is usually performed annually because more-frequent intervals are not practical.

Quest Integrity is currently developing a software system for automatically performing PCFA, and Fig.9 illustrates the system architecture. At initial set-up for a given pipeline, the user enters basic data, such as pumping station locations, pipe dimensions, elevations, and material properties. Once the system is online, it periodically imports pressure data from the PI data historian, and then processes it through the rain-flow and fracture-mechanics' algorithms. Both the pressure data input and the processed output are stored in a database and reports are generated at regular intervals based on user settings. Because the system is automated, it is possible to obtain virtually real-time updates on pressure cycling. For example, an operator may choose to generate PCFA reports on a weekly or monthly basis. It is also possible to track the growth of thousands of flaws in multiple pipelines.

Conclusions

1. Heightened public awareness of pipeline safety issues and increasing regulatory pressure mean that the maintaining the *status quo* on integrity-management is not an option.

2. Although the pipeline industry currently relies on flaw-assessment technology that is over 30 years old, improved models are available.

3. Using traditional approaches that are 'conservative' may actually lead to more risk because integrity budgets are finite, and money spent on unnecessary digs and repairs is not available to address more-critical areas.

4. Failure models for crack-like flaws that are based on finite-element analysis (FEA) are vastly superior to the ln-sec method, which has traditionally been used in the pipeline industry. A new PRCI method based on a curve-fit of FEA results provides a simpler alternative to performing custom FEA for each situation that is encountered.

5. Fracture-mechanics'-based toughness tests are more reliable than Charpy tests, especially for ERW seams.

6. Pressure-cycle-fatigue analysis (PCFA) has traditionally been time consuming, so it is typically performed no more than annually, and at a limited number of locations in a pipeline. However, an automated PCFA system that is currently under development makes real-time monitoring of pressure cycling and crack growth at thousands of locations feasible.

References

1. T.L.Anderson, 2010. Advanced assessment of pipeline integrity using ILI data. Pipeline Pigging and Integrity Management Conference, Houston, February.
2. J.F.Kiefner, W.A.Maxey, R.J.Eiber, and A.R.Duffy, 1973. Failure stress levels of flaws in pressurized cylinders. ASTM STP 536, American Society for Testing and Materials.
3. J.F.Kiefner, 2001. Modified equation helps integrity management. *Oil and Gas Journal*, 6 October, pp 64-66.
4. API and ASME, 2007. API579-1/ASME FFS-1, Fitness-for-service. Jointly published by the American Petroleum Institute and the American Society for Mechanical Engineers, June.
5. G.G.Chell, 2008. Criteria for evaluating failure susceptibility due to axial cracks in pressurized line pipe. PRCI Project MAT-8 Final Report, December.

Improving ILI benchmarking through new technology

by Michael Krywko[1], Shamus McDonnell[1], Douglas Spencer[2], and Mark Gluskin[3]

1 Hunter McDonnell Pipeline Services Inc., Edmonton, AB, Canada
2 Inline Devices LLC, Calgary, AB, Canada
3 Mears Group, Inc., San Ramon, CA, USA

IN THIS PAPER we discuss the history of in-line inspection (ILI) benchmarking, from the first magnetic markers through the current dual-clock time-based systems, including the most recent improvements made in this field. Since its inception almost 40 years ago, ILI pig technology has evolved to become a standard inspection technique for pipelines. The earliest ILI tools lacked odometers, and as a result locating anomalies on the pipeline from ILI data alone proved extremely difficult. Following the advent of odometers came the introduction of above-ground marker (AGM) systems. AGMs served to provide reference benchmarks that reduced the pipeline distances measured, thereby reducing measurement errors. The most-recent AGM developments include multiple sensor logging, capable of recording magnetic, 22-Hz, and acoustic data concurrently, along with integrated modem technologies which allow remote system monitoring. These innovations now allow safer, more-reliable pig tracking and ILI benchmarking. A case study outlining a direct comparison of two conventional AGM technologies with a new remote-monitored multiple-sensor system is discussed.

The history of benchmarking

As early as the 1800s pipelines were used to transport petroleum from producing wells to refineries. Operators noticed that after a couple of years of operation, the pipelines experienced a decrease in flow and increase in pumping pressure, indicating that deposits were building up and effectively reducing the internal size of the pipeline. Several non-invasive solutions were tried with no success. Eventually the idea of pumping an object through the pipeline was considered, and the idea of 'pigging' was born.

There are many different types of pipeline tools (pigs) within industry today, and most commercial pigs fit into one of the three general categories; cleaning, batch/displacement, or inspection. Regardless of the specific purpose or design, all pipeline pigs are propelled by the product flow and run the risk of becoming lodged. A lodged pig will either limit or stop the flow, and therefore its exact location must be ascertained for removal. The operational risks and interruption posed by a lodged pig necessitates the requirement for a process to 'track' the pig as it travels through the pipeline, and to 'locate' the pig should it become stuck.

A pig's position can be tracked through a pipeline by metering the amount of product behind or ahead of the pig; however, pressure, temperature, pig slippage, and by-pass can all adversely affect the accuracy of this method. Tracking a pig's position via metering is often only accurate to within a few kilometres. Absent a pressure spike or complete flow blockage, metering methods alone cannot conclusively determine the location of a lodged pig that is by-passing product.

Other pig-detection and location methods have been developed with varying degrees of success. Mechanical pig signals can detect pig passage, but are subject to mechanical failures and may fail to properly reset. Densitometers can often see the propagation of pressure changes in the product associated with pig passages, but this method is not considered accurate or reliable in all cases. Since mechanical signals and densitometers detect the dynamic passage of the pig, neither approach can be used to determine the location of a static (stuck) pig.

Pigs make noise as they travel through a pipeline, typically as the sealing cups hit the girth weld beads on the inside of the pipe, and this is a fact that has been exploited for tracking purposes. The noise associated with pig movement is attenuated to some extent depending on depth of cover, pipeline product, and other factors. As a consequence, acoustic-monitoring techniques benefit from amplification. Geophones have been successfully employed for this purpose for several decades. Like the mechanical pig signallers, however, the geophone can only be used to hear a pig moving or passing a location, rarely to locate a stuck pig. Recent acoustic-technology systems for locating leaks on pipelines can often detect and locate the distance to the noise created by product by-passing a stuck pig, although this is technology is very new and not available on most pipelines.

Historically, several different methods have been employed to locate stuck pigs in a pipeline. One costly and time-consuming method involves tapping the pipeline and installing pressure gauges along the pipeline's length until the location of the pressure restriction is determined. However, if the pig is stuck in a buckle or tee fitting, there may a significant amount of by-pass which serves to minimize the pressure differential, rendering the stuck pig difficult to locate. Overall, variations on this iterative search procedure have proven unsatisfactory because they are expensive and unreliable.

More recently, the need to locate a stuck pig is addressed by installing a low-frequency radio transmitter on the pig before it is launched. The radio transmitter emits a signal that can be detected above ground within a 5-10 m radius of the pig, depending on conditions. If the pig becomes stuck, the transmitter signal can be detected by walking along the pipeline with a radio receiver. Once located, the pig's precise position can be located to within centimetres. This precision locating ability is also useful to confirm that pigs are fully through trap valves before the valves are closed. The transmitter can also be used to confirm the launch of the pig, since vibrations and noise during launch often make it difficult to determine through simple observation if a pig has left the launch barrel.

The process for tracking pigs evolved to incorporate multiple technologies, including metering the product volumes and pressures, mechanical pig signallers and/or densitometers, and manually tracking the pig passage at regular intervals from above ground using the radio receiver and other sensors such as geophones. Pigs were now typically monitored through the pipeline at intervals as small as 1 or 2 kilometres, and if a pig became stuck, it could be located by walking over the line from the last identified passage location in order to detect the radio transmitter housed in the pig.

With reliable means emerging to track and locate stuck pigs, the risk of pigging was greatly reduced, and running cleaning pigs became more commonplace. The cleaning pigs eventually evolved into more-advanced data-gathering instruments. The first advances came in the form of gauge pigs to confirm internal bore, then came instrumented caliper pigs, and eventually inspection pigs that could detect and quantify metal loss and other pipeline features. These advanced inspection technologies were referred to as 'smart' pigs, a term which subsequently evolved into the more descriptive in-line inspection (ILI) tools. ILI tools are now considered the primary non-destructive testing means for surveying the condition of a pipeline to detect and identify pipeline appurtenances and other features such as metal loss, cracks, laminations, and the like.

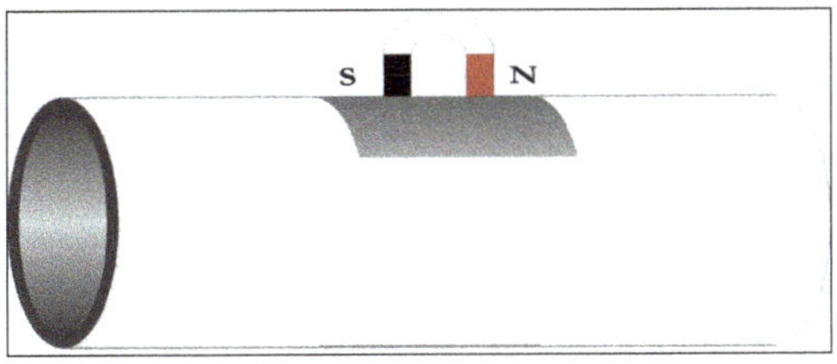

Fig. 1. Magnet benchmark diagram.

Advancing ILI-measurement technologies required improved means to track and locate ILI tools, as well as a means to locate the specific features that they were now routinely identifying. To locate an anomaly recorded on an ILI survey requires that a distance to the anomaly be determined from some 'known location' that can be referenced from above ground.

Unfortunately, the early ILI tools lacked odometers to record pipeline distances. Early analyses resorted to a count of the girth welds recorded by the ILI tool, which was then multiplied by the average joint length to obtain an approximate distance to the anomaly of interest. In the 1970s, the first odometers were included on ILI pigs: however, due to wheel-manufacturing tolerances and other accumulated errors, the footage reported by ILI tools was often not accurate enough to facilitate long-distance measuring.

Even in modern ILI tools, where odometer accuracies can often approach 0.5%, measuring distances more than three kilometres can introduces more error than can be tolerated when making a costly excavation of the pipeline (for example, 0.5% x 3000m = ±15m). Ideally, the process would incorporate two known locations at intervals less than twice the tolerable distance-measurement error, one upstream and one downstream, such that a feature location could be ascertained via measurements originating from each known location, converging at the feature of interest.

What are known locations? Certain pipeline features provide can provide one form of 'known location': for example, valves, taps, tees, and other pipeline appurtenances recorded by the ILI instrument sensors that can also be readily identified above ground are often employed. Unfortunately, these type of pipeline feature is very rarely located conveniently enough, or spaced regularly enough, to allow the feature alone to suffice. Without sufficient existing pipeline features, measuring distances greater than 2 or 3 km above ground introduces its own measurement errors, which can exceed 0.5%. Above-ground measurement errors, combined with the ILI odometer errors, can become problematic over long distances (for example, 1% x 3000m = 30m). Consequently, it becomes highly desirable to measure smaller distances between above-ground references, typically less than 3 km. These conditions give rise to the need to create more 'known locations' along the pipeline than are typically represented by existing above-ground features such as valves and taps.

The devices developed to compensate for the lack of sufficient known locations during in-line inspections are called above-ground marker(s), or simply AGM(s). The practice of using AGMs on the pipeline to provide above-ground references is known as 'benchmarking'. Because of the potentially large distance intervals, benchmarking is typically performed in combination with the pig tracking, using the same AGM site locations and personnel.

Because of the tolerances in both the ILI odometer and the above-ground measurements, benchmarking requires that the AGM location be identified on the ILI survey independent of either measurement. This is accomplished in one of two ways: either by creating AGM locations

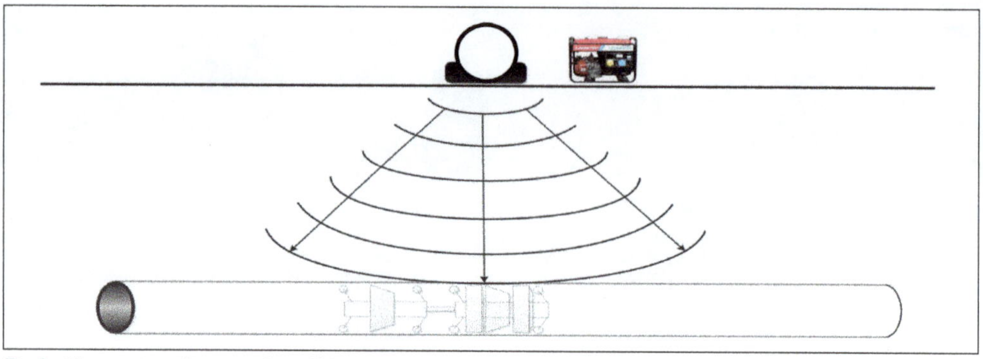

Fig.2. Magnetic pulser marking ILI sensor coil.

capable of generating a signal detected by the ILI tool, or by detecting the passage of the ILI tool through dual-clock time correlation. In both cases, the AGM site must be situated in a known (surveyed) location.

The first benchmarking system employed was the magnetic marker, which involved placing a simple magnet on the pipeline which would register directly on the magnetic-flux-leakage (MFL) ILI survey (Fig.1). Unfortunately, there were two problems with this practice. First, the pipeline had to be exposed so the magnet could be coupled directly to the pipe. Secondly, in order for the magnet to remain firmly in place for the duration of the survey, it was often necessary to remove the coating from the pipeline in order to produce sufficient magnetic coupling. This approach proved problematic with respect to coating integrity, un-compacted soil under the exposed pipe sections, and other access and placement issues. The advantages in magnetic markers were low cost, reliability, and accuracy, but these attributes were generally offset by the time and expense required to excavate the pipe for installation.

The second type of benchmarking system developed was the magnetic 'pulser' which, like the magnetic-marker system before it, would create a magnetic signature recorded on the ILI pig's MFL sensors (Fig.2). The magnetic pulser served to generate a strong magnetic field above ground that would penetrate the earth and pipe, to be detected by the ILI MFL sensors as the pig passed underneath. This above-ground solution eliminated many disadvantage associated with the magnetic-marker system; however, it also introduces several of its own new limitations. Specifically, the pulsers were relatively expensive, requiring large magnetizing coils and a heavy energy source – car batteries or portable generators were typically used.

The logistics associated with placing the number of pulsers required for an ILI survey were considerable. The pulsers could only operate for short periods of time given the significant power requirements, and they required nearly continuous operation since detection of the approaching ILI pig was required to trigger operation. Finally, the ILI tools could not reliably detect the magnetic pulses through heavy pipe wall, casings, deep cover or in areas with high AC interference.

The third evolution in AGM systems, and the one which still dominates the industry today, is the dual-clock time-based system. This system generally consists of one clock deployed within the ILI tool, and several remote timer boxes with clocks (the AGMs), each synchronized to the clock in the ILI tool. The AGMs must also deploy one more means to remotely detect ILI tool passage.

The AGMs are deployed above the pipe at pre-selected reference sites, and the AGM serves to record the time that the ILI pig passes directly under the box. With the AGM recording time and tool passage, and the tool recording inspection data and time, time becomes the common reference between these two autonomously operating devices. Post survey, the time recorded by the AGM is correlated to the time recorded by the ILI pig, effectively placing the AGM site indirectly on the ILI survey. This creates a correlation point between the above-ground reference site where the AGM was deployed, and the ILI tool odometer at the point of passage. This correlation is then used as the starting point to measure the above-ground distance to a specific underground pipeline anomaly or feature recorded by the ILI tool.

Although the dual-clock AGM system solves many of the problems inherent in the magnetic-marker and pulser systems, this approach still has theoretical limitations. Foremost among these is the accuracy of the clocks employed. If the clocks integral to the AGMs and the pipeline tool differ by even a single second, that time discrepancy can result in an error of 2.8m if the ILI tool is travelling at 10km/hr. The best ILI tools and AGM systems in use today employ highly accurate real-time clocks, download GPS time upon each start up, and periodically re-synchronize with GPS to ensure ongoing time accuracy.

To reduce false triggers, many modern AGMs also contain an automatic gain adjustment circuitry. If interference is detected, the box automatically turns down its sensitivity, and typically will not turn up the sensitivity again until it is power cycled. This requires that the AGMs be deployed away from all forms of radio, electrical and magnetic interference. This also requires that the AGM be deployed in a location where the pipe is not buried too deep for the ILI tool to be detected. Casings and excessive depth of cover will impede the AGM's ability to detect the ILI pig, while overhead power lines, wireless-communications devices, and ground vibration will all provide interference that cause the gain circuitry to reduce the timer box sensitivity.

The small size and ease of deployment of the dual-clock AGM make it very difficult to confirm that it was deployed in the correct location. If an AGM was documented at one location, but actually deployed in another, even slightly different location, the ILI odometer will be incorrectly referenced to the known above ground location. This is a limitation that is especially problematic with the small and portable dual-clock AGM – care must be taken to select, deploy, and document AGM sites carefully.

Improving ILI benchmarking

To improve ILI benchmarking in terms of accuracy, safety and reliability, a new AGM system has been recently developed and its functionality has been evaluated through a series of field trials. The new system, called the *Armadillo* AGM, combines a dual-clock AGM system with a groundbreaking multi-axis, multi-sensor ILI tool-detection capability, extensive data memory logging, and significantly improved data retrieval and communications functionality.

A summary of the key AGM improvements includes the following:

- Traditional AGMs were capable of recording only single-axis magnetic or 22-Hz radio signals. The *Armadillo* AGM system records three-axis magnetic, two-axis 22-Hz, and geophone acoustic data concurrently.

- Traditional AGMs only record a few seconds of continuous data when a pig is detected, requiring a predetermined threshold signal strength to be measured as a trigger to record tool passage. The *Armadillo* AGM system continuously records days of data from all sensors. This allows passages with signal amplitudes below the trigger thresholds to be post-processed and used successfully where other AGMs failed to record tool passage. This

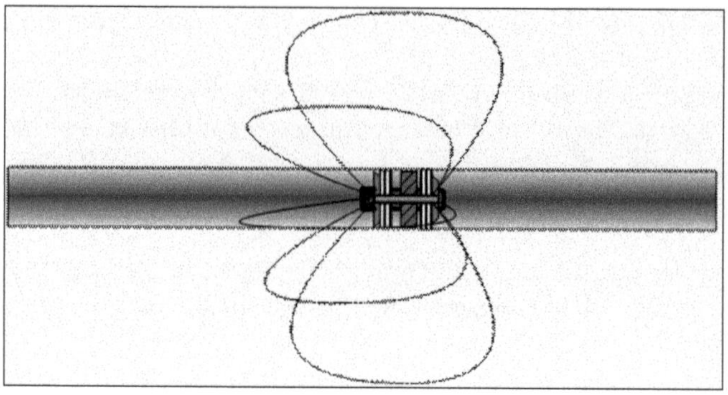

Fig.3. Magnetic field surrounding MFL ILI pig.

ability to retrieve all sensor data has proven effective in benchmarking locations with low signal amplitude and AC interference.

- Traditional AGMs with remote-communication systems only report a time when a passage trigger is encountered. The *Armadillo* AGM system incorporates a bi-directional remote-communication system, allowing the AGM to be remotely controlled, putting the AGM into battery-saving sleep mode between pig runs. The bi-directional remote-monitoring system also permits remote monitoring of real-time data, allowing the user to monitor the pig passage from anywhere in the world via the internet.

MFL sensor

Standard MFL ILI tools create a three-dimensional, torus-shaped field around the pipeline, as illustrated in Fig.3. The magnetic-field lines originate at the north pole of the magnet, travel through the magnetically-conductive medium of the pipe as well as the surrounding air and soil, and terminate at the south pole. At any point within this circuit, the magnetic fields are vector quantities, which means that they have a specific magnitude and direction, which can be represented by a three-dimensional coordinate system in the x, y, and z axes. In order to detect the very small magnetic fields generated by the tool at the surface, the *Armadillo* AGM utilizes a series of anisotropic magneto-resistance (AMR) sensors deployed in each axis to detect minute changes in magnetic-field strength.

AMRs became widely used towards the end on the 1990s. The effect, which was discovered in 1857 by William Thompson, detects the change of electrical resistance in a magnetic material in response to small variations in the environmental magnetic field. The sensor is made of a nickel-iron thin film deposited on a silicon wafer, and is patterned as a resistive strip. The properties of the AMR thin film cause it to change resistance by up to 2-3% in the presence of a magnetic field. The character of the magneto-resistive effect represents a nearly instantaneous response time, and is not limited by coils or oscillating frequencies. A typical MFL detection from the *Armadillo* AGM is depicted in Fig.4.

As indicated earlier, the *Armadillo* AGM detects the magnetic-field strength around the pipe in three orientations, MFL x, MFL y, and MFL z (see Fig.5).

x – parallel with the pipe
y – 90° off the pipe
z – perpendicular to the pipe, orientated vertically

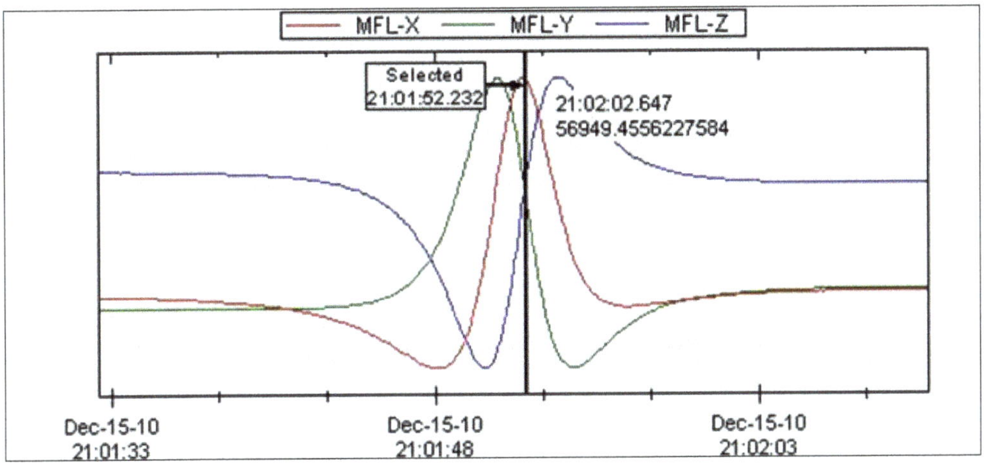

Fig.4. Magnetic signatures recorded from MFL ILI pig.

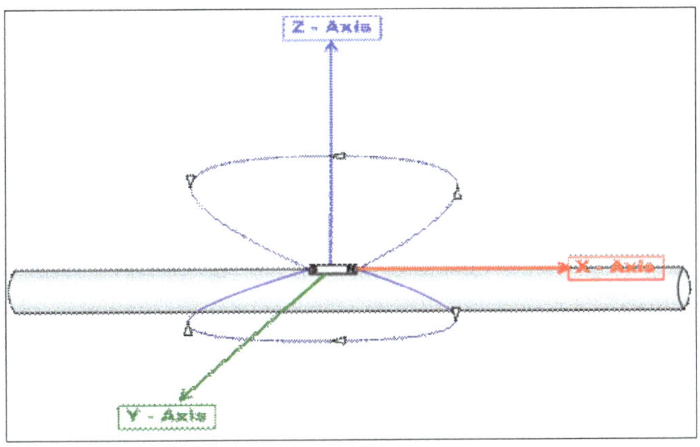

Fig.5. Orientation of 3D magnetic sensors.

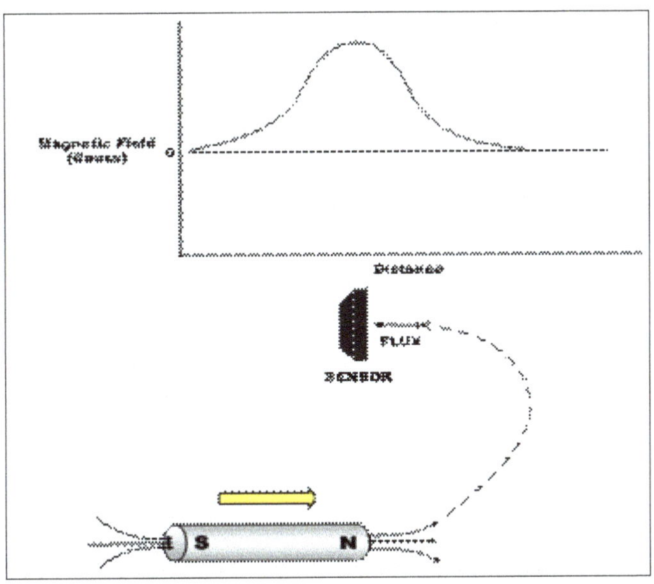

Fig.6. MFL ILI pig signature on orientation x sensor.

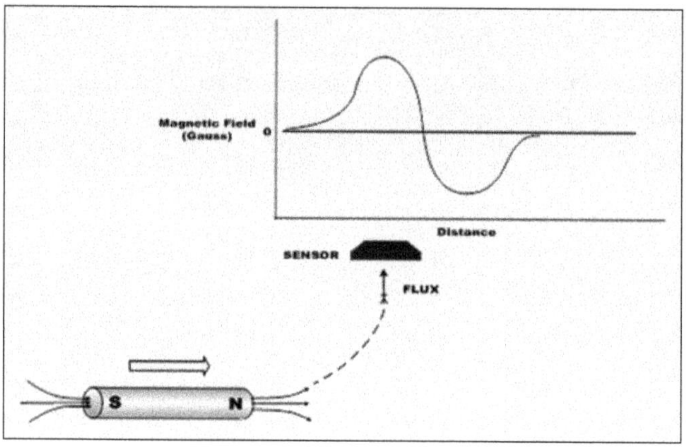

Fig.7. MFL ILI pig signature on orientation z sensor.

The MFL x standard sensor orientation and sensor output is illustrated in Fig.6. The typical MFL ILI tool-passage data will generate an exponential increase, plateau, and then exponential decrease in magnetic-field strength in response to the tool's magnetic field occurring normal to the AMR sensor face. The MFL x axis field will produce its peak amplitude when the centre of ILI tool's magnet circuit is directly below the AGM.

The MFL z sensor orientation is depicted in Fig.7. Magnetic flux emanating from the MFL tool in the z axis will result in a positive field response in the AMR as the tool approaches the sensor, and then reverse polarity as the tool passes under the AGM. The zero-crossing, or null-point, in this sinusoidal signature represents the mid-point of the MFL tool's magnetic-circuit passing directly beneath the sensor.

The MFL y sensor response depends on which side of the pipeline the AGM is placed. It will resemble the MFL z polarity illustrated above if the AGM is deployed on the left side of the pipeline (when looking downstream) and it will display an inverse polarity sinusoidal signature when deployed on the right side of the pipeline. Either polarity may be used for passage detection.

The use of multi-axis AMR sensing produces multiple independent measurements of the same tool passage. This measurement redundancy provides a high degree of confidence in the analyst's identification of the event.

22-Hz sensors

Due to the ability to readily penetrate ground, liquid, and steel, the 22-Hz electromagnetic frequency utilized in most transmitters has become the industry standard to locate and track pipeline pigs. The *Armadillo* AGM records two 22-Hz antenna orientations, vertical and horizontal, as shown in Fig.8. The horizontal antenna is aligned parallel to the pipeline axis, and exhibits superior sensitivity to the 22-Hz signal, which peaks as the transmitter passes directly under the antenna. The vertical antenna, which is aligto:ned perpendicular to the pipe axis, exhibits a somewhat lower sensitivity than the 22-Hz signal, and produces a null response when the transmitter passes directly below the antenna. The horizontal peak response in combination with the vertical minimum provides a very characteristic combined-signature response that allows analysts to reject spurious noise events and benchmark the precise time the transmitter passes directly under the AGM.

Figure 9 displays an actual dual-axis 22-Hz transmitter passage. The horizontal (peak) sensor data

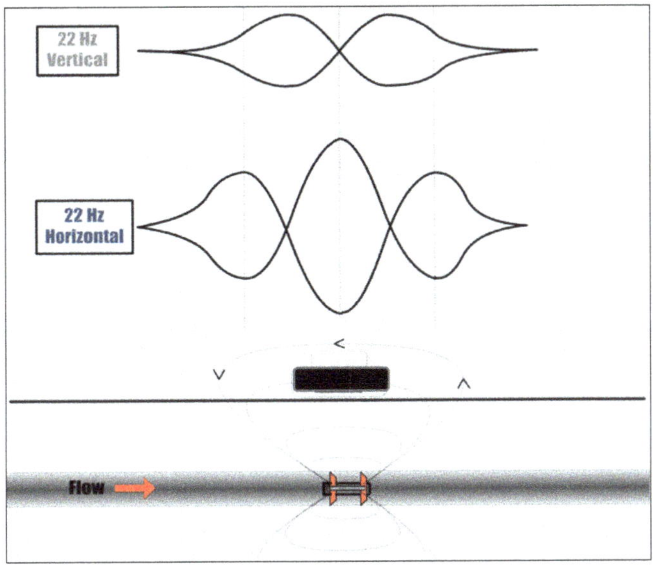

Fig.8. 22-Hz vertical (null) and horizontal (peak) passage signatures.

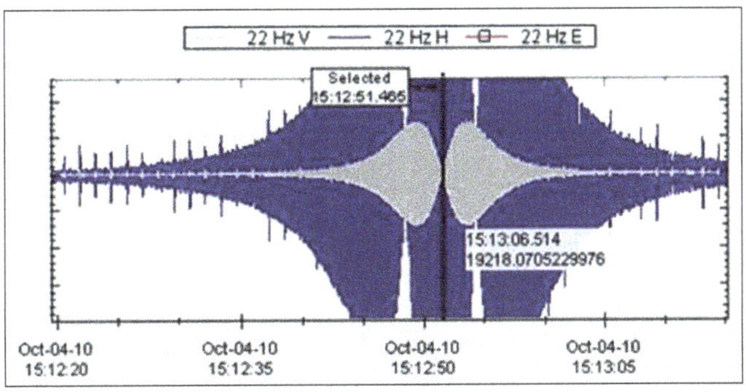

Fig.9. 22-Hz pig-passage recording with vertical and horizontal antennas.

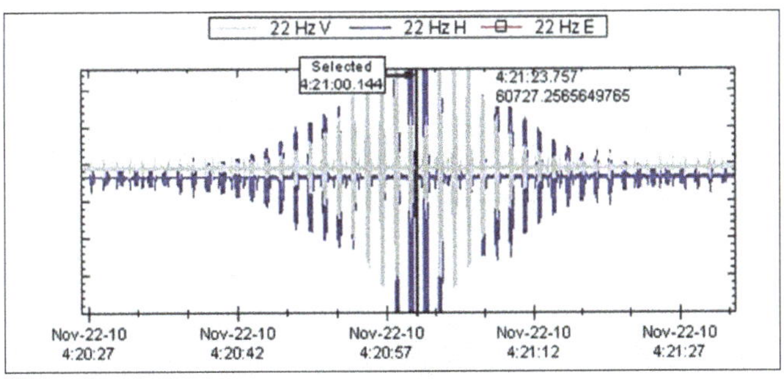

Fig10. Pulsing 22-Hz transmitter passage recorded on horizontal and vertical antennas.

is represented in blue, while the vertical sensor (null-response) data is represented in grey. The actual time of passage has been determined based on the convergence of the redundant horizontal and vertical-response signatures.

Available pig-tracking transmitters can be configured to produce either a continuous 22-Hz signal, or an intermittent (pulsing) 22-Hz signature. The pulsing transmitter design is primarily intended to conserve battery power on standard utility pigs, or to differentiate among multiple pigs run in combination. A pulsing signature detected by the *Armadillo* AGM is shown in Fig.10. The pulsing 22-Hz transmitter detection again illustrates that the tool passage is conclusively determined on the basis of convergence between the horizontal peak signature in combination with the vertical null.

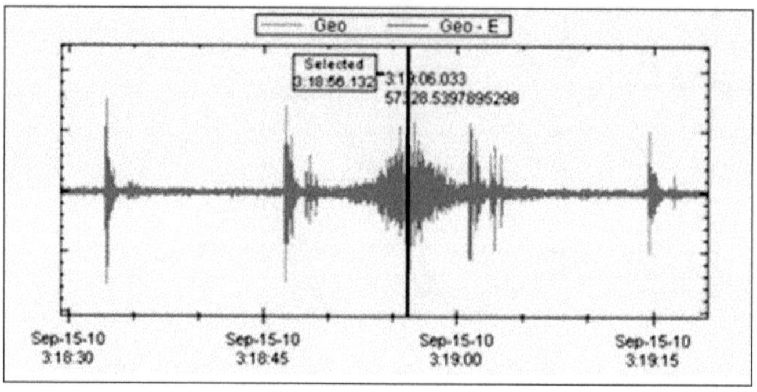

Fig. 11. Typical acoustic signature recorded from a pig passing the Armadillo AGM.

Geophone

Pipeline acoustics have been used as a primary pig-tracking tool for many years, allowing for the fact that the sound from the tool passing girth welds can be detected up to 15 km away. While simple acoustic pig-tracking methods have been in use for decades, acoustics have not been previously incorporated into benchmarking or automated AGM tracking systems. The *Armadillo* AGM design now incorporates a high-sensitivity geophone integrated directly within the AGM housing to record the full acoustic waveforms associated with tool movement through the pipeline. A typical pig-passage signature recorded by the *Armadillo* AGM is shown in Fig.11: the pig-passage time is represented by the peak decibel (dB) level.

Currently this internal geophone is utilized primarily as a data-correlation tool in combination with three-axis AMR magnetic and dual-axis 22-Hz measurements. However, ongoing development of this technology in association with operational field testing continues to reveal additional new data-extraction and correlation techniques that provide critical insight into tool passage where other techniques may fail. Some of these new techniques, such as frequency analysis, are discussed in the following sections.

In order to lay the groundwork for understanding acoustic analysis in connection with tool passage, it is necessary to examine the factors that cause large variations in pipeline acoustics and, more importantly, to understand how sound propagates in this environment. Acoustic waves do not require a conductor (such as a wire) to propagate; they can be created anywhere, and the distance they travel depends on their intensity, their frequency, the medium(s) they are travelling in, and the boundaries (i.e. absorption, reflection, refraction, diffraction).

It is natural to assume that the pipeline tool's acoustic waves travel primarily through the steel pipe, since steel is a dense material that propagates acoustic waves at nearly 6000 m/s. While the steel pipe does play a significant role in the ability of the acoustic waves to travel long distances, it is not the primary conduit for this energy because of the nature of the acoustic-wave propagation.

Acoustic waves are mechanical, as opposed to electromagnetic (EM) in nature. EM waves are capable of transmitting their energy through a vacuum, while mechanical waves require some sort of medium to conduct the energy. Sound is created by generating a pressure differential. In the pipeline, a pig cup is held back slightly as it transverses a girth weld, and when it is released it springs forward, compressing the fluid and causing a slight increase in pressure. This increase in pressure, called a condensation, travels away from the pig at the speed of sound, which is dependent on the density and temperature of the conducting medium. As an example, oil transmits sound between 400 and 1500 m/s depending on its specific gravity and temperature.

Sound	Intensity I (W/m²)	Intensity level β (dB)	Sound pressure (Pa)
Threshold of hearing	1.0×10^{-12}	0	0.00002
Rustling leaves	1.0×10^{-11}	10	-
Whisper	1.0×10^{-10}	20	0.002
Normal conversation 1m	3.2×10^{-16}	65	0.02
Inside car in city traffic	1.0×10^{-4}	80	0.2
Car without exhaust	1.0×10^{-12}	100	2
Live rock concert	1.0	120	20
Threshold of pain	10	130	-

Table 1. Sound intensity, dB, and sound-pressure relationship.

The relative intensity of sound is measured in decibels (dB). The decibel is not an absolute measure of the sound intensity *per se*, but is rather a unit-less reference system based on the threshold of hearing, which is set at 0 dB. Table 1 demonstrates how absolute sound intensity in W/m^2, the relative sound intensity in dB, and sound pressure in Pascals, relate to one another.

Acoustic energy generated at a girth weld can travel many kilometres in a pipeline, until the acoustic energy is eventually completely attenuated by the environment. The rate of attenuation is dependent on the fluid medium in the pipeline: in oil pipelines, this acoustic energy can typically travel up to two kilometres. The attenuation of the oil medium serves to absorb the acoustic energy at the rate of approximately 15 dB/km. Natural gas environments typically tend to absorb acoustic energy at a rate of approximately 3 dB/km; the gas-attenuation rate decreases as the gas pressure increases. These attenuation figures are based on an acoustic frequency of 250 Hz and temperature of 20°C.

The steel pipe itself serves to reflect approximately 97% of acoustic wave energy, thereby providing a near-perfect conduit for the acoustic energy to travel within. As the *Armadillo* AGMs are obviously external to the primary path of acoustic travel within the pipe, they must be sensitive enough to detect the very small amounts of acoustic energy that escape this conduit and travel external to the pipe. This external pathway, represented by the pipeline steel and surrounding soils, serves to transmit the small remaining balance, or less than 3%, of the total acoustic energy subsequently available to arrive at the AGM for detection and analysis.

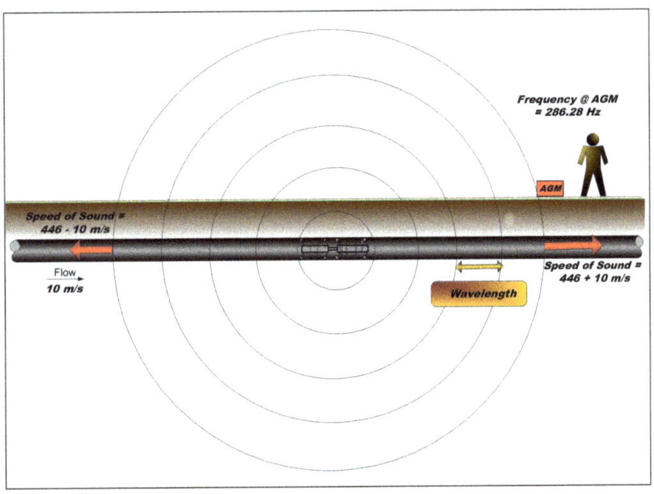

Fig. 12. Sound velocity of an approaching pig.

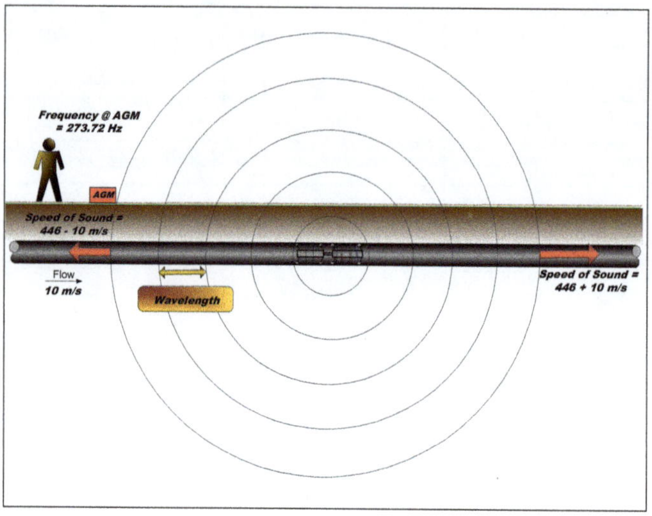

Fig.13. Sound velocity of a departing pig.

Acoustic frequency analysis and Doppler shift

When a pipeline tool passes underneath an AGM, a Doppler shift occurs due to the change in the sound velocity as the source first moves towards, and then away from, the receiver, which in our case is the AGM geophone. This phenomenon was readily demonstrated upon its discovery by the change in pitch of a railway whistle as a moving train passes a stationary observer. The Doppler shift generated by a moving object and stationary receiver creates this change in the acoustic wavelength, but because in pipeline applications the pipeline tool is moving with the conducting medium, the wavelength becomes equalized. In the case of an approaching pipeline tool, the sound wave velocity is therefore the sum of the speed of sound in the fluid, plus the speed of the tool, as shown in Fig.12. The AGM geophone frequency for the approaching tool is calculated to be 286.28 Hz.

When the pipeline tool is departing, the sound wave velocity is determined as the speed of sound in the fluid, minus the speed of the tool, as shown in Fig.13. The AGM geophone frequency for the departing tool is calculated to be 273.72 Hz. It can be seen that, while the wavelength does not vary for an approaching or departing pig, the frequency response observed at the AGM geophone site is measurably reduced by the resulting Doppler shift. The fluid medium and tool speed both affect magnitude of the phenomenon; the Doppler shift increases in response to faster tool movement, and also increases in gas pipelines, since sound travels much slower in gas environments. The acoustic frequency analysis described above will be discussed in further detail within one of the following case studies, where advanced acoustic analysis is utilized to extract tool-passage times under conditions where conventional magnetic and 22-Hz analysis fail.

Remote tracking

One of the aims of the *Armadillo* AGM design project was to simultaneously develop a remote-communications and remote-deployment technology solution, now known as the remote-tracking unit (RTU). The RTU is capable of two-way communications through GSM, CDMA, and satellite networks. In practice, the RTU allows extended and/or remote deployments to utilize an external power source and optional solar panel supply to facilitate unlimited deployment times for multiple pig passages from a single deployment. The RTU also serves to transmit passage information up

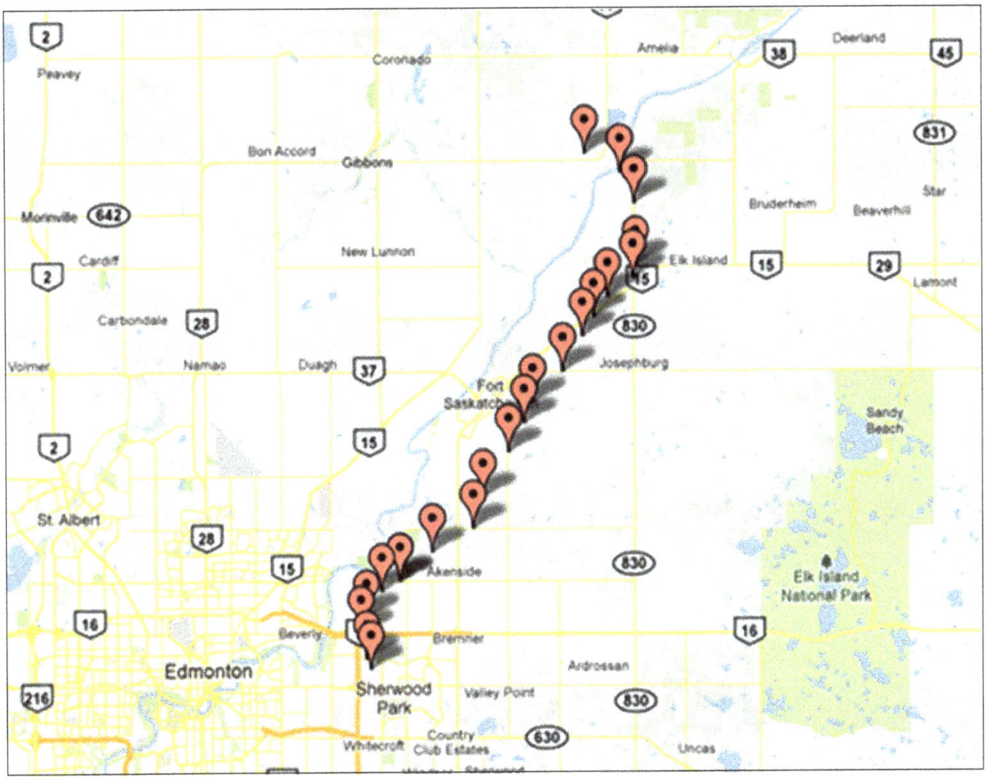

Fig. 14. Map of tracking sites for benchmarking MFL ILI pig.

to internet-based services for processing; subsequent transmissions can serve to link these data directly to clients or to a centralized database. The data stored on the server are available for further analysis, correlation applications, and research purposes. All communication paths within the RTU system are duplex, therefore providing remote command and control of the deployed AGMs through the RTU from any location in the world via a computer with an internet connection.

Case studies

Two different ILI case studies are presented, each of which involves benchmarking conditions in which there is difficulty in reliably detecting pipeline tool passages utilizing conventional AGMs. In both cases, successful results were obtained with the *Armadillo* AGM. The individual case studies include:

16-in diluent pipeline MFL ILI survey
a:22-Hz AC corridor caliper and ultrasonic ILI survey

The first case study explores an MFL benchmarking under ILI conditions which produced extremely weak magnetic signatures. The second case study examines two runs with significant detection difficulties, one utilizing a caliper tool and the other an ultrasonic crack-detection tool.

Case study 1: 1 September, 2011 – 16-in MFL run

A magnetic-flux tool was run in a 16-in diluent pipeline from an Edmonton terminal to a terminal trap near Red Water, Alberta. A total of 20 AGM-tracking sites were utilized. The depth of cover

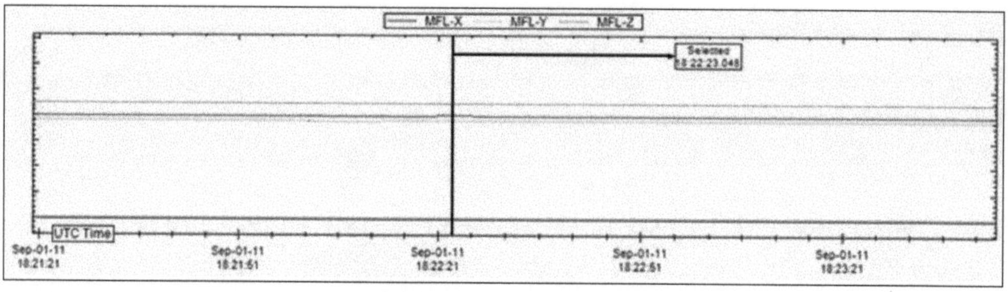

Fig.15. Site 2: extremely low amplitude magnetic data as recorded real-time by Armadillo AGM.

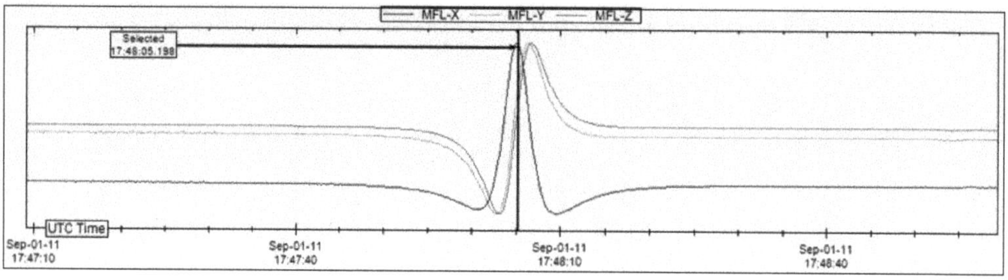

Fig.16. Site 2: memory data amplified in post-processing to reveal characteristic AMR signature.

ranged from just over 2 to 7 m, with the majority of sites at less than 4.5 m. The tool velocity remained consistent at approximately 3 km/hr. Each test site deployed AGMs produced by the three leading manufacturers, one of which was the *Armadillo*. Each AGM was set-up and used in a standard operating state, meaning that there were no custom settings or manufacturer customizations allowed.

AGM sites 2 and 3 exhibited the greatest depth of cover, up to 7 m, as previously indicated. These two sites proved difficult with respect to passage detection, with only one of two automatic triggers from an *Armadillo* AGM, and no triggers at all from any of the other AGMs. Upon post-processing, usable magnetic signatures were extracted from the *Armadillo* AGM memory logs for these two sites, and pass times for all 20 locations were generated. An overview of the benchmarking sites can be seen on the map in Fig.14.

Many of the magnetic signatures for this ILI run were very weak; a typical MFL passage signature for site 2 (extreme depth of burial) is shown in Fig.15. Despite the failure in this case to automatically detect the MFL tool at the time of passage, the ability of the *Armadillo* AGM to record full resolution data continuously for days meant that all available magnetic data from the run was stored in the unit, and available for post-processing.

Upon post-processing, the *Armadillo* software has the ability extract and re-scale the subtle magnetic response that was initially insufficient to automatically trigger a tool passage based on real-time AGM monitoring. Had an initial lower threshold been used in the AGM, the unit could have experienced a number of false triggers due to magnetic perturbations caused by vehicles, equipment, or environmental noise factors. The ability to extract from memory and analyse the AMR data in greater sensitivity is what allowed the analysts to identify the characteristic three-axis AMR response that can only be correlated to tool passage, and cannot be confused with low-level noise or other environmental factors. The amplified data for site 2, with its characteristic AMR three-axis response, is shown in Fig.16.

Fig.17. Multiple different AGMs deployed at each site.

The differentiating factor in this run was the ability to post-process the continuous AMR memory data to determine if a tool-passage signature below the automatic trigger-detection threshold was detectable, and then to use that pass time as the benchmark for the ILI survey. In this case, 100% of the AGM sites were successfully documented through post-processing of the AGM memory log to analyse extremely weak magnetic passage times recorded at sites with excessive depths of cover.

Case study 2: 22 June, 2011 – AC corridor caliper and ultrasonic ILI pig runs

In this project, two types of non-magnetic pipeline tool were tracked along a 10-in pipeline positioned within an AC electric power transmission corridor. A caliper tool was run first, followed by an ultrasonic crack-detection tool, both of which were outfitted with conventional 22-Hz transmitters. Again, two additional AGM brands from different manufacturers were deployed at each AGM site during both runs in addition to the *Armadillo* AGM.

The specifications for the pipeline are as follows:

pipeline diameter:	10 in
wall thickness:	7.8 mm
length of the run:	18.8 km
flow rate:	420 m^3/hr
product:	refined diesel

Case study 2 – caliper run

The caliper tool run started at 07:00 local time on 22 June, 2011. There were a total of 12 AGM sites between the launch and trap. Two AGMs from each of the three manufacturers were deployed at each site, for a total of six AGM devices monitoring tool passages in each location (see Fig.17). A 22-Hz transmitter placed in the rear section of the caliper tool was intended as the primary means of tracking. The caliper run proved very difficult to track. None of the six AGMs deployed at any of the 12 AGM sites triggered using the manufacturers' recommended default settings.

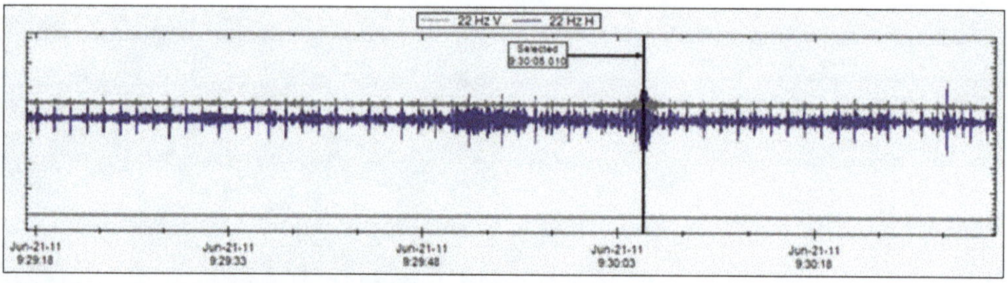

Fig.18. 22-Hz pass found using Armadillo post-processing techniques (Site 12).

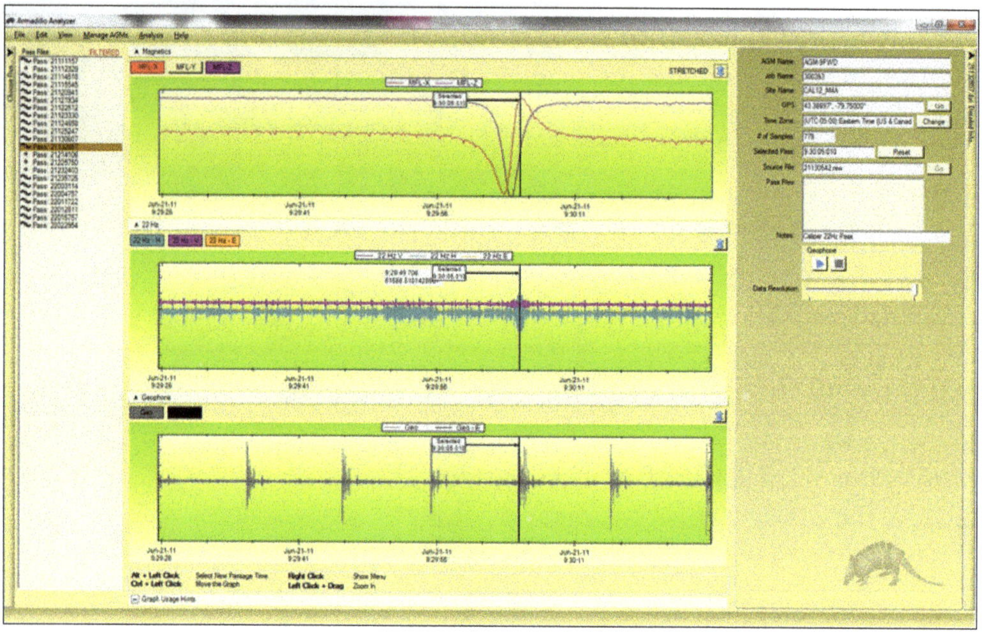

Fig.19. Armadillo raw log viewing software depicting correlation of the 22-Hz pass and AMR data. This method was subsequently used to identify passages at sites with weak 22-Hz response.

In order to counteract the initially poor performance of all three AGM models in default settings, the *Armadillo* memory data was post-processed to determine if any useful tool passage data could be extracted. Post-processing revealed one usable 22-Hz signature, found at site 12, and shown in Fig.18. The detection of only one tool-passage signature at first seemed somewhat inconsequential, but upon further analysis of the concurrent sensor data (AMR, geophone), information from the single confirmed 22-Hz passage was subsequently utilized to develop a new correlation method. This method was ultimately capable of determining reliable tool-pass times for 11 of the 12 AGM sites.

As described in the MFL sensor section of this paper, the AMR sensors detect small changes in the magnetic field when MFL pipeline tools pass. Upon further analysis, it was determined that the caliper tool's 22-Hz transmitter generated extremely low-level, but distinctive, MFL signatures that were recorded by the *Armadillo* AMR sensors at 11 of the 12 AGM sites. The conclusive 22-Hz signature identified at Site 12 made the subsequent identification and correlation of passage times based on AMR data possible. Figure 19 depicts the correlation between the AMR MFL x peak (top graph, red signature) and 22-Hz null (middle graph, purple signature). Although

Caliper Run - 06/22/2011					
Site	Number	Passtime	AGM	Comments	Placement Notes
1	M1	7:13:22.032	PPJQ	Selected pass based on magnetic signature	u/k
2	M1A	-	9PWD	No Passtime selected for this site	At Stake
3	MLV1	7:45:23.517	PPJQ	Selected pass based on magnetic signature, Valve present	u/k
4	MLV2	7:56:13.763	9PWD	Selected pass based on magnetic signature, Valve present	2m d/s of Valve
5	M2A	8:11:52.286	PPJQ	Selected pass based on magnetic signature	u/k
6	M2	8:20:17.699	9PWD	Selected pass based on magnetic signature	1m d/s of stake
7	M3B	8:26:20.724	PPJQ	Selected pass based on magnetic signature	u/k
8	M3A	8:34:14.881	9PWD	Selected pass based on magnetic signature	1m d/s of stake
9	M3	8:47:50.299	PPJQ	Selected pass based on magnetic signature	u/k
10	M4B	8:52:21.681	9PWD	Selected pass based on magnetic signature	1m d/s of stake
11	M4	9:08:15.731	PPJQ	Selected pass based on magnetic signature	u/k
12	M4A	9:30:05.010	9PWD	22Hz Pass, correlates with magnetic signature	1m u/s of stake

Table 2. Passage times identified for 11 of 12 AGM sites using the AMR correlation method.

extremely low-level, a discernible, repeatable, and characteristic signature was produced by the 22-Hz transmitter and detected by the *Armadillo* AGM system's AMR sensors. A summarized tracking sheet indicating the type of sensor data used to pick the passage times for all sites is shown in Table 2.

Case study 2 – ultrasonic crack-detection run

The ultrasonic crack-detection tool (UT) run started at 18:00 local time on 22 June, 2011. The same 12 AGM sites used to track the caliper run were also utilized during the UT run. Because a stronger 22-Hz transmitter was integrated within the UT tool, slightly better results were obtained from the default AGMs settings deployed. A total of four 22-Hz passages were identified by the *Armadillo* AGMs; no other 22-Hz passages were identified by the two alternative AGM models.

A definitive 22-Hz passage signal was observed at site 7 (Fig.20). Site 7 also produced a clear geophone passage signature which did not exhibit interference from girth welds in close proximity (see Fig.21). On the basis of the superior 22-Hz and acoustic data available from Site 7, it was determined to use this location as a test case for determining passage time solely from AGM acoustic data on the basis frequency analysis.

As described previously, acoustic-frequency analysis seeks to identify a Doppler shift (frequency drop) in connection with tool passage, the magnitude of which depends on:

- the velocity at which the pipeline tool is travelling
- the velocity of the fluid in the pipeline

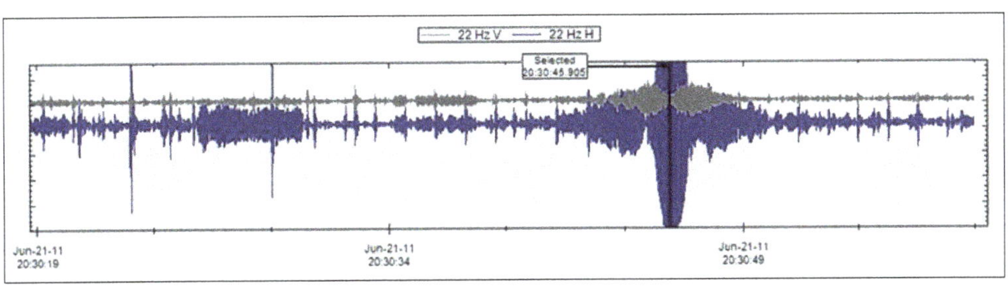

Fig.20. The 22-Hz signature found at Site 7 generated the ability to correlate passage times based on acoustic signatures.

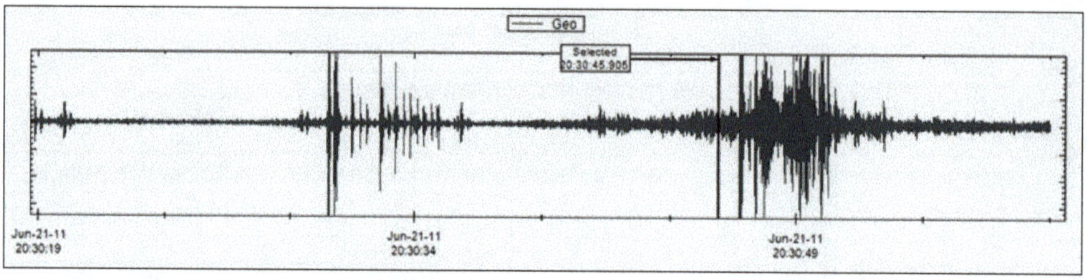

Fig.21. Geophone data for Site 7, for which a Fourier transform analysis was utilized to determine the exact time a frequency shift occurred.

- the speed of sound in the pipeline medium
- the frequency of the sound received at the AGM

Figures 22 and 23 graphically depict the acoustic-data frequency analysis employed to determine tool-pass times on the basis of acoustic (geophone) data alone. To begin with, a Fourier transform was performed on the acoustic-data signatures extracted from the AGM memory. The Fourier transform serves to represent the raw acoustic data in the frequency domain. Because the change we are seeking to identify represents a shift in frequency, the transform data allows us to identify the differences between an incoming and a departing tool (i.e. the Doppler shift).

Figure 22 illustrates the frequency domain of the geophone data from Site 7 as the tool approaches the site. The data emphasized in graphic detail reveals that the tool produced a -9 dB peak at a frequency of 96 Hz, at time 20:30:46.087. Figure 23 illustrates the frequency domain of the geophone data from Site 7 as the tool departs the site. Upon departure, analysis reveals that the tool produced a -10 dB peak at a frequency of 86 Hz, at time 20:30:46.484. The identification of the frequency shift serves to identify a very narrow time window (400 milliseconds) during which the tool passed Site 7.

The acoustic tool-passage time is considered to be the midway point of the observed Doppler shift. In this example, the 22-Hz transmitter was located in the front of the tool, therefore the 22-Hz signature would precede the acoustic Doppler shift. It is therefore necessary to calculate an offset when acoustic and 22-Hz data are used for this correlation.

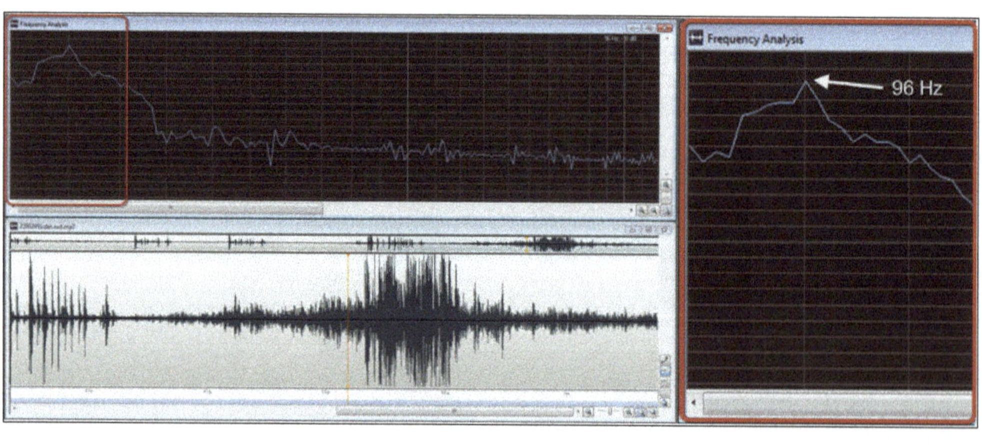

Fig.22. The frequency of the tool passage had a -9 dB and 96 Hz peak at 20:30:46.087.

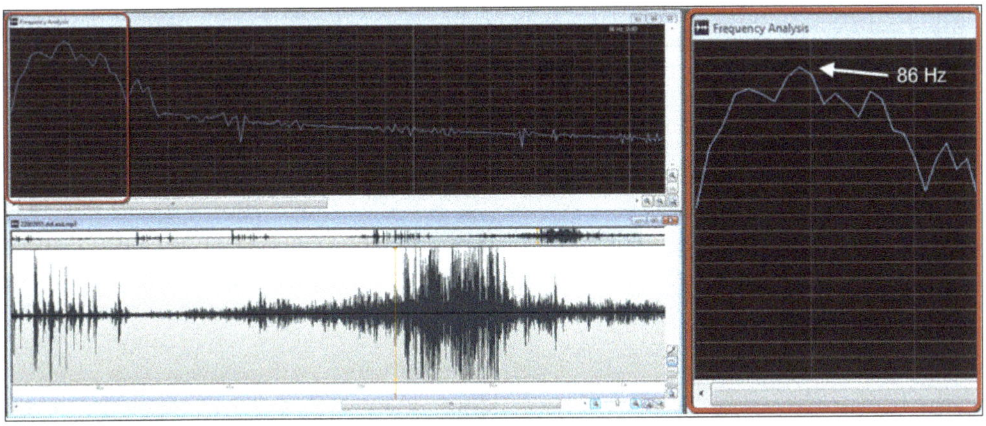

Fig.23. The frequency of the tool passage had a -10 dB and 86 Hz peak at 20:30:46.484.

The offset between a 22-Hz signature and acoustic passage time depends on where the transmitter is placed within the tool (front, back, or central) and the velocity of the tool. Transmitters placed in the front or back will have larger offsets than central transmitters, and slower tools will have larger offsets than faster ones. Once an offset for the tool configuration is calculated, differences in tool velocity between individual AGM sites must be corrected; the larger the velocity variation, the larger the correction.

In the example for Site 7, this offset is subtracted from the calculated geophone passage time in order to match a measured or predicted 22-Hz pass time. The offset is calculated as follows:

acoustic tool passage: 20:30:46.285 (average of 20:30:46.087 and 20:30:46.484)
22-Hz tool passage: 20:30:45.905
acoustic offset: 0.380 s

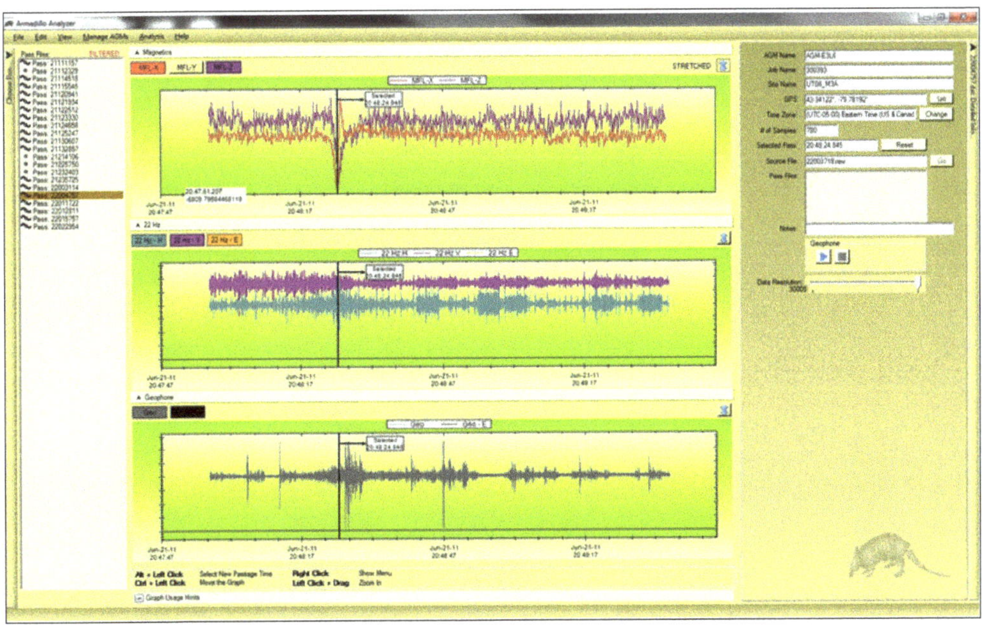

Fig.24. Identifying pass times from AGM log acoustic data using Doppler shift.

C	D	E	F	G	H	I	J	K	L	M	N
Map Chainage (ft)	Map Chainage (km)	Distance Between Sites (km)	Time of Travel Last Site (hrs)	Velocity Tool (km/hr)	Correction	Acoustic Offset (s)	Actual Arr. Time	AGM Time	Data used to Pick Passtime	Final Pastime No Vel Corr.	Final Pastime With Velocity Corr.
1737000	529.4376										
1731685	527.817588	1.620012									-
1728124	526.7321952	1.0853928	0			00:00.380	6:13	18:13:13.841	Geophone	18:13:13.461	18:13:13.461
1718840	523.902432	2.8297632	0.75	3.7730176	1.050378678		6:58	18:58:22.050	MLV		-
1713242	522.1961616	1.7062704	0.4167	4.094721382	1.139938502		7:23	19:23:30.598	MLV		-
1706952.2	520.2790306	1.91713104	0.567	3.381183492	0.941295117	00:00.358	7:57	19:57:44.621	Geophone	19:57:44.241	19:57:44.263
1703320.6	519.1721189	1.10691168	0.333	3.324059099	0.925392132		8:17		No Data		-
1700766.8	518.3937206	0.77839824	0.2167	3.592054638	0	00:00.380	8:30	20:30:45.905	22 Hz		20:30:45.905
1697399	517.3672152	1.02650544	0.333	3.082598919	0.858171501	00:00.326	8:50	20:48:25.225	Geophone	20:48:24.845	20:48:24.899
1691781.3	515.6549402	1.71227496	0.483	3.545082733	0.986923388	00:00.375	9:19	21:18:45.654	Geophone	21:18:45.274	21:18:45.279
1689735.5	515.0313804	0.62355984	0.167	3.733891257	1.039486209		9:29	21:28:55.570	22 Hz		21:28:55.570
1684599	513.4657752	1.5656052	0.45	3.479122667	0.96856062		9:56	21:56:56.578	22 Hz		21:56:56.578
1678645.5	511.6511484	1.8146268	0.55	3.299321455	0.918505365		10:29	22:29:25.338	22 Hz		22:29:25.338
1675557	510.7097736	0.9413748									

Table 3. Passage times and method of detection for UT run.

Armed with this methodology, other sites which do not have discernible 22-Hz signatures can now apply frequency analysis to the geophone data, pinpointing the acoustic passage time on basis of acoustic data alone. This approach was employed at Site 8, as shown in Fig.24. Site 8 did not produce usable 22-Hz passage data, yet acoustic-frequency analysis was successfully employed to determine tool passage on the basis of the available acoustic data. Because the UT tool's velocity profile was very consistent, there was a narrow range of acoustic offsets required. The maximum offset occurred at Site 8, where a 5.4% decrease was indicated. The Site 8 offset resulted in an approx. 50ms difference between the velocity corrected and non-velocity corrected tool pass times.

The summarized tracking sheet from the UT run in Table 3 indicates which type of sensor data was used to pick the passage times: the acoustic data was utilized to determine passage times at four of the 12 AGM sites. The valves (AGM Sites 3 and 4) produced a large amount of acoustic noise when the tool cups passed these sites. As a result, the acoustic correlation was inconclusive because excessive tool noise masked the underlying tool passage signature.

In summary, only four of the 12 AGM sites produced sufficient data to determine tool passage on the basis of the 22-Hz data alone. The addition of acoustic frequency analysis allowed an accurate time of passage to be determined at four additional AGM sites.

Summary

During design of the *Armadillo* AGM, engineers considered how to improve current AGM and pig-tracking technology. Many years of industry experience went into making design decisions. The recent improvements to benchmarking technology include:

- AMR sensors are employed for magnetic sensing and are able to detect very small changes in a magnetic field. These sensors provide the ability to record low-level MFL data while maintaining acceptable dynamic range and resolution. Weak-signal benchmarking locations are now capable of generating passage times.

- 22-Hz detection is recorded in two axes. The combined peak and minimum indications of the two axes provide a definitive passage time. The secondary axis also provides redundancy in noisy environments and other poor signal conditions. The 22-Hz signal can also be detected by the unit's AMR sensors.

- All AGM sensor channels are recorded continuously. Detailed acoustic, AMR, and 22-Hz analyses can be performed via post-processing. Pipeline tool passages with low signal amplitudes or noisy environments can be retrieved.

- Three types of sensor data are recorded no matter what type of tool is being tracked. This capacity provides the ability to correlate one tool-passage data set with another.

- Remote-tracking units that are capable of two-way communications through GSM, CDMA, or satellite networks. The RTU is able to control, download, and listen to the AGM remotely. Sensor data snapshots are provided to verify passage times.

Through research and field trials, the operations of tracking and benchmarking have been made more reliable and safe. The *Armadillo* AGM hardware, along with its analysis software, provides greatly enhanced capability for obtaining accurate tool-passage times. The remote-tracking capabilities being tested now will further reduce or eliminate the need for personnel to deploy and monitor benchmark systems during a pig run, increasing safety while reducing costs.

Section 7: Operations

Commissioning of the world's longest LPG pipeline and retrieval of stuck pigs: a case study

by Partha Jana

GAIL (India) Ltd, Jamnagar, Gujarat, India

GAIL (INDIA) LTD is the country's largest natural gas company, having a market share of 78% in gas transmission and 70% in gas marketing. Apart from these activities, the company has diversified business interests in petrochemicals, city gas projects, LPG transmission, and exploration and production activities. The company operates internationally in a number countries including Egypt, Burma, China, and Oman.

At the time of writing (in 2008), the company is planning to lay eight new gas pipelines which will link to the India's integrated natural gas grid. The new pipelines are expected to increase GAIL's gas transmission capacity from 148 to 300 MMscmd, and the existing trunk pipeline network from 6662 to 11,931 km.

LPG transportation

The Government of India has promoted the use of LPG in domestic as well as commercial sectors for protection of the environment. The population growth in India has resulted in LPG consumption growth to more than 200% between 1990-91 and 2002-03, which has also resulted in an increase in road and rail traffic congestion across the country. LPG transportation by pipeline made a modest beginning in 2002, and by 2006-07, its share in the country's LPG transportation was 24% (11.2 Mt/yr), the balance being by road and rail transport.

The unique physical properties of LPG (including the formation of highly flammable vapour cloud on leakage, as LPG is a vapour under ambient conditions) compared to other liquid hydrocarbon products, poses a greater risk to both public and property during transportation. Unlike other hydrocarbons (which are stable under ambient condition) where any leakage during

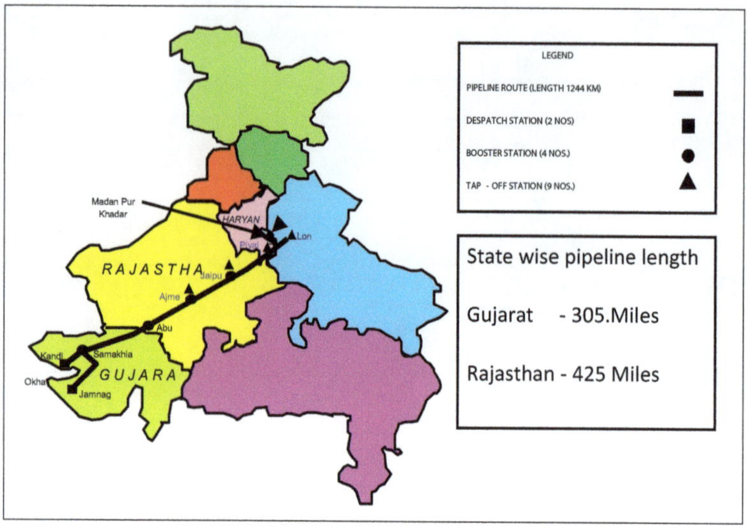

Fig. 1. The Jamnagar-Loni pipeline route.

transportation in bulk results in spills, LPG leakage quickly picks up heat from the surroundings and the soil to evaporate quickly and results in flammable vapour clouds which travel along the ground, in the direction of the wind, and result in fire/explosion on coming into contact with a source of ignition. This prompted GAIL to carry out a feasibility study on the bulk transportation of LPG by pipelines versus rail and road. Based on the confidence gained in the transportation of natural gas through cross-country pipelines for over a decade and the study result, GAIL first decided to transport LPG in bulk through a cross-country pipeline in 1998, and initiated the task of designing, laying, and operating the world's first and longest exclusive cross-country LPG pipeline with a length of 1290 km and diameters of 8, 12, and 16 in, from Jamnagar in Gujarat to Loni in Uttar Pradesh; Fig.1 shows an overview of the route of the resulting Jamnagar–Loni pipeline (JLPL).

Among the benefits to the country from LPG transportation by pipeline are the following:

- safer and economic mode of transport
- environment friendly
- reduction in surface traffic
- minimal transit loss and pilferage

Commissioning of the JLPL

Because there was no experience available in the country relating to LPG transportation by cross-country pipeline, it was a challenging task right from the commissioning of the pipeline to its operation and maintenance, to maintain the integrity of the pipeline which transports hazardous liquid hydrocarbons and passes through various types of terrain and geographic conditions. The operation and maintenance procedures were established using existing international standards (including ASME B 31.4 and 31.8, API 610, API 1104, API 1110, and NACE 0169), and modified over a period of time with the experience gained.

Precommissioning checks

Precommissioning checks were carried out for the pipeline to ensure that the system, including the distribution network and pipeline installations such as valve stations, intermediate pigging

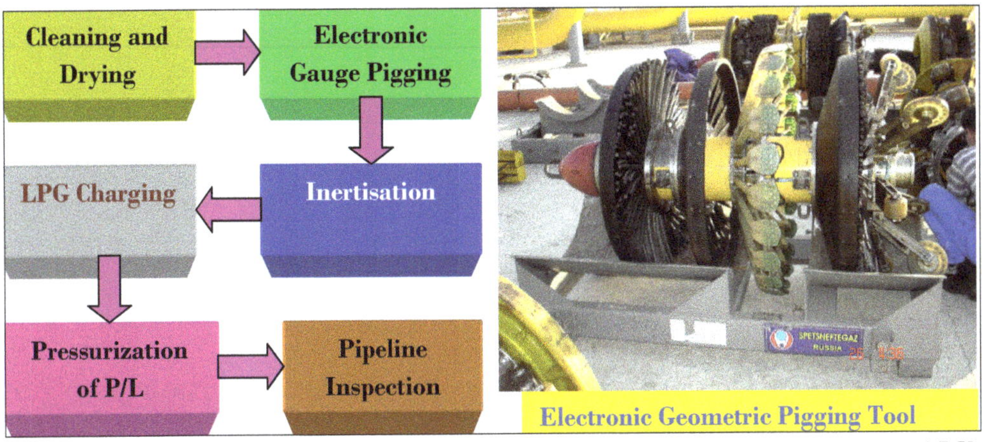

Fig.2. Flow diagram of commissioning and EGP.

Section no.	Section identity	Diameter (in) /length (km)
1	Jamnagar-Samakhiali	14 / 166.4
2	Samakhiali-IP1	16 / 141.3
3	IP1 - Aburoad	16 / 128.8
4	IOCL Kandla - DT Kandla	12 / 6.9
5	DT Kandla - Samakhiali	8 / 58.4
6	Abu Road -IP2	16 / 143.2
7	IP2 - IPS Nasirabad	16 / 161.4
8	IPS Nasirabad- IPS Mansaram-pura	12 / 121.3
9	IPS Mansarampura- IP4	12 / 156
10	IP4 - DT Loni	12 / 151.2
11	TOT 1 - IOCL	8 / 10.9
12	TOT 2 - RT Sanganer	8 / 36.8

Table 1. Details of the Jamnagar-Loni pipeline.

stations, and the terminal stations, were mechanically complete in all respect. The checks included:

- mechanical integrity check
- electrical distribution system check
- instrument control and interlocks check
- communication system and utility check
- survey of the pipeline and it's installations
- ready reckoner

Commissioning activities

After completion of the precommissioning checks, the pipeline was declared 'ready for commissioning', the sequence of activities for which is shown in Fig.2. The JLPL was divided into

Fig.3. A typical cup pig and N2 tanker with vaporizer.

Fig.4. A detachable hot flare and LPG flaring in the night.

12 sections for commissioning purposes, details of which are given in Table 1. The salient features of the commissioning phase included:

- Being the first exclusive LPG transporting pipeline in the world, no reference was available on the post-commissioning experience, and it was therefore a learning experience for GAIL. The company developed the commissioning procedures without involvement of any outside parties.

- Inerting of the pipeline and charging of LPG was an uphill task with respect to quantity, length of the pipeline, the hazardous nature of the contents, and the available infrastructure.

- Bi-di and cup pigs (Fig.3) in combination were used for proper sealing to minimize by-passing of the LPG.

- It was endeavoured to maintain a liquid column of about 5km between two consecutive pigs, although in practice, at the receiver, the pigs were all more or less together within a span of about 800m.

- It was observed that N2 and LPG columns overtook the pigs. However, the N2 column was maintained sufficiently ahead of the LPG column in all the pipeline sections to avoid the formation of explosive mixture. A typical pig, N2, LPG schedule is given in Table 2.

- GAIL installed detachable hot flares (as shown in Fig.4) – which operate without electricity or compressed air – so as to be able to flare LPG at any location if the situation demanded it.

Section no.	Pig tracking location	Section length (km)	Details of activity (pig launching/ receiving/ N2 and LPG charging/ receiving) in 2000	N2 detection	LPG detection	Remarks
1	Start	0	1st pig: 16:40 on 12 Nov2nd pig: 01:30 13 Nov3rd pig: 16:00 14 Nov4th pig: 06:15 on 15 Nov	16:40 on 12 Nov	06:15 on 15 Nov	LPG charged
2	A	13.2	1st pig: 08:552nd pig: 09:053rd pig: 10:004th pig: 12:10 on 15 Nov	08:15 on 15 Nov	12:00 on 15 Nov	LPG has by-passed 4th pig
3	B	19.9	1st pig: 17:502nd pig: 18:253rd pig: 21:454th pig: 21:45 on 15 Nov	14:15 on 15 Nov	17:30 on 15 Nov	LPG has by-passed all four pigs and is travelling behind N2 column
4	C	9.9	All four pigs between 06:20 and 06:25 on 16 Nov	18:45 on 15 Nov	21:45 on 15 Nov	All four pigs have formed a pig train behind the LPG column
5	D	11.2	All four pigs at 13:00 on 16 Nov	23:15 on 15 Nov	06:45 on 16 Nov	
6	E	14.3	All four pigs between 22:00 and 22:15 on 16 Nov	07:00 on 16 Nov	19:30 on 16 Nov	
7	F	8.1	All four pigs at 03:00 on 17 Nov	18:45 on 16 Nov	02:00 on 17 Nov	
8	G	13.7	All four pigs at 13:00 on 17 Nov	00:35 on 17 Nov	07:45 on 17 Nov	
9	H	11.0	All four pigs at 17:45 on 17 Nov	10:15 on 17 Nov	13:00 on 17 Nov	
10	I	12.9	All four pigs at 00:45 on 18 Nov	16:15 on 17 Nov	18:00 on 17 Nov	
11	End	14.5	All the 4 pigs were retrieved during the commissioning of next section of the pipeline		02:15 on 18 Nov	Pumping halted at 02:30

Table 2. Typical pig, N2, and LPG movement details.

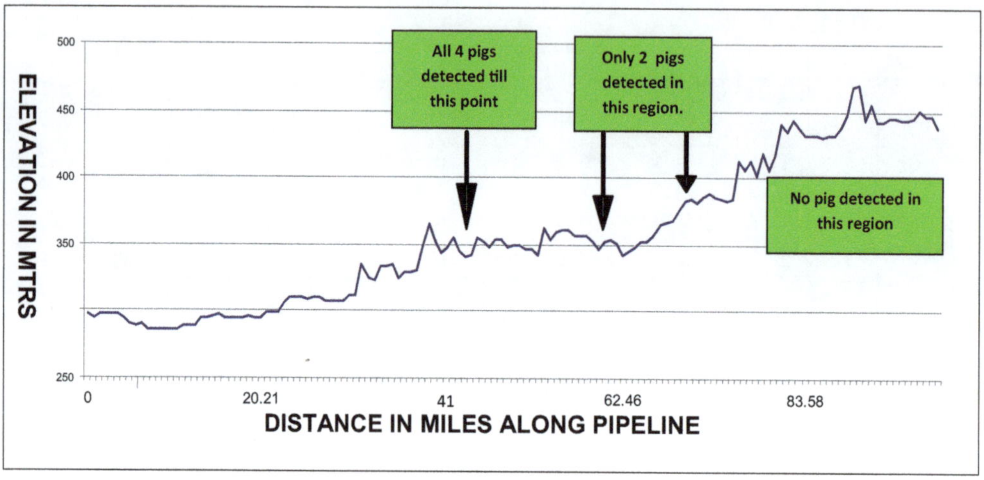

Fig.5. Section 7 vertical profile.

- In Section 7, all four commissioning pigs became stuck. GAIL tried various methods of retrieving the pigs, including pressurizing and depressurizing the section, and flowing LPG in reverse flow through receiver barrel, but without success. Before any future pigging operations, it was necessary to retrieve all these stuck pigs to make the pipeline section free from all obstacles; despite this, the flow through the JLPL was found to be normal with a 100% flow capacity.

Section 7: scenario and problem identification

The general commissioning of the pipeline was undertaken using a combination of four-cup uni-directional and bi-directional pigs. However, for this section, only four-cup uni-directional pigs were used. Normally the pigs from the previous section are retrieved during commissioning of the next section; however, all the four commissioning pigs used in Section 7 could not be retrieved, even after commissioning of the three following sections.

The commissioning of this 161.4-km long IP2-Nasirabad section was carried out in 2000; the altitude profile is shown in Fig.5, and other details are as follows:

section size	: 16 in x 161.4 km
wall thickness	: 7.1 to 8.7 mm
operating pressure	: 63 - 83 bar
flow rate	: 230 - 280 Mt/hr
no. of sectionalizing valves	: 8
no. of offtakes	: 1, 8-in diameter
service	: LPG
date of commissioning	: 21-27 November, 2000

Analysis of commissioning pigging activities

A detailed analysis was carried out of the data recorded during commissioning the pipeline, and the following observations were made:

- LPG charging was from 06:00 on 24 November to 10:35 on 27 November, a total duration of 76 hrs 35 mins.

- The flow of LPG at 150-155 Mt/hr in the section was maintained to attain pig speed of approx 0.6 m/sec.

- The pressure along the route were: Jamnagar – 65 bar; Samakhiali – 48 bar; Abu Road – 24.5 bar; IP2 – 16.7 bar; and Nasirabad - 6.4 bar, i.e. higher than the LPG vapour pressure.

- Based on the average speed of the pigs and assuming that all pigs were moving as one cluster, the pig receipt time would have been 12:00 hrs on 27 November. However, LPG was received 85 mins before.

The lengths of the commissioning pigs were as follows:

pig 1: 600 mm
pig 2 580 mm
pig 3: 540 mm
pig 4: 570 mm

In view of the above observations, retrieval of the four commissioning pigs after more than four years of operation of the pipeline was a most challenging job in itself, and it was essential to take maximum care in carrying out this operation in what had become a lifeline for Northern India.

The most optimistic outcome was retrieval of all four pigs in first pigging operation; the worst situation envisaged was removal of stuck pigs by a stoppling operation, making a by-pass, and cutting the pipeline at each stuck pigs location, i.e. four times. As part of its planning, GAIL had the necessary equipment available for such stoppling and pipe-cutting activities.

Contingency plan

The most optimistic scenario was retrieval of the stuck pigs by a single high-density foam pig run, while the worst-case scenario was removal of each stuck pigs by cutting the pipeline four times, at four locations. GAIL needed to be ready for the worst possible situation during this pig-retrieval operation, which had to be undertaken with minimal loss time, and so a detailed contingency plan was prepared by an experienced team and all resources were identified and kept ready to move onto site at short notice, if needed. The contingency plan activities are listed below:

- Identification and readiness of the required hot-tapping machines, stoppling equipment, fittings, and accessories.

- Locating the pipeline sections where pigs were stuck, and pinpointing the exact location of each pig.

- Mobilization of the hot-tap and stoppling machines and fittings (including by-pass arrangement), pre-hydrotested linepipe, accessories, cold cutting and welding machine, etc., at short notice.

- Excavation of the pipeline sections.

Fig.6. Foam and cup pig with brush, ready for launching.

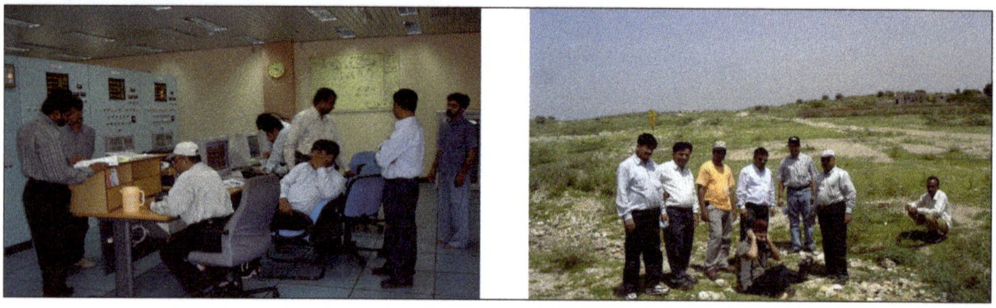

Fig.7. Control room monitoring and pig tracking in the field.

- Removal of the coating and radiography to confirm the position of the pigs in the pipeline.
- Welding of the hot-tapping and stoppling fittings and by-pass line.
- Cold cutting of the pipeline and removal of the pigs.
- Restoration of the pipeline section to normal operation

The above operations would be required only after the failure of the foam pig to retrieve the stuck pigs, and after confirmation of its disintegration due to high differential pressure. A brush pig would then be launched, incorporating flow by-pass to allow 30% by-pass in case it, too, became stuck. In this case, the pipeline by-pass were required to be made ready within 72 hrs. During this period, 30% of the flow (approx. 85 Mt/hr) could be maintained and a minimum supply provided to the pipeline's customers. The main line by-pass arrangement would allow 90% flow, i.e. 250 Mt/hr, which could then be maintained after the approx. 116 hrs it would take for the by-pass work to be completed.

Co-ordination with customers

During the pig-retrieval operation, close coordination with GAIL's customers was a most important task, as sufficient storage space needed to be created in order to maintain a stable flow rate during the pigging operation. This was carried out by reducing the extraction and pumping rates at the customer's offtakes and at the dispatch terminals, respectively, 15 days in advance.

Fig.8. All four stuck pigs along with the foam pig, as they were received at IPS-Nasirabad.

Pig tracking locations in Section 7	Station interval distance (km)	Cumulative LPG flow from Abu-road (Mt)	Liquid velocity (m/sec)	Pig velocity (m/sec)
Start point	0	0	0	0
A	11.05	884.8	0.95	0.79
B	14.51	986	0.97	0.95
C	14.13	851	1.13	1.04
D	12.10	915	1.17	1.02
E	19.84	1387	1.19	1.13
F	25.94	1768	1.18	1.15
G	10.69	703	1.19	1.16
H	24.05	1671	1.17	1.11
I	17.98	1349	1.19	1.03
End point	11.58	637	1.19	1.16
Total	161.39	11151.8		
Average fluid velocity: 1.03 m/sec		Average pig velocity: 0.95 m/sec		

Table 3. Pig detection record with geophone.

Safety aspects and preparedness

Utmost care was to be taken to maintain uninterrupted LPG flow to customers. Various teams were formed to keep a close watch on the line pressure profile and for tracking the movement of the foam pig. Fire tenders and ambulance services were kept ready for use in case of any emergency, and close co-ordination maintained with local authorities along the route.

Retrieval activities and execution

Two run sequences were planned for retrieval of the stuck pigs with the following tool specifications:

- foam-pig: 760-mm long polyurethane-coated pig which can disintegrate at 20 to 30 bar differential pressure (Fig.6)

Fig.9. Stuck pig no 1, as received.

Fig.10. Stuck pig no 2, as received.

- wire-brush pig: 4C-1D *Vantage* pig (Fig.6) with wire brush, which provided with 25-30% flow by-pass in case of sticking during operation.

The activities undertaken were as follows:

1. Pumping through the JLPL was stopped on 20 August 2005 at 17:45, to create sufficient space at customers' storage to facilitate smooth pigging operation.
2. Pigging activity started at 06:00 on 22 August.
3. Pumps at upstream of IP2 (i.e. Abu Road) were started at 06:48 and at Nasirabad station, the by-pass valve was opened at 06:59.
4. The foam pig was launched at IP-2 at 07:07 on 22 August.
5. LPG flow through JLPL was maintained at 230 Mt/hr.

Pig tracking and data logging

Teams (Fig.8) were mobilized and positioned at the first tracking location downstream of the start point A in Table 3). The initial pig velocity was about 0.54 m/sec. To increase the velocity, the pumping rate at Jamnagar-DT (the origination point of the JLPL) was increased from 230 Mt/hr to 280 Mt/hr at 08:30 on 22 August. The pig was detected by geophone at each location shown in Table 3 with the exception of location I. The pig could not be detected at location I, although the passage of the pig was recorded by the team, based on the fluid velocity.

Pig receipt

The following sequence of activities were carried out for receiving the pig at the receiver:

- The receiver was put online at 23:00.
- Flow through JLPL was maintained at 280 Mt/hr.
- The pig signaller before the receiver detected the pig's arrival at 00:30 on 24 August.
- The basket-filter differential pressure started rising, and a stand-by filter was also brought online.
- Flow through receiver was assured, and all pigs would be received at the trap.
- The pig-detection signaller showed pig passage at the receiver at 01:15.
- The receiver was isolated and all relevant safety measures were carried out.

Fig.11. Stuck pig no 3, as received.

Fig.12. Stuck pig no 4, as received.

Fig.13. Foam pig, as received.

- The receiver was depressurized by hot flaring and was opened at 03:30: all the stuck pigs and the foam pig were taken out for inspection, as shown in Fig.8.

Conclusion

All the stuck pigs (Figs 9-12) and the foam pig (Fig.13) were thoroughly inspected. The commissioning pigs were found to be in a damaged condition. The average liquid velocity during pigging operation was 1.03 m/sec, and the average foam pig velocity during the operation was 0.95 m/sec. Total duration of the retrieval operation was 41.4 hrs.

The cumulative length of the pig train was 3100 mm, and the length of receiver barrel was 3200 mm. Pig-train retrieval from the receiver barrel was a delicate task as pig train's last pig, i.e. the foam pig, might stick in the neck of barrel which would have raised critical safety issues. Consequently, the barrel opening operation and pig retrieval from the barrel needed special attention, as the foam pig might have acted like a cork in a pressurized bottle due to entrapped pressurized LPG. To compensate for this, the pipeline section was depressurized as far as possible, and well-thought through safety measures avoided a major mishap.

The best possible solution for retrieving the stuck pigs was achieved at the first try itself. A steady flow and dedicated team effort, with complete co-ordination, resulted in achievement of the planned activities. The "hope for the best but prepare for the worst" strategy had built-up enough confidence in team to put the plan in place.

Factors affecting the design and selection of pigging tools for multi-diameter pipelines

by Karl Dawson

Pipeline Engineering, Catterick Bridge, UK

THIS PAPER CONSIDERS the process involved in pigging-tool selection for pipelines with two or more significant internal diameters; the tools need to be capable of negotiating the different internal diameters whilst also carrying out the necessary pipeline cleaning operation.

The paper includes an analysis of pipeline features that affect pigging-tool selection and then goes on to look at other variables that determine pigging-tool design; this includes a step-by-step guide outlining how a tool is designed, the development of prototype pigs, and the importance of testing and validation prior to final deployment in operational pigging programmes.

WITH ITS track record of engineered design solutions to dual-diameter and related pigging problems, the application by Pipeline Engineering of proven techniques, together with new and innovative concepts, has allowed the development of multi-diameter pigs capable of negotiating multiple pipeline diameter changes and geometry conditions, together with specific launch and operational parameters.

Historically the need for a pipeline to be of single-diameter construction with a constant bore, and bend radii of five times the internal diameter, was a requirement of pipeline inspection companies. This was to enable the clearance between their tools and the pipe wall to allow collection of the required data. If a pipeline followed this configuration it was deemed to be 'piggable'.

The drive for cost-effective design highlighted the potential savings in space, weight, fabrication, and installation costs. It was found that if topside pipework, risers, and subsea manifolds were to be of a smaller diameter than the main pipeline, a considerable reduction in cost could be achieved. The reduction in bore necessitated smaller valve configurations, branches, and welded fittings such as tees and bends, which naturally led to reduced costs. The weight savings in these assemblies also reduced fabrication and installation outlay which also contributed to the overall reduction in cost.

The joining of lines within a field to a main transmission line and then to a central processing location provides a source of dual and multiple diameters. It is more cost-efficient to tie-in to an available existing line than to lay a new line, with a benefit being shared maintenance and a reduced overall installation lead time. The size of a branch line can be smaller than the mainline, and is determined by the production output of the joining location.

The continuing development of deepwater fields has emphasized the requirement for economical design. The deeper water depths dictate higher pressure ratings and therefore thicker-walled pipe systems, valves, and fittings. With increasing field water depths come exponentially escalating construction costs, and as such any potential area for saving must be explored. With this, connectors, valves, and features have been scrutinized with the result being that rather than

Fig. 1. Petal-type pig.

reducing the overall diameter of the component, it is acceptable to reduce the internal diameter to achieve the thicknesses and cavities needed for form and function. This then creates the opportunity for a vast quantity of internal diameters due to the array of manufacturers producing components to be included in assemblies.

A prime design consideration is that the line to be installed is piggable. This factor is generally never discounted when applying varying diameters, as flow assurance is a mandatory aspect to be addressed. A flow-assurance programme ensures the line condition is maintained at a predetermined level, optimum flow conditions are achieved, and product quality is retained. With these factors taken into account, the drive for savings is still pressing and a direct approach can be achieved by pushing the boundaries of the term 'piggable'. A balance must therefore be struck between economy and functional viability.

The process of pig selection

Suitable pig selection is crucial to ensure that the desired task is carried out to the standard specified, and within the project timescale and to the allocated budget. With this, the drive for an engineered solution, which has been proven to be successful, the need for accurate information and provision of operating conditions is essential.

Foam and conical-cup construction pigs can negotiate reductions in diameter, but are not specifically designed to cope with changes in diameter for considerable lengths of run. To fulfil the requirement of functioning within a dual or multi-diameter line, the pig is needed to be suitably designed to negotiate the predefined diameters, and to pass through the diameter-specific features.

Step-by-step design guide

To design a pig capable of negotiating a multi-diameter pipeline, the parameters must firstly be clearly defined. Within the term 'parameter' the following factors need to be considered:

- internal diameters
- bend radii
- feature definition and configuration
- lengths
- transitions
- location of features
- flow and pressure conditions

Fig.2. The patented paddle-type pig.

Fig.3. Wheeled-suspension pig.

- medium
- expected debris or internal line condition
- pig trap
- interaction of pig characteristics to negotiate features

Internal diameters

The diameters present in a line need to be defined as accurately as possible, as all variations of the stated diameters can have an effect on the boundary conditions. The range of diameters needs to be broken-down into a range for each core diameter. This could involve grouping schedules for each major diameter, or more likely similar sizes to allow a number of defined ranges to be identified. The pig seal and support elements would then be sized to suit the ranges. If the ranges are found to be too great for the elements to accommodate, the ranges could be broken down further to necessitate additional elements for cover. The type of seal and support element and configuration will be selected based upon the range step changes, together with the length of run in each diameter and transitional conditions. The seal element could be a range of specially sized sealing discs (see the case study below), or an overlapping petal style disc (Fig.1). The support element could be a modified traditional-style support disc (see the case study) or a hybrid paddle support (Fig.2). For larger diameters, it may be necessary to employ a wheeled spring-suspension arrangement to maintain alignment to the pipe centreline due to the increased weight of the tool (Fig.3).

Bend radii

The bend radii need to be defined together with the specific diameter in which the bend is formed. The portion of the bend in angular terms, and the method in which the bend is formed - such as induction bending or lobster-back field fabrication - are also key factors for consideration. The pig length is of major consideration here, as a longer body is less likely to be able to traverse the bend, but a short pig would be unstable through straight runs. The pig length is also influenced by the combination of features within the pipeline system.

Feature definition and configuration

Definition of the feature and its particular configuration in the application require detailing. An example would be a tee, which could have a barred branch for pigging, or it may be a flow tee with through-bore flow-matched linepipe. The pig design needs to provide a positive seal across the feature to allow an efficient passage with no loss of drive which would lead to stalling. A wye piece is another example of branch which requires careful design consideration.

Lengths of each section

The length of each section in relation to its diameter needs to be clearly defined to assist the review of the main diameters. This also provides a basis for selection of materials resistant to wear for the stated length.

Transition between diameters

The transitions between different diameters and features need to be investigated and simulated to ensure that they are not too abrupt, which could cause loss of a positive seal and therefore drive, and may also prevent the switch between the two sealing elements occurring as required in the transition between the major diameters.

The length of run to each feature needs defining so that a map of the pig run can be built-up for analysis purposes to enable the optimum pig design to be generated. The distance to each of the features, and the order in which they occur in the line, are key pieces of information without which a suitable design cannot be produced.

Flow and pressure conditions

The stipulated flow and pressure conditions need to be taken into account and recommendations are to be made to ensure pig speeds are kept at the optimum level to prevent unnecessary wear and damage, but also to ensure an optimum cleaning speed as required. By-pass can be introduced to maintain flow but reduce pig speed, whilst introducing an efficient cleaning mechanism.

Medium and environment

The medium and environment which the pig is to transit can be corrosive, and as such the materials and design must therefore be suitably resistant for successful receipt. A medium which is not self-lubricating, such as a dry gas line, can present a particular challenge as the seal and support elements can wear at a faster rate than in a lubricated line. Careful material selection of the affected elements ensures a suitable pig is designed for the task.

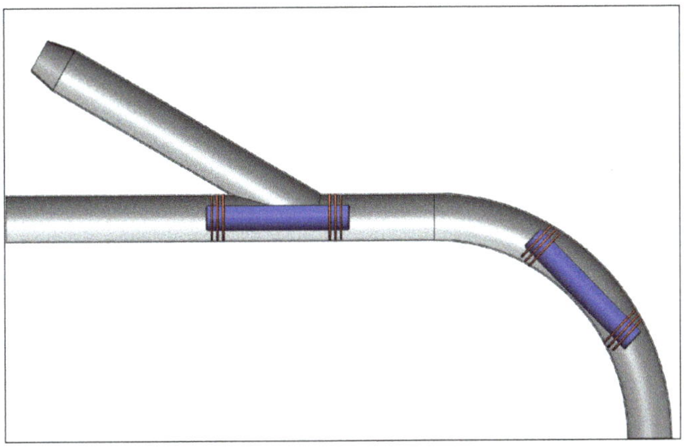

Fig.4. Layout of pig in wye and bend.

Expected debris and internal line condition

Depending upon the internal condition of a line and the medium transmitted, varying types and quantities of debris can be present, and this dictates a specific approach; for example, a by-pass pig to allow through flow to suspend black powder in front of the pig to prevent a blockage and overloading of the receiver facilities.

Pig launcher and receiver

The onsite launching and receiving facilities can restrict the overall length of the pig, and hence prevent the pig being designed to best suit the line geometry any feature combinations. An example of this is an ITAG pigging valve, which has a strict maximum length to allow a pig to be inserted and rotated into the main flow of the line to be launched.

Interaction of line features

The interaction of individual line features may not at first appear to have a large bearing on pig design, but this can never be sufficiently stressed as an underestimated design premise. It is the interaction of pig's characteristics designed to negotiate and traverse separate line features which can potentially have an impact on passage through a feature in which it is not required to be active. An example of this is when a pig is designed to seal across a wye piece: the body is considerably longer than that of a standard pig. The pig could also be required to traverse a bend, but due to the revised length, the pig may not be able to do this as the increase in length could have lowered its position in the bend causing a clash between the inside of the bend and the body material. Figure 4 shows the layout of such a scenario.

The severity of the clash would be dependent upon the radius of the bend and may result in a loss of seal rather than a clash; this may able to be rectified with a modification to the disc pack configuration. If the disc pack cannot be modified, the tool could be split into two modules with an articulated joint between the two pig bodies, and this would allow passage around the bend and sealing across the wye.

Pipeline data are critical

The provision of line diameter information and feature details are fundamental inputs into to the pig-design process. As previously stated, to achieve an optimum design all available line data are

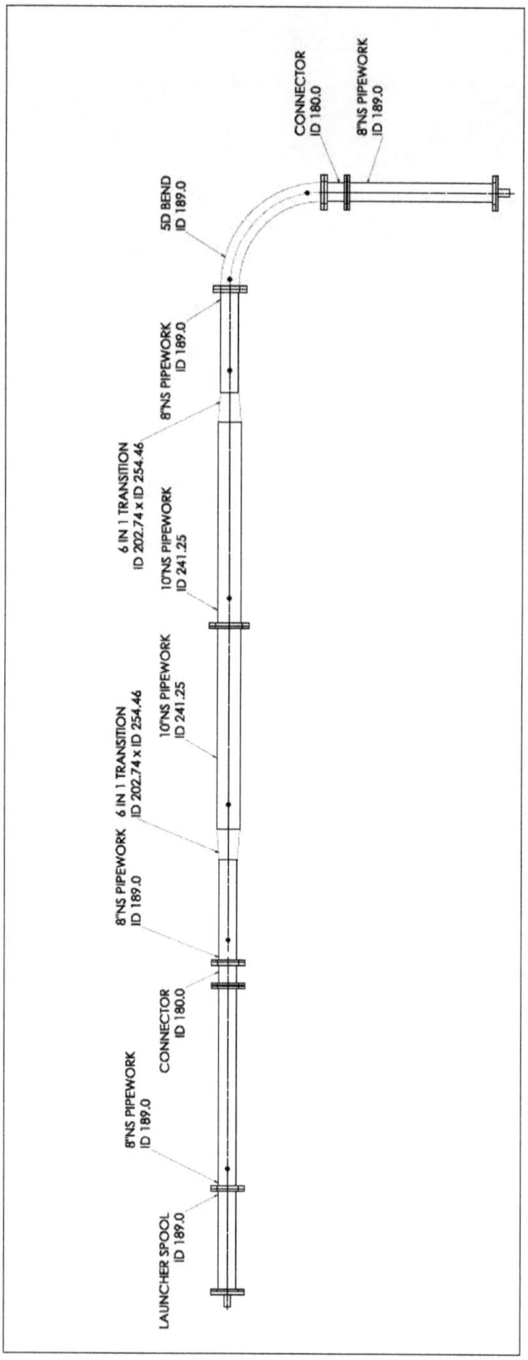

Fig.5. Test rig layout.

required, and where information is found missing measurements need to be taken where viable for the full picture to be obtained. If the aforementioned is not obtained, the process of design will be extremely difficult to complete and, depending upon the missing information, may not be possible. The objective is to provide a pig to suit the application: it must be kept in mind that when engineering a suitable solution, assumptions and estimations must not take the place of fact; if information is found lacking, a halt must be called to the design process until the information can be provided.

Prototype development and the importance of testing and validation

When a design has been developed to suit a particular application, it is trialled using CAD modelling through the diameters and features to be negotiated. The design basis and previous trial data are used to refine the design to achieve the most suitable solution. The true test - and therefore validation - of the design is to manufacture a prototype of the design solution and test the pig in a purpose-made test rig. The test rig is to be designed to simulate the worst-case scenario features and diameters which the pig will be subjected to when running through the field line. When testing the conditions under which the pig will operate in the field, parameters such as flow and pressure are simulated to ensure the test is as true a representation of the operational conditions as possible. This will therefore validate the pig for use in its intended application in the field. Data collected from testing can used to benchmark the flow and pressure readings in the simulated features, and these can be compared to operational data to review performance.

It must be noted that testing is generally under ideal conditions with no pipe wall deposits such as wax, and no corrosion. It is however possible to apply such build-ups and replicate corrosion pits and scours, to enable a true assessment of pig performance.

When testing, it may be necessary to amend disc diameters and disc-pack configurations to allow a smoother, more-efficient passage through the features. A particular parameter to be noted when developing a dual or multi-diameter pig is by-pass: modifications, where possible, are made to keep this to a minimum. By-pass can be reduced when then pig is traversing a straight pipe section and also in a bend, but it is at the transition to a larger diameter where it can only be reduced as the sealing elements respond to the variations and effect a positive seal.

Together with the validation of pig performance, testing is an activity imperative to validate the functionality of a new or special pig design. Gaining data which can be used for operational purposes is a useful exercise, but testing the pig through the simulated field geometry and conditions is invaluable: should a design feature not perform as intended, or an unexpected clash between the body and pipe wall occur and the pig become stuck, it can easily be removed from the test rig and the design rectified. The number of modifications and retests are unlimited, but when the operation requiring the pig takes place, only a single opportunity exists for success. The cost of recovering a stuck pig from a subsea manifold would be substantial and would undoubtedly delay a project with certain further financial impacts. With this in mind, the costs incurred in performing test-loop trials are minimal by comparison, and could prevent a series of events detrimental to the success of a project.

Case study: 8-in x 10-in pipeline offshore India

Pipeline Engineering was approached to supply a pigging solution to negotiate 8-in to 10-in major diameters for commissioning activities and production pigging. For dewatering the line, the pig was to be propelled with nitrogen. The pig was to be back-loaded into an 8-in vertical subsea launcher which was then to be connected to a pipeline end termination through a reduced-bore mechanical connector and into a 90° 5D bend. The pig was to perform a mandrel body roll flip and pass though the connector and 5D bend, then pass into a 10-in line pipe section in which it was to travel 3.2 km before negotiating a reduction in to 8-in pipe, a 90° 5D bend, and a further reduced-bore connector before being received at the subsea manifold.

Fig.6. 8-in x 10-in pig: initial design.

Pig operational requirement

The operations were to be carried out subsea with both launch and receipt at 600m water depth. The pig was extensively tested and developed to ensure functionality was maintained under the parameters. The pig was required to negotiate the following:

8-in launcher and pipework ID	= 190.5mm
connector ID	= 179.8mm
5D bend ID	= 190.5mm
10-in line ID	= 241.3mm
tapered 1:6 transition	
length fixed at 400mm due to laydown head design	

Pig functional requirements

- Remove construction debris
- Flood line for hydrotest
- Dewater line

Pig design development and validation testing

The pig design could not incorporate a suspension system, or a paddle-support system, due to the bi-directional and back-loading requirements, and the restriction on length. A segmented support system was employed for pliability through the reduced-diameter connector, and to provide support in both the minor and major diameters. Dual seals were used for the 10-in section, and single seals for the 8-in.

When the trials commenced, the design was found to be unsuccessful at negotiating the features, due to the reduced-bore connector damaging the disc packs, preventing formation of an effective seal in the 10-in pipework. It was found that the annular clearance in the 8-in pipework was too small to allow for the 10-in seal discs, and the required proportion of the support discs, to compress into.

Fig.7. 8-in x 10-in pig: successful final design

The pig was subsequently re-designed and the prototype modified for further trials. A combination of radially grooved supports, arranged in a petal formation, was applied to support the pig in both diameters. Two 10-in seal discs were removed and the disc-pack spacing and body-flange positions were revised for compression in the 8-in pipework.

The pig was run through the test rig to fine-tune the disc diameters, with the end result being that the pig was found to be successful.

The 8-in x 10-in pig will be used to flood and dewater lines in the field. It was therefore a requirement to test the pig using gas as a pigging medium to dewater the test rig. The main criterion for the dewatering test was that the pig can be received into the 8-in pipe section with gas as the pigging medium. This test was carried out and design was again found to be successful.

Testing results

As stated in the previous section, the final pig design was found to be successful in the trials and was therefore validated as fit-for-purpose. The following information details the differential pressures in each feature for water-to-water pigging:

flip launch	= 8.0 bar
8-in pipework	= 7.5 bar
connector	= 15.6 bar
5D 90° bend	= 13.6 bar
10-in pipework	= 0.9 bar
pass through reducer	= 17.4 bar

The differential pressures were quite high in the 8-in diameter pipework due to the compression of the 10-in elements, with the main length of run having a differential as would be expected in this diameter.

The above results were mirrored with the air-water test exercises. The pig design was successfully launched and received in a number of field operations, and performed as required during these operations.

Summary

The process of pig design can be eased by the interaction between the client and the vendor in which a free flow of information is present. It is only under these circumstances that a true appreciation of the impact of line geometry upon the final pig design and operational capabilities can be gained. When developing a pigging tool suitable for a specific task, it is essential that knowledge of the operations to be carried out is held by both parties.

Dual and multi-diameter pigs have long been proven to be successful during validation testing and field usage. Each design diameter difference has to be approached and appraised on a case-by-case basis, with individual minor changes being considered together with the overall major change. The interaction of the changes with the features must also be considered for a suitable design solution to be engineered.

With the cost of pipeline recovery and deepwater operations, validation testing is a necessary step to ensure a successful design solution has been supplied, and the risk to the project has been reduced to as low as reasonably practicable.

Design and construction of a 42-in liquids'-pipeline batch-pig facility

by Robert W Kratsch, PE

Enbridge (US), Inc, Superior, WI, USA

ENBRIDGE'S CURRENT MAJOR expansion called Southern Access is a 42-in liquid crude oil pipeline running 321 miles from Superior, WI, to Delavan, WI, in 2008 and continuing another 133 miles to Flanagan, IL in 2009. As part of the goal to achieve and maintain a high quality pipeline system, an automated batch pig system was required to remotely launch the batch pigs, operated from the Control Centre in Edmonton, Alberta, Canada.

The project team has designed and developed a unique batch pig system that allows the loading and unloading of multiple pigs. The 42-in pigs can be remotely launched or received one at a time without having to open the pig launcher or receiver to atmosphere. These facilities allow pigs to be launched remotely, separating the various crude types being transported. The launcher and receiver have been designed to accommodate remote launching or receiving up to four pigs without having to open the traps. The facilities are designed for quick loading and unloading of the launcher and receiver to reduce the time the trap is open and reduce labour requirements. The receiving facilities incorporate pig washers and a pig maintenance shop to service the pigs as they are received. Specialized material handling equipment has been engineered to facilitate the safe and efficient movement of the pigs used for this operation. The launcher and receiver barrels can also be utilized for routine cleaning and inspection operations.

This paper discusses the key features and challenges of the design and construction of the batch pig systems implemented for the new 42-in liquids pipeline. Of particular interest are the practical requirements included in the design for operation of the facilities in a safe and efficient manner.

ENBRIDGE (US), INC, owns the US portion of the world's longest petroleum pipeline system. Combined with the Canadian portion of the pipeline system operated by Enbridge Pipelines, Inc, the system spans more than 8,000 miles (13,000km) from western Canada through the Great Lakes states, to eastern Canada. The total system transports over 2 million barrels of crude oil per day.

In today's competitive marketplace, it is crucial for pipeline companies to be prepared to quickly react and evaluate business expansion opportunities. To be successful, these evaluations must be efficient and accurate. Combined with the competitive nature of the business, regulatory demands are also becoming more complex and are demanding more from the pipeline developer.

For this expansion project, an automated batch pig system with remote launching capabilities was required for several major reasons:

- to provide a high-quality pipeline during operation by providing mechanical batch separation to prevent crude oil contamination during transportation

- to accommodate a high range of flow rates for the operation of the 42-in pipeline (400,000brl/d initially) and through various pipeline flow states (laminar or turbulent)
- to reduce labour requirements for the operation of the facilities.

Batch pig system design basis

The initial step for design of the batch pig facilities was to identify the key design parameters and capture them in a design basis. Among these major parameters required for the design were flow rates, crude characteristics, operating conditions, batch sizes, pig cleaning, and pig transportation. The pipeline flow rates and batch sizing played a critical role in determining the frequency of which the batch pigs are required to be launched and received. Knowing the number of batch pigs to be launched and received on a daily basis helped determine the size and layout of facilities to accommodate a safe workflow.

In developing the design basis, meetings were held with the project stakeholders to determine their requirements for the pipeline operation in order to meet industry demands. The primary stakeholders involved were pipeline control, petroleum quality, facilities management, shipper services, and regional operations. The key operational parameters identified were the following:

- the system was required to initially accommodate a nominal flow rate of 400,000brl/d (63,600cum/d) and capable to be easily expanded to run at a nominal flow rate of 600,000brl/d (95,400cum/d)
- minimum batch size of 63,000brl (10,000cum)
- provide true mechanical batch separation
- a launcher capable of remotely launching up to four batch pigs without reloading
- a receiver capable of receiving up to four batch pigs without unloading
- redundancy of critical systems, valves, pig signals, etc., to reduce maintenance and pipeline downtime
- pigs that could be handled relatively easily
- pigs that could be rebuilt easily
- ability to accommodate cleaning and in-line inspection tools
- reduce labour requirements for operation
- safety: overall system design to reduce the time the launcher or receiver doors are open to atmosphere during the loading or unloading operations.

Several logistical studies were performed to further develop the launcher and receiver design basis. A cycle-time study was performed to determine the time required for loading the pigs into the launcher and unloading the pigs from the receiver, and this was critical to determine the final design of the barrels and supporting equipment and operations' personnel requirements.

Also included in the initial studies were calculations for the number of pigs required for continuous operation based on several factors:

- number of pigs in the pipeline based on batch sizes
- number of pigs being washed and waiting for inspection or requiring repairs
- number of pigs in transit from the receiver site to the launcher site
- determination of a quantity required for a warehouse stock of pigs at the launcher facility.

At an initial flow rate of 400,000brl/d (63,600cum/day), the pigging frequency is anticipated to be approximately seven pigs launched per day assuming one pig at each batch interface with a minimum batch size of 63,000brl (10,000cum). Based on launching requirements and environmental conditions, it was determined that at least a four-day supply of batch pigs was required to be kept at the launching facility. This equates to one day's supply ready for launching and three days' supply on site just in case weather conditions do not permit transport of the batch pigs from the receiving site. Also factored in were the number pigs in transit between the sites and pigs waiting to be cleaned or rebuilt.

The areas around the launcher and receiver barrels were evaluated to determine the hazardous classifications. To maintain an overall unclassified area under the trap shelters, the shelters were designed as open as possible to keep them defined as 'open structures': this meant that there had to be 50% or more of the wall area open. This was accomplished by having walls only where needed to protect equipment and the operators from the weather. With this design, only specific pieces of equipment required hazardous classification limits. This design also defined hazardous boundaries at the receiver site to locate the cleaning equipment and rebuilding areas for the pigs.

Batch pig operations are not common for 42-in crude oil pipelines, and there are currently no templates for facilities to accommodate this type of operation. The design basis proved to be a very critical tool for the successful design of facilities.

Batch pig launcher and receiver system design

The overall design of the 42-in batch pigging system included a launcher, receiver, batch pigs, load and unload trays, trap drain and sump systems, pig washers, and automation for remote launching capabilities that could be integrated into current station control programming.

The design of the batch pig launcher and receiver was not a typical pig trap design. In the past, this type of batch system would incorporate the use of spherical pigs launched from an angled barrel launcher using one or more mechanically-actuated pins. The system proposed incorporated the basis of the spherical pig launching system, but utilized a specially-designed mandrel batch pig, pre-loaded four at a time and launched from a horizontal barrel [1].

Batch pigs have been used in automated systems before, but not typically on this large a pipe diameter, nor with this many preloaded pigs ready for launching. In an effort to provide the highest level of batch quality and reduce crude contamination as much as possible, the decision was made to use multi-lip cups in a disc-cup or DC-DC construction. Many modifications were made to the pig body: it was extended beyond the second disc-cup set to provide proper spacing of the pigs in the launcher; holes were added to the end of the body in a special pattern to allow better fluid flow from the kicker lines in the launcher for launching the pig and for increased draining of the crude oil out of the pig body in the receiver trap; and a bumper was added to the front of the pig in order to allow stacking of the pigs within the trap barrels. The 42-in diameter batch pigs weigh approximately 980lbs and are 75in long (Fig.1). Once the design of the batch pig was completed, the launching and receiving system could be designed.

The launcher barrel design (Fig.2) incorporated the capability to remotely launch up to four pigs. The launcher incorporates multiple kicker lines, electrically-actuated pins in front of each pig, and pig signals to detect what position the pigs are in and to detect a successful launch. The kicker lines are sized and positioned at the tail end of the pigs to provide the necessary flow and differential pressure to launch the pigs. The electrically-actuated pins are positioned in front of each pig in the barrel to prevent a pig from prematurely launching. The pig signals are positioned on the trap to detect the launch position of each pig in the barrel; signals are also located downstream of the

Fig. 1. Specialized batch pig.

launcher and mainline by-pass tee to detect a successful pig launch. The launcher is capable of holding up to five pigs when the barrel is fully loaded: the first four pigs in the barrel are positioned for launching while the fifth pig, which is closest to the barrel closure, is loaded into the launcher to serve as a spacer and to be pre-warmed in the event of an immediate launch when the trap is reloaded. This pre-warming feature helps to prevent the urethane cups and discs from being too hard and not pliable to properly seal inside the 42-in pipe when cold weather (-20°F) is experienced at the location of the launcher.

A load tray was fabricated to assist with loading the pigs into the launcher barrel, and consists of a tray with wheels that move on a track to allow it to be lined-up to the barrel and a mechanical pusher mechanism to insert the pigs a specified distance into the barrel. The pigs are inserted into the launcher one at a time, and the pusher ensures that each pig loaded into the barrel is properly positioned between the kicker lines, pig signals, and pins as it is inserted into the launcher.

The receiver barrel design (Fig.3) incorporated the capability to receive up to four pigs without unloading, and was designed to allow the full flow rate of the pipeline through the receiver to receive the pigs. This design required two by-pass outlets from the barrel to the by-pass piping. The receiver also incorporates an internal tray to receive the pigs and to facilitate removal of the pigs from the barrel. Pig signals are positioned upstream of the receiver, and on the receiver barrel to detect a pig entering the receiver. The redundancy of the pig signals helps to ensure that a pig has successfully entered the receiver.

An unload tray was fabricated to assist with unloading the pigs from the receiver barrel. The unload tray consists of a tray with grooved wheels that move on a track to allow for line-up to the barrel, and a winch to remove the internal tray loaded with pigs. This winch is also used to insert the empty internal tray into the receiver barrel.

A trap drain skid was developed to assist with draining the launcher and receiver barrels. The trap drain skid incorporates a high volume/low pressure pump and several electrically-actuated valves to drain the trap to the sump tank. The pump is used to quickly drain the barrel to help reduce

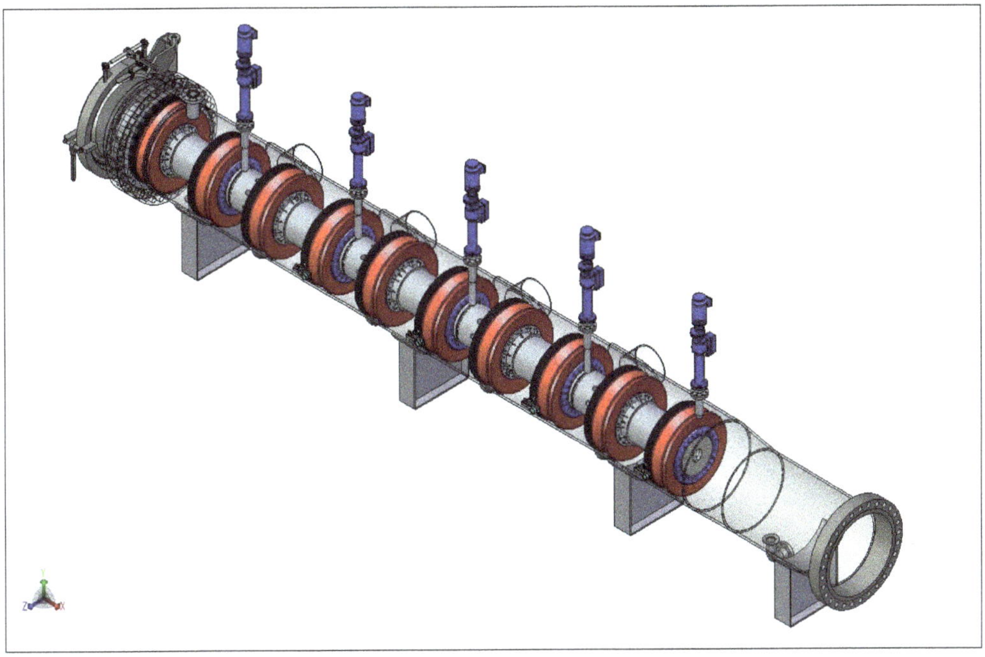

Fig.2. Launcher isometric drawing.

the cycle time for loading or unloading the traps. If for any reason the pump is not operational, a by-pass valve on the skid can be opened to allow for gravity drain of the barrel to the sump tank.

One other important feature incorporated into the design of the launcher and receiver was the closure. A review of past trap failures indicated that not being able to properly close the closure door after it has been opened played a significant part in pipeline downtime associated with pigging facilities. In light of this, a flanged closure was implemented using the closure welded to

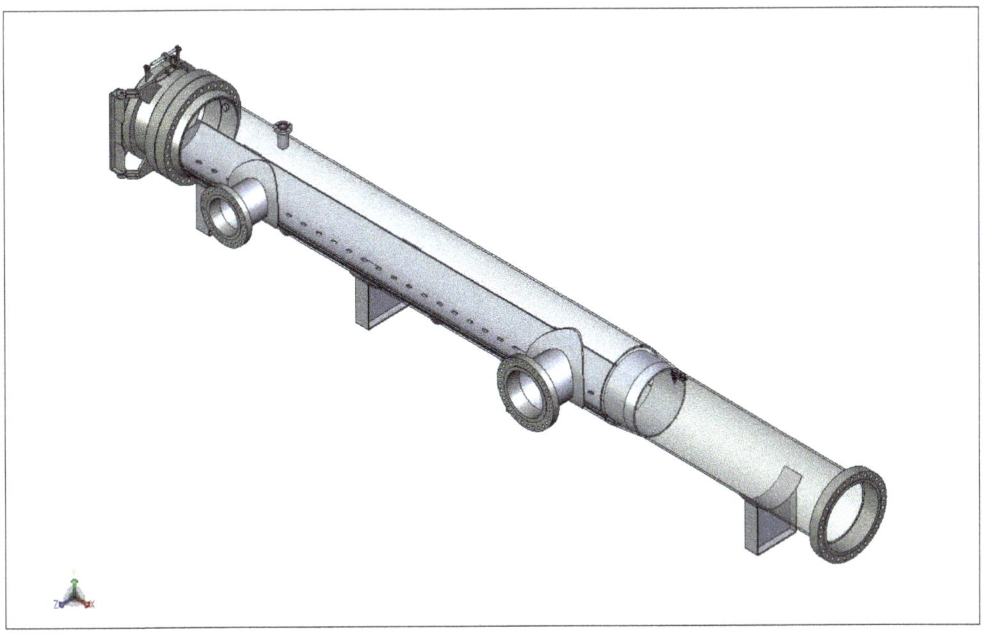

Fig.3. Receiver isometric drawing.

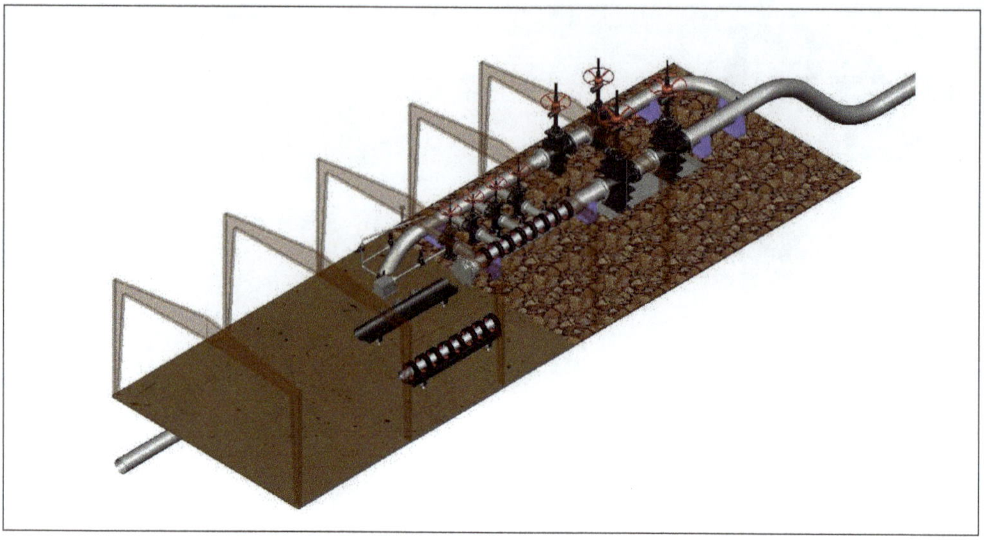

Fig.4. Launcher site conceptual layout.

a flange. Spare closures were purchased and located at each site, allowing the closure to be changed out in its entirety when a major closure issue arises. It also reduces the pipeline downtime and time when the batch pigs can not be launched or received.

Batch pig facility design and layout

To help achieve the goals that the design basis described, the equipment required at each facility had to be identified, quantified and, in a few cases, invented. The design team conducted several brainstorming sessions to evaluate conceptual facility layouts to optimize handling efficiencies when loading the launcher barrel and unloading the receiver barrel.

The initial facility layouts were based on the requirements of the design basis, site constraints and the climates where the facilities were located. Since batch pig facilities of this size and scale do not exist, several options were explored for the launcher and receiver site layouts.

Launcher facility

The launcher site incorporated the aspects of storing the batch pigs and staging them to be easily accessed during the loading of the launcher.

Many factors were taken into account to develop the launcher site. Work flow patterns by the launcher operators and maintenance groups were evaluated to determine the proper layout of the launcher, direction of the closure door swing, access requirements, protection from weather, controls location, storing of equipment, and emergency access.

Safety of the operators to load the launcher was top priority. Due to the large size and weight of the batch pigs, lifting and handling the pigs required forklifts and overhead bridge cranes to assist the operators. The physical size of the pigs and the use of machinery to handle the pigs necessitated more space to operate around the launcher.

Other considerations specific to the design of the launching site were redundant valves on the

Fig.5. Launcher site final layout.

mainline and by-pass piping to reduce maintenance downtime, dedicated sump tank for draining the launcher for loading operations, a shelter over the launcher to allow operations in harsh weather, and specialized lifting and handling equipment to move the batch pigs. With all the design parameters, site constraints, and major logistical considerations taken into account, the conceptual layout was developed (Fig.4), and included a shelter (approximately 50ft x100ft) that included an overhead bridge crane to lift the pigs and a drive bay for trucks to drive through and unload the pigs. The layout allowed for access to all the major equipment that would need maintenance or repair. The larger diameter valves were located outside of the shelter to facilitate easier maintenance or removal. The launcher barrel was located so the closure was covered and protected from the elements and to allow for 24/7 operations even in harsh weather conditions.

There were very few design changes from conceptual design of the launcher facility to the final detailed design (Fig.5), the major ones being:

- the launcher by-pass piping was routed outside the building to eliminate piping under the concrete floor
- a dedicated double-walled fibreglass sump tank was added for draining the launcher barrel
- platforms were added for access to the large-diameter valves for maintenance of the actuators
- a wall with large overhead doors was added to the north side of the shelter to allow for protection from the prevailing winds and elements while providing access to the launcher.

Receiver facility

The receiver site incorporated many pieces of equipment and work areas, including a pig receiver, an unloading tray, washing facilities, pig rebuilding and maintenance shop, storage of the pigs, and loading of the pigs for transport to the launcher site. The receiver was designed for the same flow parameters and frequency of receiving pigs as the launcher site. There are no intermediate launching and receiving traps for the initial 321 miles of 42-in pipeline.

Similar to the launcher site, many factors were taken into account, including evaluating work flow patterns by the receiver operators and maintenance groups to determine the proper layout of the receiver and building orientation, as well as the direction of the closure door swing, access

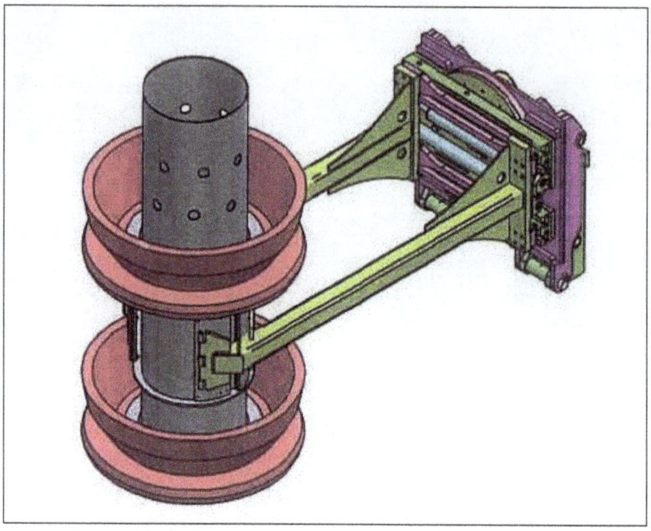

Fig.6a. Specialized pig-handling device (conceptual design).

Fig.6b. Specialized pig-handling device (mounted on forklift).

requirements, protection from weather, controls location, storing of equipment, and emergency access.

Operator safety during the receiver unloading procedure was top priority. Due to the large size and weight of the batch pigs, a specialized forklift-mounted pig-handling device was designed and fabricated specifically for the pigs. The device was fabricated to handle the pigs by the pig body, therefore, so as not to damage the cups or discs. This device provides safe means for handling the pigs at the facility (Figs 6a and 6b).

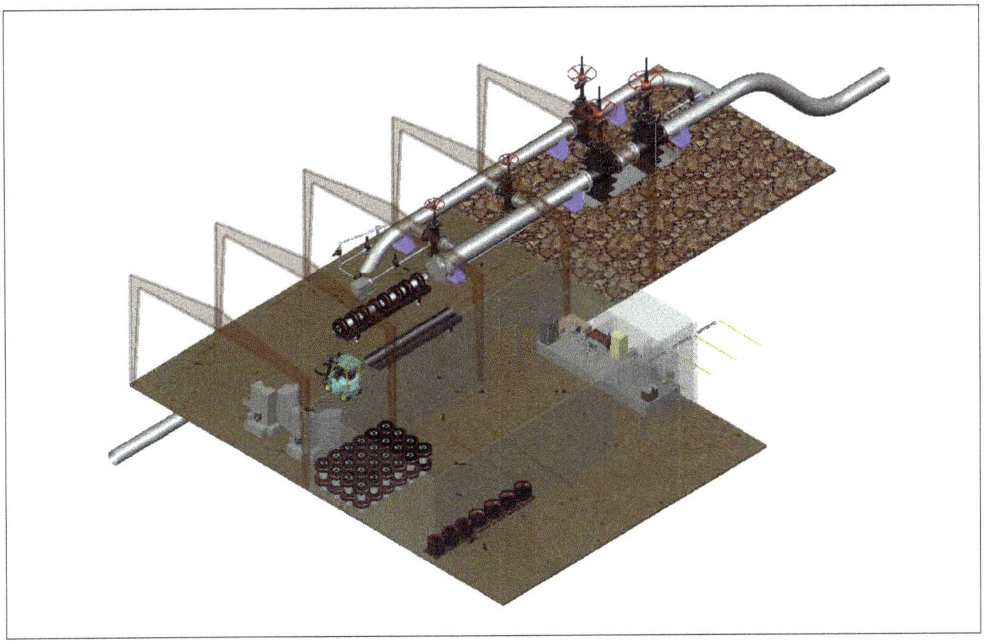

Fig.7. Receiver site conceptual layout.

Other considerations specific to the design of the receiver site were redundant valves on the mainline to reduce maintenance downtime, a dedicated sump tank for draining the receiver during unloading operations, a shelter over the receiver to allow operations in harsh weather, a wastewater tank for pig cleaning, a building for maintenance, storage and rebuilding the pigs, and an area for loading the pigs on a truck for transport to the launcher site. One major design consideration was that the receiver site will only be used for approximately 18 months, after which construction of the mainline pipe to the Flanagan Terminal in Illinois will have been completed. With all the design parameters, site constraints, and major considerations taken into account, the conceptual layout was developed (Fig.7).

The receiver conceptual layout included a shelter (approximately 50ft x 100ft) that included an overhead bridge crane to lift the pigs, space for the pig washers and a 36-ft x 75-ft shop area for rebuilding and storing the pigs. There was also a drive-through area for loading the pigs on trailers for transport to the launcher site. This layout allowed for access to all the major equipment that would need servicing. The larger-diameter valves were located outside of the shelter to facilitate easier maintenance or removal. The receiver barrel was located under the shelter area and out of the elements as much as possible to allow for 24/7 operations even in harsh weather conditions.

The receiver site layout (Fig.8) changed significantly from conceptual design ideas to the final detailed design. The major changes were:

- the receiver facility was mirrored to accommodate the site conditions, to reduce noise transmission to neighbours and to shelter the receiver from the prevailing winds
- the receiver by-pass piping was routed outside the building to eliminate piping under the concrete floor
- dedicated double-walled fibreglass sump tanks were installed to drain the receiver barrel; based on high bedrock elevations, two tanks were incorporated to reduce the depth of rock removal

Fig.8. Receiver site final layout.

- the 42-in mainline pipe routeing through the site was modified to allow for future removal of the receiver barrel, by-pass piping, and associated equipment
- platforms were added for access to the large-diameter valves for maintenance of the actuators
- a fabric shelter was chosen to be installed over the receiver barrel and pig washers for ease of future removal
- a jib crane was chosen as a backup to the fork lift in place of the overhead bridge crane to assist with removal of the pigs from the unloading tray.

Design of operational sequencing and automation

The operation for launching and receiving the batch pigs is designed to be controlled remotely from the pipeline system Control Centre in Edmonton, Alberta, Canada (over 2200km away). However, the loading of the batch pigs into the launcher and unloading the batch pigs from the receiver will still be a task that is performed by the local operations and maintenance groups.

Extensive studies were performed to determine the procedures for loading and unloading the traps. Operational sequencing documents were created with the design of the equipment and facilities to ensure the overall facility functionality is safe and efficient. These documents were key to ensure a functional facility that would meet the established design basis.

The launcher is automated for the Control Centre to remotely launch the batch pigs at the batch interfaces. The design team's automation and controls group created a logic sequence that was developed into the programming to operate the facilities and launch the batch pigs. An operational sequence document was developed which identified the steps required to load the pigs into the launcher by the local operations group at the launcher facility. Some of the steps required to do this are: depressurizing, draining, loading the pigs, refilling, and equalizing pressure in the launcher with the mainline.

The operation of the launcher is initiated when the normal operation of the pipeline is by-passing the launcher, and the trap has at least one batch pig in launch position. When a batch interface is detected upstream of the launcher, a signal is sent to the Control Centre operator to start the batch pig launch sequence. The launch sequence automatically cycles various valves at the facility in a predetermined order to divert the flow through the corresponding kicker line and launch the

Fig.9. Launcher site under construction (launcher barrel).

Fig.10. Launcher site under construction (shelter and platforms at mainline valves).

pig into the pipeline. When a successful launch is detected by the pig signals downstream of the trap, the valves are cycled back to their original position and the system is prepared to launch the next pig. Once all the pigs are launched, a signal will alert local operations that the trap is empty and needs to be reloaded.

The launcher-loading sequence is a manual operation with logic incorporated into various controls to ensure safe operation of the workers to load the launcher. Prior to opening the launcher barrel, it needs to be depressurized, drained, and then checked to make sure that all the fluid has drained properly. With this done, the launcher closure can be opened. To load the pigs, the load tray is pushed up to the face of the open launcher and secured in place. The pigs are then

Fig. 11. Receiver site under construction (receiver and jib crane).

loaded on the tray using the overhead bridge crane and pushed into the launcher. This step is repeated until the desired number of pigs is loaded into the launcher. When the pigs are in the launcher, the closure is closed and the barrel is filled and pressurized. When the launcher is fully pressurized, the valves around the launcher can be cycled to return the launcher to the 'ready to launch' state. The pig signals on the launcher barrel will indicate the number of pigs in the launcher that are ready to be launched and their position.

The receiver is designed for normal pipeline flow through the receiver and out the multiple by-pass lines. With this design, it is always ready to receive a batch pig until it is full and placed in by-pass mode. The design team's automation and controls group created a logic sequence that was developed into the programming to operate the facilities and accurately count the batch pigs as they enter the receiver. An operational sequence document was also developed which identifies all the steps required to unload the pigs from the receiver by the local operations group, some of which are: depressurizing, draining, unloading the pigs, moving the pigs from the internal tray, refilling, and equalizing pressure in the receiver with the mainline.

The operation of the receiver is initiated when the normal operation of the pipeline is flowing through the receiver and the trap has less than four batch pigs in launch position. When a batch pig enters the receiver barrel from the mainline, it is detected by the pig signals upstream of the receiver barrel and on the receiver barrel. The pig signal redundancy helps to detect whether a pig has been successfully received or is stuck upstream of the receiver. The pigs are counted by the pig signals until there are four pigs in the receiver. When the third and fourth pigs are received, a signal is sent to the local operations group that the trap is nearly full, then full, and needs to be unloaded. At this point, the Control Centre cycles the valves to place the receiver in by-pass mode.

The receiver unloading sequence is a manual operation with logic incorporated into various controls to ensure safe operation of the workers to unload the receiver. Prior to opening the receiver barrel, it is depressurized, drained, and then checked to make sure that all the fluid has drained properly. With this complete, the receiver closure can be opened. To unload the pigs, the unload tray is pushed up to the face of the open receiver and secured in place. The pigs are unloaded from the receiver using a winch attached to the unload tray that pulls the internal tray

Fig. 12. Receiver site under construction (maintenance building).

Fig. 13. Receiver site under construction (receiver shelter).

out of the barrel. Then the pigs are removed from the tray using a forklift with the specialized handling apparatus. When all the pigs are removed from the tray, the winch is used to pull the internal tray into the receiver. The closure is closed and the barrel filled and pressurized. When the receiver is fully pressurized, the appropriate valves are cycled to return the pipeline to flow through the receiver. The pig signals on the receiver barrel will be reset to indicate the receiver is empty and ready to receive pigs.

Batch pig facility construction

The construction of the batch pig facilities encountered several risks involved throughout the construction process that proved challenging. The major challenges that were identified in the construction process were: materials, site and access constraints, and winter construction.

1. Material availability and deliveries were key in the sequencing of construction activities. The launcher and receiver barrels, trap drain skid, sump re-injection skid, load tray and

unload tray were fabricated off-site. The goal was to have the launcher and receiver barrels at each site prior to major construction activities to allow for on-site fabrication and construction to be focused around these major pieces of equipment.

The large 42-in and 36-in valves at each site were also very critical pieces of equipment. These were ordered over 42 weeks prior to construction and proved to be a critical path item to tie all the piping systems together to the launcher and receiver barrels.

2. The launcher site conditions were complicated by construction of the adjacent pump station facility that feeds the batch pig facility. Due to later-than-expected receipt of permits, the construction schedule of the pump station was delayed and caused an overlap of construction activities for the pump station and batch pig facilities. This overlap caused resource constraints for construction of both facilities. Through resource management and identification of the critical path items, a schedule was developed to construct the facilities to achieve a 'ready for service' date that maintained project schedule objectives.

   The receiver site conditions were complicated by the high elevation of the bedrock at the site. The high bedrock elevation posed issues with setting the piping and achieving proper compaction of the soils under the equipment and building footings. To help eliminate the compaction issues, the equipment and building concrete footings were raised by a foot. This allowed for a thicker cushion below the piping and concrete footings to the bedrock.

   The newly-constructed adjacent pump station caused site constraints and limited access for multiple trades to work in the area. Only one trade could work in one area at a time. This extended the schedule for installation of the receiver barrel, piping systems, and maintenance building.

3. Winter construction conditions added complexity to both the launcher and receiver sites. Typically, construction activities are limited in the winter. However, due to the overall pipeline construction schedule constraints, the construction had to continue through the harsh Wisconsin winter. Both sites used ground-thaw systems and temporary heated shelters to install the concrete foundations. A glycol mix was used for hydrostatic testing the piping systems during below-freezing weather.

Facility commissioning

A commissioning team was assembled to perform a physical check of all the mechanical and electrical equipment at each facility. A functional check was also performed for the programming that was created to run the facilities.

The commissioning of the batch pig facilities encountered several difficulties throughout the process. The major challenges were:

- tracking changes during the design and construction process to ensure the facilities were constructed correctly
- working with new equipment specifically created for these facilities
- working with a new automation sequence and control programs
- commissioning as equipment within the facilities were installed and not at the end of construction once the whole facilities were complete.

As a final commissioning activity, the local operations team conducted several dry-runs of the launching and receiving systems to verify the logic sequencing, equipment operation and functionality of the facilities. These dry-runs also proved valuable to assist with the creation of detailed operation and training manuals.

Summary

The 42-in liquids pipeline batch pig facility has been a multi-faceted experience of innovation and problem-solving from development of the design basis to the commissioning of the facilities. Determination of the design parameters along with the establishment of the project schedule served as the foundation and the framework used to focus efforts toward the completed product. Specialized batch pigs, innovative pig traps, unique material handling devices, and custom automation and control systems worked in concert to achieve the end goals of pipeline product integrity and reduced operator labour.

Work flow patterns, on-site conditions, safety needs, and future maintenance concerns were factors that helped guide the construction project from conceptual graphics to detail design. Overall, material availability, site situations, access constraints, and weather conditions proved to be the areas of major risk and concern during the construction phase of this endeavour. Finally, commissioning of these facilities was challenging and rewarding as this first-of-a-kind batch pig system neared operation.

Acknowledgements

LHB Engineers & Architects, Duluth, MN.
T.D. Williamson, Inc., Tulsa, OK.

References

1. Chritian J Cloyde, 2008. Automating batch pigging. *PipeLine and Gas Technology*. T.D. Williamson, Inc., Tulsa, OK, March.

Ethanol transportation: status of research, and integrity management

by Dr John Beavers[1], Patrick Vieth[1], and Dr Narasi Sridhar[2]

1 CC Technologies, Inc (a DNV Company), Dublin, OH, USA
2 DNV Research and Innovation, Dublin, OH, USA

THE PIPELINE INDUSTRY is undertaking considerable research to determine the best approach to manage the potential for internal stress-corrosion cracking (SCC) to occur while transporting fuel-grade ethanol (FGE). Based on the results to date, it appears that FGE meeting the ASTM D 4806 specification can cause SCC of carbon steel. The parameters that affect the potential for SCC (oxygen, water, etc.) are understood, and the research is now focused on methods to reduce the likelihood of SCC. The current state of the research is discussed.

THE US Energy Policy Act of 2005 (amended in 2007) established a nationwide renewable fuels standard starting from 15 billion litres (4 billion gallons) of all biofuels in 2006 to 136 billion litres (36 billion gallons) in 2022. Ethanol will constitute almost 90% of this renewable fuel. As the price of gasoline has oscillated, the economic viability of alternative fuels also is undergoing re-evaluation. However, the long-term need for biofuels, both for reducing gasoline dependence and carbon footprint, is undeniable. Biofuels can be broadly classified into several generations depending on their status of commercial production readiness. The ethanol produced from sugars (such as sugar cane, beets, and grapes) and starch (corn, wheat) is considered to be a first-generation biofuel. The production techniques for these feedstocks are well established, and world-wide commercial production of ethanol from these sources was approximately 50 billion litres (13.2 billion gallons) in 2008.

The ethanol produced from grasses (such as switch grass), agricultural/food processing wastes, and other cellulosic materials requires enzyme treatments that will require significant additional process development. The ethanol (or alcohol) from these sources is referred to as second-generation ethanol (and also as cellulosic ethanol). A further development in alcohol production will be the use of transgenic materials (low-lignin trees), which will require advanced enzymatic treatments, and the resulting alcohols will be the third-generation cellulosic fuel. A somewhat similar categorization exists for biodiesel production.

The ethanol supply chain is illustrated in Fig.1. Ethanol is produced in bio-refineries and must be transported to terminals, where it is blended with gasoline to produce the most commonly used blends E-10 (10% ethanol) and E-85 (85% ethanol). As shown in Fig.1, rail and truck are currently the predominant means of transporting ethanol in North America. Brazil has a history of transporting ethanol via pipelines and ships. In terms of the volumes transportable by the different modes shown in Fig.1, one barge load is roughly equivalent to 15 to 20 rail cars or 60-80 truck loads. In comparison, a 16-in pipeline can transport an equivalent of 15 barges on a daily basis. The number of new rail cars constructed has to rise substantially, and new terminals that can accommodate unit train shipments have to be constructed, to allow rail shipment of the future anticipated fuel volumes. Barge transport can benefit substantially by a pipeline delivery system, while increasing the truck transportation poses significant logistical problems, including training a much larger number of drivers than anticipated to be available in the future. Thus, pipeline transportation is the most cost-effective mode of transporting large volumes of ethanol.

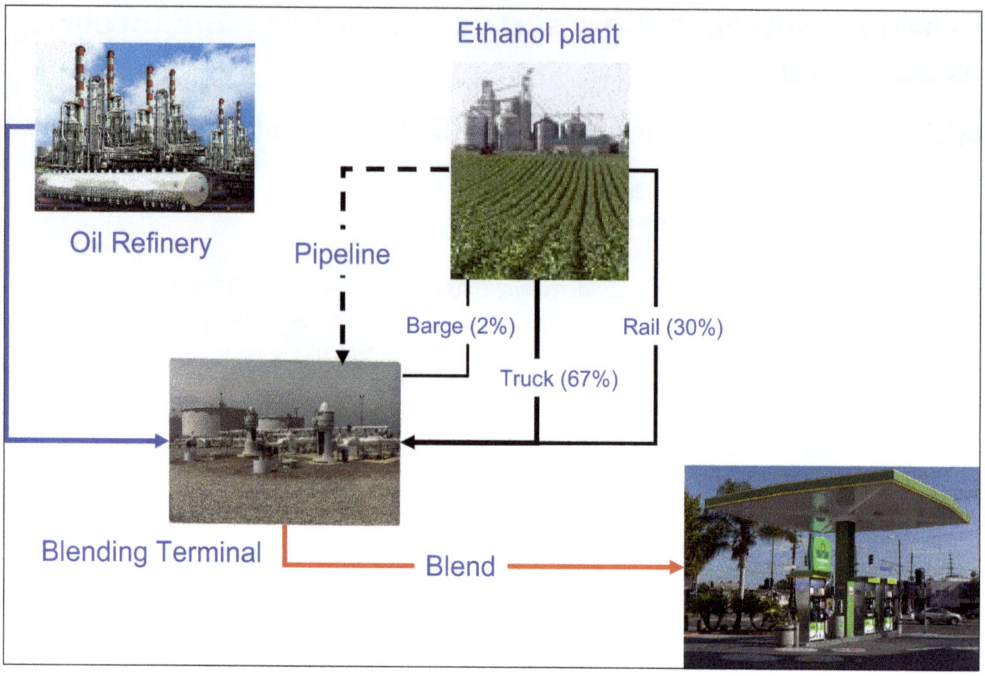

Fig. 1. Ethanol supply chain for North America.

Figure 2 shows that most of the bio-refineries in the US are located close to the middle of the continent, whereas the population centres are along the coasts. Most of the current hydrocarbon pipelines move products from the Gulf of Mexico region to the east and west coast and the midwest. Thus, new pipelines will be required to transport the fuel-grade ethanol (FGE) from the bio-refineries to the population centres.

Background

A surve of published literature and service experience with SCC in FGE was published by the American Petroleum Institute (API) in 2003 [1]. Documented SCC failures of equipment in users' storage and transportation facilities have dated back to the early 1990s: the majority of the cracking has been found at locations near welds where the primary stresses leading to SCC have been residual welding stresses. No cases of SCC were reported in ethanol manufacturer facilities, tanker trucks, railroad tanker cars, or barges, or following blending the FGE with gasoline. All occurrences of SCC were at the first major hold point (the FGE distribution terminal) or in the subsequent end-user gasoline-blending and -distribution terminals.

An example of SCC in terminal piping is shown in Fig.3: note that the leak is near a girth weld adjacent to a piping tee.

The API survey did not pinpoint what causes ethanol SCC, but the failure history suggests that the SCC may be related to changes in the FGE as it moves through the distribution chain over a period of days, weeks, or months. These observations led to an industry-sponsored research programme to identify the causative factors. A 'Roadmapping Workshop' held in October, 2007, identified a number of research gaps in safely transporting FGE via pipelines [2], which were divided into four areas:

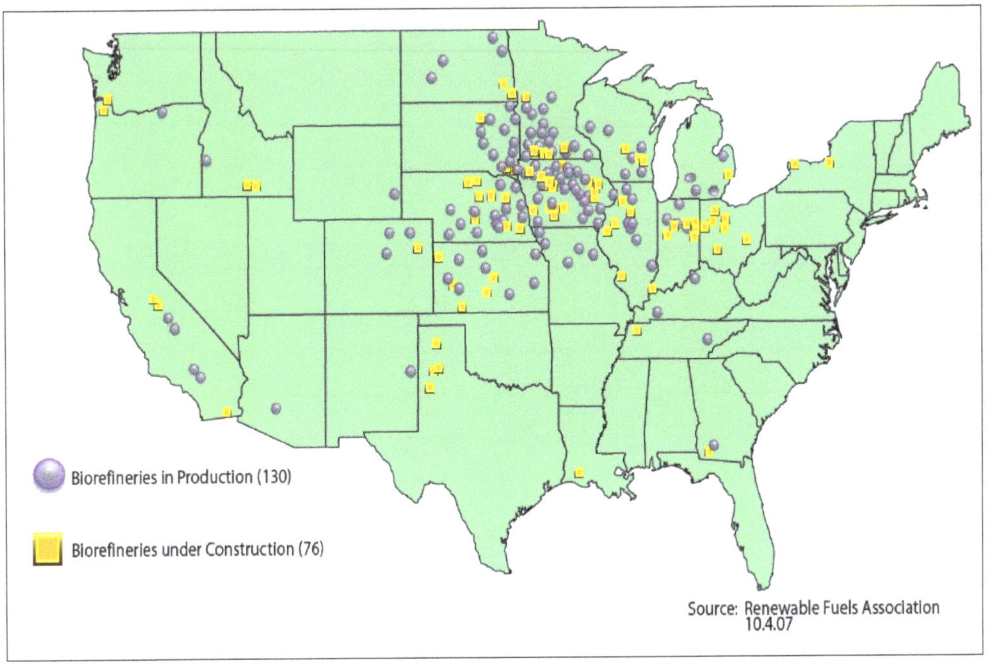

Fig.2. Ethanol production locations in the US.

Fig.3. SCC observed in terminal piping system containing FGE.

(i) ethanol sources and quality,
(ii) pipeline operations,
(iii) standards, guidelines, and training, and
(iv) pipeline integrity.

Ethanol SCC potentially impacts all four of these areas and research is continuing or planned to address these gaps. A number of factors were identified as contributors to SCC, and SCC-mitigation strategies are being developed. This paper summarizes the current state of the research.

Requirement	ASTM Limits *	
	Minimum	Maximum
Ethanol, vol. %	92.1	-
Methanol, vol. %	-	0.5
Solvent-washed gum, mg/100 ml	-	5.0
Water content, vol. %	-	1.0
Denaturant content, vol. %	1.96	4.76
Inorganic chloride, ppm (mg/L)	-	40 (32)
Copper, mg/kg	-	0.1
Acidity (as Acetic Acid CH3COOH), mass % (mg/L)	-	0.007 (56)
pHe	6.5	9.0

Table 1. Specification of fuel-grade ethanol.

Environmental factors affecting SCC in FGE

The results of research on chemistry effects on SCC have demonstrated that FGE that meets applicable API standards (Table 1) is a potent cracking agent in the presence of oxygen [3, 4]. Several research programmes have examined the effects of the contaminants (such as chloride) or the denaturant in FGE on SCC behaviour in aerated ethanol solutions. Studies by Sridhar *et al.* [5] and Beavers *et al.* [6] showed that chloride significantly increased the susceptibility of carbon steels to SCC in ethanol. Furthermore, the fracture mode changed from predominantly intergranular to predominantly transgranular as the chloride concentration increased from 0 to 40ppm. Methanol also appeared to increase SCC susceptibility [5]. The water content of the FGE has also been shown to affect the SCC behaviour: anhydrous ethanol will not promote SCC [4] and water contents above about 4.5% by volume completely inhibit SCC [7]. Between these limits, water does not appear to have a significant effect on SCC [5, 7].

Factors that have not been shown to have a significant influence on SCC in FGE include acidity, one common general corrosion inhibitor, and the denaturant [4, 5]. SCC was observed in SSR tests over a wide range of pHE and acetic acid concentration. Sridhar *et al.* [5] showed that one common corrosion inhibitor added to FGE to protect against automotive corrosion (*Octel DCI-11*) did not have any effect on SCC of steel.

A statistically-designed study by Sridhar *et al.* [5] showed that dissolved oxygen is the most important factor affecting SCC in FGE: no SCC occurred under any circumstances without the presence of dissolved oxygen. Based on the oxygen concentration, a "critical" potential regime was identified for SCC [8], Fig.4, which depends on chloride concentration. In the presence of chlorides, SCC extends to lower corrosion potentials.

At high corrosion potentials in some ethanols, SCC was not observed, and the reason for this behaviour is still unclear. Beavers *et al.* [6] showed that removing oxygen by chemical, mechanical, or electrochemical methods all resulted in suppression of SCC in slow-strain-rate (SSR) tests in a simulated FGE. Oxygen removal also caused a negative potential shift in the free corrosion potential, as shown in Fig.5. It is well known that dissolved oxygen increases SCC susceptibility of steel in other non-aqueous environments, such as ammonia and methanol. Therefore, it is not surprising that dissolved oxygen is a major contributor to SCC in FGE.

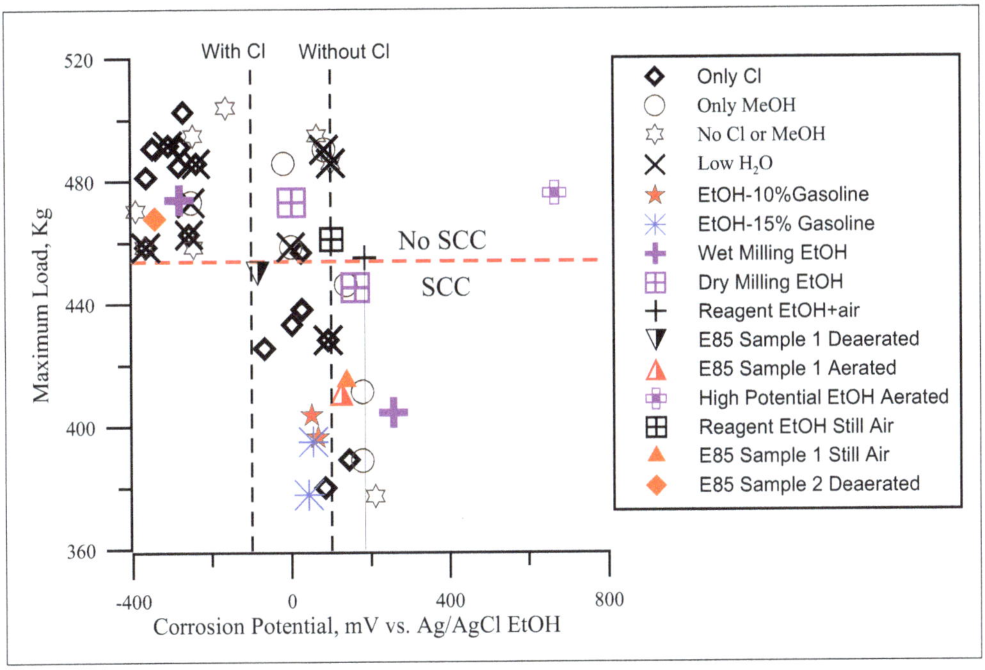

Fig.4. SCC vs corrosion potential indicating a critical potential (dependent on chloride level) below which SCC was not observed [8].

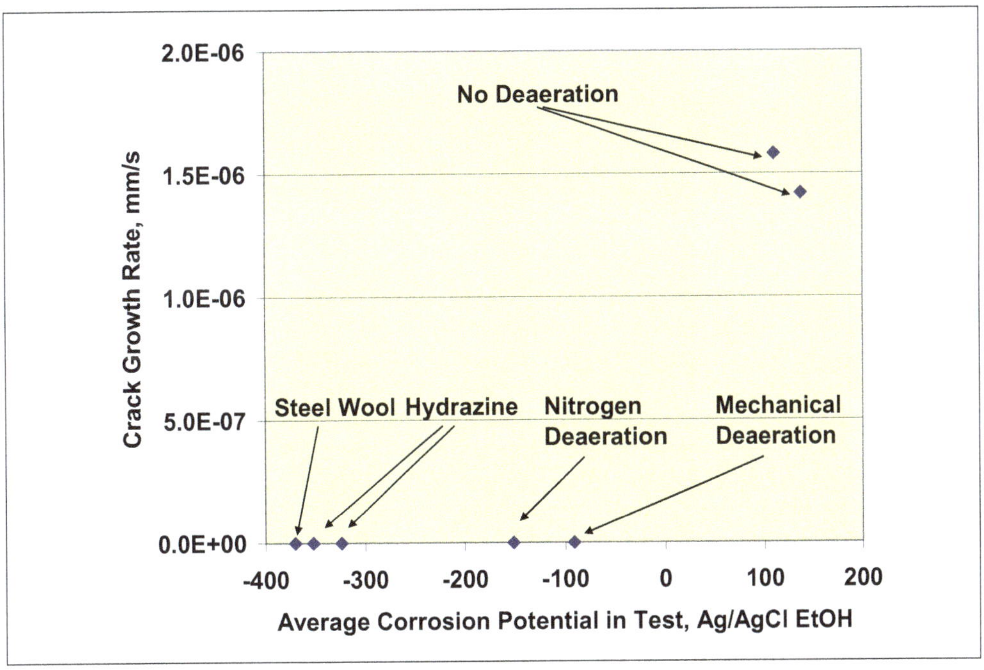

Fig.5. Crack growth rate as a function of average potential for SSR tests in simulated FGE with various deaeration methods [6].

The earlier research, funded by API, demonstrated that FGE as well as E-85 (85% ethanol - 15% gasoline) promoted SCC [4]. More recently, Beavers *et al.* [9] evaluated the effect of ethanol-gasoline blend ratio on SCC in a research project funded by PRCI. The study was performed with

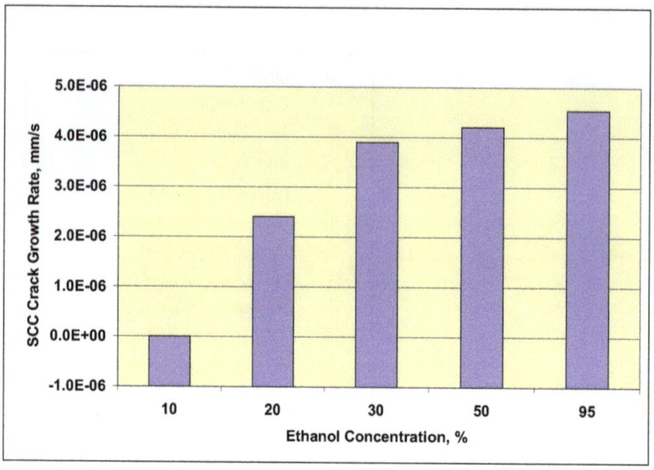

Fig.6. Crack growth rate as a function of ethanol concentration for X-46 linepipe steel specimens tested in simulated FGE-gasoline blends [9].

notched SSR specimens of an X-46 linepipe steel in a simulated FGE. No SCC was observed in gasoline or E-10 (10% ethanol blend), but SCC susceptibility increased rapidly with increasing ethanol concentration for E-20 and higher blends. Surprisingly, E-30 was nearly as susceptible to SCC as FGE, as shown in Fig.6.

Studies [8, 9] have shown that no two ethanols are created equally in terms of SCC tendency. Some ethanols do not cause SCC even at high dissolved oxygen levels; others cause significant SCC. Aging of ethanol samples appears to alter their SCC tendency significantly. The variations in the ethanol chemistry and their impact on SCC behaviour are the subject of ongoing studies.

Metallurgical factors affecting ethanol SCC

Field experience and laboratory testing indicate that severe straining is required for ethanol SCC to occur. SCC of ethanol storage tanks has been observed only in severely-strained areas associated with non-post weld heat-treated welds and/or in tanks with design/installation issues [1]. For example, floor areas that were not adequately supported experienced SCC as a consequence of cyclic loading from filling and withdrawal of ethanol. Some of the earliest laboratory studies of SCC in ethanol were conducted using U-bend specimens. SCC was not observed in these tests unless a "bad" welding bead perpendicular to the stressing direction and an extremely severe bending mode were included. In SSR tests with un-notched specimens, SCC was observed near the necked region of the specimen [6]; notched-SSR tests exhibited SCC at the notch root [9]. All these observations suggest that severe plastic deformation and the presence of dynamic plastic strain are necessary for SCC to occur. In more-recent crack-growth tests using compact tension specimens, the presence of a cyclic loading component has been shown to exacerbate SCC [7].

Recent studies reported by Beavers *et al.* [9] have shown that the extent of SCC was not dependent on steel grade ranging from X-42 high frequency electric-resistance welded pipe material to cast steel for pumps. For one grade, the weld area of a double submerged arc weld appeared to be slightly more resistant to SCC than the base metal.

Mitigation of ethanol SCC

The field experience and research results specifically addressing ethanol SCC, as well as broader experience with other forms of SCC in the pipeline and other industries, point to potentially-effective methods for mitigation of ethanol SCC. The research on oxygen effects on ethanol SCC clearly demonstrates that, regardless of how the oxygen is removed, SCC can be mitigated. Both mechanical deaeration and one chemical oxygen scavenger were shown to be effective. It is probable that the oxygen is absorbed in the ethanol during the transportation process and it might be possible to minimize oxygen contamination, as opposed to removing it once it is already in the ethanol.

True SCC inhibitors also potentially could be effective. Research by Beavers *et al.* [6] showed that some film-forming amines have an inhibiting effect on ethanol SCC. The identification of the best possible inhibitors or inhibitor packages, taking into consideration diverse issues such as toxicity, compatibility with combustion engines, cost etc., requires further research.

The association of SCC in the terminals with residual stresses provides another mitigation avenue for new ethanol pipelines. Post-weld heat treatment of all welds could minimize SCC, although the hoop stresses from the internal pressure in transmission pipeline might play a bigger role in the SCC process. Grit blasting prior to coating has been shown to play a role in the mitigation of external SCC of gas transmission pipelines [10]. The compressive residual stress imparted by the grit blasting process has been shown to effectively overcome the effects of residual stresses and the tensile hoop stress from internal pressurization. A similar process might be effective for the mitigation of ethanol SCC.

Summary

Large increases in production and transportation volumes of FGE are expected as a result of new energy policies dictating substantially-higher usage of alternate fuels. Ethanol has been shown to cause SCC of steel in the presence of dissolved oxygen and chloride. Significant advances have been made in understanding the various parameters that can affect SCC and in identifying mitigation strategies. Going forward, this information will be needed to manage the integrity of ethanol pipelines.

References

1. R.D.Kane and J.G.Maldonado, 2003. Stress corrosion cracking of carbon steel in fuel grade ethanol: review and survey. API Technical Report 939-D, American Petroleum Institute, Washington, DC, September.
2. Energetics, Inc., 2007. Safe and reliable ethanol transportation and storage technology roadmapping workshop, October 25-26, Dublin, Ohio.
3. R.D.Kane, N.Sridhar, M.Brongers, J.A.Beavers, A.K.Agrawal, and L.Klein, 2005. *Materials Performance*, **44**, 12.
4. R.D.Kane, D.Eden, N.Sridhar, J.Maldonado, M.P.H.Brongers, A.K.Agrawal, and J.A.Beavers, 2007. Stress corrosion cracking of carbon steel in fuel grade ethanol: review, experience survey, field monitoring, and laboratory testing. API Technical Report 939-D, 2nd Edn, American Petroleum Institute, Washington, DC, May.
5. N.Sridhar, K.Price, J.Buckingham, and J.Dante, 2006. *Corrosion*, **62**, 8, pp687-702.
6. J.A.Beavers, M.P.Brongers, A.K.Agrawal, and F.A.Tallarida, 2008. Prevention of internal SCC in ethanol pipelines. NACE, Corrosion 2008 Conference, New Orleans, LA, March, Paper 08153.
7. J.A.Beavers and N.Sridhar, 2008. Unpublished results, PRCI SCC Program.
8. J.G.Maldonado and N.Sridhar, 2007. SCC of carbon steel in fuel ethanol service: effect of corrosion potential and ethanol processing source. Corrosion, Paper 07574, Houston, TX, NACE International.
9. J.A.Beavers, N.Sridhar, and C.Zamarin, 2009. Effects of steel microstructure and ethanol-gasoline

blend ratio on SCC of ethanol pipelines. NACE, Corrosion 2009 Conference, Atlanta GA, March, Paper 095465.

10. J.A.Beavers, N.G.Thompson, and K.E.W.Coulson, 1993. Effects of surface preparation and coatings on SCC susceptibility of line pipe: Phase 1 - laboratory studies. Corrosion, NACE Paper 597, New Orleans, LA, March.

The fundamentals of pigging systems and the importance of trap assessments

by Christian J Cloyde

TD Williamson, Inc., Tulsa, OK, USA

THE PIGGING OF pipelines has been a necessity in the energy industry for many years. Whether a pipeline operator pigs to improve production through-put, displace one product for another, empty a pipeline for decommissioning, insert a physical barrier (pig) between two different products, or to inspect the integrity and condition of the pipe wall, pig launchers and receivers will always be needed equipment on the pipeline. In fact, ever since TD Williamson designed the first pipeline pigs in the 1940s, the company has been designing, fabricating, and/or delivering quality pig traps for the pipeline industry around the world. Launchers and receivers – or pig traps – are fairly simple pieces of equipment to design, fabricate, and install. However, a basic understanding of the components, launching and receiving sequences, and design aspects is essential for each pipeline operator.

Pig launchers are used to introduce a pig into the pipeline and there are certain minimum components needed for the safe and proper operation of a pig launcher. There is a difference between pig launchers and pig-launching systems, and there are minimum recommended dimensional parameters for the necessary features of a launcher. Pig receivers are used to retrieve a pig from the pipeline and there are certain minimum features needed for the safe and proper operation of a pig receiver. In addition, there is a difference between pig receivers and pig-receiving systems, and there are minimum recommended dimensional parameters for the necessary features of a receiver. The launching and receiving sequence is very practical and methodical. Performance-enhancing features for pig traps come in the form of equalization lines, inspection tool pull-through nozzles, additional vents, and additional drain nozzles.

Pig traps should be designed based upon the mechanical characteristics of the pipeline to which they will be connected, as well as for the types of pig they will accommodate. There are many different factors that should be considered when locating or positioning a trap or pigging system. Pig-trap designs are based upon various codes, and the cost of the trap can be affected by the particular code used.

As pigging systems age, safety and operational efficiency can deteriorate. An effective trap-assessment programme assembles pertinent information for each piece of pigging equipment in the pipeline system and evaluates the performance and safety of that unit. In some cases, a corrosion-monitoring programme can be utilized to estimate the service life of a trap based upon monitored corrosion rates within the trap. TD Williamson has provided trap-assessment services for large pipeline companies with existing pigging assets that have been in the field over 20 years.

WHEN THE DECISION was made to create a tool that would improve the flow capacity of a pipeline, the next question had to be: "How do we get the tool into and out of the pipeline?" At that point, pigging equipment – or pig traps – became a necessary commodity on

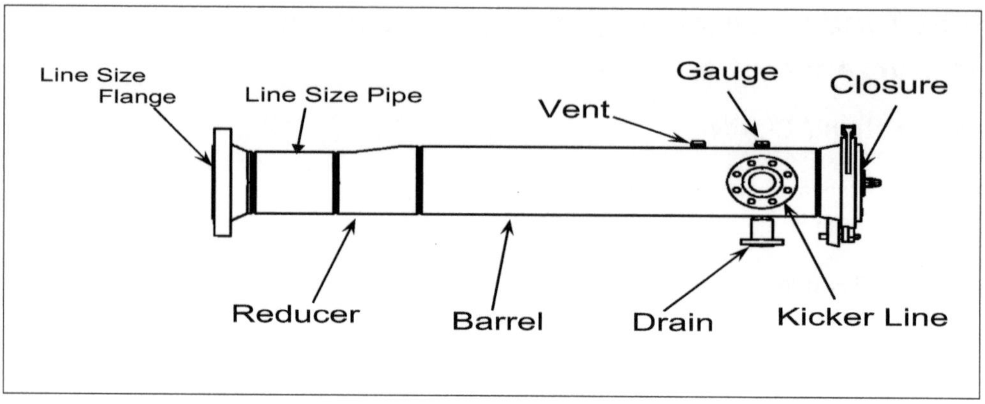

Fig. 1. A typical pig launcher.

the pipeline system. This pipeline equipment has gone by many names over the years and throughout the world, and pig traps, scraper traps, launchers, receivers, barrels, and pigging systems are some of the many names by which this equipment has been identified at different times. The purpose of a pig trap is to introduce and remove a pipeline tool into a pipeline without interruption of the pipeline flow. The last part of the previous sentence is extremely important to the pipeline operator and owner because their livelihood is based upon the uninterruption of product flow through their pipeline. Pig traps are very simple pieces of pipeline equipment: in some cases, the pig trap can be as basic as a piece of pipe with a blind flange or pipe cap.

Some may assert that pig traps are the simplest examples of pipeline equipment. Even though pig traps are typically made up of a few pieces of pipe, a closure, and some valves, there are different levels of complexity or sophistication that can be added to a pig trap for various reasons. A basic pig trap is composed of two pieces of pipe, a reducer, a closure, and a few nozzles, and it is commonly installed in a horizontal orientation. A pigging system is made up of everything necessary to launch or receive a pig in the pipeline by connecting the pipeline to the system in two places. In addition to the pig trap, a pigging system contains valves to isolate the trap from the pipeline, valves to divert the pipeline flow through the pig trap, and it may include pipe supports and pig-handling equipment. Pig traps used to launch and receive spherical pigs have a slanted or sloped barrel in order to allow gravity to assist in the launching and removal of these pigs from the pipeline. In areas where there is limited horizontal space for the installation of a pig trap, it is necessary to orient the barrel in a vertical configuration. This pig-trap configuration is often found in offshore platforms and within refineries where horizontal floor space is at a minimum. In recent years, automation has been added to the pigging operations. Automation on a pig trap allows for the loading and retrieval of multiple pigs in a trap barrel at one time. This also allows for the pigging operator to launch and receive a pig without personnel at the pigging station. Automation controls can be configured so that pigs can be launched either on timed intervals, or by an operator at a remote location, or manually by on-site personnel.

Nomenclature

- Pig trap: a generic term used to represent either a pig launcher or pig receiver; pipeline equipment used to insert and retrieve a pipeline tool into and out of a pipeline section.

- Pig launcher: pipeline equipment used to introduce a tool into a pipeline section without the interruption of product flow.

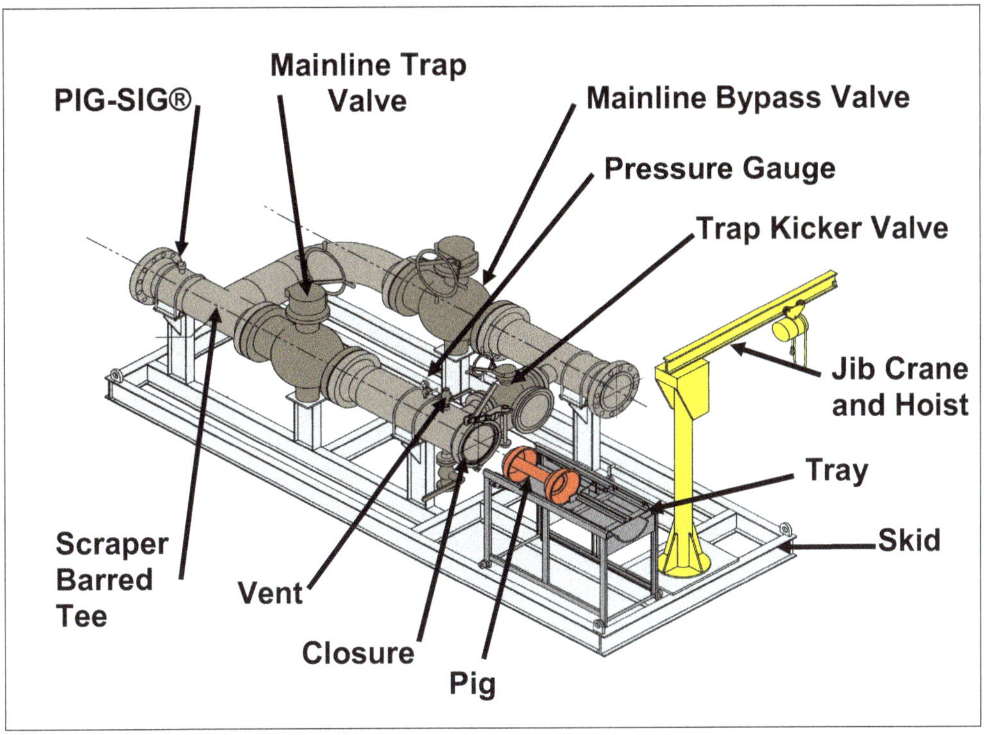

Fig.2. A skid-mounted pig-launching system.

- Pig: name for a pipeline tool used to clean, inspect, provide batch separation, and displace product in a pipeline.
- Pig receiver: pipeline equipment used to remove a tool from a pipeline section without the interruption of product flow.
- Pigging system: generic term used to represent either a launcher system or a receiver system.
- Launcher system: an arrangement of pipes and valves used to launch a pig into the pipeline without interruption of product flow.
- Receiver system: an arrangement of pipes and valve used to receive a pig from a pipeline without interruption of product flow.
- Trap assessment: an evaluation of the components of the pipeline equipment used for pipeline tool insertion and retrieval. This assessment deals with the evaluation of the existing pigging equipment or the pigging system used for launching or receiving pipeline tools.
- Piggability assessment: an evaluation of an existing pipeline for the purpose of determining the necessary modifications to make a pipeline section capable of safely launching, running, and receiving pipeline tools.
- ANSI: American National Standards Institute
- ASME: American Society of Mechanical Engineers

- NDE: non-destructive examination
- SMYS: specified minimum yield strength

Launchers and launcher systems

A pig launcher (Fig.1) is used to insert a pig or pipeline tool into a section of pipeline. A pig launcher includes an oversized pipe section, reducer, various-sized nozzles, line-size pipe section, and a quick-opening closure. Typically, a pig launcher is identified by its line-size pipe section, oversized pipe section, and its ANSI pressure class in that order. For example, a pig launcher on a 12in diameter pipeline with a 16-in diameter oversized barrel and 600 ANSI pressure class would be designated as a 12-in x 16-in 600# launcher. The components that make up a pig launcher are:

- Line-size flange: for connection to the pipeline or mainline isolation valve of a pigging system.
- Line-size pipe section: pipe connecting the line-size flange to the reducer which aids in the conveyance of the pig from the pig trap to the pipeline. With the addition of nozzles, this can also aid in the loading of inspection tools.
- Reducer: typically an eccentric reducer has its flat side on the bottom of the trap and provides a transition from the oversized barrel of the trap to the line-size section of the trap. A pressure seal, which provides the pressure barrier necessary to create differential pressure behind the pig, is created at this reducer.
- Over-size barrel: sometimes called a barrel of a trap, this is a pipe section larger than the pipeline diameter which is used to load the pig into launch position inside the trap reducer. This section connects the reducer to the closure.
- Closure: a door connected to the over-size barrel which allows for the sealing of the trap and introduction of the pig into the trap.
- Kicker nozzle: an opening on the launcher located on the over-size barrel which is used to fill and pressurize the trap, as well as to transfer product flow and pressure behind the pig. This transfer of product flow and pressure provides the force to move the pig into the pipeline. Therefore, the kicker nozzle is located toward the closure end of the over-sized barrel.
- Pressure-gauge nozzle: an opening on the trap for connecting a pressure gauge located close to the closure door in order to allow a clear view for the operator at the closure.
- Vent nozzle: an opening on the trap which aids in the venting of air from the trap during filling and depressurization of the trap during the emptying of the trap.
- Drain nozzle: an opening on the trap used for emptying the trap of liquids prior to opening the closure door.

There are some general guidelines for minimal sizing and spacing of the different components of the launcher. The distance between the kicker nozzle and the over-size part of the reducer should equal the longest pig length to be run on the pipeline section. A 0.5-in diameter threaded nozzle should be adequate for connecting a pressure gauge to the trap. For pipelines up to 22in diameter, a 1-in (minimum) diameter nozzle should be adequate for the vent nozzle, while a 2-in (minimum) diameter nozzle should be adequate for venting launchers connected to pipelines of 24in diameter and above. Drain-line nozzles should be sized accordingly:

- for less than 4in pipeline diameter, use a 1.5-in diameter drain nozzle;
- for pipelines of 6-18in diameter, use a 2-in diameter drain nozzle; and
- for pipelines 20-in and above in diameter, use a 4-in diameter drain nozzle.

The kicker nozzle should be a minimum of one third the diameter of the pipeline diameter. For pipelines of less than 12in diameter, the oversize barrel should be one pipe size larger than the line-size pipe; for pipelines of 12-in and larger diameters, the over-size barrel should be at least two pipe sizes larger than the line-size pipe. However, if it is planned for the pipeline section ever to have an inspection tool run through it, it is recommended that the over-size barrel be at least two pipe sizes larger than the line-size pipe no matter what the pipeline size is.

There are some performance-enhancing and safety features that can be added to a pig launcher. An equalization line consisting of a 1-2in diameter pipe and a valve can be added to the kicker line and connected to both sides of the kicker valve; this will help protect the kicker-line valve seats by eliminating the need to operate that valve against the full pipeline differential pressure. An equalization line should also be added to the trap barrel, with one end connected to the line-size pipe on the trap and the other end connected to the over-sized barrel of the trap: this allows for filling and pressurization of the trap in front of and behind a pig seated in the reducer. In addition to this equalization line, an extra vent and pressure-gauge nozzle should be added to the line-size pipe section of the trap to allow the air to vent during filling and for equalization verification. Three nozzles can be added to the line-size pipe to aid in the pulling of inspection tools into the launcher.

A launcher system (Fig.2) contains everything needed to launch a pig into the pipeline and is connected to the pipeline in two locations. Many times the launcher system is supported by legs connected to skid. The launcher is connected to a mainline trap valve, which is itself connected to a barred tee. The other end of the in-line branch of the tee is connected to a short piece of pipe with a flange on the end and a pig signaller on the top. The branch connection of the barred tee is connected to a section of by-pass piping, within which there is a mainline by-pass valve upstream of which is a nozzle connected to the kicker valve. The kicker valve is connected to the kicker nozzle on the launcher. Sometimes, pig-handling equipment (such as a pig tray and jib crane) will be included in a launching system.

The basic procedure for launching a pig into a pipeline section is practical and methodical. Considering a trap that is pressurized and full of product, the mainline trap valve, the mainline by-pass valve, and the kicker valve are open and the drain and vent valves are closed. In order to isolate the trap from the pipeline, the mainline trap and kicker valves are closed. The trap is depressurized and emptied by opening the vent and drain valves. Once the launcher has been depressurized and emptied, the closure door is opened and the pig is inserted into the reducer. The closure door is closed and the drain valve is closed, and the trap is filled by partially opening the kicker valve. Once the trap is full of product, the vent valve is closed, the trap is equalized to the pipeline pressure, and the kicker valve is closed. Once the trap is fully pressurized, the mainline trap valve is opened, and the kicker valve is opened. The pig is now ready to launch. The mainline by-pass valve should then be partially closed to increase the flow through the kicker valve and into

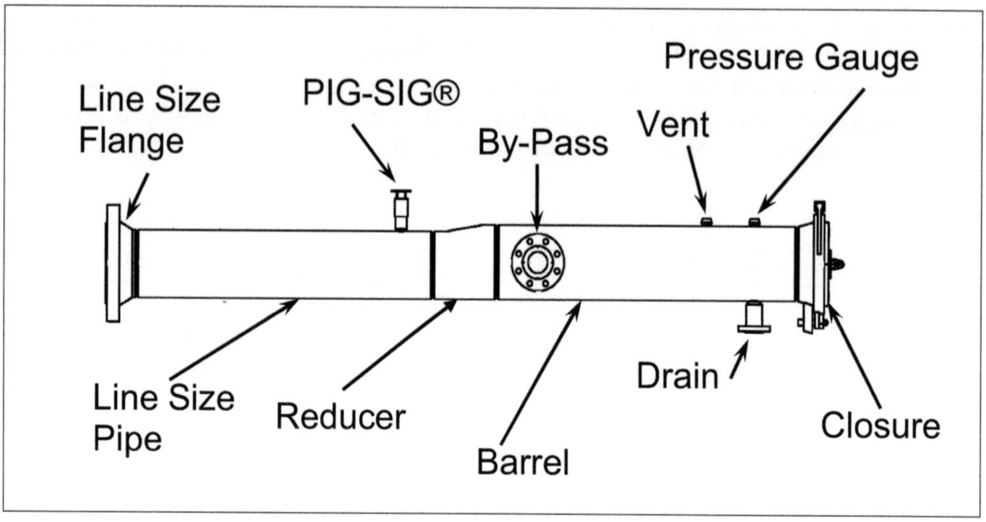

Fig.3. A typical pig receiver.

the launcher behind the pig. Opening of the mainline by-pass valve is continued until the pig leaves the launcher and activates the pig signaller downstream of the barred tee. Once the pig has entered the pipeline, the mainline by-pass valve is opened fully.

Receivers and receiver systems

A pig receiver (Fig.3) is used to retrieve a pig or pipeline tool from a section of pipeline without the interruption of product flow, and includes an oversized pipe section, reducer, various-sized nozzles, a pig signaller, line-size pipe section, and a quick-opening closure. Similarly to the launcher, a pig receiver is identified by its line-size pipe section, oversized-pipe section, and its ANSI pressure class, in that order. For example, a pig receiver on a 12-in diameter pipeline with a 16-in diameter oversized barrel and 600 ANSI pressure class would be designated as a 12-in x 16-in 600# receiver. The components that make up a pig receiver are:

- Line-size flange: for connection to the pipeline or mainline isolation valve of a pigging system.

- Line-size pipe section: pipe connecting the line-size flange to the reducer which aids in the conveyance of the pig from the pipeline to the pig trap.

- Reducer: can be either eccentric (see above) or concentric (when its centreline is a continuation of the main-line centreline), and connects the line-size pipe section to the over-size pipe section.

- Over-size pipe section: sometimes called the barrel of the trap, this is a pipe section larger than the pipeline diameter which is used to remove the pig and any liquid or debris brought in by the pig from the pipeline. This section connects the reducer to the closure.

- Closure: a door connected to the over-size barrel which allows for the sealing of the trap and access to the pig within the trap.

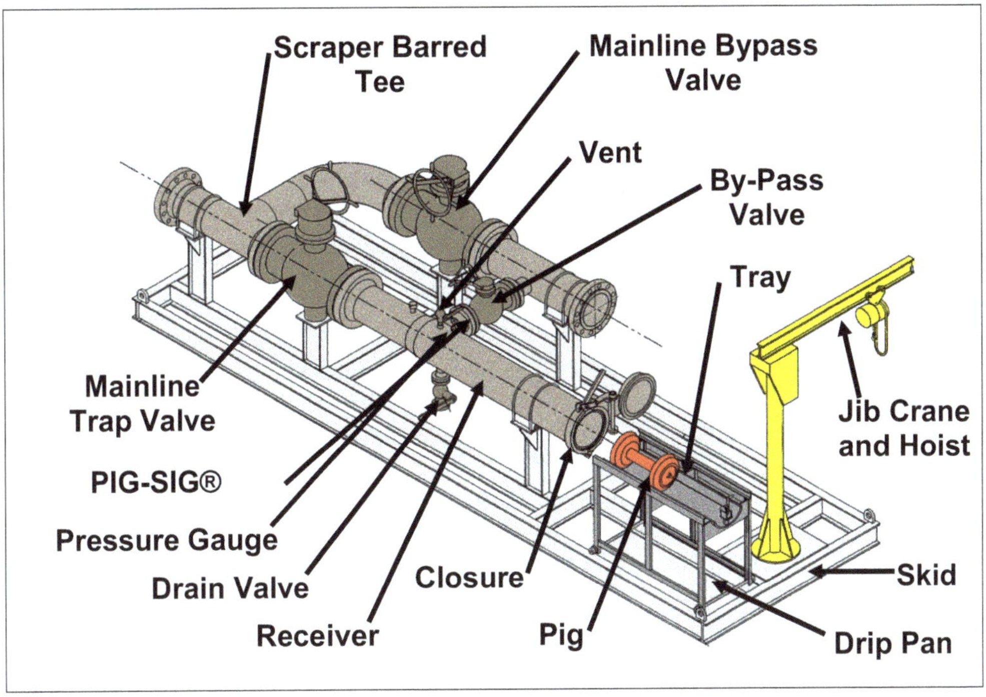

Fig.4. A skid-mounted pig-receiving system.

- By-pass nozzle: an opening on the receiver located on the over-size barrel which is used to fill and pressurize the trap, as well as, divert product flow out of the receiver. Once the flow is diverted from behind the pig, the pig will slow down and stop inside the barrel of the trap. Therefore, the by-pass nozzle is located toward the reducer end of the barrel.

- Pressure-gauge nozzle: an opening on the barrel for connecting a pressure gauge located close to the closure door in order to allow a clear view for the operator at the closure.

- Vent nozzle: an opening on the trap which aids in the venting of air from the trap during filling and depressurization of the trap during the emptying of the trap.

- Drain nozzle: an opening on the trap used for emptying the trap of liquids prior to opening the closure door.

- Pig signaller: located on top of the line-size pipe near the reducer, this is used to verify that the pig has come out of the mainline trap valve and entered the barrel of the trap.

There are some general guidelines for minimal sizing and spacing the different components of the receiver. The most important dimension on a pig receiver is the distance from the pig signaller to the face of the line-size flange: this distance should be the length of the longest pig to be run in that pipeline section. If an inspection tool is to be run through the pipeline section, the distance from the pig signaller to the face of the line-size flange should be at least as long as the length of the inspection tool. If this distance is shorter than the length of the inspection tool, then the pig will not clear the mainline trap valve, and the operator will be unable to retrieve the pig from the receiver because the trap will not be able to be isolated.

The distance between the by-pass nozzle and the inside face of the closure door should be equal to the length of two cleaning pigs or one inspection tool. A 0.5-in diameter threaded nozzle should be adequate for connecting a pressure gauge to the trap. For pipelines of diameter up to 22ins, a 1-in (minimum) diameter nozzle should be adequate for the vent nozzle, while a 2-in (minimum) diameter nozzle should be adequate for venting launchers connected to pipelines of 24in diameter and above. Drain-line nozzles should be sized accordingly: for pipelines less than 4in in diameter, use a 1.5-in diameter drain nozzle; for pipelines of diameters 6-18in, use a 2-in diameter drain nozzle; and for pipelines of diameters above20in, use a 4-in diameter drain nozzle. The by-pass nozzle should be a minimum of one-third the diameter of the pipeline diameter. For pipelines less than 12in diameter, the oversize barrel should be one pipe size larger than the line-size pipe, while for pipelines of 12in and above, the over-size barrel should be at least two pipe sizes larger than the line-size pipe. However, should the pipeline section ever have an inspection tool run through it, it is recommended that the over-size barrel be at least two pipe sizes larger than the line-size pipe for all diameters.

There are some performance-enhancing and safety features that can be added to a pig receiver. An equalization line consisting of a 1-2-in diameter pipe and a valve can be added to the by-pass line and connected to both sides of the by-pass valve: this will help protect the by-pass valve seats by eliminating the need to operate that valve against the full pipeline differential pressure. An equalization line should also be added to the trap barrel with one end connected to the line-size pipe on the trap and the other end connected to the over-sized barrel of the trap: this allows for depressurization of the line-size pipe section of the trap should a pig become lodged in the line-size pipe of the receiver. Another way to relieve pressure behind a pig lodged in the line-size portion of the receiver is to add an extra vent and pressure-gauge nozzle on the line-size portion of the receiver. If a receiver has only one drain nozzle, there is a possibility that a pig or debris could block this when a pig is received in the trap. An operator may not realize that this has happened until the closure door is opened and a barrel full of liquid and pipeline debris issues forth. One possible solution to this dilemma is to add an additional drain nozzle to the bottom of the trap.

A receiver system (Fig.4) contains everything needed to retrieve a pig from the pipeline and is connected to the pipeline in two locations. Many times the receiver system is supported by legs connected to a skid. The receiver is connected to the mainline trap valve, and the mainline trap valve is connected to a barred tee. The other end of the in-line branch of the tee is connected to a short piece of pipe with a flange on the end and a pig signaller on the top. The branch connection of the barred tee is connected to a section of by-pass piping. Within this piping there is a mainline by-pass valve, and upstream of this valve is a nozzle connected to the by-pass valve, which itself is connected to the by-pass nozzle on the receiver. Sometimes, pig-handling equipment (such as a pig tray and jib crane) will be included in a receiving system. In addition, a drip pan can also be welded into the skid to collect spills from the opening of the closure door.

The basic procedure for receiving a pig from a pipeline section is practical and methodical. Considering a trap that is empty and depressurized, the mainline trap and the by-pass valves are closed and the mainline by-pass, the drain, and the vent valves are open. In order to receive a pig, the conditions inside the trap need to match those within the pipeline. Therefore, close the drain valve and open the by-pass valve. Once the trap is full of product, close the vent valve, and allow pressure to build-up and equalize with that of the pipeline. Open the mainline trap valve, and the trap is now ready to receive the pig. When the pig arrives, it may not come into the receiver, and it may stop either between the barred tee and the mainline trap valve or in the mainline trap valve. Partially close the mainline by-pass valve which will create an increase in differential pressure behind the pig and push the pig through the mainline trap valve, through the line-size pipe section, activating the pig signaller, and into the barrel of the trap. In order to isolate the trap from the pipeline, the mainline trap and by-pass valves are closed. The trap is then depressurized and emptied by opening the vent and drain valves. Once the receiver is depressurized and emptied, the closure door is opened and the pig is removed. Lastly, the closure door is shut.

Pig trap design considerations

A pig trap must be designed to match the pipeline section design specifications. The mechanical design characteristics of the pig trap should meet or exceed the design pressure, have the same design factor, have compatible material type, be designed using the same design code, and be suitable for the same temperature range as the pipeline section that it serves. Also, a pig trap must be dimensionally suited for the type of pigging that is expected on the pipeline section. The critical lengths of the barrels and line-size pipe sections mentioned previously must be long enough to accommodate the longest pig that will be used in the pipeline section.

When deciding where to locate a pig trap, there are various things to consider. The pig trap should not be placed near any open flames or ignition sources. Many building codes and pipeline companies have rules and regulations about what type of powered equipment is allowed within certain distances of an opening in the pipeline, such as a closure door. If the pig trap is to be located in an area where horizontal space is not at a premium (such as on an offshore platform or a refinery), then care should be taken to provide sufficient work space adjacent to the closure door for pigging operations. These operations can take the form of loading and unloading long inspection pigs, removal of liquids and debris from the pipeline and into a waste container, installation and operation of a temporary separator, etc.

Another consideration that is important to the safe and efficient operation of a pig trap is how the barrel is oriented at the pigging station. Any valves or instrumentation associated with the operation of the pig trap should be given adequate space to allow routine maintenance or replacement. The closure door should face away from other equipment and places where people typically congregate (i.e. break areas or parking lots). There have been rare occurrences where pigs have shot out of pig traps and damaged equipment, as well as injuring people. The over-sized pipe section of a pig trap is not named 'barrel' by coincidence.

In recent years, the energy industry has become more focused on what effects its operations have on the environment, and the location of a pig trap is also a concern in this area. When a pig trap is vented or a closure door is opened, forethought should be taken to minimize or eliminate the occurrence of hazardous contaminants within a pipeline from reaching the outside atmosphere or contaminating the nearby ground or water.

Pipeline companies that operate large-diameter pipelines should consider the use of material-handling equipment when it comes to conducting pigging operations. Mandrel or spherical pigs used in a pipeline that is 20in in diameter or larger can be too heavy or awkward for one or two people to handle safely. In addition, even small-diameter inspection tools are typically too heavy and long for one or two people to easily manipulate into or out of a pig trap. There are various designs of pig trays available on the market, some of which have wheels while others are stationary. There are other pig trays that have automation for pushing a pig into or pulling a pig out of a pig trap. Many pig trays are fitted with drip pans for collecting liquids or fine debris that may fall off of a pig once it is out of the receiver. In some cases, lifting equipment may be necessary to move large pigs into position; jib cranes, gantry cranes, and fork lifts are all examples of pig-handling equipment.

As mentioned above, pig traps and pigging systems should be designed according to the same design codes as the pipeline to which they are connected. The predominant codes used for pipeline design in many countries are written by ASME, of which those commonly encountered in the pipeline industry are ASME B31.4 (which governs the design of liquid pipelines), ASME B31.8 (which governs the design of gas pipelines), ASME B31.3 (which governs the design of process piping), and ASME Section VIII, Div. 1 and 2 (which governs the design of pressure vessels, and which is sometimes referred to as the Boiler Code). There are other codes in use that govern the design of pig traps such as CSA Z-662 in Canada or ASME B31.11 for slurry pipelines.

It is helpful to the purchaser of pipeline equipment to understand some of the differences between the commonly used ASME codes.

- ASME B31.4 *Pipeline transportation systems for liquid hydrocarbons and other liquids* (including crude oil, liquid petroleum gas, anhydrous ammonia, alcohols, and carbon dioxide) allows for design with certain steel materials such as ASTM A694 F42 to F70, A707 L3 CL3, A105, A350 LF2, A182 F316, A182 F51 (Duplex), and others. The design maximum allowable stress values are determined by design factors (0.72 or 0.6) multiplied by the specified minimum yield strength (SMYS) of the material. The pipe-wall thickness is given by $wt = PD/2SF$ (where wt = wall thickness; P = design pressure; D = pipe diameter (OD); S = allowable stress; F = design factor) based upon the allowable hoop stress of the material in question. The welding standard is according to API 1004.

- ASME B31.8 *Gas transmission and distribution piping systems*. Gas (not gasoline) as used in this code commonly refers to natural gas, manufactured gas, and liquefied petroleum gas distributed as a vapour, and the code allows for design with similar materials as in ASME B31.4. The maximum allowable design stress values are determined by design factor (0.8, 0.72, 0.6, 0.5, or 0.4) multiplied by SMYS of the material, and are ˜related to the population density in proximity of the pipeline. The pipe-wall thickness is again given by $wt = PD/2SF$, and is based upon the allowable hoop stress of the material in question. The welding standard is according to API 1004.

- ASME B31.3 *Process piping* (also referred to as refinery piping) covers allowable materials that are restricted to B31.3 'listed' materials, which usually includes A105, A350 LF2, and A182 F316. Some commonly used high-yield materials (including A694 and A707) are not permitted under this code. The maximum allowable design stress values are determined by the lesser of ($1/3 \times S_u$ (tensile strength)) or ($2/3 \times S_y$ (yield stress)); the allowable stress values are found in B31.3 as "tabulated" values. Overall, material thicknesses are calculated using B31.3 tend to be more conservative or thicker than those calculated using B31.4 or B31.8. the pipe-wall thickness is given by $wt = PD/2(SE+PY)$ with similar definitions to those above but where E = quality factor, and Y = a coefficient based upon the tensile strength of the material. The welding standard is according to ASME Section IX.

- ASME Section VIII Division 1 – ASME *Boiler and pressure vessel code rule for construction of pressure vessels* covers allowable materials that are restricted to ASME Section II 'listed' materials, which are usually SA105, SA350 LF2, and SA182 F316. Some commonly used high-yield materials (such as A694 and A707) are not permitted under this code. The maximum allowable design stress values are found in ASME Section II as 'tabulated' values. Overall, material thicknesses calculated using ASME Section VIII Div.1 tend to be more conservative or thicker than those calculated using B31.3. As above, the pipe wall thickness formula is $wt = PR/2(SE\text{-}0.6P)$ where P = design pressure; R = pipe radius (inside radius); S = allowable stress [the lesser of (S_u (tensile strength) divided by 3.5) or (2/3 multiplied by S_y (yield stress))]; E = quality factor) based upon the tensile strength of the material.

- U Stamp is the official Code U symbol for stamp (marking) on the vessel or closure to denote inspection and testing in compliance with code requirements.

All of the above codes can be used to design pig traps, although inspection criteria vary between these different codes. Generally, given the same pipeline design parameters, a pig trap designed using ASME B31.3 will tend to be costlier than for one designed using ASME B31.4 or B31.8 because of the difference in material grades and thicknesses. In addition, a pig trap designed from ASME Section VIII Div.1 will tend to be more expensive than one designed from ASME B31.3 for the same reasons.

Pig-trap/pigging-system assessments

As with any other piece of equipment connected to the pipeline, pig traps should be assessed at regular intervals for various reasons. The pipe and fittings that make up a pig trap will age and deteriorate over time. Pipeline companies may acquire existing pipelines with pig traps and it will be important to know the condition of these used assets. Some existing pipelines undergo a change in use, whether to do with a reversal of flow direction or a change in product being transported. Existing pig traps can change the way they are used: for example, a pig trap sized for cleaning pigs may need to be modified so that it can accommodate inspection pigs. A launcher may need to be changed from a manually operated pigging system to an automated pigging system. A receiver may need to be modified so that it can receive more than one pig at a time. The initial design of the pig trap may be inappropriate for the current pipeline conditions. At some point in the history of the trap, modifications may have been made that were inappropriate for the proper performance of the pigging system. These are all reasons for performing an assessment on a pig trap or pigging system.

The time it takes to perform a trap assessment depends on the level or levels of assessment required, the experience of the trap-assessment team, the working conditions where the trap is located, the remoteness of the trap to be assessed (on- or offshore) and the operational circumstances of the pipeline section at the time of assessment.

There is a difference between trap assessments and piggability assessments. A trap assessment is an evaluation of the piece of pipeline equipment used for introducing or retrieving a pipeline tool from the pipeline without interruption of pipeline flow. This assessment deals with the evaluation of an existing piece of pigging equipment or pigging system used for launching and receiving pigs or pipeline tools. In contrast, a piggability assessment is an evaluation of an existing pipeline for the purpose of determining the necessary modifications in order to make a pipeline section capable of safely launching, running, and receiving pipeline tools.

Levels of trap assessment

A trap assessment can range in complexity and sophistication, and there are many levels of trap assessments that can be conducted. Below is a description of each level of trap assessment: it may be noted that each level of assessment increases in complexity.

The first level, or Level 1 trap assessment, is called a 'research' assessment. This level of assessment explores the history and design parameters of the pig trap. It notes any modifications that have been made to the pig trap from the time of installation to the present, the mechanical design limitations of the pig trap, the physical location or designation of the trap or pipeline section, the trap dimensions, and the location and use of each nozzle on the pig trap.

The Level 2 trap assessment is called an 'operational' assessment. This level of assessment is concerned with the current-day operational condition of the pig trap and aspects of the overall pigging system. This assessment observes whether the closure opens, closes, and seals properly, whether the pressure-warning device on the closure operates correctly, whether the various valves on the pigging system seal adequately, whether the pig signaller and pressure gauge work as they should, and whether the kicker or by-pass nozzles are sized properly.

The Level 3 trap assessment is called the 'functionality' assessment. This level of trap assessment determines if the pigging system is performing to its peak effectiveness. If it is desirable to launch or receive inspection tools, is the trap or the surrounding area dimensionally capable of handling this operation? Are there physical obstructions (handrails, stairs, piping, etc.) that make it difficult to safely load or unload pigs? Are piping modifications needed to allow for inspection pigging? Should an equalization line be added across the trap reducer for safety or to improve pigging operations? Should additional vent and pressure-gauge nozzles be added to the line-size pipe for safety? Should additional drain nozzles be added to the pig trap? These are all questions that this level of trap assessment seeks to answer.

The Level 4 trap assessment is called the 'corrosion' assessment. This level of assessment is the most complex and typically will require a qualified NDE technician or engineer to be on the trap-assessment team. This evaluation seeks to determine the existence of corrosion agents acting on the components of the pig trap and whether or not these corrosion agents have affected the structural integrity of the carbon steel enough to cause the trap to be unsafe to operate. Are liquid or debris samples being taken? If so, are the samples analysed for corrosion agents? Are there sampling ports for obtaining liquid or debris samples from the pigging system? Have any inhibitors or biocides been applied to this pipeline section? If so, what was the name of the inhibitor or biocide used and what was the interval of application? Did the inhibitor or biocide have a positive effect or not? Have in-line inspections been conducted on this pipeline section? Has any form of NDE been conducted on the trap since it was installed? If so, have the data been analysed to assess minimum pipe wall thicknesses? Is NDE performed regularly on the traps to monitor corrosion growth rates? If previous NDE data are provided, corrosion growth rates can be used to estimate the time when repair or replacement of the trap would be necessary.

Trap-assessment team

A trap-assessment team (Fig.5) should be composed of the following members as a minimum:

- Team leader/project manager: responsible for the assessment team in the field and ensure that the necessary data are collected for the technical writer to create the assessment report.

- Project engineer: the technical expert on the design and operation of pig traps and pigging systems. This member can assume the role of team leader/project manager for economy of workforce.

- Technical writer: assembles the data collected into a technical report which explains to the client the findings of the assessment.

Fig.5. One of TD Williamson's trap-assessment teams

- NDE technician (optional member, for Level 4 assessments only): performs the non-destructive examination on the trap and provides the data to the project engineer for mechanical integrity evaluation.

On-site trap-assessment procedure

1. Assemble as much information about the trap and pipeline section as possible before conducting the on-site assessment. Note the history of the trap, pipeline/trap design parameters, location, etc.

2. On-site assessment

   Compare the existing trap with the as-built drawings. If there are any differences, note and sketch them.

   If an as-built drawing is not available, make a sketch of the trap with dimensions. Note nozzle sizes and use. Also note valve types, makes and condition in the pigging system.

   Question the operators and pigging crews about the pigging type, frequency, and the operational condition of the different components of the pigging system.

   Take pictures of the trap. Care should be taken to capture any areas of concern on the trap or pigging system. It has been said that a picture is worth a thousand words. These pictures will be useful as illustrations within the assessment report.

   If possible, look inside the trap and note the condition of the inside pipe wall and closure door.

   If a Level 4 assessment is conducted, the NDE technician should take ultrasonic test readings and record them for further evaluation.

   Assemble the data in an organized fashion and transmit the data to the technical writer.

3. Write the assessment report and submit it to the client.

Conclusion

The development of the pig trap has occurred over many years and will continue as long as there remains the need to pig a pipeline. An understanding of the components, the function of each component, and certain performance-enhancing and safety features for a launcher and receiver helps to grasp the function of the overall pigging system and procedures for launching and receiving a pig. Design considerations should extend beyond the limits of the pig trap to the boundaries of the pigging station. Trap assessments are extremely valuable to the responsible pipeline operator that is concerned with the condition of the pipeline equipment and the safety of the pigging crews in the field.

Multi-diameter, bi-directional pigging for pipeline precommissioning

by Magne Andreas Vik[1], Alf Åge Kristiansen[1], Simon Sykes[2], Steve Hutcheson[3], and Dr Aidan O'Donoghue[4]

1 StatoilHydro, Haugesund, Norway
2 FTL Seals Technology, Southampton, UK
3 Pipeline Pigging Technology, Chesterfield, UK
4 Pipeline Research Ltd, Glasgow, UK

THIS PAPER EXAMINES the issues associated with multi-diameter, bi-directional pigging specifically for pipeline precommissioning. The technique can be used to flood and subsequently dewater a pipeline without the need for temporary subsea traps. An example is the Alve pipeline in Norway: this 16-km flowline from the Norne platform to the Alve manifold includes 10-in and 12-in pipe sections. The line was flooded from Norne using the pig with oxygen-scavenged seawater and then dewatered using nitrogen and produced gas from the well. The pigs needed to have a high sealing efficiency since very low velocities were used to flood the line, and in order to avoid hydrates on dewatering. Multi-diameter wheel pigs were employed with non-buckling disc-type seals. This paper describes the design of the pigs and the seals to achieve the required functionality. The test facility and testing performed to verify the pig performance is also illustrated. Finally, an overview of the offshore pigging operation is provided.

IN ORDER TO FLOOD and subsequently dewater the Alve flowline, a number of high-seal, multi-diameter and bi-directional pigs were required. The pipeline contains several internal diameters from 10in to 12in: since no pigging from the Alve manifold was possible (no launcher), all operations needed to be performed from Norne FPSO.

Four pigs spaced with MEG were launched from Norne with oxygen-scavenged water, propelled through the pipeline, and then stopped in position just upstream of the manifold. Before start-up of the pipeline and introduction of hydrocarbon gas, the pigs were required to be reversed with nitrogen and travel back through the pipeline, with no gas by-pass, and be received back on Norne. The pressure was first raised to 50bar with nitrogen for pigging and to 80bar with hydrocarbons from topside to give back-pressure for start-up. A field schematic is shown in Fig.1.

Performing this operation without any pigs was initially considered but, after a number of studies, the hydrate risk was considered to be too great. The need for high-seal pigs was identified. A number of additional scenarios for the operation were considered which impacted on pig design:

- Reversal of the pigs from the manifold, just before the inline isolation valve: the risk is that the pig will travel too far and will not be reversible from the 5-in inlet line (pumping into the middle of the pig rather than upstream);
- Reversal of the pigs from before the expansion spool: the implication is that the pig does not need to operate negotiate any bends in the large-diameter line.

The base case was the second option, but consideration needed to be given to the first option as a potential contingency. Testing would be performed to establish pig efficiency in all components, including the 12-in bends, and to establish if the first pig in the train was reversible from the valve

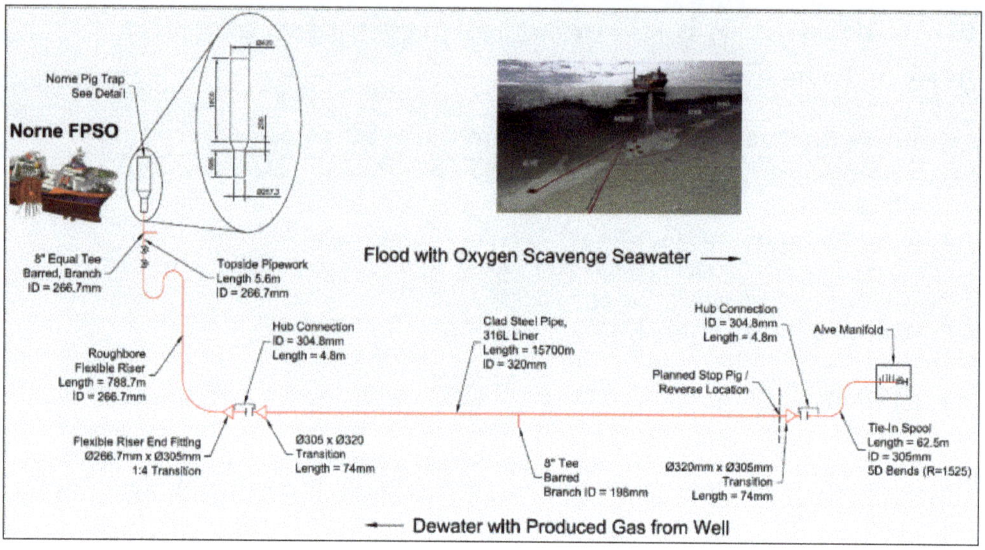

Fig. 1. Field schematic.

location. If this proved to be difficult then additional procedural steps would be taken to avoid the train reaching the manifold.

A pig train consisting of four pigs with MEG separation was required. The main pipeline features were as follows:

10-in vertical launcher
10-in topside piping at launcher, with 257mm internal diameter
10-in topside and riser, with 267mm internal diameter
12-in pipeline, with 320mm internal diameter, 15.7km in length
12-in tie-in spools and manifold, with 305mm internal diameter with 5-D bends.

The following functional requirements were discussed and agreed with the project:

- the pigs must be fully bi-directional with high sealing ability in both directions;
- low flow rates were expected, in the region of 300-400l/min, resulting in a pig velocity of 0.03 to 0.08m/s. The pig must be able to operate at such low velocities;
- good seal efficiency and pig support/centralisation were required to ensure safe negotiation with minimum by-pass through all components along the system. The risk of gas by-passing on return to Norne could result in hydrate formation;
- the ratio between pig-flip differential pressure (pressure to flip the seals forward and cause them to fail) and running differential pressure to be at least 5:1;
- the drive differential pressure in all pipeline components was requested to be less than 7bar;
- the pigs to be fitted with isotope holder for tracking purposes;
- pig handling to be considered for vertical launch and receipt.

The final aspect that needed to be considered as a contingency was the possibility of the pig travelling too far into the manifold, and the provision of a method of reversal from this location. This may mean that the pig straddled the manifold inlet used for driving the pig back to Norne.

Fig.2. Initial pig concept.

Pig selection

The timescales for the project were relatively short, with initial feasibility in August, 2008, and required pig delivery in December, 2008. This only allowed three months to establish concepts, perform detailed engineering, test to verify the pig functionality, and provide four units for the operation.

An initial feasibility study was undertaken with the aim of selecting a single pig type for development for this application. Several different types of multi-diameter pig were considered for this:

- traditional multi-diameter pig with slotted guides and seals of various diameters
- wheel pig or *Varipig* from FTL Seals Technology
- *Paddle Pig* from Pipeline Engineering
- other approaches from other suppliers

It must be stressed that whilst multi-diameter pigs have been successfully developed and used on many occasions, the project team was not aware of any projects which have developed a multi-diameter bi-directional pig and with such a high emphasis on sealing (i.e. no visible leakage in any pipeline component). The pros and cons of each technology were discussed, and it was concluded that – given the timescales – the wheel pig would be the best choice with the highest possibility of success. On the other hand, it is noted that with more time, the other methods could also be made to work.

No other pig was considered for this project from this point onwards. It is considered the best approach to concentrate all efforts on one chosen approach with a high probability of success rather than to dilute the effort by having several different competing pig prototypes which have lower chance of success and take up excessive testing time. Running a competition for pig development is considered inefficient in general, and it is better to establish the base case in a feasibility phase and then develop this further.

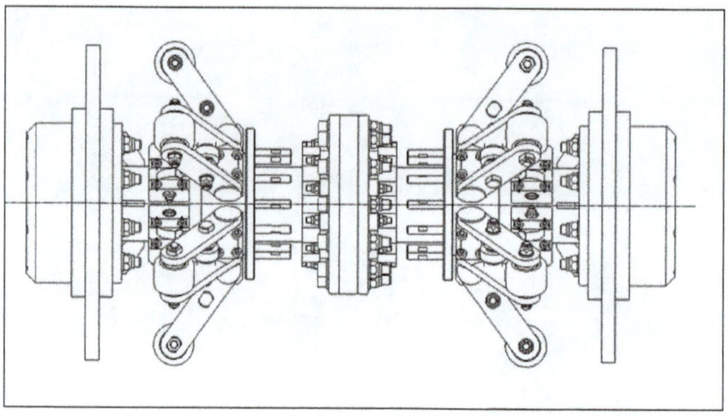

Fig.3.Initial axi-symmetrical design.

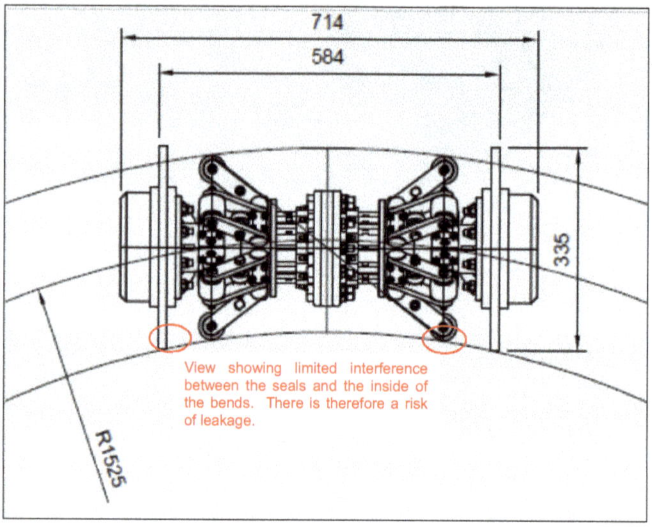

Fig.4. Possible leakage at the bends.

Pig design

The pig's mechanical design was performed by FTL Seals Technology with input and guidance from Pipeline Pigging Technology and Pipeline Research Ltd. In addition, StatoilHydro ensured that the requirements from the project were communicated as soon as possible. This is especially important in a tight timescale project and where small changes to the operation philosophy can have significant implications on the pig design. This was managed effectively throughout the development.

The outline concept pig design is shown in Fig.2. The pig consists of two wheel modules with interlinked suspension arms. The pig travels on the centreline of the pipe and so it is easier to specify seals that will provide a good sealing action. The spring force in the suspension units is greater than the weight of the pig and so if the pig drops below the centreline, then the restoring force is greater. The geometry of the wheel arms provides a mechanical advantage which results in a flat force / deflection curve, i.e. the force require to deflect the arms does not increase significantly in smaller diameters. As a result, the load on the wheels and bearings remains at an acceptable and determinable level.

For the Alve pig, these wheel units are facing each other with seals at either end. The pig is axi-symmetrical in design, which guarantees full bi-directionality (Fig.3). It was decided early on that

Fig.5. Additional seal at centre of the pig to avoid leakage at bends.

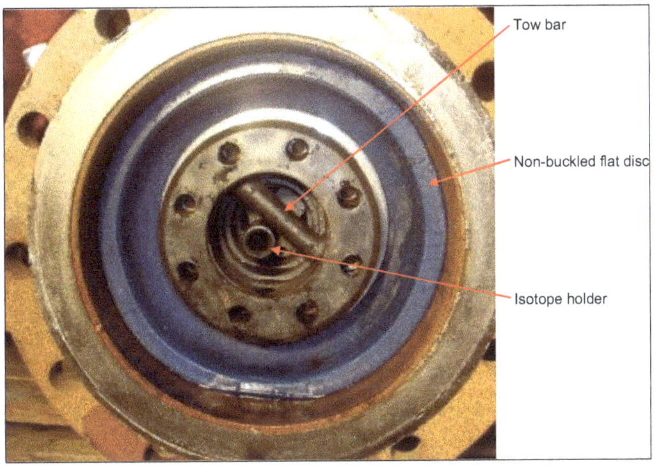

Fig.6. Isotope holder and towing arm.

a single, non-buckling seal would be used for both line sizes (10in and 12in). This is discussed in detail below.

Detailed engineering of this concept followed, and it became clear that in the event that the pig needed to travel through the 5-D bends at the manifold, then there could be leakage past the pig, and this is demonstrated in Fig.4. This is not acceptable for these functional requirements, and to solve the problem an additional seal was introduced in the centre of the pig – see Fig.5. Other issues associated with the layout of the pig include:

- Installation of an isotope holder: this is shown in Fig.6.

- Provision of a lifting bar at the rear of the pig (see Fig.6): the pig is loaded and removed from Norne as it is not handled subsea.

- The front pig in the train was also a special, known as the Type 1 pig, as this pig could potentially end up in the manifold and come to rest near the ball valve at the end of the manifold straddling the inlet line. This then required a slightly longer bumper nose to

Fig.7. Examples of buckled seals.

ensure that a seal was always downstream of the manifold off-take. The reversal of the pig from the manifold in the event of over-travel was subject to additional testing and modification as described later in this paper.

Seal design

The design of the seals for this pig was critical. One advantage of the wheel pig is that it supports the pig on the pipe centreline with the result that the seal diameter can be set just greater than the internal diameter of the largest bore and still provide a very good wiping action. Coupled with this, there has been good success lately with using a single disc seal to span several line sizes without buckling in the smallest size. This is known as the 'single seal' concept.

The idea is that a single oversized disc has the ability to work and provide a good seal at a range of smaller and smaller diameters before it finally buckles. The following scale of 'buckling' has been investigated previously:

no buckle
buckles when forced, but recovers
buckles when forced, but does not recover
buckles even when not forced to do so.

To be safe, for this application, it is important that the seal does not buckle or, if forced to do so, it returns to a full seal. Over the years much experience has been gained on buckling and non-buckling of seals for dual- and multi-diameter pigging. Figure 7 shows some examples of where the large-diameter seals are intentionally buckled into the small-diameter line in order to allow smaller-diameter seals to take over. This has been used to good effect in large-diameter change projects where 'buckle inducers' are used to force the seal to fold into the small-diameter line.

The opposite is now proposed: using seals that do not buckle when they enter the small-diameter line. The advantage of using such a seal in this development is that a single seal can be used at the front and the rear of the pig. As a result there is no interference between small-diameter and large-diameter seals over a limited pig length.

A routine has been developed to establish if a seal will buckle or not, and four criteria must be met to ensure that the seal will behave in the required way for different line sizes. This is based on a buckle model of the seal coupled with test and field data, and the output is shown in Fig.8 for this development. Based on this analysis, a number of seal sizes were selected, both for the main seals either end of the pig and also for the central seal positioned to avoid leakage in the 12-in bends.

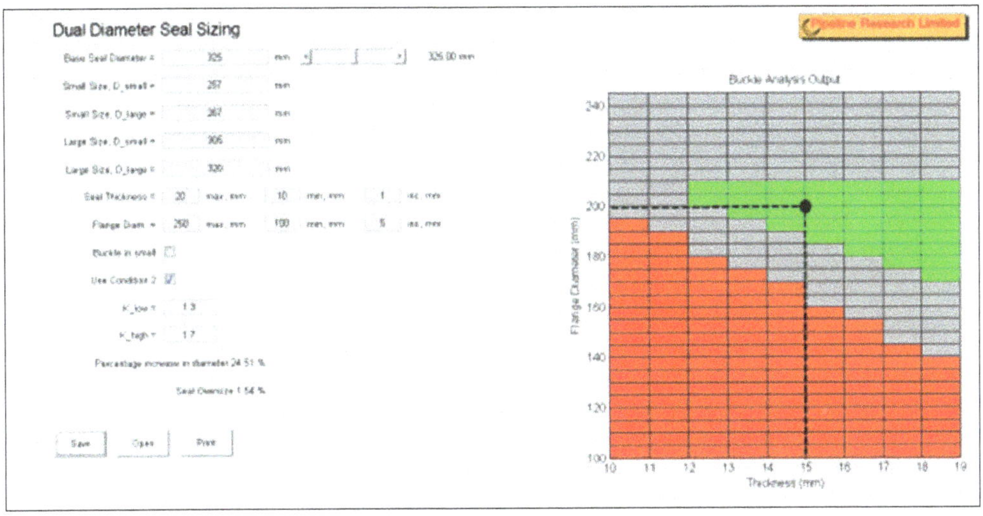

Fig.8. Seal sizing for buckling or non-buckling.

Fig.9. Test facility.

A base-case pig was also established for initial use in testing. The aim is always to arrive on the test site with a base-case design and a number of spares and alternatives to help solve any problems with the pig during verification testing.

Testing

The tests were performed at K-Lab at Kårstø in Norway, the test facility at which is shown in Fig.9. The facility consisted of the main components in the Alve flowline:

launcher (horizontal, for test purposes)
tight 10-in section at the beginning, 257mm ID
10-in topside and riser piping, 267mm ID
10-in x 12-in transition
12-in spool with 12-in equal tee, 307mm ID
12-in pipeline, 323mm ID (320-mm ID test pipe was unavailable)
12-in manifold pipe, 305mm ID
12-in bend, 305mm ID.

Fig.10. Buckle test.

Fig.11. Flat disc seal in small diameter.

A manifold spool with two 6-in tees was also included for reversal tests.

All the testing was performed open-ended to allow the pigging to be observed. This is for assurance that the pig was not visibly leaking, and that the seal was adequate and fit-for-purpose. Testing in a closed loop hides many problems, and only demonstrates that the pig travels from launch to receipt; it does not establish that it travels reliably from launch to receipt. Proper risk-assessment procedures and testing with water drive ensured that the HSE risk was minimal.

Launcher inlet pressure, flow-rate, and pig location using magnetic signallers were recorded during all tests. The set of tests shown in Table 1 was performed: each test was repeated if required, and to verify pig parameters. Any problems with the pig during the test were discussed in the light of data output and drawings of the pigs in the various features of concern. A clear line of communication was maintained with the project to understand any changes in the precommissioning / RFO procedure which might impact on the pig design.

The buckle test on the seal is highlighted in Fig.10 with stills taken from a video of the test. A screwdriver was forced into the seal and levered to make the seal buckle, and water was shown coming from the buckle. On withdrawal of the screwdriver, the seal recovered unaided. Figure 11 shows a close-up of the 325-mm diameter disc seal in the small, 257-mm, diameter line. The disc seal takes on a cup-like shape.

Test	Description	Parameters
1	**Full facility test** Test pig through the full test facility.	Measure pig velocity over length of test rig, running pressure and flow rate. Observe leakage past the pig.
2	**Reverse in full facility** Reverse the pig through the full test facility.	Measure pig velocity over length of test rig, running pressure, reverse pressure and flow rate. Observe leakage past the pig.
3	**Initial spools test** Launch 257.3mm – 266.7mm – 305mm straight and flip.	Measure running pressure, flow rate and flip pressure. Observe leakage past the pig.
4	**Observation of rear of pig** Stop pig in 266.7-mm section and observe rear of pig for buckling.	Stop the pig in the 266.7-mm section, remove trap, observe rear of pig, try to induce buckle in seal.
5	**Main pipeline test** Launch 257.3mm – 266.7mm – 305mm – 320mm straight and flip. Repeat at very low and low flows.	Measure running pressure, flow rate and flip pressure. Observe leakage past the pig.
6	**Pig to 305-mm section** Launch 257.3mm – 266.7mm – 305mm – 320mm – 305mm straight.	Measure running pressure and flow rate. Observe leakage past the pig.
7	**Bend test** Launch 257.3mm – 266.7mm – 305mm – 320mm – 305mm – 305mm bend	Measure minimum flow in bend before pig stall. Observe leakage past the pig.
8	**Bend test flip** Launch 257.3mm – 266.7mm – 305mm – 320mm – 305mm – 305mm bend and flip.	Measure running pressure, flow rate and flip pressure. Observe leakage past the pig.
9	**Manifold test 1** Launch 257.3mm – 266.7mm – 305mm – 320mm – 305mm – 305mm bend into manifold and dead head.	Measure running pressure, manifold pressure and flow rate. Record position of pig in Manifold. Reverse pig slowly from Manifold. Observe leakage past pig on reverse.
10	**Manifold test 2** Launch 257.3mm – 266.7mm – 305mm – 320mm – 305mm – 305mm bend into manifold and stop at second off-take.	Measure running pressure and flow rate. Record position of pig in Manifold. Reverse pig slowly from Manifold. Observe leakage past pig on reverse.
11	**Permanent set test 1** Leave pig in 257.3mm spool over night (12 hours minimum). Launch into 266.7mm – 305mm – 320mm straight.	Measure running pressure and flow rate. Observe leakage past the pig.
12	**Permanent set test 2** Leave pig in 266.7mm spool over night (12 hours minimum). Launch into 266.7mm – 305mm – 320mm straight.	Measure running pressure and flow rate. Observe leakage past the pig.

Table 1.

Table 2 summarizes the basic pig parameters. No visible leakage was observed coming from the seals during the tests, which were performed at very low velocity to replicate the actual scenario offshore - around 0.03m/s. The pig was also fully reversible and the flip capacity of the discs deemed to be adequate to make pigging acceptable and safe.

The final test undertaken was to see if the pig would reverse when positioned against the manifold ball valve, a position which meant that the pig would straddle the inlet as shown in Fig.12. To allow the pig to reverse from this position, by-pass ports were opened in front of this pig which allowed pressure to be transferred from between the pig seals to the ball valve, to allow the pig to move backwards (the net force on the pig pushing it in reverse). The size of the ports was critical as the flow needed to generate the necessary reversal pressure must be able to pass through them. It was anticipated that this would prove to be difficult, given the limitations on by-pass size and also on available flow into the off-take.

Parameter	Drive DP (bar)	Flip DP (bar)
257-mm / launch into 10-in	2.2	–
267-mm ID straight pipe	1.8	7.2
323-mm ID straight pipe	0.1	1.2
305-mm ID straight pipe	0.3	1.6
305-mm ID bend	0.5	1.3

Table 2.

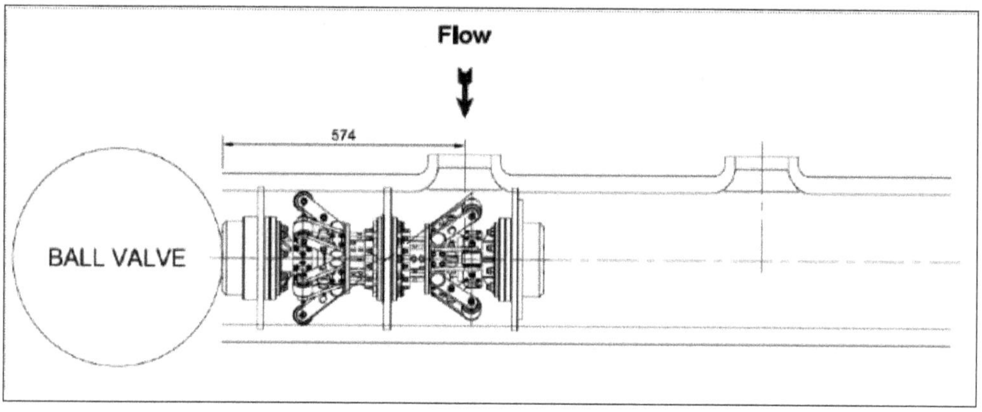

Fig.12. Reversal position at valve.

The problem is outlined in Fig.12: there is a trade-off between the ability to get the flow through the by-pass ports to displace the pig and the ability of the rear seal to hold this pressure without leakage. This has been achieved in other projects, but on those occasions the balance was easier to achieve. Sleeper discs were used to attempt to increase the pressure capacity of the rear seal but this was ineffective. The final position, where some degree of reversal was possible at the ball valve or straddling the off-take, was where the rear two seals were upstream of this off-take (Fig.13). This could not be guaranteed, as the front of the pig would have to be extended, resulting in an unwieldy design and problems negotiating the bends. As a result, the emphasis was put back on the operation to avoid the pig reaching this position in the first place, and this was ensured by increasing the tracking effort subsea.

Offshore operation

The operation took place in March, 2009; it was a success, and the pigs performed well and no gas by-pass was observed.

Four pigs were launched from a temporary vertical pig launcher at the topside on Norne. Before the first pig entered the expansion spool at the manifold, the pig train was planned to be stopped. Due to a delay in communication and the short distance from detection to spool, the first pig finally stopped inside the spool, having passed the first 5-D bend.

After all the pigs had been located using isotope tracking, the pig train was reversed and discs flipped with MEG before being returned with nitrogen.

For both outbound flooding with water and return pigging with nitrogen, the pressures experienced were consistent with the pigging trials that had been performed.

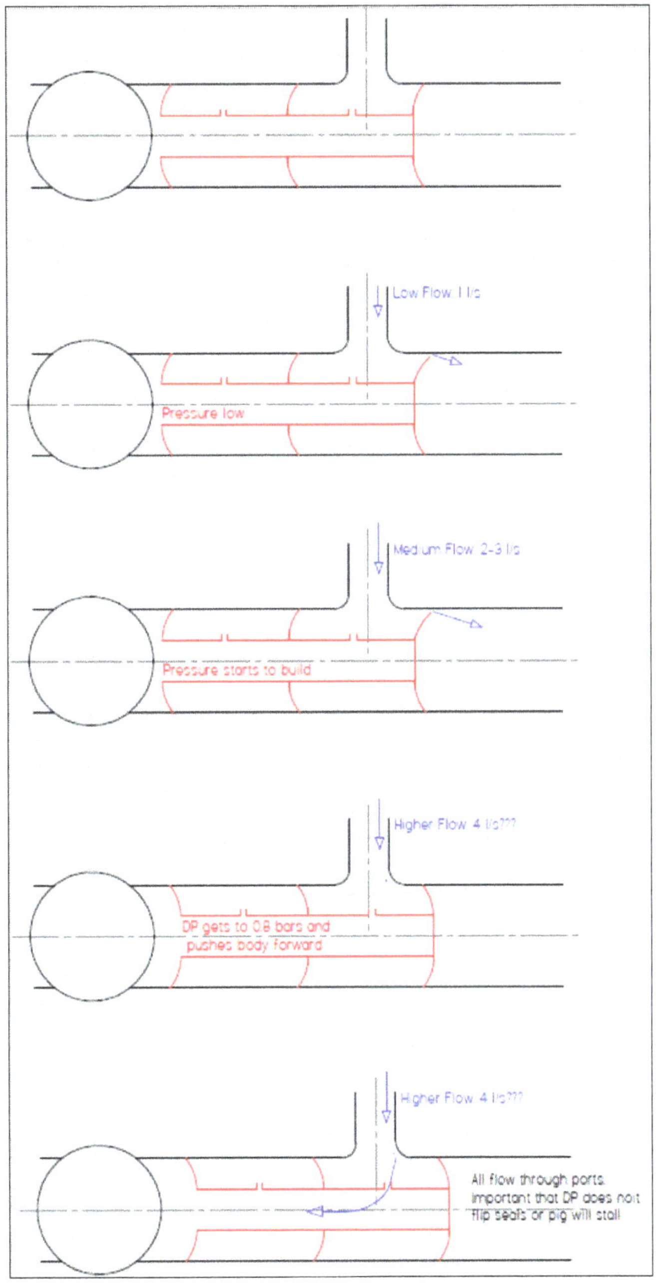

Fig. 13. Reversal at the ball valve – story board.

Conclusion

The multi-diameter bi-directional approach to precommissioning RFO ('ready for operation') is being looked at in more detail, as it potentially rules-out the need for a subsea receiver or launcher and an extra support vessel. The ability to make a single-disc seal work over a wide range of diameters is key to this development, as is the wheel pig to allow the pig to be maintained on the centreline. The Alve pipeline has an approximately 25% increase in diameter. StatoilHydro is now examining a 12-in x 16-in case with a 41% change in diameter, where a similar approach is being adopted with further work on the single seal concept being examined.

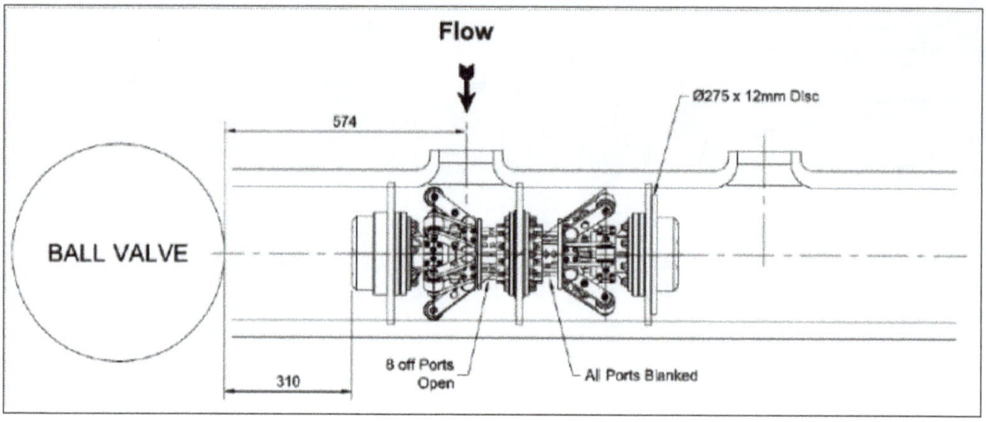

Fig. 14. Reversal position at valve.

Fig. 15. Final pig design.

Acknowledgement

The authors thank Olaf Erland and Tor Grindheim at K-Lab in Kårstø for their assistance in this development.

Capabilities of MFL inspection in Duplex steel pipelines

by Hendrik Aue[1], Werner Thale[1], Age E Pedersen[2], and Samuel Moe[2]

1 Rosen Technology and Research Centre Germany, Lingen, Germany
2 Total E & P Norge, Stavanger, Norway

DUPLEX STAINLESS STEEL is commonly used for offshore pipeline applications. Duplex combines the advantages of ferritic and austenitic steel – corrosion resistance, high strength, and toughness – therefore making it ideal for use on riser sections exposed to wave loads and bending. Duplex pipe is relatively expensive and usually only used for the riser, whereas the rest of the pipeline consists of conventional carbon steel. This mixture of pipeline materials combined with the special magnetic properties of Duplex create a challenging environment for in-line inspection tools utilizing magnetic-flux leakage (MFL) technology.

Rosen inspected a Total pipeline with a Duplex riser in 2008, and then came together in 2009 to investigate the results of the MFL inspection. This paper discusses the results of this investigation based on pull tests in a 12-in' Duplex test pipe with artificial metal loss features.

ROSEN INSPECTED A Total pipeline using an in-line inspection corrosion-detection tool. The riser close to the end of the line is made of Duplex steel, which has significantly different magnetic properties from the rest of the line. To get a better understanding of the magnetic properties of the Duplex pipe material, and to allow an adequate identification and sizing of the detected features, it was decided that pull tests would be necessary using Duplex pipe joints from Total to analyse Duplex steel samples gathered from the test joints.

Rosen, together with Total, performed a series of pull tests in 2009 using the 12-in corrosion-detection tool (CDP). This paper discusses the capabilities of MFL in-line inspection (ILI) in Duplex steel, as well as the results from the pull tests, and a detailed analysis of Duplex material samples.

Duplex pipeline applications

Duplex steel combines the advantages of ferritic and austenitic steel - extreme strength, and resistance against stress-corrosion cracking (SCC) and degrading corrosion - making it especially suitable to resist the extreme forces found on platform riser sections (Fig.1).

Duplex steel is useful for offshore platforms in terms of linepipe and other process applications. The amplified strength of Duplex steel allows for reduced wall thickness and reduced weight. Duplex is also used for onshore applications, for example in pipelines where high erosion rates are present. Carbon steel elbow installations have been replaced by Duplex material in high flow velocity gas pipelines with erosion due to solid particles. In addition, it is used for other pipeline installations such as valves and tee-pieces. Furthermore, this steel is useful for pipelines in cold regions because it also retains its strength in low ambient temperatures, for example down to -40°C. Relatively long Duplex pipeline sections can be found in Alaska; however, due to the expense, Duplex is usually only used for special pipeline applications, as mentioned above.

Fig.1. An example of an offshore pipeline riser.

Duplex material

Duplex steels are called 'Duplex' because they have a mixed two-phase microstructure of grains of austenitic and ferritic steels (Fig.2), each having a content of about 50%. This is why Duplex steel combines the advantages of ferritic and austenitic steels as corrosion, erosion, and SCC resistance, as well as amplified strength and toughness.

Although Duplex steel has a higher tolerance, it is still susceptible to metal loss due to corrosion, erosion, milling features, or third-party damage.

Austenitic steels are non-magnetic while ferritic steels are ferromagnetic. Duplex as a mixture of both is somewhere 'in between', depending on several factors (such as he chemical composition).

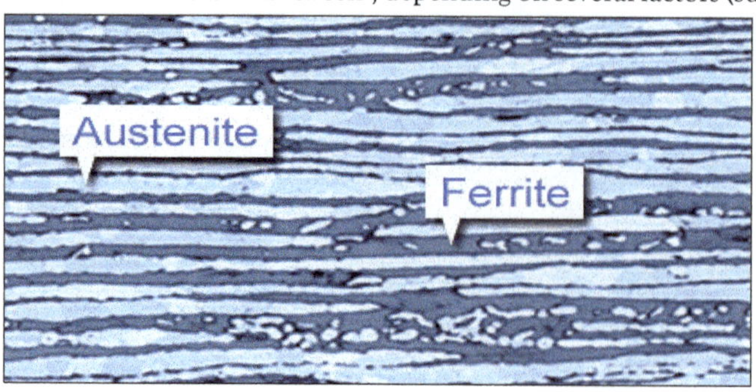

Fig.2. Duplex steel sample under a microscope, showing the two-phase microstructure of austenite (light blue) and ferrite (dark blue) grains.

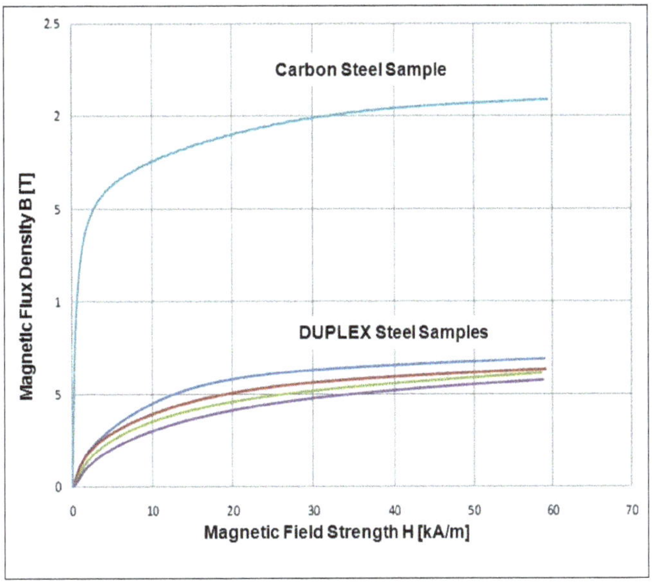

Fig.3. B-H curve comparison between Duplex steel and carbon steel.

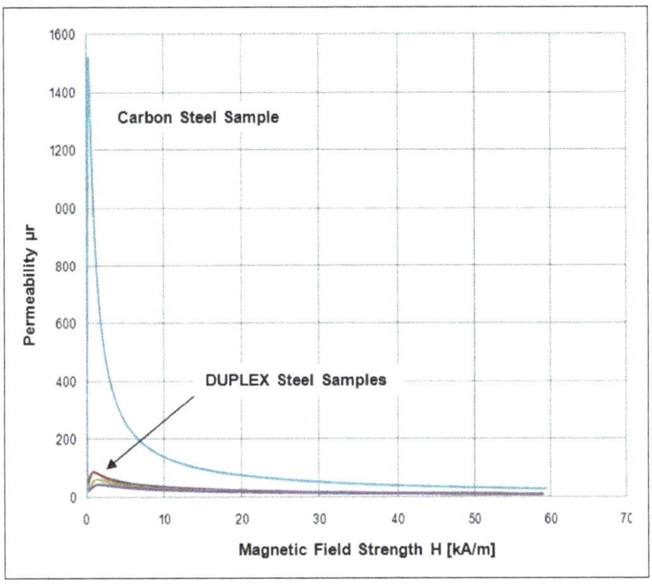

Fig.4. Permeability comparison between Duplex steel and carbon steel.

The investigation described in this paper shows the magnetic properties of Duplex and, as a result, the capabilities of MFL inspection in Duplex pipelines.

Duplex sample analysis

Four samples were taken from two Duplex pipe joints received from Total (14.0 and 16.7 mm wall thickness, cut out in the axial and circumferential pipe directions) and sent to an external institute for analysis purposes. The B-H curves (showing magnetic material properties, see Fig.3) were measured and prepared for input into finite-element method (FEM) software. The investigations on the B-H curves of the Duplex steel show significant differences in the magnetization compared to that of carbon steel material.

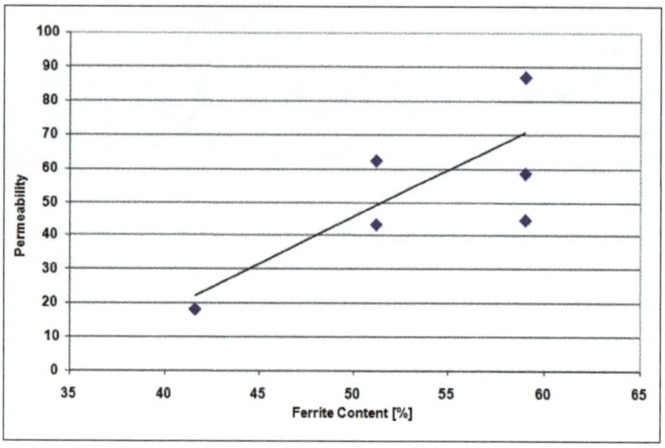

Fig.5. Permeability as a function of the ferrite content.

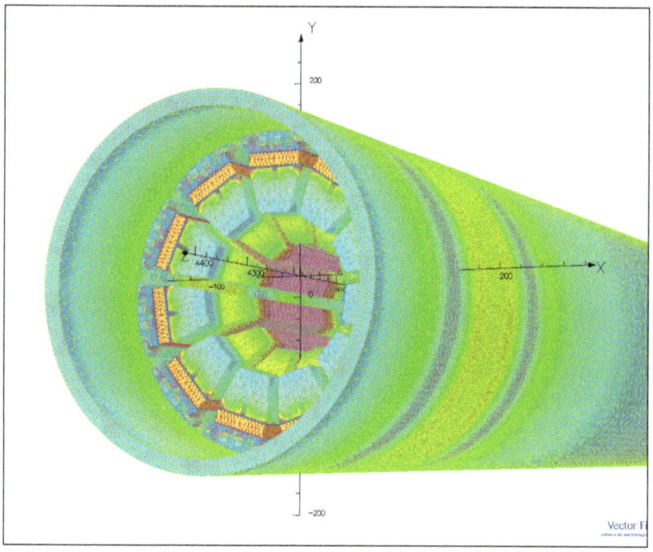

Fig.6. FEM-model of the Duplex pipe including the magnet circuit of the inspection tool.

Figure 3 shows the results of the measurements and compares them with the carbon steel B-H curve. The graph illustrates that the saturation flux density is about three times smaller than that of carbon steel.

For permeability, the effects are even greater, and can be seen in Fig.4. A factor of more than 10 at its maximum can be observed between the properties of Duplex steel and carbon steel. Additionally, the saturation state is completely different: here, the permeability is much smaller, so that the magnetic flux cannot be conducted by the pipeline, as is the case with carbon steel.

Figure 5 shows a Total investigation which visualizes the permeability as a function of the ferrite content. The permeability increases with increasing ferrite content.

FEM calculation

FEM calculations were conducted simulating the MFL ILI tool in the pipeline (Fig.6). The model reflects the identical situation of the pull test discussed below. Using the information from the measured B-H curves, the magnetic field generated by the ILI tool in the pipe wall was calculated.

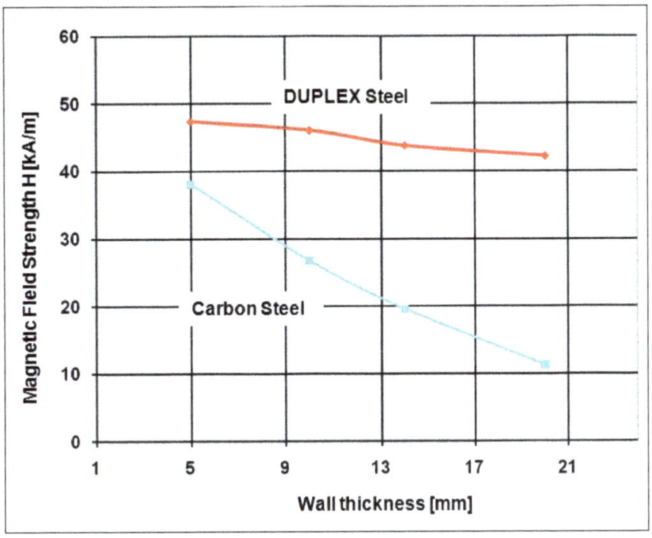

Fig.7. Magnetic field strength vs wall-thickness curve of Duplex in comparison to that of carbon steel.

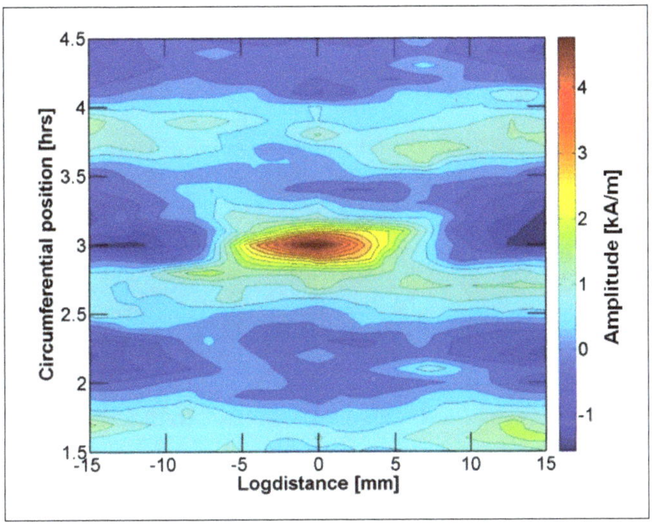

Fig.8. FEM calculation result for internal 20% deep 10-mm diameter effect in Duplex.

The resulting magnetic field strength was plotted as a function of the wall thickness of the pipe (Fig.7).

As input for the FEM calculation, an average B-H curve extracted from the individual Duplex steel samples (Fig.3) was used. As a result of this, Fig.7 shows the comparison of the magnetic field strengths of the Duplex pipe to those of the carbon steel pipes.

Compared with carbon steel, the field strengths of Duplex steel are much higher with the same magnet circuit. For the magnet circuit of the inspection tool used for the pull tests, field strengths higher than 40 kA/m were calculated at the specified wall thickness range in standard carbon steel.

For the simulations of defects in the Duplex pipeline, a full model of the magnet circuit of the inspection tool was needed. This can be seen in Fig.6, where the meshed model is shown, including yoke, magnet-package, brush, and pipeline. The colours represent the strength of the magnetic-flux density: blue indicates low flux density values, whereas red marks strong flux densities.

Fig.9. Cylindrical flat-bottomed EDM feature in 12-in Duplex pipe (red box).

Fig.10. Cylindrical through-wall, and rectangular, EDM features at girth weld (red boxes).

The FEM calculations determine feature amplitudes of the same magnitude and with comparable behaviour (amplitude vs depth, etc.) for simulated defects in Duplex as in standard steel, which indicates that a comparable sizing procedure can be applied to both Duplex and standard pipeline steel. Figure 8 shows the FEM calculation results for a 20% deep and 10-mm diameter internal defect.

Pull test investigation

A pull test series was performed by Rosen and Total at the Rosen Technology and Research Centre in 2009 using a 12-in corrosion-detection tool (CDP). Two welded together Duplex joints (14.0mm and 16.7mm wall thickness) were provided by Total.

A set of artificial features was prepared in the pipe body to investigate the detection and sizing capabilities of the CDP in Duplex pipe. Additional test features were prepared at and next to the girth weld. All test features were prepared with electric-discharge machining (EDM). Figures 9 and 10 show the cylindrical and rectangular EDM features.

Figure 11 shows that all features are visible in the MFL data: even the smallest external feature with 10mm diameter and 30% depth is clearly visible.

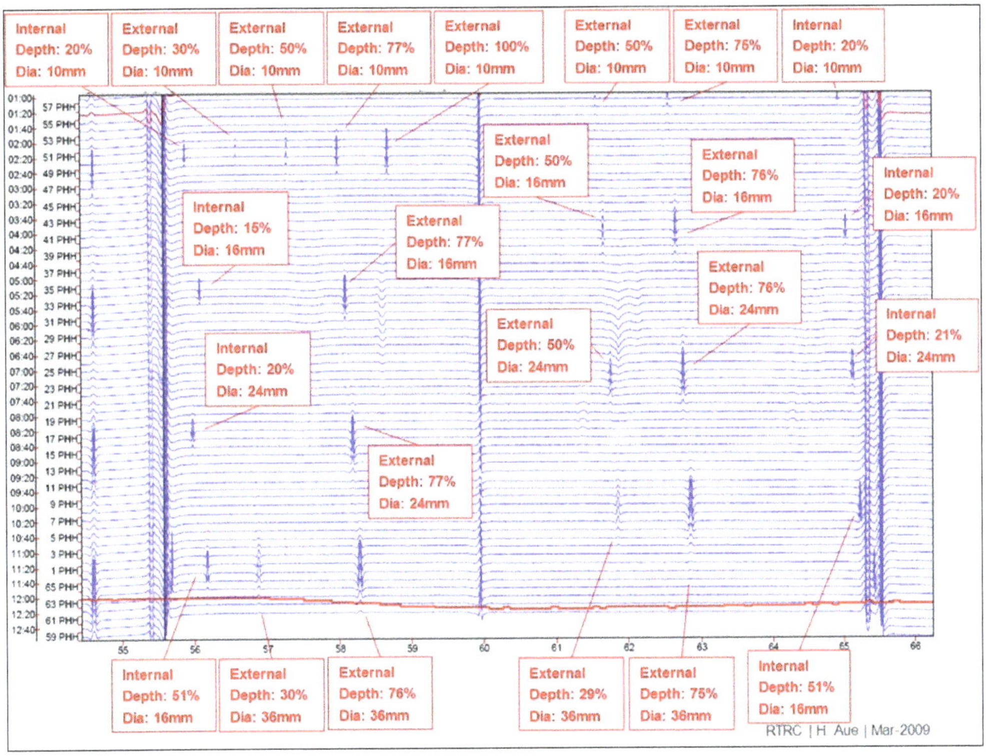

Fig. 11. Line plot of primary horizontal Hall (PHH) sensors of Duplex test joint. All artificial test features are visible in the data (labelled with given dimensions).

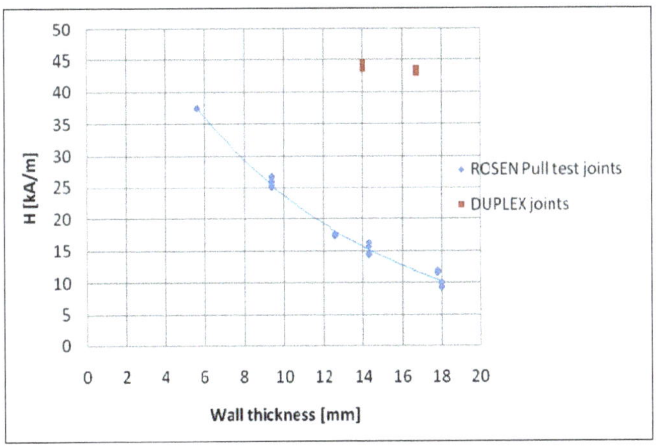

Fig. 12. Comparison of measured magnetic field strength vs wall thickness for Duplex and carbon steel pipe.

The calculated behaviour of magnetic-field strength vs wall thickness based on the measured magnetic properties of the Duplex test segment (with FEM) was confirmed by the pull-test results. Figure 12 shows the measured magnetization levels of the two Duplex joints compared to the magnetization curve of the 12-in pull-test joints of the Rosen pull-test rig.

The first important result is that the CDP is not only capable of detecting external metal loss features, but also that the MFL amplitudes of the external test features are comparable with the corresponding test features in standard steel pipe (such as API 5L grade X52). Figure 13 shows the signal amplitudes of the external test features in the Duplex test joints with 14.0 mm compared to the corresponding features in the carbon steel pull test joint with comparable wall thickness.

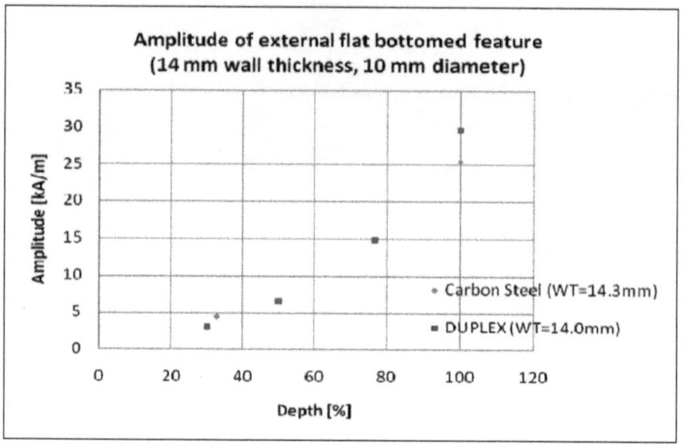

Fig. 13. Comparison of feature amplitude vs depth.

While external features show a similar behaviour, the MFL amplitudes of internal features strongly differ from the corresponding features in carbon steel, especially shallow internal features which have much higher amplitudes in Duplex than in standard pipe steel.

From the above, it follows that a special sizing model has to be used for the inspection of Duplex and that some minor restrictions have to be considered: for example, a restricted detection probability for shallow external features and a reduced sizing accuracy, especially for internal features.

Apart from the smallest internal feature, all internal features show clear signals on the internal / external discrimination channels; therefore, it is estimated that the internal / external discrimination in Duplex is comparable, or only slightly reduced, compared to standard pipeline steel.

The Duplex test segment consisted of two test joints welded together with an intentionally defective girth weld. At girth welds (on standard steel pipelines) the magnetization is usually lower than at the pipe body, due to the extra metal at the cap and the root. At the Duplex girth welds, it was observed that the magnetization was higher than at the pipe body. This is probably due to fact that the magnetic properties of the girth weld materials differ distinctly from those of the pipe body.

Total prepared three girth-weld anomalies: lack of fusion, lack of penetration, and excessive root penetration, each extending over about one third of the circumference. The artificial test features machined at the girth weld (Fig.10) were not suitable for assessing the sizing accuracy of the welding areas, particularly as they are superimposed on the intentionally prepared 'natural' girth-weld anomalies (lack of fusion and lack of penetration). Nevertheless, these features were visible in the data (Fig.14), although it must be emphasized that the detection capabilities were reduced and a sizing accuracy cannot be specified.

In addition to the girth welds, extra metal was detected in the pull-test data for the Duplex joints. This means that not only metal-loss features, but also references such as extra metal, valves, or tees, can be reported for Duplex pipelines.

Conclusion

Duplex steel known as a useful material for protecting pipelines against, for example, stress-corrosion cracking, shows magnetic properties which allow for inspection with a high-resolution

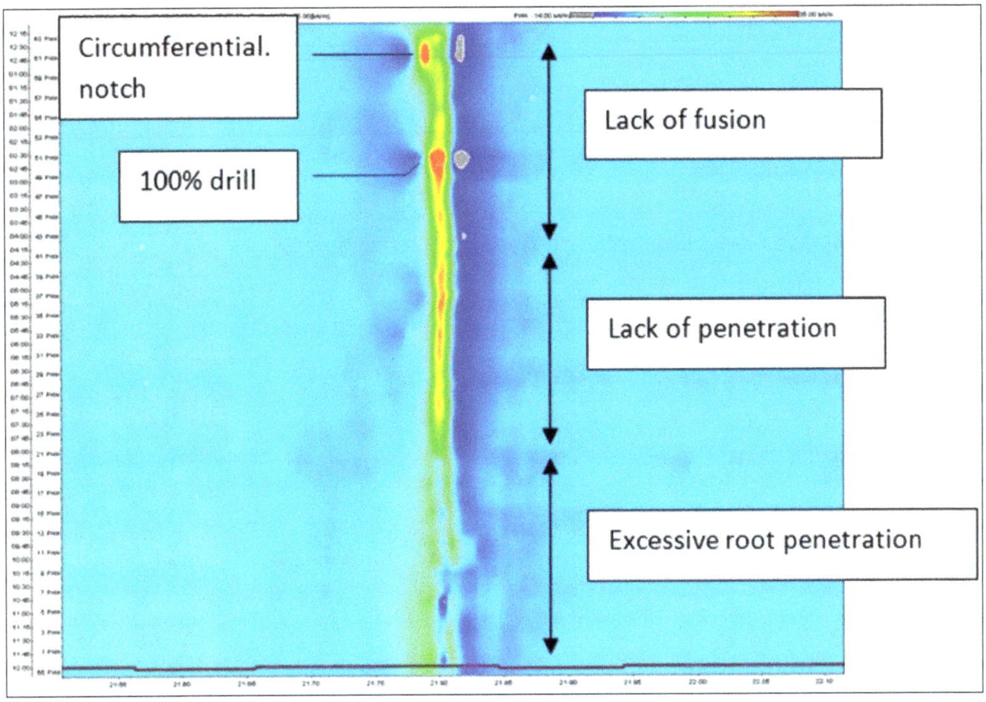

Fig. 14. Girth weld on the Duplex test segment with intentionally prepared girth-weld anomalies and additional artificial test features.

MFL ILI tool. The pull tests showed that metal-loss feature detection and sizing is possible with Rosen's corrosion-detection tools.

With help of the pull-test results, a special calibration for MFL feature sizing was generated. The CDP is not only capable of detecting external metal-loss features, but also the MFL signal amplitudes of the external test features are comparable with the corresponding test features in standard steel pipe (such as API 5L grade X52). The data evaluation showed that the metal-loss defect internal/external discrimination in Duplex is comparable, or only slightly reduced, to that of standard pipeline steel.

Deep metal-loss features in girth welds, as well as girth-weld anomalies such as excessive root penetration, severe lack of fusion, or lack of penetration, were visible in the data. Also features such as extra metal, valves, or tees can be reported for Duplex pipelines. Minor MFL detection and sizing restrictions are also discussed in this paper.

References

H.-J.Bargel and G.Schulze, 2008. *Werkstoffkunde (Materials Science)*. 2008.

W.Thale and H.Aue, 2009. In-line metal loss inspection investigation of Duplex pipeline. Pull Test Report for Total, Rosen.

Augmenting ILI tools to assess external coatings

by Dr J Bruce Nestleroth[1] and Jason K Van Velsor[2]

1 Energy Systems, Battelle Memorial Institute, Columbus, OH, USA
2 FBS, Inc., State College, PA, USA

Introduction

THE COATINGS USED TO protect oil and natural gas pipelines can degrade over time, enabling corrosion and stress-corrosion cracks to initiate and grow. Pipeline companies use in-line inspection (ILI) tools to detect these anomalies, and repair methods to mitigate the result of a failed coating. This project developed inspection sensors that could prevent these anomalies from occurring in the first place by monitoring the integrity of the external protective coating of the pipeline. This coating assessment, which could be performed during a typical ILI, could help pipeline owners assess the general health of the coating protecting their pipeline system. A goal of the design was to keep these sensors simple so that an implementation would not add substantial cost or complexity to a typical magnetic-flux leakage (MFL) or caliper survey.

In this development, a sensor system was designed to generate the proper wave type and modes to assess coating conditions. Non-contact electromagnetic acoustic transducers (EMATs) were designed to send guided waves around the circumference of the pipe. With the use of guided-ultrasonic waves, as opposed to bulk-wave ultrasound, very few ultrasonic sensors were required for implementation. For pipes less than 20in diameter, only two are required: one for sending the wave, and a second for receiving. For larger-diameter pipes, four EMATs were used for 100% circumferential coverage, two EMATs reserved for the excitation of ultrasonic energy and two for receiving the signal. This number of EMATs is an entire order of magnitude less than the number of bulk-wave ultrasonic transducers that would be required to obtain only partial circumferential coverage.

The coating-assessment capability was experimentally demonstrated using a prototype EMAT ILI tool, and all three detection features were shown to perform well in an ILI environment. These demonstrations were carried out in pull rigs at Battelle's Pipeline Simulation Facility and at BJ Inspection Services. Improvement to the prototype were made between each test, the most significant of which was the design and construction of a novel set of thick-trace transmitting and receiving printed-circuit board (PCB) EMAT coils. These coils were designed very specifically to be capable of handling the high current densities created by the 1200-V amplifier. Implementation variables, such as moisture and soil loading, were shown to have a minimal influence on the results.

Coating assessment using ultrasonic waves is not entirely new. Ultrasonic pigs designed to detect stress-corrosion cracks are often influenced by coating condition, and most ultrasonic-based stress-corrosion cracking (SCC) tools are typically good coating-detection tools, and are sometimes marketed for this application. However, the implementation is typically complex, with the number of sensors and wave properties chosen to detect and size small cracks. In contrast, this development was focused on developing a coating-assessment tool, with modelling and experiments to establish an optimal configuration for coating assessment, and the result of this approach was a fundamental improvement over existing methods.

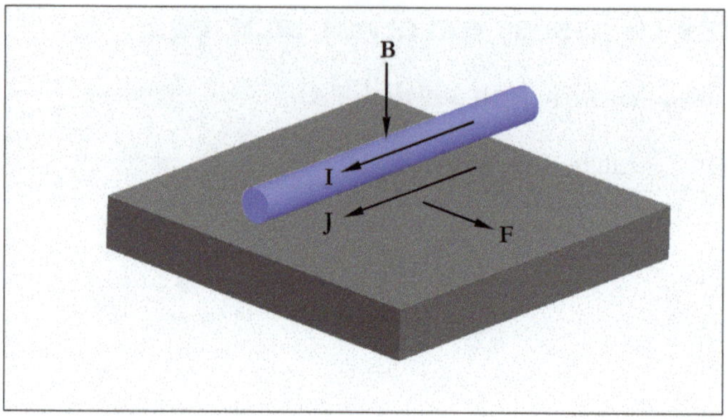

Fig.1. Lorentz EMAT transducer principle.

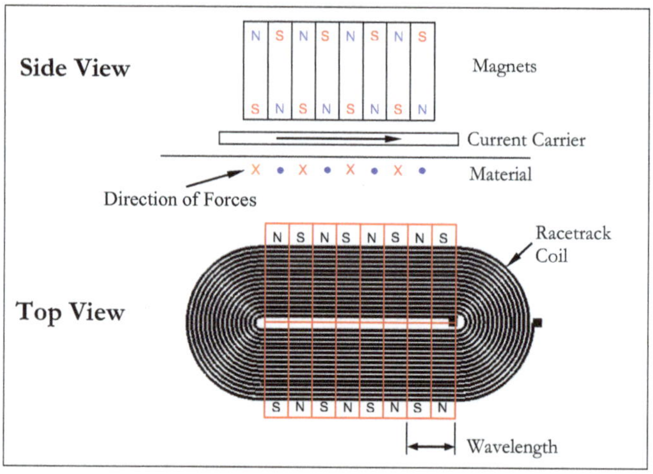

Fig.2. SH-wave EMAT transducer.

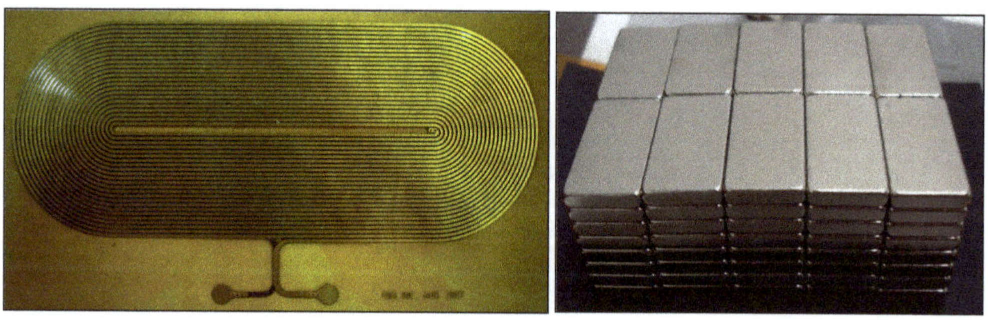

Fig.3. (a - left) Dual-layer EMAT racetrack coil; (b - right) neodymium rare-earth magnet array.

A common approach for assessing coating condition is to assess the amplitude of the received signal; low amplitude means that the coating is good, because the ultrasonic energy went into the coating and was absorbed; while high signal amplitude means that coating was not intact. While this works reasonably well, the pitfall in this approach rests with the fact that the amplitude is affected by many inspection variables including surface roughness, pig speed, and debris. By taking a more fundamental approach to the design in this development, new features for assessing coatings were established, a unique one of which was the arrival time of the ultrasonic wave. For the wave type and frequency selected, the wave velocity is different for bare and coated pipe. Therefore, a disbonded or missing coating can be detected by monitoring the arrival time of the

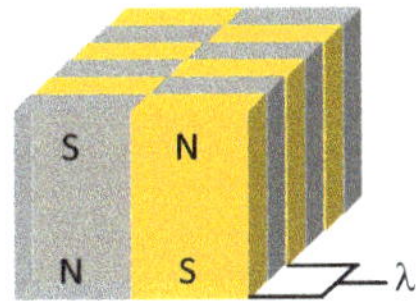

where $\lambda = \frac{c_P}{f}$

EMAT	*f (MHz)*	c_P (mm/µs)	λ (mm)	Magnet Size (mm)
1	0.13	3.23	24.85	12.42
2	0.3	3.23	10.77	5.38

Table 1. Illustration and table showing desired wavelength and magnet dimensions to generate a 130-kHz SH0 mode in a bare pipe.

ultrasonic wave, a feature that is amplitude independent. Another feature for assessing coatings, the absorption of selective frequencies, was also demonstrated.

Along with the benefit of knowing a coating's condition, this technology could help justify longer re-inspection intervals for corrosion surveys. For lines with a few manageable corrosion anomalies, as demonstrated by an MFL survey, verifying that the protective coating is intact would help justify that the threat is properly addressed; an additional benefit would be improved assessment of the SCC threat. One method to assess whether SCC is present on a pipeline is to conduct bell-hole excavations, which are sometimes focused by soil modelling to establish that a susceptible environment is present. The coating-assessment results available from this new technology could be used to focus digs at locations with coating faults, and fewer excavations could therefore be performed to establish the viability of the threat.

The project team was comprised members from the US Department of Transportation (DOT), the Pipeline Research Council International (PRCI), BJ Inspection Services, Battelle, and FBS Inc.

Implementation

For a practical ILI implementation, the sensors should not require any type of coupling liquid and should be capable of efficiently generating shear-horizontal (SH) waves in the pipe wall. EMATs were determined to be the most-appropriate sensor type, as they generate and receive ultrasound by coupling magnetic fields to the flow of current within a specimen. EMATs can be non-contact, operate at elevated temperatures, work on rough or oxidized surfaces, and operate at high speeds. Depending on the configuration of the magnetic field and eddy currents, Lamb- and SH-guided waves can be both generated and received.

The EMATs used in this project are Lorentz-force EMATs, the concept of which is illustrated in Fig.1. The first component in the Lorentz-force transduction mechanism is an eddy current (J) which is induced by passing a current (I) through a wire or trace in close proximity to the specimen. The part to be inspected must be conductive for this to occur. In addition to the eddy current, a static magnetic field (B) must be present; when the current is pulsed in the presence of the magnetic field, a force (F) is induced in the specimen. The direction of the force can be determined by the right-hand rule, and its magnitude and direction are given by Equn 1, where F is the force per unit volume, J is the induced dynamic current density, and B is the static magnetic induction.

$$F = J \times B \tag{1}$$

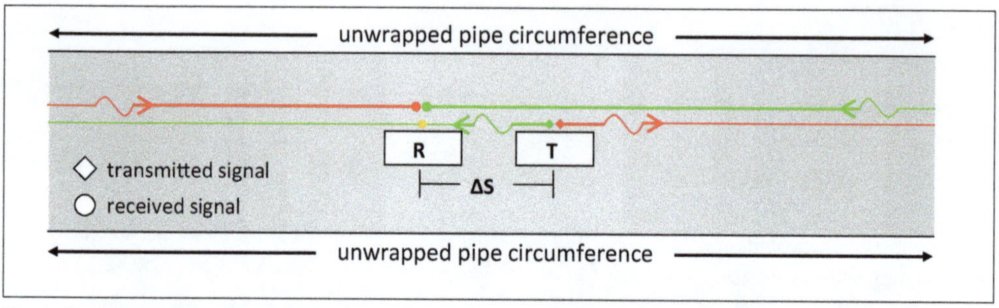

Fig.4. Sensor configuration which allows for the normalization of the received circumferential pulses. The received reference pulse (orange dot) is used to normalize the first complete traverse of the pipe circumference (green dot). Note that the 'red' pulse has not completely traversed the pipe circumference.

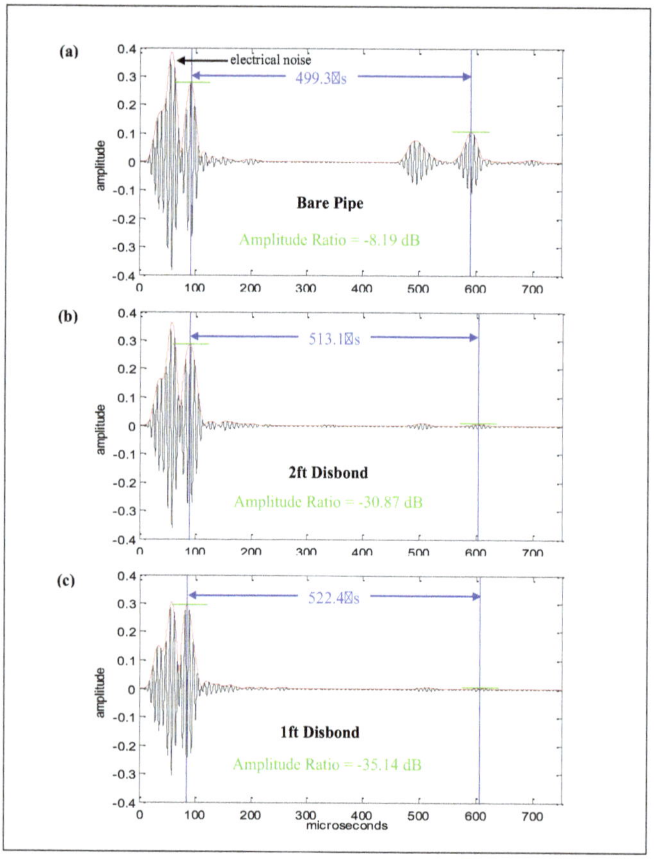

Fig.5. Ultrasonic waveforms obtained from a 20-in diameter schedule 10 pipe with a coal-tar enamel coating with a (a) bare pipe, (b) 2-ft disbonded pipe, (c) 1-ft disbonded pipe.

Figure 2 shows the typical configuration of an SH wave EMAT; the wavelength of the induced wave can be changed by altering the thickness of the magnets. In both the Lamb-wave and SH-wave EMATs, changing the wavelength of the sensor allows the designer to sweep-through the dispersion curve space. A given wavelength activates a line on the dispersion curve that originates at the origin, with a given slope, and the slope of the line can be altered by changing the spacing. A specific mode can then be activated by exciting the transducer at a set frequency.

Table 1 summarizes the desired wavelengths and corresponding magnet sizes for the 130-kHz SH wave that was proposed for detection of disbonded coal-tar enamels. The actual dimensions of the obtained magnets are 12.6mm, resulting in a frequency of 128kHz. Photographs of the core

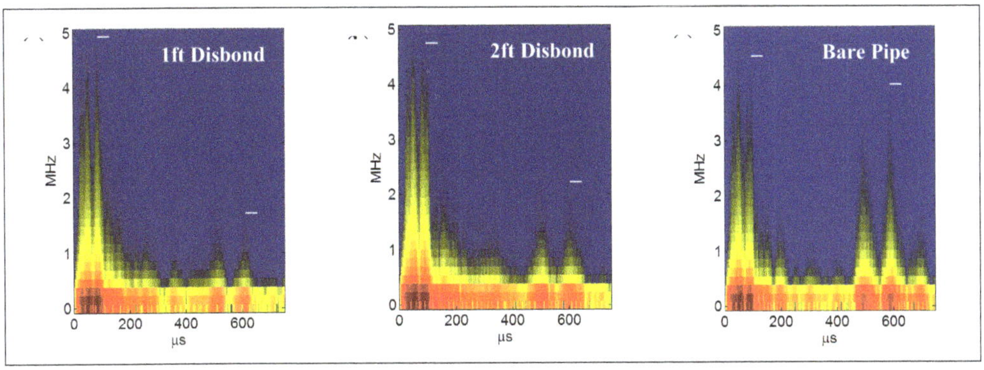

Fig.6. STFTs of RF-waveforms for a (a) 1-ft disbonded area, (b) 2-ft disbonded area, and for (c) bare pipe. Results obtained using a 64-point Hanning window with 32-point overlap.

components of the EMAT components are shown in Fig.3: Fig.3a shows the dual-layer EMAT racetrack coil that was designed specifically for the disbonded-coating detection task, while Fig.3(b) shows an array of 80 N-50 grade neodymium rare-earth magnets stacked in ten columns of eight. The individual magnet dimensions are 0.5in×1in × 0.125in, resulting in a total array height of 1in and a sensor wavelength of 25.7mm.

A sensor configuration was adopted that allowed for the normalization of all received pulses to an initial reference pulse, and an illustration of the sensor configuration is seen in Fig.4. In the configuration, the transmitter (T) and receiver (R) are separated by an arc length (ÄS). The reference pulse is the pulse that travels directly from the transmitter to the receiver, and its point of reception is indicated by the orange dot in the figure. The reference pulse can be used to normalize subsequently received signals in the amplitude, time, and frequency domains. Note that in Fig.4, the 'green' signal is the first signal to completely traverse the circumference of the pipe, whereas the 'red' signal never traverses the area in between the transmitter and receiver prior to first reception. For this reason, the received 'green' pulse is the one used to extract information regarding coating integrity.

Figure 5 shows the results from a disbonded-coating detection study that was completed using the initial prototype sensor with the sensor configuration. A 20-in diameter pipe with a coal-tar enamel coating was used for the study, and disbonds were created by removing the coating in fixed-size areas. In the figure, the first pulse to complete one traverse of the pipe circumference is compared to the reference pulse (see the crosshairs). It is seen that a bare pipe (a), a 2-ft disbond (b), and a 1-ft disbond (c), are easily distinguishable. The first pulse seen in all three waveforms is noise from the EMATs and electronics. From this figure it is obvious that the disbonded area's size affects both the received signal amplitude and time-of-flight, as predicted by the theoretical and numerical modelling. There is more than a 20-µs difference between the bare pipe case and the 1-ft disbonded case, and nearly a 10-µs difference between the 1-ft and 2-ft disbonded cases. Accounting for the noise level of the system and experimental error, time-of-flight differences in excess of 2µs can be reliably measured.

The tendency of attenuation to increase with frequency can be used as a disbonded coating detection feature: the absence of coating will result in a frequency spectrum with higher-frequency content. As the amount of well-bonded coating increases, the higher-frequency content will be filtered-out by absorption. An experimental demonstration of this concept is shown in Fig.6, in which the short-time Fourier transforms (STFTs) of the data sets displayed in Fig.5 are plotted. The difference between the two white lines, marking the maximum frequency content of the reference

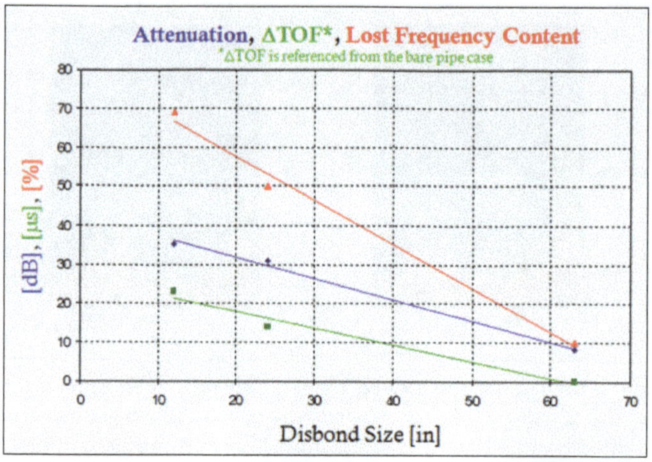

Fig.7. A plot showing the time-, frequency-, and amplitude-disbondment-detection features for three different disbondment sizes in a coal-tar enamel coated pipe.

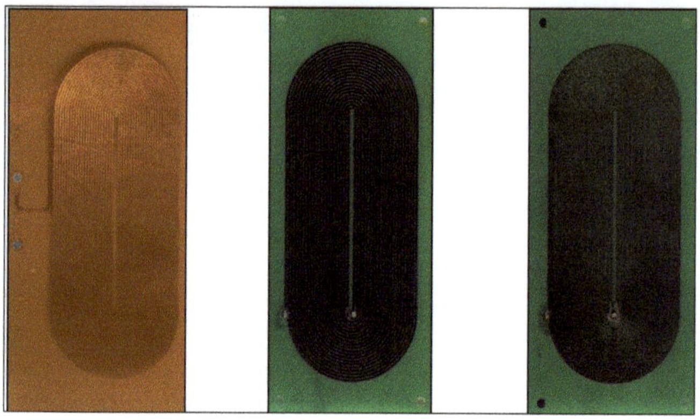

Fig.8. Scanned images of mylar film (left), thick-trace PCB (centre), and thin-trace PCB (right) coils.

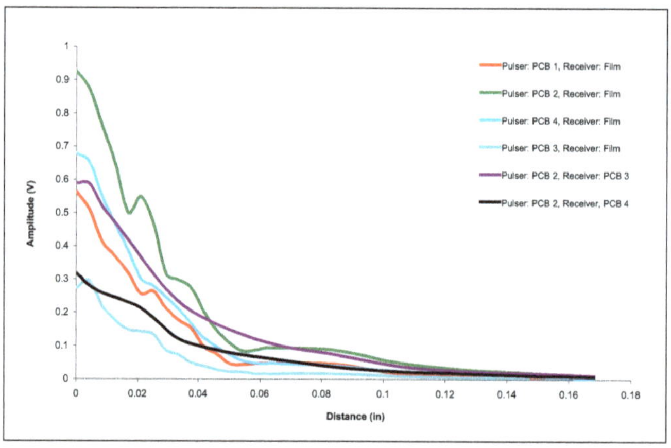

Fig.9. Plot showing the received signal amplitude vs sensor liftoff for the best pulser/receiver combinations.

pulse and the first counter clockwise (CCW) traverse, represents the amount of lost frequency content after one complete circumferential traverse of the pipe. Figure 7, in which all three features are plotted on the same scale, summarizes the results of the disbonded coating proof-of-concept study. The sensitivity of the technique can be increased by combining the three features into a single feature, such as through addition or multiplication. It should be noted that no discernable reflections were obtained from the boundaries of the disbonded-coating regions: it is highly likely that they are very small in amplitude and are absorbed or otherwise lost in the noise floor.

	No. of layers	Approx. turns / in	Approx. trace width (in)	Approx. trace thickness (in)	Approx. substrate thickness (in)
Film	2	25	0.03	0.00125	0.005
PCB 1	1	50	0.01	0.01	0.03
PCB 2	1	21	0.035	0.01	0.03
PCB 3	2	50	0.01	0.01	0.015
PCB 4	2	21	0.035	0.01	0.015

Table 2. Specifications of the different EMAT coils used in performance evaluation

Sensor design

One of the most critical design factors in EMAT heads was optimizing penetration power and maximizing sensor liftoff. Table 2 includes the specification of all the coils tested. The coils consisted of one printed on mylar film ('film') and four on printed-circuit boards ('PCB').

Figure 8 shows scanned images of the three primary coil geometries. From Table 2, it can be seen that the primary differences between the PCB coils were the width of the traces, and whether or not the PCB had traces printed on both sides (two-layer). The most significant difference between the film coils and the PCB coils was the trace thickness, with the PCB traces nearly ten times thicker than that of the film coils. By changing the cross-sectional area of the traces, the electrical impedance and current density of the coil are changed.

Sensor lift-off experiments were performed with an arbitrary wave generator connected to a 1200-V amplifier, and it was found that the load applied by the amplifier was very near the operational limit of the film coils. For this reason, the film coils were not used for pulsing in the 1200-V tests. An impedance-matching network was used between the amplifier and pulsing coil in all tests.

Figure 9 shows the results of the sensor lift-off study for several of the best combinations of pulsing and receiving coils. It is seen that the single-layer thick-trace PCB coil, used as a pulser, and the film coil, used as a receiver, are the optimal sensor pair. For nearly all lift-off distances, this combination of coils provided the highest amplitude. Also of interest is the PCB2/PCB3 coil combination: this is because these two coils are very similar in construction and are, in general, slightly more robust than the film coils. From an implementation standpoint, a more-robust coil may be preferred over several decibels of signal amplitude.

A comparison of the PCB2/film coil combination for both the 1000-V and 1200-V systems was also performed, switching between systems resulted in a gain of nearly 8dB in the signal amplitude. This proves that moving from a 1000-V system to a 1200-V system is incredibly advantageous despite the need for a more 'heavy-duty' pulsing coil.

Pull test results

Four pipes were prepared for pull testing at Battelle's pipeline simulation facility. All pipes were 24-in diameter, and three had coatings applied to their outer surfaces. A photograph of the four samples can be seen in Fig.10, and a description of each pipe is given in Table 3. The internal surfaces of all four pipes had been sandblasted and coated with primer to prevent corrosion.

Fig.10. Photograph showing four pipes used for pull testing at the PSF.

Pull location(in, measured from origin)	Disbondment size	Amplitude loss (dB)	Time-of-flight(μs)	Lost frequency content (%)
1	100%	-13.5	589.2	19
27	approx. 30%	-29.1	601.3	46
99	approx. 30%	- 25.9	596.5	41
170	approx. 30%	-27.8	599.9	46

Table 3. Description of pipe samples used for pull tests at the PSF.

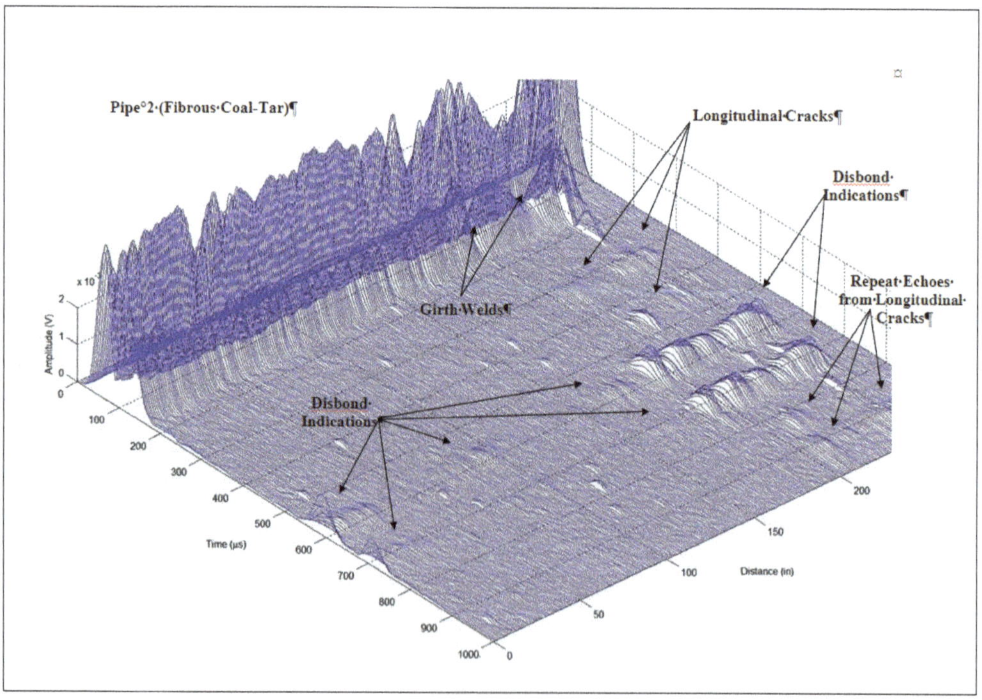

Fig.11. Three-dimensional plot of analytic envelopes of ultrasonic data acquired on Pipe 2, which is coated with a fibrous coal-tar coating.

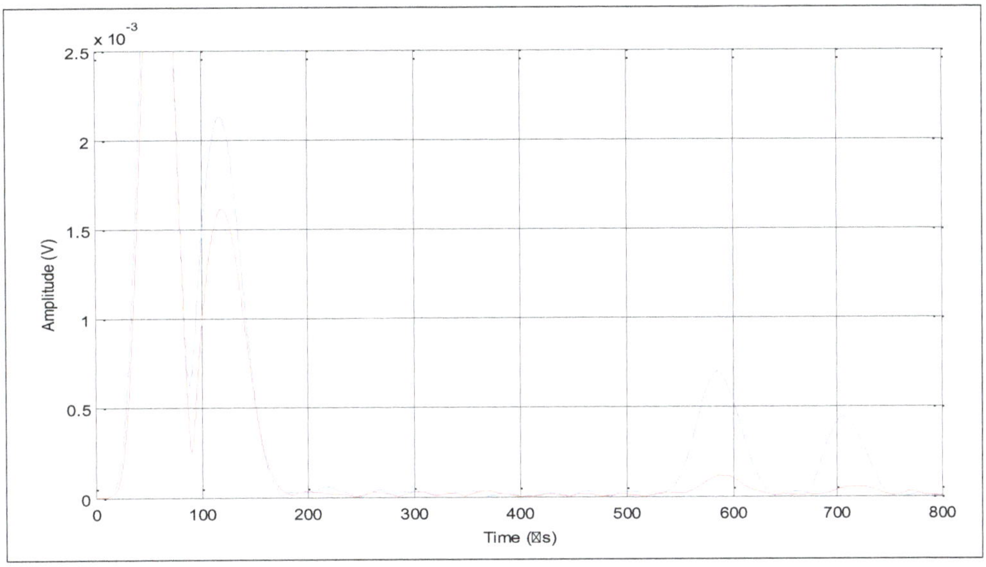

Fig.12. Two-dimensional plot of analytic envelopes of ultrasonic data acquired on Pipe 2 at in into the pull length (blue) where the pipe was bare, and at 27in into the pull length (red) where an approximate 50% circumference disbondment existed.

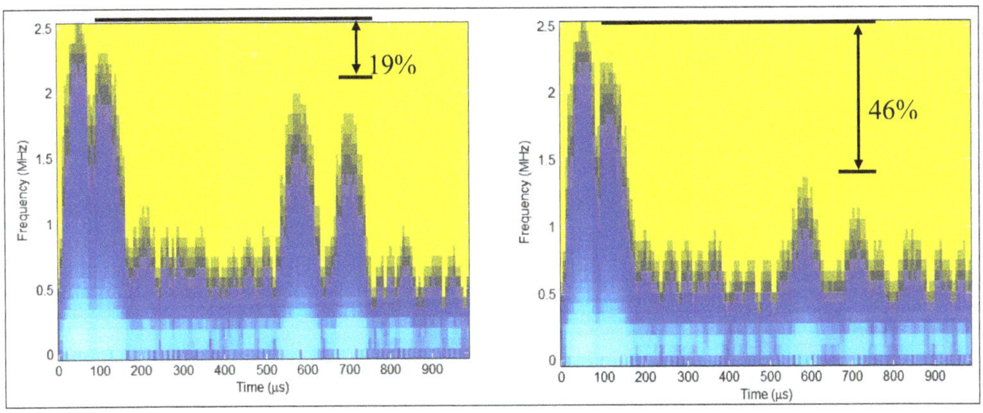

Fig.13. Short-time Fourier transform of ultrasonic data acquired on Pipe 2 at 1in into the pull length (left) where the pipe was bare, and 27in into the pull length (right) where an approximate 50% circumference disbondment existed. A 64-point Hanning window with 32-point overlap was used to obtain these plots.

Runs were completed on each of the four pipes. To generate the plots, the analytic envelope of the RF signal was plotted versus the axial location at which it was obtained, and the result serves as a quick reference for the evaluation of each data set. Figures 11, 12, and 13 show the results obtained from Pipe 2, coated with a fibrous coal-tar wrap. Several coating-disbonded regions, as well as other features, can be seen in Fig.11, and Table 4 summarizes these results along with the results for several other axial locations containing disbondments. It is seen from these figures that, though the amplitude is low, the traverse that travels around the full circumference is successfully able to detect all 24-in disbondments using the amplitude-, time-, and frequency-based detection features. An 8-in disbonded area between locations 53in and 92in was not detected because the signal was completely attenuated by the coating that was well bonded. This is an indication that an actual implementation will need at least two sets of sensor heads.

Pull location(in, measured from origin)	Disbondment size	Amplitude loss (dB)	Time-of-flight(μs)	Lost frequency content (%)
1	100%	-13.5	589.2	19
27	approx. 30%	-29.1	601.3	46
99	approx. 30%	- 25.9	596.5	41
170	approx. 30%	-27.8	599.9	46

Table 4. Summary of disbondment-detection results for several pull locations for Pipe 2 (fibrous coal-tar coating).

Conclusion and future direction

The primary goal of this research was the development of a more-reliable and robust guided-wave disbonded-coating detection technique than that which is currently available. Some of the key contributions of this work are outlined as follows:

- Identification and experimental verification of time-, frequency-, and amplitude-based disbondment-detection features. Prior to this work, the time- and frequency-based features were never used for disbondment detection.

- Development of a sensor arrangement such that all amplitudes can be normalized to some reference pulse, allowing for a more-reliable use of amplitude-based features. This effectively accounts for such things as variation in sensor lift-off.

- Design and construction of a novel set of thick-trace transmitting and receiving PCB EMAT coils. These coils were designed very specially to be capable of handling the high current densities created by the 1200-V amplifier.

- Experimental demonstration of the disbonded-coating detection capability using an actual prototype EMAT ILI tool. All three detection features were shown to perform well in an ILI environment.

- Experimental demonstration of the disbonded- coating detection capability for thin (< 1mm) coatings using a time-based detection. Future work will be needed to optimize this technique through the selection of the ideal wave mode and frequency.

Though a significant contribution toward the reliable detection of disbonded coatings using guided waves has been made, there is always more work to be completed. Because the guided-wave ILI market is still in its early developmental stages, and there are not many competing technologies available, there is significant opportunity to make lasting contributions in this area. It is strongly believed that some of the results of this work will eventually be incorporated into an industrial inspection technology.

Section 8: Administrative and regulatory issues

Integrity first: voluntary performance reporting in a goal-oriented regulatory environment

by Ziad A Saad, Kim J McCaig, and Brenda Kenny

Canadian Energy Pipeline Association, Calgary, AB, Canada

IN 2007, the Canadian Energy Pipeline Association (CEPA) published a report titled Integrity First *which strives to achieve two goals:*

- *For the pipeline industry to communicate performance with its stakeholders and regulators in the areas of pipeline integrity, health and safety, and environmental performance.*
- *To define performance success quantitatively with appropriate metrics and statistics.*

This paper will focus on discussing the second goal and, most specifically, on how voluntary reporting of performance metrics is a necessity in an era of goal-based regulations.

For a regulatory agency to effectively manage its dual responsibility to protect the public while facilitating efficient energy transportation, it can be argued that goal-based regulations allow for the best compromise to satisfy both responsibilities. In theory, such regulations 'set the bar' at a level that is acceptable to society and it is up to the pipeline company(ies) to determine the most sensible method to achieve the intended goals. Arguably, the pipeline company is in the best position to make decisions on how to safely operate the pipeline with the least amount of risk to workers, the public, and the environment while ensuring financially viable operations. However, there must be some mechanism to demons :trate transparently to the regulator (and ultimately the public) that the company is meeting the intent of the regulations and not allowing conflicting interests to supersede safety, reliability, and environmental responsibilities.

The Canadian Energy Pipeline Association

CEPA represents Canada's transmission pipeline companies. Its members transport 97% of Canada's daily crude oil and natural gas production from producing regions to markets throughout Canada and the United States.

The public context of pipeline development in Canada

As public attitudes have changed during the last 30 years, so too have the social, economic, and environmental parameters within which the pipeline industry operates. The industry's primary objective remains the safe, reliable, and efficient transport of energy resources to market, but this fundamental activity now occurs within a radically different climate of public opinion and regulatory oversight.

Permitting, as well as constructing and operating, a pipeline is becoming an exceedingly complex endeavour. Issues of personal safety and environmental protection dominate the industrial agenda in recognition of growing public expectations and boundless scepticism about corporate trustworthiness. Government regulators, aware of and sensitive to the shifting sands of public opinion, increasingly encourage direct company-stakeholder resolution of concerns, and routinely incorporate those expectations into their project decisions. "Consultation between pipeline companies and regulators has historically been excellent in Canada and that reputation has to be extended to people working and living near pipelines"[1]. Many pipeline companies have tackled these challenges head-on with enthusiasm and remarkable innovation on an individual basis. Others, it is fair to say, have been surprised by the changes and complexity of the regulatory climate, and in some instances their efforts may appear haphazard or half-hearted. Even with application of industry best practices, companies have witnessed an unfortunate mixture of project delay, escalating costs, mounting stakeholder discontent and deepening regulatory confusion[1]. The situation reassures no one, yet remains intractable.

The pipeline industry has come to this impasse after decades of regulatory evolution. Initially, regulators prescribed solutions that relied largely on the expertise of pipeline companies to establish construction standards. Such standards were based almost exclusively on engineering considerations and did not address many of the issues of concern to individual landowners, special-interest groups, and other stakeholders. As time went on and expectations changed, regulators gradually adopted a performance-based approach that relied more on consensus-based standards[2] and laid out goals and performance targets without prescribing the means to their achievement. The evolution of regulation in Canada is described in some detail in a paper entitled *Goal-based regulation of pipelines in Canada* [2]. While more flexible and more effective in producing results than prescriptive regulation, performance-based regulation can seem vague. As such, it has created challenges in assuring that changing stakeholder expectations are met. Those shortcomings are most noticeable around non-quantifiable objectives such as building community capacity to accommodate impending socio-economic change or the design of public consultation programmes that need to be timely, inclusive, and thorough.

From time to time regulators have supplemented their decisions and recommendations with additional guidance notes, while the industry itself has gradually developed more-comprehensive

1. Regulatory delays in the Mackenzie pipeline project are a prime example of these difficulties.

2. Most pipeline regulations in Canada adopt the requirements of the CSA Z662 standard to address technical requirements for design, construction and operation of pipelines.

voluntary codes of practice. Despite these evolving and well-meaning efforts, the Canadian pipeline industry continues to face expanding demands from stakeholders.

Goal-oriented and performance-based regulation remains the preferred means of addressing this persistent impasse. Like all regulation, goal-oriented regulation sets the height of the bar for industry performance. During the last decade in particular, regulators have shifted toward a more-balanced consideration of the full range of economic, social, and environmental issues inherent in pipeline construction. Indeed, balance is the pivot on which goal-oriented regulation turns. Yet finding the appropriate balance among competing interests, and clarifying what success looks like, remains highly elusive. It is anticipated that this uncertainty will not only persist but also intensify as North America enters a period of unprecedented infrastructure rehabilitation and expansion[3].

The need for industry-driven solutions

Regulatory authorities invariably set the standard for industry performance at a level that is publicly acceptable, but finding appropriate ways in which to meet or exceed that standard must remain the province of pipeline companies and, by extension, of the pipeline industry. While struggling with heightened public expectations, pipeline companies remain in the best position to determine how to build, operate, and maintain their infrastructure with the lowest degree of risk to workers, the public, and the environment while maintaining sound financial performance.

Many pipeline companies have responded to heightened public and regulatory expectations with remarkable innovation and, as a result, have experienced a lesser degree of difficulty when embarking on significant pipeline-development projects. Notwithstanding many individual successes, CEPA member companies determined that public confidence in their stewardship will grow in lockstep with principled and observable progress within the industry as a whole. It was necessary for the industry to present a united front and proactively establish a common set of principles, practices and metrics that can be presented to stakeholders as a consistent reflection on the entire industry. It is thus that the *Integrity First* programme and publication were launched in 2007.

From the pipeline industry's perspective *Integrity First* is intended to:

- provide positive visibility for the pipeline industry;
- enhance the industry's public image;
- support an environment of favourable regulation and policy making;
- showcase the industry's commitment to public safety and the environment; and
- strengthen public understanding that pipelines are indispensable infrastructure and there is no practical substitute for them.

The *Integrity First* programme is comparable to similar programmes adopted by other resource industries. For example, in 1983 the Canadian Chemical Producers' Association developed its self-administered Responsible Care Programme [3] to promote and demonstrate continuous improvement in environmental, health, and safety performance. This occurred in response to public concerns. Three years later, this landmark programme was adopted and spread around the world by the Chemical Manufacturing Association in the United States following Union Carbide's catastrophic release of toxic chemicals at Bhopal, India. Similarly, in 1993, timber

3. Pipeline companies in Canada have proposed, or are proceeding with construction on over C$20 billion in new pipeline projects in next decade.

companies responded to consumer demand by launching the Forest Stewardship Council (FSC) [4], an international certification and labelling system that "guarantees that the forest products you purchase come from responsibly managed forests and verified recycled sources." Participation in the FSC has now grown to include 640 members from 67 countries. In 2003, the Canadian Association of Petroleum Producers (CAPP) created a Stewardship Programme [5] that promotes "responsible resource development and continuous improvement in environmental, safety, and social performance". No upstream petroleum producer can belong to CAPP without adhering to the principles of the Stewardship Programme. More recently, the Canadian Mining Association developed a stewardship initiative called Towards Sustainable Mining [6] in recognition of the fact that "the *status quo* is not sustainable. Public views and goals are changing and the mining industry must improve its performance, both socially and operationally, in order to remain in step with broader community values." These, and similar initiatives in disparate resource-based industries, are dedicated to the simultaneous advance of industry standards, regulatory satisfaction, and public credibility.

In order to succeed in achieving the industry's objectives, the *Integrity First* programme must satisfy some basic criteria:

- present a common set of principles and commitments that all CEPA members will uphold;
- confirm minimum operating standards and measurable performance reporting metrics for members; and
- demonstrate a commitment to continuous improvement and transparency through annual public reporting.

Linking goals and performance

In order to credibly deliver on its objectives, *Integrity First* must incorporate comprehensive performance indicators. In general, the selected performance indicators must be aligned towards addressing public concerns yet appropriate for regulators to utilize in support of new project development. To that end, CEPA decided on four main criteria that all performance indicators must embody.

Criterion 1: Meaningfulness

Today's pipeline companies routinely collect, analyse, and interpret voluminous data on many different topics. Sometimes, as is frequently the case with financial data, the analysis and reporting is prepared for internal decision-makers only or perhaps for private review by outside financial institutions.

Typically, it is only analysis for regulatory purposes that rests in more generally available company-wide data and finds its way into a printed or online report. Even then, these data may include topics as obtuse to the ordinary reader as environmental non-compliance statistics, formulaic safety statistics, and greenhouse-ggas (GHG) emission rates expressed as CO2 equivalents.

Needless to say, there is no deliberate deception or obfuscation. Rather, the report authors have neglected to identify their readership in its entirety. Moreover, it must be remembered that it is rare for two distinct report audiences to need or expect the same information. Customarily, report writers are focused on the specific data they need for their particular analysis. While this may satisfy an internal need, the data are usually too narrow in scope and technical in nature to address the concerns of a wider audience.

Secondly – and this is discussed more thoroughly under Criterion 2: Transparency – the choice of language in a corporate (or industry) document can further understanding or it can hinder it. In short, the criterion of 'meaningfulness' is really a plea for clarity and relevance. Any data that pipeline companies put before a wider audience in the hope of encouraging understanding must be germane to the concerns of that external audience and be presented simply and clearly. As is so often the case, plain language is the key to good communication.

CEPA anticipates that its annual *Integrity First* report will always be predicated on the needs of a largely non-technical audience. For example, when presenting the yearly review of pipeline-integrity management, CEPA expects to offer an analysis of leaks or substance releases from pipelines. In doing so, CEPA would be careful to describe plainly the operational conditions resulting in leaks, sources of such leaks, root causes, response, and environmental-mitigation efforts. In other words, CEPA intends to identify issues of public and regulatory concern, discuss their implications, and offer an analysis of the entire industry's performance, good or bad, in this area. Ideally, the report will focus on the main social, economic, and environmental impacts of the pipeline industry's activities.

In short, *Integrity First* is committed to offering data that are meaningful to both industry and its stakeholders in terms anyone can understand.

Criterion 2: Transparency

Numerous third-party studies have shown that companies which routinely and voluntarily provide stakeholders with credible information about their activities enjoy and benefit from a more-positive public reputation. Reduction of what is sometimes called 'reputational risk' enhances corporate relations with communities, reduces friction over land access and related rights-of-way issues, diminishes the need for lengthy and expensive hearings into project applications, and often lessens the degree of public cynicism and hostility when adverse incidents occur. By extension, the same benefits should accrue to an industry when thorough, ongoing communication can be expected from the organization which represents the industry.

In transparent reporting, the basic issues are what is communicated, to whom, and how. *Integrity First* is committed to annual preparation of a report that identifies performance metrics common to CEPA members. While the precise nature of those metrics is yet to be determined, it is possible to say that they will deal with issues such as pipeline integrity and related safety matters, emissions, product releases, and environmental reclamation. The annual report will be freely available to anyone desiring a copy either in print form or online, or in both formats.

Most importantly, the content of the report will be presented in plain language, supplemented with meaningful graphics and whenever possible, comparative charts that show industry trends in the main areas of concern. In 2008 CEPA expects to be able to present baseline data for all indicators that will be tracked annually. Over time, this will permit the development of comparative charts. The methodology for selecting, analysing and presenting the data will also be explained.

Finally, *Integrity First* will be at pains to ensure that the numbers used to calculate the metrics can be verified independently, and that the methods of calculation can be reproduced. Both are essential to demonstrating transparency.

While the general public has never had a single source for information like this on the Canadian pipeline industry, CEPA's *Integrity First* reports are also expected to be an asset to individual pipeline companies that wish to benchmark their performance against that of the industry as a whole. As studies have shown, the lack of standardized metrics actually slows the diffusion of industry best practices. CEPA believes that access to cumulative industry data has the potential, over time, of elevating the performance of the entire Canadian pipeline industry.

Criterion 3: Apples-to-apples comparisons

The pipeline industry has long prided itself on being the safest way to transport oil and natural gas over land. That position is based in a comparison of pipeline safety records with those of rail and truck carriers. While this comparison happens to favour pipelines, the example is more important in the context of this paper because it compares apples with apples. By contrast, to introduce ocean-going tankers into the comparison would be inappropriate.

The same logic must apply to the comparison of pipeline data within *Integrity First* reports. For example, if *Integrity First* chose to discuss risks that pipelines pose to public safety, the comparison would of necessity include data from transmission pipelines, gathering pipelines, and distribution pipelines, but would need to clarify the unique nature of those lines. Comparisons between types of pipeline would need to clarify the differences in risk frequency and potential consequence.

Furthermore, *Integrity First* will undertake to establish an unambiguous definition of each comparative metric that can serve as the standard for the collection and analysis of data associated with the indicated metric. Without such a set of rules, neither individual companies nor external stakeholders could be confident about the message that the performance indicators provide.

Criterion 4: Consistency over time

Performance indicators should always be relevant to the uses they are intended to serve, able to be measured with existing tools and at reasonable cost, and capable of comparability. This latter point – the ability to track indicators over time or compare them company-to-company – is particularly important when one of the overriding goals is to enhance performance on an ongoing basis.

One of the chief benefits of an initiative such as *Integrity First* is its ability to discern and communicate about industry trends. This is as important for individual pipeline companies as it is for external stakeholders. Their motivations in reviewing metrics over time may be different, but their analytical needs are the same.

Meaningful comparisons over time are possible, however, only when the same data sources, collection methods, and analyses are used to arrive at the metrics. This is particularly challenging when different companies are involved over time, or if they alter the way in which they assemble data and perform their calculations on that data.

By subscribing to the *Integrity First* programme, member companies will endorse a common set of practices that will facilitate the desired industry-wide consistency over time.

In addition to the four general criteria discussed above, it was clear that the performance indicators must also reflect a full range of social, economic and environmental values. In that regard CEPA determined that the performance indicators must include industry statistics on:

- health and safety such as total recordable incident frequency rates (TRIFs), driving incident frequency rates, etc.

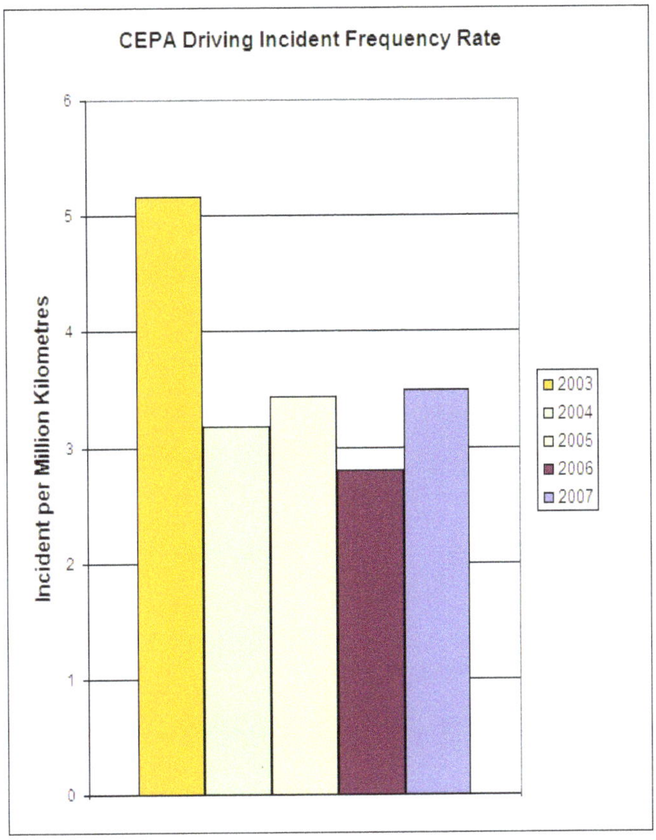

Fig. 1. A typical example of data: five-year driving record.

- pipeline integrity, such as pipeline defect numbers, frequency of inspections, spills, and releases, etc.
- the environment, such as levels of ground disturbance during construction and maintenance, completed land-remediation efforts, wild-habitat restoration, air emissions, etc.

Leading versus lagging indicators

Lagging indicators are, of course, those that measure the result at the conclusion of a process. They are almost invariably quantitative in character, easily understood and, it must be said, generally preferred by members of the public and regulatory bodies because of their unequivocal nature. The annual volume of fugitive emissions from mainline compressor stations would be a lagging indicator.

Leading indicators, on the other hand, are not definitive but rather suggestive of outcomes. They are often qualitative in nature. For example, a marked increase in the number of employees who receive specialized driver training in a given year may suggest a future reduction in the number of vehicular accidents. Numerous studies have demonstrated that using leading indicators often influences future behaviour for the better. Unlike lagging indicators, leading ones allow for course correction.

Integrity First's reports will use both lagging and leading indicators. While the former establishes clear, repeatable, benchmarks, the latter promotes awareness, fosters discussion, and potentially results in significant new solutions to vexing problems.

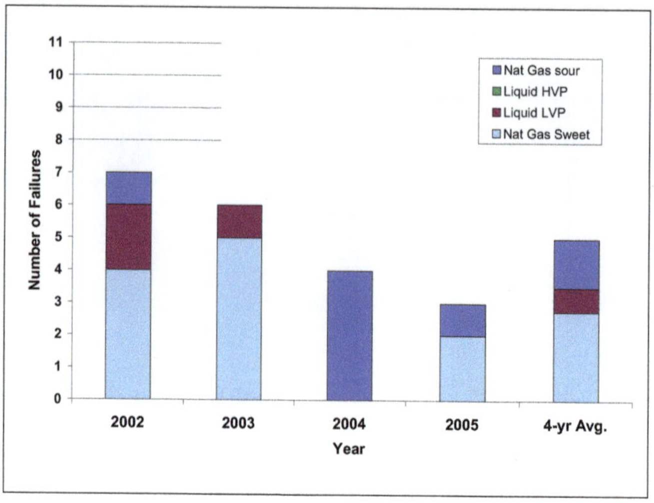

Fig.2. A typical example of data: tracking number of significant failures.

Expected results

Adoption of a holistic perspective toward the customary activities of pipeline companies may be expected to resonate positively and gain acceptance at every level of the corporation. Boards of Directors will appreciate the way in which *Integrity First* dovetails with the process of strategic planning and due diligence. Senior executives will find it easier to clearly enunciate policy and performance expectations. Project engineers will be empowered to honour the injunction of The Canadian Council of Professional Engineers to "provide leadership to advance the quality of life through the creative, responsible, and progressive application of engineering principles in the global context". And field representatives will gain a distinct advantage in dealing with contentious local issues and feel supported by the company's leadership as they do so.

CEPA is confident that *Integrity First* will also find champions among a wide circle of public and regulatory stakeholders. If, for example, a county or municipal representative is called upon by local constituents to explain and justify a council decision to allow a controversial land re-zoning application for a pipeline right-of-way, he or she should be able to turn to the most recent annual *Integrity First* report and find accurate information about the industry's safety record, its approach to environmental protection and sustainability, its track record on clean-ups, and its respect to the property rights of private landowners and First Nations. These cumulative industry data will serve as a reassuring context for information about the specific company that intends to construct the pipeline. Such reports will, in the course of time, become the most reliable and trusted source of data on the overall performance of the Canadian pipeline industry.

Ultimately, *Integrity First* will provide the industry with a credible tool to demonstrate that it is well-tuned to changing public and regulatory trends and is proactive in responding to stakeholder needs. Progressively, the programme will contribute to greater uniformity of practice within an industry that prides itself on continuous improvement. A growing corporate ability to identify and use industry best practices, as well as to take notice of industry benchmarks, will gradually raise the bar for everyone. Realistically, the cumulative data may not always show continuous improvement, yet that is the price of public transparency. Ideally, public response to the industry's view of itself will encourage greater forward momentum on all performance measures.

Conclusions

Integrity First is about three things: continuous improvement in the performance of the pipeline industry; providing regulators with information that would enhance their ability to do their jobs effectively; and earning and retaining the confidence of neighbours and other key stakeholders. The success of the initiative can be established only with reference to the responsiveness of the pipeline industry to those interrelated needs.

The initiative will facilitate this by giving individual pipeline companies the unprecedented ability to compare their performance metrics with those of the industry. Simultaneously, transparent reporting can be expected to elevate both public understanding of and expectations about the industry's performance. In so doing, *Integrity First* will encourage the industry's best performers to innovate further and its worst performers to improve competitively. And, over time, it is anticipated that the continuing evolution and adoption of best practices will be the norm within the industry. Through *Integrity First*, exceptional performance will become the standard by which our industry's ethical integrity is measured.

Such a transformation will not occur overnight. A great deal of discussion and debate must occur first, especially about the selection of appropriate performance metrics. In the short term, there may be miscommunication and missteps and even mistrust. Over the longer term, regulatory guidance and public feedback will be important in refining our approach. But with persistence and goodwill CEPA believes that this important initiative will eventually foster a public belief in our industry's ethical integrity that matches our enviable reputation for pipeline integrity.

References

1. K.Vollman, 2000. Towards goal-oriented regulation. Proc. Int. Pipeline Conf., October 2000, Calgary, Alberta, Canada.
2. K.Paulson, 2004. Goal based regulation for pipelines in Canada. 4th Int. Conf. on Pipeline Technology, May, Ostend, Belgium.
3. http://www.responsiblecare.org, Global Charter
4. http://www.fsccanada.org
5. http://stewardship.capp.ca/About/what_is_stewardship.html
6. http://www.mining.ca/www/Towards_Sustaining_Mining

Dealing with uncertainty in pipeline integrity and rehabilitation

by Rafael G Mora, Dr Alan Murray, Joe Paviglianiti, and Sara Abdollahi

National Energy Board, Calgary, AB, Canada

DETERMINING THE ongoing fitness for service of an energy transmission line, whether in response to an incident or as part of a due-diligence review, involves conducting an engineering assessment. Many pipeline standards and regulations refer to such assessments without providing much detail as to their expected extent or proof of adequacy. This lack of clarity creates difficulties for both the pipeline operator and its governing regulatory body. Recently, several standards and recommended practices have been published which have attempted to provide a framework for threat identification to establish due diligence and assist in the development of integrity-management programmes. With the exception of Annex O in the Canadian Z662 pipeline standard, the approaches offered are deterministic in nature and no guidance is given on how to deal with the uncertainties contained in establishing a baseline condition, the defect-assessment methods used, or the quality of their input data. This paper discusses measurement, modelling, and interpretation errors that could affect the validity of integrity assessments. As a first phase of this development, this paper introduces a case study that identifies the uncertainty effects of in-line inspection accuracies during the criticality assessment of reported metal-loss anomalies that could fail by leak or rupture, and proposes some industry technical approaches on how to deal with uncertainty in the development of integrity verification and rehabilitation programmes.

THERE ARE A number of circumstances in which a pipeline operator and its regulatory authority are faced with making a determination of the current conditions of a section of pipeline and assessing its fitness for intended service. Examples range from a change in service conditions – such as flow reversal or permitted operating pressure increase – through re-activation of a deactivated line to dealing with a change in service fluid. Latterly the National Energy Board (NEB) has dealt with applications involving one or other of these circumstances. In addition, there is a continuing requirement to investigate incidents and oversee the development and effective implementation of integrity-management programmes to ensure the continuing safety of existing pipeline systems. The Canadian oil and gas pipeline standard CSA Z662-2007, adopted by reference in the Board's Onshore Pipeline Regulations OPR-99, requires that an engineering assessment be performed to establish system adequacy in the case of changes in service, while it can also be useful when determining the root cause of an incident.

Inherent in any such assessment is the consideration of risk and the need to deal effectively with uncertainty. The publication of the ASME B31.8S Standard in 2004, as well as the NACE recommended practice RP579 [1], provide excellent sources of potential threats that should be considered and either addressed or eliminated as a result of the assessment. These threats are classified as being either stable or time-dependent, and are evaluated using an assortment of theoretical models – most of which have their basis in fracture mechanics – such as ASME B31G [2], DNV_RP_101 [3], and BS7910 (2005). All require a careful examination of their underlying assumptions and valid range of use as well as the input data quality.

Uncertainty

As noted above, a pipeline may be subject to a number of individual or combined threats to its integrity. ASME B31.8S (2004), for example, provides a list of 21 different categories, most of which are amenable to physical modelling of their underlying process(es). It is difficult to argue that the 21 categories are incomplete, so the issue here might be one of establishing whether, in a particular circumstance, they act singly or in combination. If the answer to that question involves a combined effect - corrosion plus cracking, for example - then a proven highly accurate representation is not yet available.

It is this absence, or incompleteness, of information which gives rise to uncertainty when attempting to assess a pipeline's fitness for service. It may be useful to consider uncertainty in the present context as having two components: descriptive uncertainty, where one lacks the set of variables that would fully describe the physical behaviour of a pipeline under various threats; and measurement uncertainty, where there is an inability to be categorical about the exact value assigned to each variable. In what follows we address the first of these only in a qualitative sense and it is the latter on which we focus a quantitative assessment. The pipeline operator, however, would do well to consider both when performing an assessment.

Introducing errors

Modelling errors

With respect to the availability and adequacy of models, at the outset of an engineering assessment one should ask:

- Is the model valid, and if so, over what range?
- Are the assumptions reasonable?
- Do the model predictions match the observed data?
- How uncertain are the results?
- How can we assess uncertainty and its effects?

Clearly a good model is one which is realistic, reliable, and valid over a wide range. The models used in determining fitness-for-purpose for pipelines are generally descriptive and predictive in nature, and sometimes include empiricism wherever it has proved difficult to fully describe the underlying physical process. None of them explicitly contains a term to describe random variation; rather, if the effect of uncertainty is to be addressed, it is done through performing a sensitivity analysis of the key variables.

The test of whether model predictions match the observed data and loading conditions can be illustrated by considering the models used to characterize metal loss due to corrosion. The best known of these is the ASME B31G manual first published in 1973. Although supported by data from over 300 full-scale tests, the results produced from using it were later perceived to be conservative, so refinements were made to the underlying concepts leading to the development of the modified B31G, and later still, the RSTRENG effective-area method [4]. Essentially the methods differ in the simplifying assumptions made in their derivation, especially describing the profile of the defect, the characterization of flow stress, and the representation of localized bulging due to weakening of the pipe wall (the Folias factor). The dependency upon flow stress derives from the assumption that corrosion defects will fail as a result of plastic collapse, and is thus controlled by the tensile properties of the linepipe. As pipe yield strengths have increased and the Y/T ratio moved closer to unity, then it may be reasonable to question the assumption of plastic collapse for these types of steel and to use other criterion for pipe axial-flaw failure assessment.

There have been continuing improvements to the methods for assessing corrosion defects, such as enhancements to B31G made in 1996 as a result of a joint-industry study undertaken by Advantica (British Gas at the time). This project produced guidance for the assessment of single and interacting defects as well as a means for determining the actual shape of the defect. Changes were made to the definition of flow stress and the Folias factor. Det Norske Veritas (2004), in another joint-industry study, examined the effects of axial and bending loading on the bursting strength of corroded pipe and produced recommended practice DNV–RP-101 which includes equations for assessing single defects under combined loading.

Thus it can be seen, that there can be a number of models available to describe a particular failure category, so the user needs to be mindful of the particular circumstance when making a choice.

Remaining with the modelling of corroded pipe, though equally applicable to other types of defect assessment, it is readily seen that the material and dimensional properties of the pipeline are important parameters. A deterministic approach to defect assessment relies upon assigning single values to these parameters. In reality there will be random variability associated with all of them, albeit minimized by good quality control. Nevertheless, the plate-manufacturing process ensures non-isotropic material properties which also vary around the circumference of the pipe. There is also variability between pipe joints since, in a sizeable project, pipes will come from different heat numbers. Using small data sets from which to select representative values for key variables of the whole pipe therefore introduces uncertainty into the modelling process.

Similarly there may be a considerable degree of variability associated with the in-service loads acting on a pipe from which the appropriate values of load need be determined for use in a model.

Measurement errors

In addition to material properties, corrosion-defect assessment requires knowledge of the operating conditions of the pipeline and a description of the geometry of the defect(s). These inputs are obtained as a result of measurements. However measured values are meaningless without some statement of their accuracy. No measurement is exact, and repeated measurements of the same quantity will yield slightly different values, though they are inclined to cluster around the true value. The deviations from the true value are referred to as errors which can vary either randomly or systematically (for example, contain an inherent bias in the measuring device). If the data spread is narrow then it is usual to use the mean value as an approximation for the true value.

Operating conditions such as pressure and temperature will vary along the length of the pipeline but are only measured at discrete locations. The measuring instruments are calibrated and serviced regularly but are subject to inaccuracy generally contained within specific limits. As will be described later, the measurement errors associated with in-line inspection (ILI) tools can contain both random and systematic components. The sizing accuracy of an ILI tool, run under optimal conditions, is given by the tool vendor as +/- values associated with a confidence limit. There are also conditional probabilities associated with the probability of the detection and identification of a defect.

Detection as well as sizing capability may be a function of the size and number of sensors on the inspection tool, but are definitely related to its speed of travel and the cleanliness of the internal pipe surface.

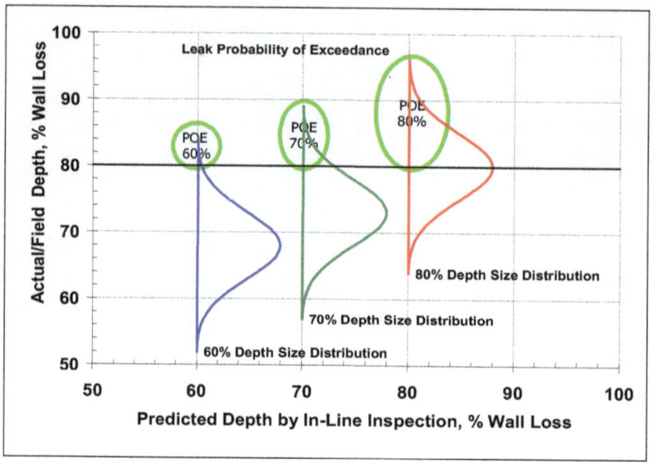

Fig. 1. Depth and factor of safety probability of exceedance.

Interpretation errors

Another posible cause of uncertainty with inspection data lies in the interpretation of the sophisticated signals, and in particular correlating information for the same defect from successive tool runs. Even determining the spatial location of a defect can be done erroneously, so it is important to correlate tool information with as-built pipeline-alignment sheets. A recent incident on an NEB-regulated pipeline involving delayed third-party damage illustrates the point. The operator erroneously assumed that a signal from an ILI tool run, indicating denting, was instead the effect of tool lift-off as it rounded a bend. A check against the alignment sheet would clearly have shown no bends in the vicinity.

More recently, following a pipeline rupture, a review of the tool data from an earlier ultrasonic inspection showed the signal associated with the anomaly had been masked. m:Hence the user needs to be aware that while the accuracy of ILI tools in terms of detection, identification, and sizing has improved considerably, the effects of uncertainty need to be examined further as the following case study demonstrates.

Case study: sizing uncertainty in criticality assessments of metal-loss features reported by ILIs

The purpose of this case study is to identify the effects of uncertainty on ILI sizing accuracies during the criticality assessment of reported metal-loss anomalies that could fail by leak or rupture, and propose some technical approaches on how to deal with this uncertainty in the development of integrity verification and rehabilitation programmes.

Case-study terminology

- *Accuracy* refers to the agreement between a measurement and the true or correct value.
- *Error* refers to the disagreement between a measurement and the true or accepted value.
- *Uncertainty* of a measured value is an interval around that value such that any repetition of the measurement will produce a new result that lies within this interval.
- *ILI accuracy* is a measure to determine the level of performance of an ILI in terms of detection, identification, and sizing.

- *Sizing accuracy* is a measure comprising both tolerance (i.e. +/- 10% of the nominal wall thickness) and uncertainty (i.e. 80% of the time).

Case-study background

As illustrated in Fig.1, the probability of exceedance (POE) approach [5] was used to determine the probability, or chance, that a reported metal-loss feature could exceed a critical depth or leak criterion (i.e. > 80% of the pipe's wall thickness) and critical safety factor; or a rupture criterion (i.e. < 100% of the maximum operating pressure – MOP). POE also accounts for sizing accuracy, meaning that the actual dimensions of the metal-loss features found in the field may be more or less severe than those reported by the in-line inspection.

Case-study methodology

The methodology comprised six steps:

- regulatory and industry practices framework review
- ILI sizing-accuracy simulation for metal-loss features
- POE leak and rupture scenarios
- correlation of POE scenarios to industry safety or reliability levels from N.America and Europe
- analysis of results
- conclusions and recommendations

Regulatory and industry practices framework review

A literature review was conducted of the current regulatory and industry practices framework including the latest ASME International Pipeline Conferences (IPC) papers as well as:

- DNV-RP-F101 *Corroded* pipelines, DNV-OS-F101 *Offshore pipelines*
- CSA-Z662-2007 Annex D *Guidelines for in-line inspection of piping for corrosion imperfections*
- ASME B31.8S-2001 *Management system integrity of gas pipelines*
- NACE 35100 *In-line non-destructive inspection of pipelines*
- NACE Standard RP0102 *In-line inspection of pipelines*
- National Energy Board *On-shore pipeline regulation, 1999*
- API 1160, *Managing system integrity for hazardous liquid pipelines*, and
- API 1163 *In-line inspection systems qualification.* [6]

The review indicated that accuracy and uncertainty effects are proposed to be identified within the process of conducting criticality and integrity assessments using ILI data by some industry standards such as the Canadian CSA-Z662-2007 Annex D.10 *Assessment of report accuracy*, stating that "Where appropriate, an allowance for errors in the reported dimensions shall be taken into consideration when assessing the need for further excavations and the acceptance of reported imperfections that do not require excavation"; or the European recommended practice DNV-RP-F101-1999 *Corroded Pipelines* stating that "Uncertainties associated with the sizing of the defect depth and the material properties are specifically considered" (i.e. partial safety factors).

However, industry standard and/or regulatory guidelines related to the utilization of minimum uncertainty effects and reliability targets during the integrity assessment and verification processes, and/or implementation through mitigation or rehabilitation programmes are needed.

Depth tolerance with 80% uncertainty scenarios (% of nominal wall thickness -NWT-)	Factor of safety tolerance with 80% uncertainty due to depth variability (% maximum operating pressure -MOP-)
+/-5% NWT	+/- 8% FOS
+/- 10% NWT	+/- 12.1% FOS
+/- 15% NWT	+/- 18.1% FOS
+/- 20% NWT	+/- 23.5% FOS
+/- 25% NWT	+/- 28.6% FOS
+/- 30% NWT	+/- 33.0% FOS
+/- 35% NWT	+/- 36.7% FOS

Table 1. Depth accuracy effect on FOS.

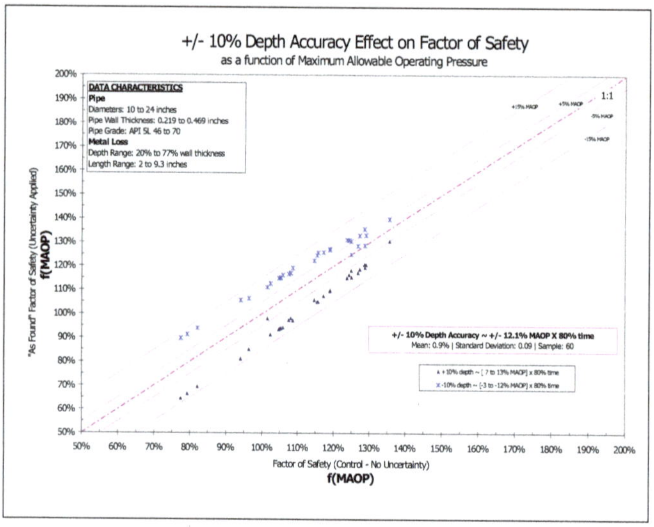

Fig.2. Depth accuracy effect on factor of safety.

ILI sizing accuracy simulation for metal loss

A sizing-accuracy simulation was built using accuracy specifications from six major ILI vendors. Depth and length tolerances and uncertainties were used for defining the leak and rupture probability-of-exceedance models. As illustrated in Fig.2, depth accuracy scenarios (i.e. +/- 5%, +/-10%, +/-15%, +/-20%, +/-25%, +/-30%, and +/-35% of the nominal wall thickness) were also used for assessing the effect on the factor-of-safety (FOS). An statistically significant sample of metal-loss features was created with normally distributed depth and length sizes, pipe diameters ranging from 273 mm (10.75 in) to 609 mm (24 in), pipe wall thicknesses from 5.6 mm (0.219 in) to 11.9 mm (0.469 in), and pipe grades from API 5L 317 MPa (X46) to 483 MPa (X70).

As illustrated in Table 1, the effects of depth accuracy on FOS were determined by calculating the predicted burst pressures using ASME B31.G and Modified B31.G or 0.85dL RStreng methods, indicating the variability or tolerance as a percentage of FOS for 80% of the time or uncertainty. The FOS tolerances ranged from +/-12.1% of maximum operating pressure (MOP) to +/-36.7% of MOP for depth variability from +/- 10% to +/- 35% of the nominal wall thickness. In addition, the effects of both depth and length variability were also determined for representative length accuracy cases.

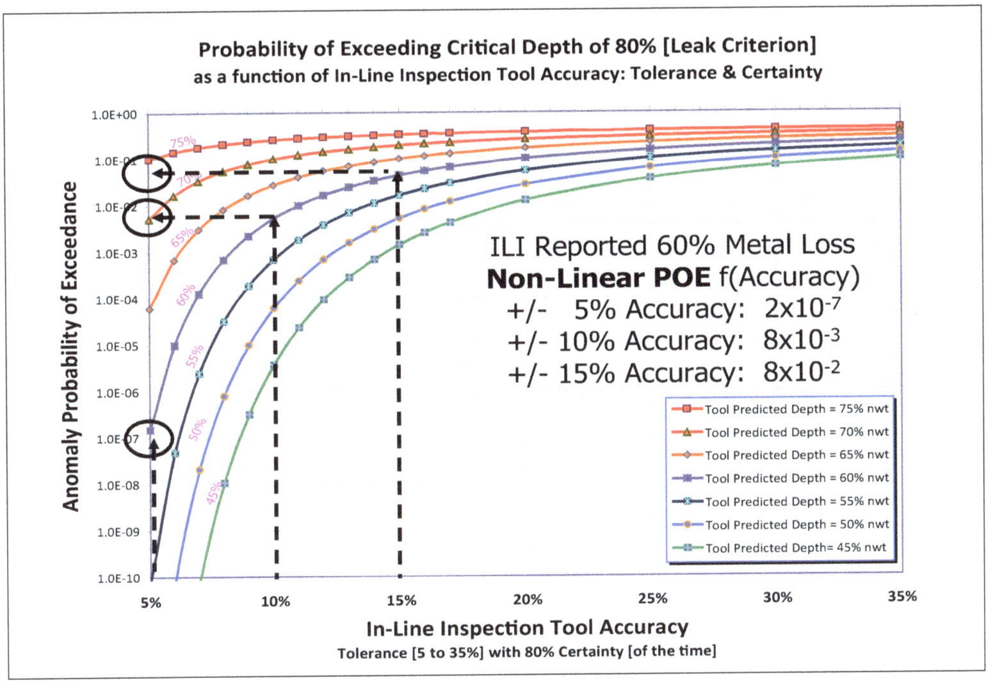

Fig.3. Probability of exceeding critical depth of 80% NWT as a function of depth accuracy.

POE leak and rupture scenarios

Probability of exceedance (POE) scenarios for leak and rupture were determined as a function of the ILI accuracy (tolerance and uncertainty) based on the depth and FOS accuracies identified during the simulation.

As illustrated in Fig.3, the POE values for a given ILI reported depth (i.e. 60% of the nominal wall thickness) for different depth accuracies are not linear (i.e. POE = 2 x 10^{-7} for +/-5% depth accuracy; POE = +/-8 x 10^{-3} for +/-10%; and POE = 8 x 10^{-2} for +/-15%) so the practice of adding the absolute value of the accuracy (i.e. 10, 15, or 20) should be revised in light of safety or reliability levels for assessing the additional effect of the uncertainty into the criticality assessment.

Similarly, Fig.4 shows the POE values for a given ILI reported factor of safety (i.e. 125% of the MOP) for different FOS accuracies associated to previously determined depth accuracies (i.e.: POE = 5 x 10^{-5} for +/-8% FOS or 5% depth accuracy; POE = +/-6 x 10^{-3} for +/-12.1% FOS or +/-10% depth accuracy; and POE = 7 x 10^{-2} for +/-18% FOS or +/-15% depth accuracy). The next step in the methodology correlates POE leak and rupture to some industry practices in North America and Europe.

Correlation of POE scenarios to industry safety or reliability levels from N.America and Europe

Two industry approaches providing minimum safety or reliability levels were correlated to the POE leak and rupture scenarios in order to determine potential excavation, mitigation, or rehabilitation criteria per safety level based on ILI-reported depth and factor-of-safety, and their associated to ILI tolerance and uncertainty.

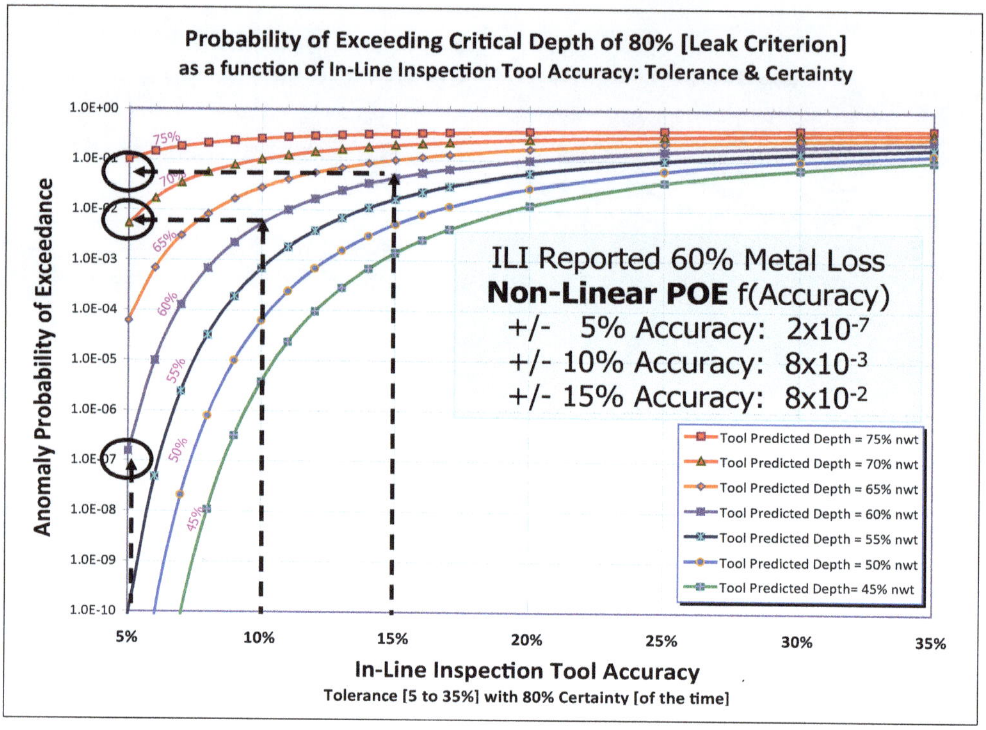

Fig.4. Probability of exceeding critical factor of safety of 100% MOP as a function of depth accuracy.

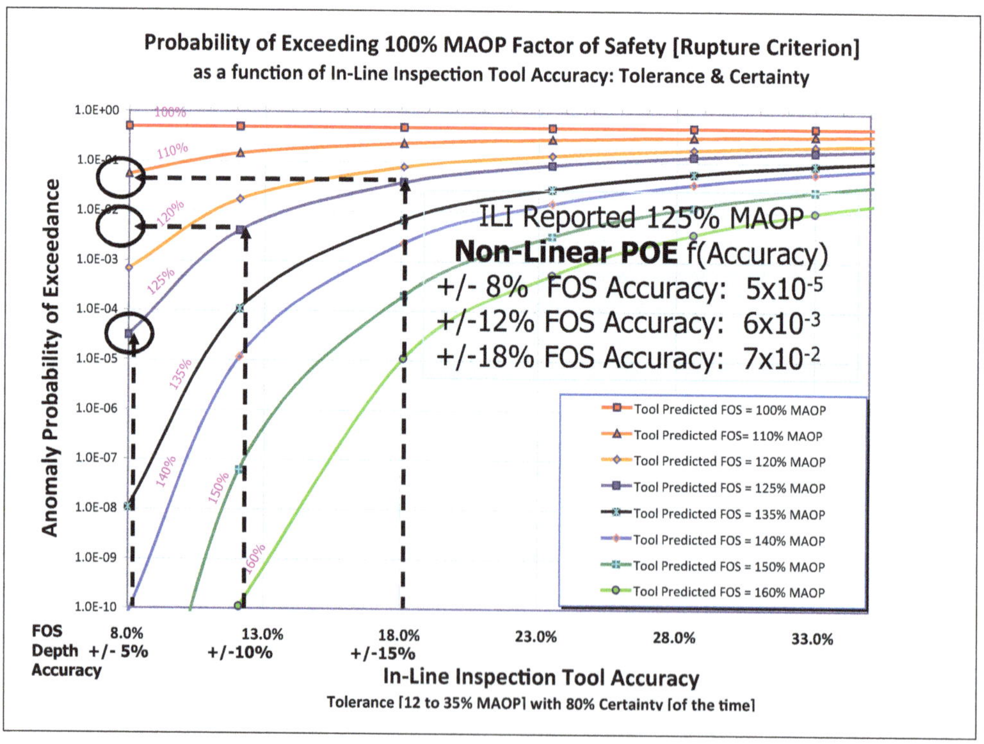

Fig.5. Case A Europe: ILI reported 60% feature and low/normal/high safety levels.

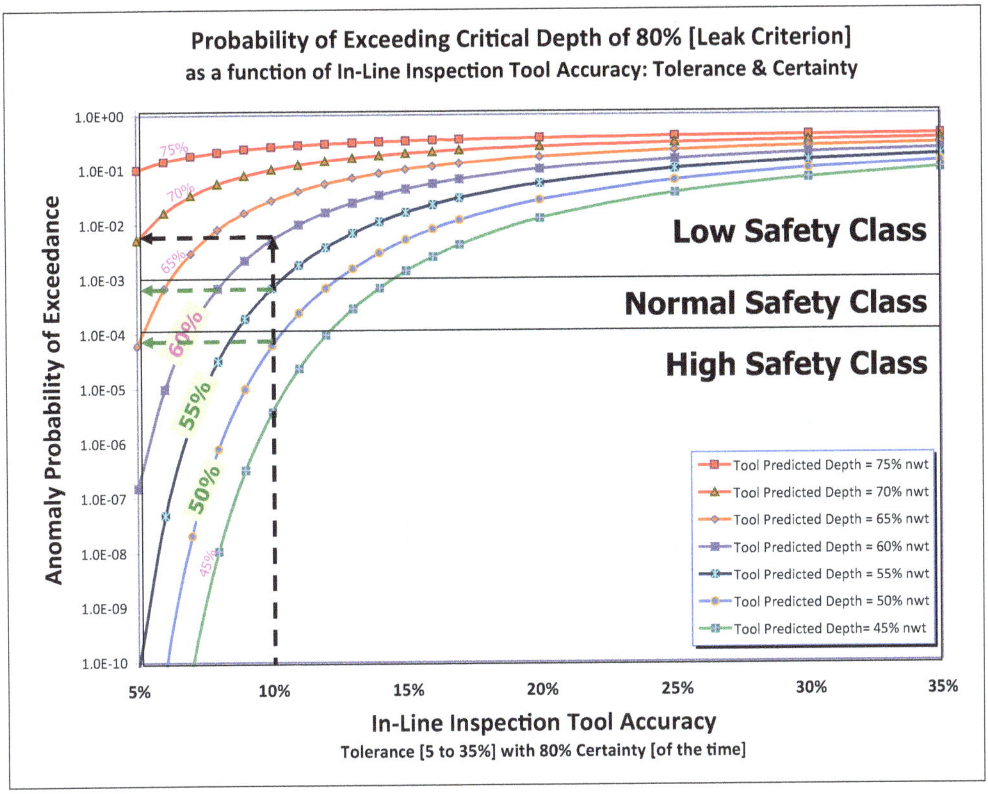

Fig.6. Case B North America: ILI reported 60% MOP feature and fixed reliability target.

Case A was defined based on a European industry approach outlined in DNV-OS/RP-F101 recommended practice that proposes safety classes (low, normal, and high) associated to target failure probabilities for ultimate (ULS), serviceability (SLS), fatigue (FLS), and accidental limit states (ALS). In this standard, 'low' safety class is defined as "where failure implies low risk of human injury and minor environmental and economic consequences", which is usually applied for installation/construction conditions. The 'normal' safety class is defined "for temporary conditions where failure implies risk of human injury, significant environmental pollution, or very high economic or political consequences", which is usually applied for areas with non-anticipated frequent human activity. The 'high' safety class is similarly defined as the 'normal' safety class, but for "operating conditions".

Case B was defined on a hypothetical N.American industry approach of utilizing a reliability level of < $1 \cdot 10^{-6}$ that would establish the acceptable region under the anomaly POE curve. More specifically, PRCI developed reliability targets by class location accounting for population density and pipeline characteristics for design and assessment of gas transmission pipelines. Case B approach is to apply a specific safety or reliability level of one for comparison purposes only.

Analysis of results

As illustrated in Fig.5, if Case A European safety levels were used for selecting metal-loss features to be field investigated with an ILI accuracy of +/-10% of the nominal wall thickness and an uncertainty of 80%, features with a depth greater than 60%, 50%, and 40% would fall under low, normal, and high safety classes, respectively. This would imply that the higher the safety level, the

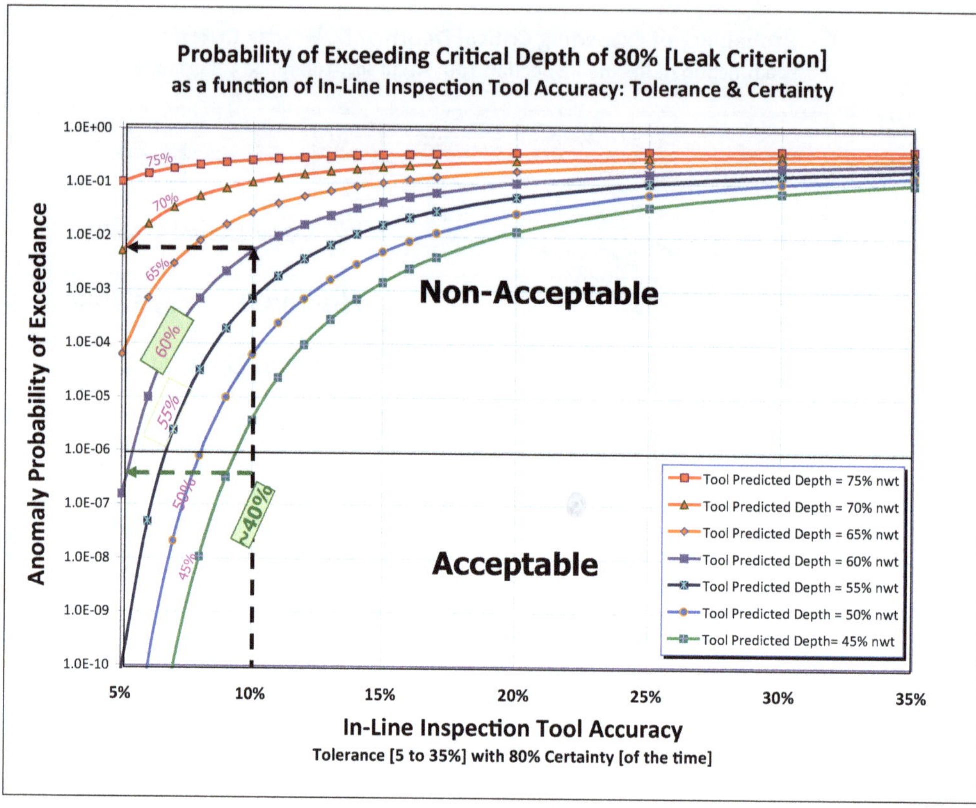

Fig.7. Case A Europe: ILI reported 125% MAOP feature and low/normal/high safety levels.

lower the reported depth of the metal-loss feature required for field investigation based on the tolerance and uncertainty of the ILI. Similarly, in Fig.6, if Case B hypothetical N.American reliability level was used, features with a depth greater than 40% of the nominal wall thickness would be required for field investigation, which coincides with the high safety class requirement of this simulation.

As illustrated in Fig.7, if Case A European safety levels were used for selecting metal-loss features to be field investigated with an ILI accuracy of +/-12.1% FOS and an uncertainty of 80%, features with a FOS smaller than 125%, 135%, and 140% MOP would fall under low, normal, and high safety classes, respectively. This would imply that the higher the safety level, the higher the reported FOS of the metal-loss feature required for field investigation based on the tolerance and uncertainty of the ILI. Similarly, in Fig.8, if Case B hypothetical N.American reliability level was used, features with a FOS greater than 145 to 150% MOP would be required for field investigation, which is slighter higher than the high safety class requirement of this simulation.

Case-study conclusions and recommendations

Based on the results from the case study, three main conclusions can be drawn:

- Criticality assessment exclusively based on information reported by ILI (as-is) may lead into potential leak and rupture conditions of the pipeline system.

- Uncertainty has a considerable effect on the criticality assessment of reported features due to their inherent in-line inspection accuracy (i.e. depth, length, and FOS).

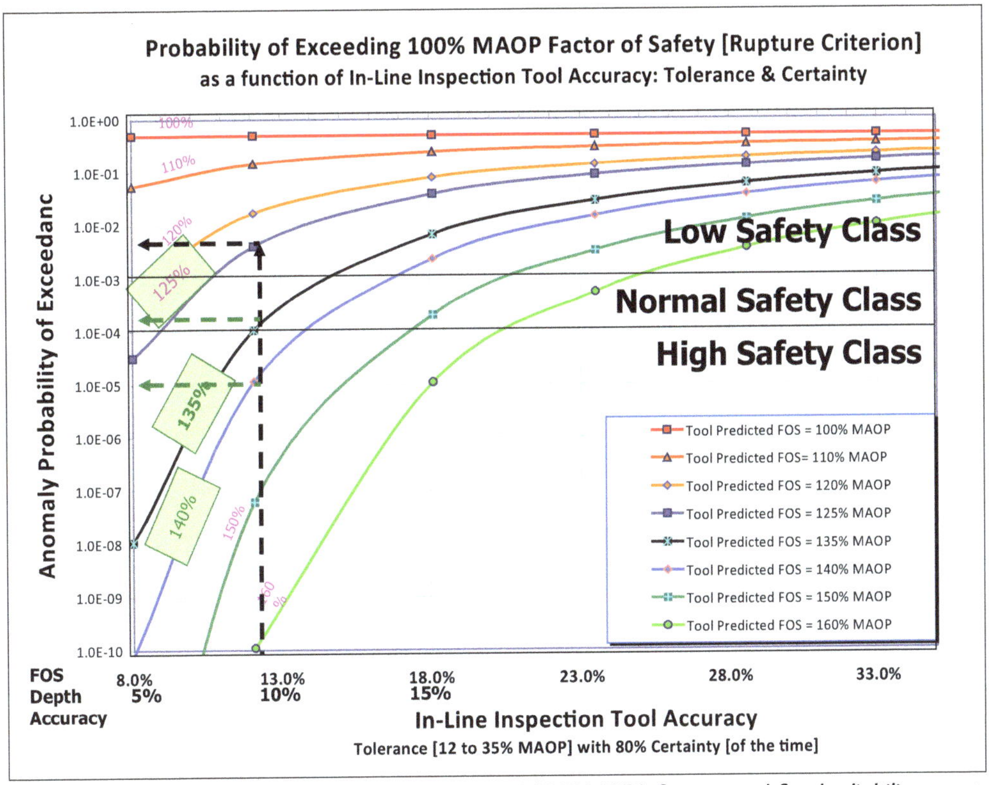

Fig.8. Case B North America: ILI reported 125% MOP feature and fixed reliability target.

- Consideration of ILI accuracy for depth and FOS can significantly reduce uncertainty, allowing the development of technically sound and cost-effective rehabilitation / mitigation programmes.

Therefore, regulatory and industry standard acceptance criteria in conjunction with reliability targets (i.e. safety class/empirical levels) should be used for developing rehabilitation / mitigation programmes in order to achieve realistic levels of safety, environmental protection, and a reliable service

Detection uncertainty

In regards to ILI detection performance, the world-wide pipeline industry has experienced several failures caused by features detected by ILIs but not reported due to multiple factors such as to sensor data integration (i.e. length not fully captured on angled features), manual detection analysis with low data analysis experience (new or under-development tools), ˜or automatic detection with unreliable software. All these factors, and others, contribute to increase the level of uncertainty driven by detection capabilities of ILI technologies.

As illustrated in Fig.9, an angled stress-corrosion cracking (SCC) feature was detected as a discontinuous off-axis crack-field by an ultrasonic crack-detection ILI. The feature was not reported by the vendor as the "'red box' marked by the anomaly algorithm did not meet its length-reporting threshold", which also did not include the remaining angled signal. Detection of off-axis features is one of the limitations of current crack-detection technology.

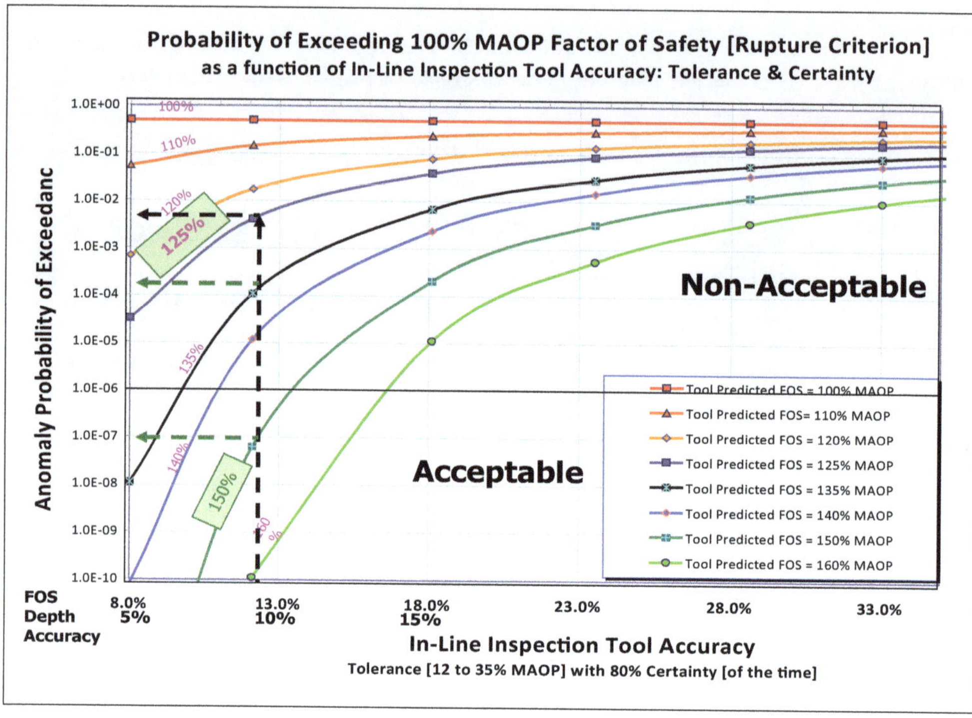

Fig.9. Stress-corrosion cracking field versus detected angled/fractioned feature.

Therefore, pipeline operators and regulators should be aware of the limitations of each ILI technology so alternative quality-assurance methods can be implemented. Recently, operators world-wide have initiated the use of third-party, independent, subject-matter experts on data analysis of ILI data. This quality-assurance approach consists of conducting either spot or full checks on the ILI raw data in order to identify potential features that could have been missed during the reporting process such off-axis features, short high amplitude features with shading areas, etc.

Identification uncertainty

Several unnecessary digs due to misinterpretation of classification or identification of features reported by ILIs have been conducted. Furthermore, failures have occurred due to features reported as appurtenances instead of critical features (i.e. wrinkle reported as a tee), seam-weld defects reported as magnetic disturbances, or cracks reported as notch-like features. Correct identification or classification allows the selection of appropriate criticality assessment methodologies and growth mechanisms. As well as detection, reduction on the identification uncertainty can be assisted by third-party independent subject-matter experts that conduct initial feature selection for validation and customize their criteria based on the findings discovered during the excavation programme. This analysis, called ‘confidence analysis’, provides higher confidence in the development of cost-effective mitigation programmes.

Conclusion

This paper discussed the importance of dealing quantitatively as well as qualitatively with the uncertainties that are inherent in performing criticality and integrity assessments as part of the continuing fitness-for-service cycle required within an effective integrity-management programme. The uncertainty effects should be taken into consideration in the development of technically sound and cost-effective pipeline integrity and rehabilitation programmes.

Acknowledgement and disclaimer

The authors would like to thank the National Energy Board for permission to publish this paper, which represents their personal views and should not be taken as the views of the Board

References

1. NACE, 2002. International recommended practice 102: In line inspection of pipelines.
2. ASME, 1991. Manual for determining the remaining strength of corroded pipelines. ASME B31G-1991, A supplement to ASME B31 Code for pressure piping. ASME, New York.
3. DNV, 2004. Corroded pipelines. Recommended practice DNV-RP-101, Det Norske Veritas, Hovik, Norway, October.
4. J.F.Kiefner and P.H.Vieth, 1989. A modified criterion for evaluating the remaining strength of corroded pipe. Final report on project PR3-805, Batelle Memorial Institute, Columbus, Ohio.
5. R.Mora, C.Parker, P.H.Vieth, and B.Delanty, 2002. Probability of exceedance (POE) methodology for developing integrity programs based on pipeline operator specific technical and economic factors. Proc. 4th Int. Pipeline Conf., Paper IPC02-27224. Calgary. ASME, New York.
6. API, 2005. In line inspection systems qualification standard. API 1163, 1st Ed. August, American Petroleum Institute, Washington DC.

Section 9: Stress-corrosion cracking

Re-assessment intervals for managing stress-corrosion cracking in pipelines

by Dr Raymond R Fessler[1] and Steve C Rapp[2]

1 BIZTEK Consulting, Inc., Evanston, IL, USA
2 Spectra Energy, Houston, TX, USA

PIPELINES FOR WHICH stress-corrosion cracking (SCC) has been identified as a threat of concern typically are assessed by hydrostatic testing, in-line inspection (ILI), or direct assessment (DA). Because SCC is a time-dependent mechanism, it is necessary to re-assess those pipelines periodically to ensure the continued integrity of the line. Intervals between subsequent re-assessments should be short enough to avoid in-service failures but not so short as to involve unnecessary pressure cycles, service interruptions, or expenses. A recently developed method for establishing appropriate intervals for hydrostatic re-testing requires only the test pressure, the maximum allowable operating pressure, and the probable maximum tensile properties of the steel. The method involves relatively short initial intervals followed by progressively longer subsequent intervals. Based upon a number of case studies of pipelines that have been subjected to multiple hydrostatic tests following discovery of SCC, it has been shown that, compared to equal intervals over time, this method would be more effective at preventing in-service failures while requiring fewer tests. In principle, the method also can be used for establishing intervals for ILI and SCC DA, although other options can be considered..

HYDROSTATIC TESTING, in-line inspection (ILI), and direct assessment (DA) are the primary ways to demonstrate the structural integrity of a pipeline that has exhibited evidence of stress-corrosion cracking (SCC). Such evidence could come from an in-service failure due to SCC, a hydrostatic-test failure that initiated at stress-corrosion cracks, ILI, or direct observations during a bell-hole examination. However, since very small stress-corrosion cracks may exist in the pipeline following a demonstration of structural integrity, and those cracks might continue to grow, it usually is advisable to reassess the pipeline at certain intervals to be sure that the surviving cracks have not grown to a size that would approach the critical size for failure at operating pressures. Choosing an appropriate interval between assessments is important because intervals that are too long carry the risk of an in-service failure, while unnecessarily short intervals subject the pipeline to needless pressure cycles and the company to unnecessary expense.

It is relatively straightforward to calculate the size of the largest crack that could survive the hydrotest and the size of a flaw that would cause a rupture at the maximum allowable operating pressure (MAOP). That size difference divided by the crack-growth rate would indicate the maximum safe time between assessments. Unfortunately, the crack-growth rate depends upon many unknown factors, such as the condition of the coating, the chemical composition of any liquid in contact with the pipe, the electrochemical potential under a disbonded coating, and the susceptibility of the steel. Because of these unknowns, pipeline companies have been forced to make arbitrary decisions about appropriate re-assessment intervals.

This paper describes a model [1] for determining hydrostatic re-test intervals based just upon what is known about the pipeline: the hydrostatic-test history (pressures and dates), and the range of tensile properties of the steel, which can be obtained from mill records. The model addresses the intervals after the second hydrostatic test; it does not specifically treat the first interval. It also considers only ruptures; it does not consider leaks. The model is applicable to high-pH SCC and near-neutral-pH SCC. In fact, it is not necessary to know which type of SCC is on the pipeline. The assumptions upon which the model are based have been verified by comparing its predictions against the field experience of a number of pipeline companies that have conducted multiple hydrostatic tests on pipelines that contained stress-corrosion cracks.

This paper also describes approaches for establishing re-assessment intervals for ILI and SCC DA. Some of those approaches are extensions of the hydrostatic re-test interval model and others are independent of it.

Hydrostatic re-test model

Assumptions

The hydrostatic re-test model is based upon the following assumptions:

- The pipeline in question contains stress-corrosion cracks. (If it does not, the choice of an interval is not critical to the safety of the pipeline.)

- The growth rate for a surviving crack will be less than the previous growth rate for a crack that already failed. This seems to be reasonable, because the combination of environmental conditions and steel susceptibility associated with the failed crack must have been more severe than those conditions associated with a crack that is smaller.

- A crack that initiates in the future will not fail before some existing crack does. Similar to the previous argument, the conditions where a crack has not yet started are expected to be less severe than those where a crack is already growing.

- Future operating conditions (pressure levels, pressure cycles, cathodic-protection levels, and temperature) are no more severe than past operating conditions.

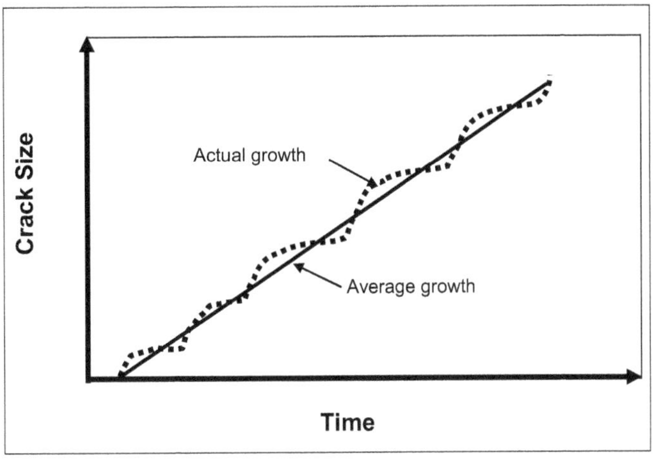

Fig. 1. Substituting the average crack growth rate for the actual variable rate.

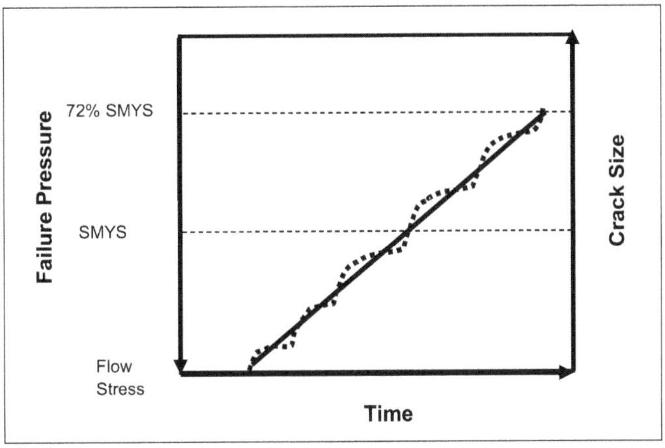

Fig.2. Using failure pressure to represent flaw size.

- Although the crack-growth rate probably is not constant over time, it is acceptable to represent the growth rate as the average over time. This is illustrated schematically in Fig.1.

Although the preceding assumptions appear to be reasonable, since they cannot be proved, predictions from the model have been tested against field experience to validate the assumptions and the model.

Structure of the hydrostatic re-test model

Since there is a direct relation between the size of a defect and the pressure at which it would cause a rupture, and because the pressures on a pipeline can be measured accurately, whereas the size of a defect usually is not known (unless good ILI data are available), it is convenient to use the failure pressure of a defect as an indirect measure of the size (see Fig.2). In fact, the primary reason for knowing the size is to be able to calculate the failure pressure.

Consider a pipeline that has been found to contain stress-corrosion cracks and has been subjected to two hydrostatic tests, the second one occurring t_1 years after the first. Referring to Fig.3, the maximum prior growth rate of a surviving crack can be determined from the test pressure (P_t) and the flow stress. The flow stress is the stress at which an infinitesimally small flaw would cause a failure. For most line-pipe steels, the flow stress can be calculated as the average of the yield strength and the ultimate tensile strength or, alternately, 10,000 psi plus the yield strength.

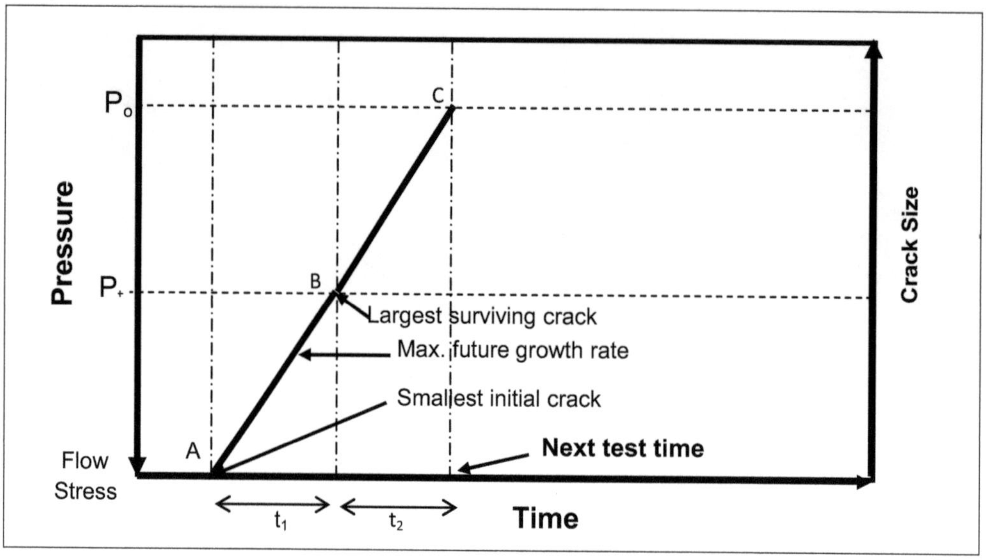

Fig.3. Extrapolating the maximum prior crack growth rate to establish the interval for the next re-test. P_o is the maximum allowable operating pressure, and P_t is the hydrostatic test pressure.

Assuming that some sub-critical stress-corrosion cracks survived the first hydrostatic test, Point A in Fig.3 represents the smallest that it could have been at that time, and Point B represents the largest size that could have survived the second hydrostatic test. The slope of Line AB therefore is the maximum average growth rate that could have occurred during time t_1. In reality, the initial size probably was somewhat greater, and the final size probably was somewhat smaller, which means that the actual highest growth rate was less than the calculated maximum. Thus, using the maximum possible prior growth rate as an estimate of future growth introduces considerable conservatism into the approach.

According to the assumptions of the model, Line BC represents the maximum size of the largest flaw that could have survived the second hydrostatic test and continued to grow at the prior maximum rate. That hypothetical worst defect would be large enough to cause a failure at the maximum allowable operating pressure (MAOP) at Point C. Therefore time t_2 in Fig.3 represents the maximum safe interval to wait before re-testing the pipeline again.

Figure 4 illustrates how each subsequent interval can be calculated based upon the total time since the first hydrostatic test following the discovery of SCC in the pipeline. Implicit in the structure of Figure 4 is the assumption that the pipeline still contains a few cracks that existed at the time of the first hydrostatic test. Using the principle of similar triangles, it can be shown that the ratio of the next interval (t_n) to the difference between the test pressure (P_t) and the operating pressure (P_o) is equal to the ratio of the sum of the previous intervals (t_p) to the difference between the pressure corresponding to the flow stress and the test pressure.

$$t_n/á = t_p/â \quad (1)$$

$$t_n = t_p\,(á/â) \quad (2)$$

where *á* equals P_t minus P_o, and *â* equals the pressure corresponding to the flow stress minus P_t. As is shown in Fig.5, both the test pressure and the flow stress have strong influences on the ratio of the future intervals to previous intervals.

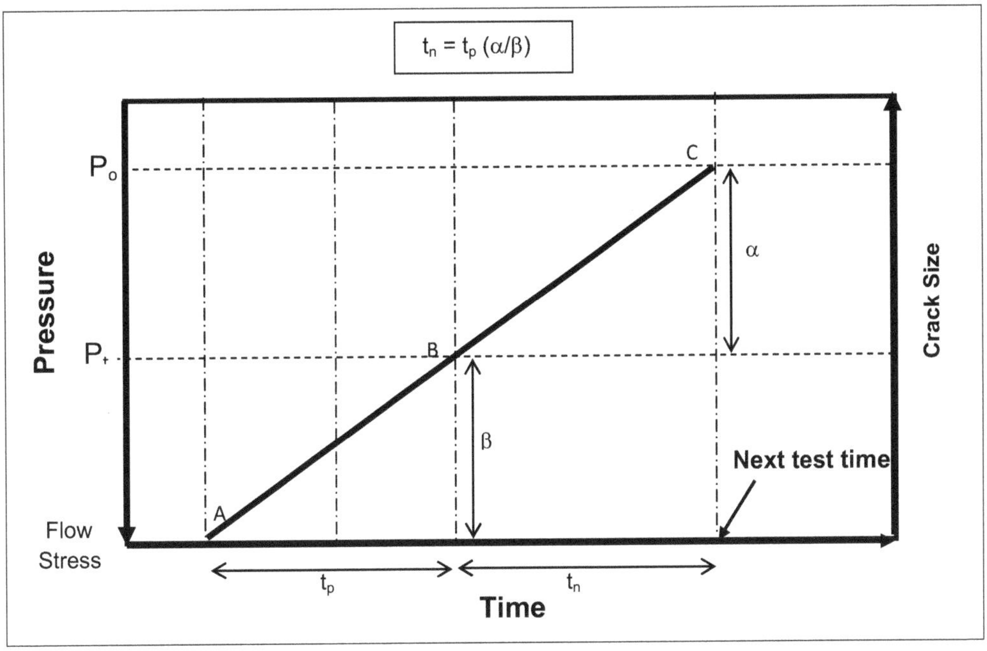

Fig.4. Establishing subsequent intervals based upon previous intervals.

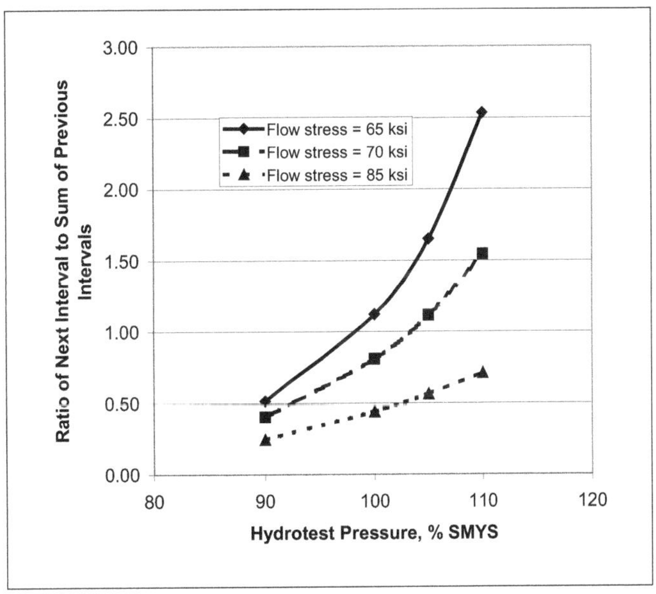

Fig.5. Effects of hydrostatic test pressure and flow stress on length of subsequent intervals between re-tests for an X52 pipeline operating at 72% SMYS

A key result of applying this model is that the duration of intervals after the second interval can be significantly longer than either of the first two. For example, if *á* = *â*, the second interval would equal the first, the third would be twice as long as the first, the fourth would be four times as long, and the fifth could be eight times as long as the first.

According to this model, establishing subsequent intervals does not depend upon whether any failures occurred during any of the previous hydrostatic tests. It is only necessary to know the maximum growth rate for cracks that ultimately survive the prior tests, since all cracks with higher growth rates would have been removed during the prior test.

Case	Time from 1st hydrotest to service failure	Number of hydrotests following 1st	Number of hydrotests with failures	Comments
1	NA	3	2	
2	3, 27	10	8	90% SMYS hydrotest and high flow stress
3	7	3	0	
4	17	6	2	
5	NA	8	1	37 years to 1st hydrotest failure
6	4	8	0	
7	NA	6	0	
8	NA	2	1	
9	NA	1	1	Hydrotest failures above 98% SMYS after 38 years
10	22	2	1	
11	6	3	0	
12	8	2	0	
13	NA	2	2	

Table 1. Case studies of valve sections with SCC and multiple hydrostatic tests.

Case studies

In order to check the predictions of the model against field-experience, data were obtained for 13 valve sections that had experienced either high-pH SCC or near-neutral-pH SCC and had been subjected to multiple hydrostatic tests. The histories of these valve sections are summarized in Table 1. Data also were obtained for 132 additional valve sections from the same pipeline systems; those valve sections also had been subjected to multiple hydrostatic tests but had not failed during those tests.

Representative examples of how the predictions from the model compared with field experience are illustrated in Figs 6 and 7. Figure 6 represents a valve section that was hydrostatically tested to 110% of the specified minimum yield strength (SMYS) in 1968, during which four SCC ruptures occurred (open stars). Subsequently, a service failure due to SCC occurred in 1972 (filled star), after which eight hydrostatic re-tests were conducted, none of which produced failures (open circles). The dark slanted lines represent the maximum crack growth rates that would be predicted by the model for various times. The model assumes that the first re-test would have been conducted three years after the first test, and it predicts that the joint that actually failed in service in 1972 would have failed during the 1971 hydrostatic re-test at some pressure above 900 psig. Subsequently, three additional re-tests would have been conducted, none of which would have produced failures. In summary, following the model would have eliminated one service failure and demonstrated the integrity of the valve section with four fewer hydrostatic re-tests.

Figure 7 represents a valve section that experienced several hydrostatic-test failures in 1987, after which three hydrostatic re-tests were conducted, the latter two each producing a rupture due to

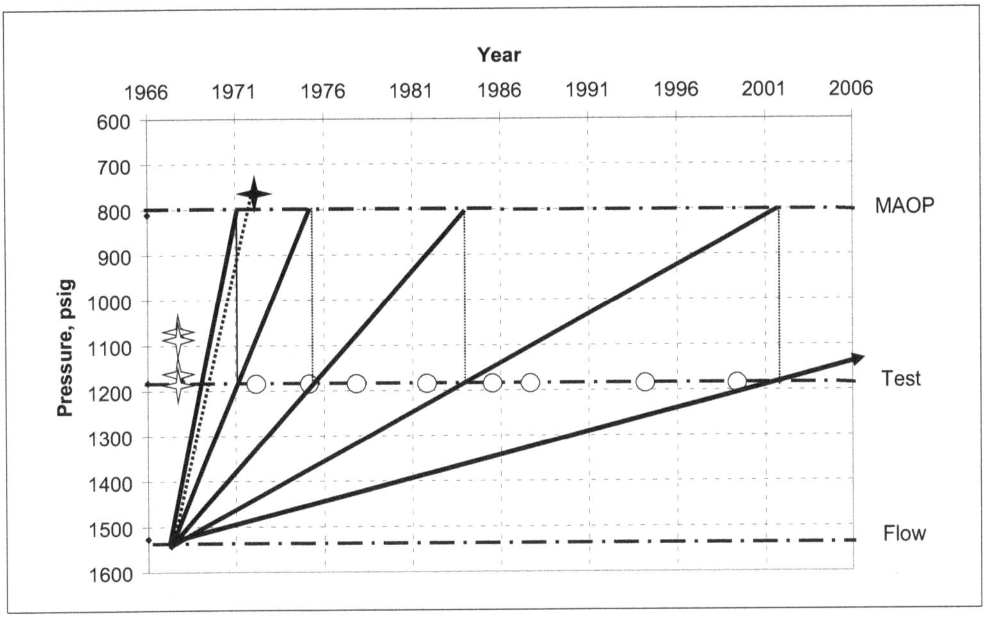

Fig.6. Comparison of service history with predictions of model for Case 6. Open stars represent hydrostatic-test failures, closed star represents a service failure, and open circles represent hydrostatic re-tests without failures. Dark slanted lines represent model predictions for maximum crack growth rates at various times.

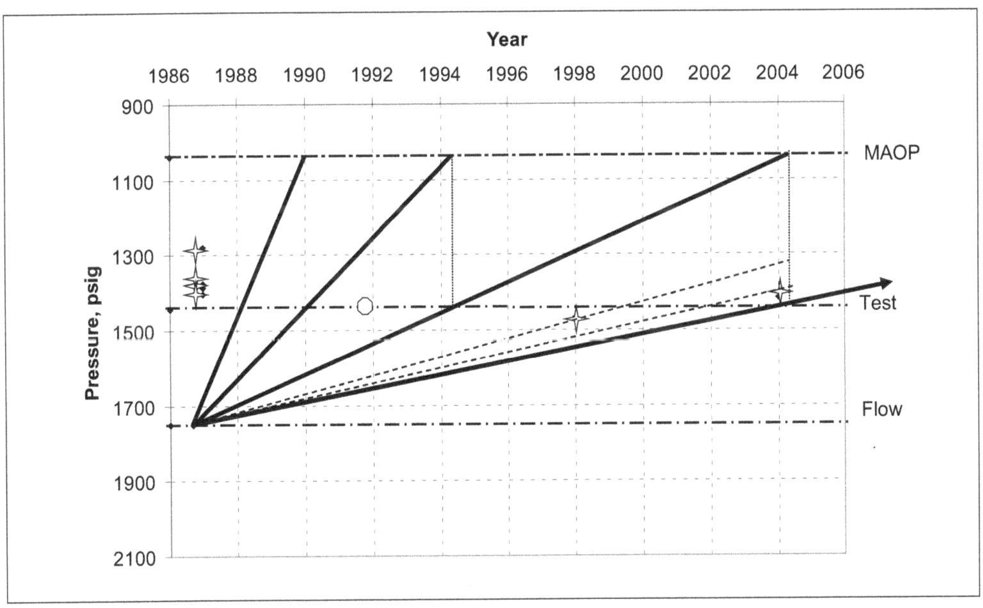

Fig.7. Comparison of service history with predictions of model for Case 1. Symbols are as described for Fig.6.

SCC very near the maximum test pressure of 105% SMYS. In this case, the model would have predicted the same number of re-tests and test failures, but both failures would have occurred in the 2004 re-test at pressures above 1300 psig.

Events after first hydrotest	Actual number	Predicted from model			
		t1 = 3 years		t1 = 5 years	
		Number	Difference	Number	Difference
Service failures	8	2	-6	3	-5
Hydrostatic retest failures	56	46	-10	42	-14
Number of hydrostatic re-tests	56	50	-6	38	-18

Table 2. Summary of comparisons of prediction from model with 13 case studies from actual service experiences.

Comparable analyses that were completed for all 13 valve sections are summarized in Table 2. Comparisons were made for first intervals of three years and five years. Of the eight service failures that occurred after the initial hydrostatic tests, five or six probably would have been prevented if the intervals from the model had been used rather than the ones that were, but no more re-tests in total would have been required. The only two service failures that would have occurred with the model intervals and a three-year first interval occurred on a valve section that had been tested to only 90% SMYS. In addition, the pipe in that valve section had unusually high values of flow stress, which further reduces the effectiveness of a hydrostatic test. In terms of Fig.4, the relatively low test pressure and high flow stress produce a small value for á and a large value for â.

The additional 132 valve sections that had been tested without producing SCC failures had been subjected to 370 hydrostatic tests (238 in addition to the original 132). Had the predictions from the model been used to establish the intervals, about 236 additional re-tests would have been conducted. As with the original 13 case studies, using the model to establish re-test intervals would not have required any more re-tests than were actually conducted.

Limitations of the hydrostatic re-test model

There are several circumstances that are not covered by the model, but they are believed to be rare, and, if they do occur, would be difficult to prevent under any approach. One is the possibility that two or more nearly co-linear sub-critical cracks could coalesce to form a critical size flaw. That would cause a discontinuous step in the growth curve, which is not consistent with the model. Another possibility is that a coating defect could develop after the first hydrostatic test and a severe chemical environment might develop under the defective coating, which might produce a relatively rapidly growing crack. However, initiation of a new crack in an otherwise crack-free pipe is always a possibility and is not predictable.

If either of those possibilities were not highly improbable, some cases of the model failing to match field experience would have been expected, but that is not the case. Therefore, although use of the model cannot guarantee prevention of all service failures, the assumptions upon which it was built appear to be reasonable representations of conditions on existing pipelines.

Modifying intervals following re-test failures

According to a strict interpretation of the method, the lengths of future intervals do not depend on whether or not failures have occurred during previous re-tests. Any joint of pipe that would

	Hydrotest pressure	Years since first hydrotest					
		3	6	7	9	12	>21
% of valve sections with no in-service rupture within time	>90% SMYS	97	94	90	84	83	80
	>100% SMYS	100	96	96	96	96	90
% of valve sections with no in-service or hydrotest rupture within time	>90% SMYS	89	79	71	68	52	48
	>100% SMYS	97	89	88	84	67	50

Table 3. Percentages of valve sections not experiencing failure following first high-pH SCC hydrotest (based upon 38 valve sections).

have failed in service during the next interval would have been removed during the current re-test. Crack-growth rates in the surviving joints would be so low that the pipe would survive until the next re-test. Even if a rupture occurred very near the MAOP during the re-test, it would not violate the assumptions of the method.

In view of the multiple levels of conservatism that are built into the method, it is highly unlikely that re-test failures would occur much below the test pressure, and industry experience bears that out. The vast majority of failures in re-tests following an initial test above 100% SMYS have been at or near the test pressure.

However, in the unlikely event that a re-test failure did occur near the MAOP, that would be an indication of a relatively small safety factor, and some modification to subsequent intervals would provide a higher level of confidence. Therefore, an approach has been devised to modify subsequent intervals if a failure occurs during any re-test, the amount of reduction in subsequent intervals being greater the further the failure pressure is from the test pressure. If the test failure occurred very near MAOP, the next interval would be half of the previous interval; if the test failure occurred at or near the maximum test pressure, the next interval would be calculated based upon the original model. Failure at intermediate pressures between MAOP and the maximum test pressure would lead to proportionate intermediate amounts of shortening. The following formula can be used to calculate the length of the next interval consistent with the above discussion:

$$t_n = t_p (S_1 + S_3/2 - S_2)/S_2 \quad (3)$$

where

t_p = sum of all previous intervals
S_1 = flow stress – maximum operating stress
S_2 = flow stress – failure stress
S_3 = test stress – failure stress

To add still more conservatism, the origin point for calculating subsequent intervals would be moved from the first test to the most recent test in which a failure occurred.

The first interval

The method described above can be used after two hydrostatic tests have been conducted, the first test being one that either produced a failure due to SCC or one that was conducted after an SCC service failure occurred. It cannot be used to establish the interval between the first two tests. Unless a company has specific information about crack-growth rates on its system, its best option is to rely upon general industry experience. As part of a joint-industry project, relevant data were obtained for 38 valve sections that had experienced high-pH SCC and 11 valve sections that had experienced near-neutral-pH SCC, all of those sections having been subjected to at least two hydrostatic tests following discovery of SCC.

The key piece of information is for how long after a hydrostatic test that a valve section has remained in normal service without experiencing a service failure. As is shown in Table 3, that depends somewhat on the level of the first hydrostatic test; longer lives have been experienced for test pressures of 100% SMYS or higher compared with test pressures between 90 and 100% SMYS. For test pressures of 100% SMYS or higher, there were no service failures within the first three years and only one within 12 years. 90% of the valve sections that have been in service for more than 20 years beyond the first test have not experienced a service failure. Almost 90% of the valve sections survived at least six years without even experiencing a hydrostatic re-test failure.

As is shown in Table 4, a similar behaviour pattern has been observed for 11 valve sections that had experienced near-neutral-pH SCC. All of those valve sections had been tested to at least 100% SMYS.

Based upon the above data, it appears that a reasonable and prudent choice for the length of the first interval would be three to seven years, the shorter time being selected where SCC is thought to be more aggressive, either because of an in-service failure or multiple failures during the first hydrostatic test. The longer time would be appropriate if SCC were discovered at a very high pressure during a hydrostatic test.

A three to seven-year first interval also is consistent with crack-growth rates that have been deduced from metallographic examinations of cracks that had survived a hydrostatic test several years earlier. The most aggressive of those rates have been on the order of 0.03 in/yr. Typically, a crack that survived a hydrostatic test at 105% SMYS would have to grow another 0.10 in in depth to fail at 72% SMYS, which, at the aggressive growth rate of 0.03 in/yr, would take about three years and probably more than seven years at typical growth rates.

Re-assessment intervals for ILI

ILI has become an important part of SCC integrity management with a number of liquid pipeline operators, but it is used by very few gas pipeline companies because of the difficulty of getting reliable defect-size data without using a liquid couplant. However, in a few special cases, ILI is the best alternative even for gas pipelines, and companies that use it need to establish appropriate re-inspection intervals.

An important part of an ILI is establishing the minimum size flaw that is detected and the uncertainty in the sizes of large and small flaws. This usually is accomplished with confirmatory excavations. Flaws that are judged to present an unacceptable risk are removed or sleeved. The maximum size of any remaining flaw is the critical parameter that determines the appropriate re-inspection interval. The company's policy for what size flaw should be removed or sleeved, and the uncertainty in determining flaw size from the ILI data, determine the largest flaw that might remain in the pipeline.

Depending upon the type of ILI data available to the pipeline company, there are at least two options for establishing appropriate re-assessment intervals:

	Years since first hydrotest				
	3	6	7	9	12
% of valve sections with no in-service rupture within time	100	91	90	78	75
% of valve sections with no in-service or hydrotest rupture within time	73	64	60	44	38

Table 4. Percentages of valve sections not experiencing failure following first near-neutral-pH SCC hydrotest (based upon 11 valve sections, all tested >100% SMYS).

- If the growth of individual cracks can be followed with successive runs, the actual growth rates can be determined by dividing the change in size by the time between the two runs [2].
- If such data are not available, the maximum size of flaw that is left in the line can be used to establish an equivalent hydrostatic test pressure, and the hydrostatic re-test model can be used.

Crack-size data from successive runs have been used to establish growth rates of individual cracks, and the value at the 95th percentile can be used as a conservative estimate of the growth rate. Then that growth rate can be imposed on all of the cracks that were left in the line to calculate a minimum time to failure for each crack. Those results can then be used to schedule inspections to verify the flaw sizes and make necessary repairs. Although that procedure theoretically should prevent any future failure, it may be advisable to conduct another ILI run in about seven years to validate the assumptions.

Alternatively, an equivalence with a hydrostatic test can be established by determining what hydrostatic-test pressure would be required to remove the largest remaining flaw. So long as the maximum flaw size that can remain in the pipeline is smaller than the largest flaw that could survive a hydrostatic test of a certain pressure, the ILI run can be considered to be at least equivalent to such a hydrostatic test, and the guidelines for establishing hydrostatic re-test intervals can be used for the ILI re-inspection intervals.

Re-inspection intervals for SCC DA

In principle, the procedure for establishing re-inspection intervals for SCC DA can be essentially the same as for ILI. Once the DA process establishes the probable maximum size flaw that might be in the pipeline, that size can determine an equivalent hydrostatic-test pressure, and then the procedure for establishing hydrostatic re-test intervals can also be used for SCC DA.

However, the appropriate action following SCC DA will depend upon the severity of cracks that are discovered, and it may be something other than another DA. If relatively large cracks are found, it may be prudent to conduct a 100% inspection (hydrostatic test, ILI, or 100% magnetic-particle inspection) rather than additional DA. If the largest crack is near critical size, a temporary pressure reduction until the 100% inspection is completed should be considered. It will be necessary to assume a growth rate and critical crack size, from which it will be possible to calculate a reasonable re-assessment interval based upon the largest flaw that is likely to remain in the pipeline.

If no cracks are found at the location that is expected to be most susceptible, no additional actions should be required before the next scheduled assessment, which may be dictated by regulations.

Industry experience suggests that, for every joint of pipe that contains a colony of cracks that is severe enough to cause a service failure, there probably are thousands to tens of thousands of colonies with minor cracking. Furthermore, those minor colonies are not randomly distributed throughout the system; they tend to be preferentially located near the more-severe cracks. Therefore, if any segment that is being assessed contains a colony of cracks that is severe enough to cause a service failure within seven years, for example, and if a joint of pipe is chosen for DA based upon it having the highest probability in that segment of having SCC, then the probability of that joint of pipe not having any stress-corrosion cracks would be extremely low. In other words, if the joint of pipe with the highest probability of SCC contains no cracks, it is highly unlikely that another joint of pipe within that segment has cracks that are large enough to cause a service failure within seven years.

Summary and conclusions

A model has been developed that provides a technically sound basis for establishing intervals between subsequent hydrostatic tests of portions of a pipeline that might contain stress-corrosion cracks. The only input data needed for the model are the prior hydrostatic test history and the range of tensile properties of the steel in the pipeline. Assumptions upon which the model was developed were validated by comparing predictions from the model with field experience on a number of pipelines that contained either high-pH or near-neutral-pH stress-corrosion cracks.

Based upon the model, it is possible to justify extending intervals for subsequent hydrostatic re-tests, regardless of whether failures occurred in a previous test. Furthermore, short early intervals followed by successively longer intervals are more effective than repeated uniform intervals.

Based upon 13 field case studies, hydrostatic re-test intervals established from the model would be expected to prevent more service ruptures with fewer tests. In all but one of the cases, all of the subsequent service failures would have been prevented, and with fewer hydrostatic tests, on average. In the one exception, the previous tests were at only 90% SMYS, and the flow stress was very high.

It is possible to use the same model to establish intervals for ILI and SCC DA, provided that equivalence is established between those assessment methods and a hydrostatic test. Such equivalence would be based upon the failure stress of the largest flaw that is left in the pipeline. However, other approaches also are possible for ILI and SCC DA.

References

1. R.R.Fessler and S.Rapp, 2006. Method for establishing hydrostatic re-test intervals for pipelines with stress-corrosion cracking. Proc. 6th Int. Pipeline Conf., paper IPC2006-10163.
2. D.Katz, S.Limon, M.Gao, R.McNealy, R.Krishnamurthy, and R.McCann, 2006. SCC management and integrity planning in a gas pipeline. Proc. 6th Int. Pipeline Conf., paper IPC2006-10180.

Self-excited eddy currents for the detection of SCC

by Richard Kania[1] and Grant A Coleman[2]

1 TransCanada Pipelines Ltd, Calgary AB, Canada
2 BJ Pipeline Inspection Services, Calgary, AB, Canada

STRESS-CORROSION CRACKING (SCC) is a serious integrity issue for operators of oil or gas pipelines. The consequence of a failure is extremely high, both financially and environmentally. A reliable inline inspection (ILI) technique for crack detection would be the preferred method of detection and certification. There are several techniques capable of detecting cracks and similar features; however many are not suited to the harsh pipeline environment or cannot be run autonomously.

There exists a need in the industry to develop new techniques for the detection of SCC in fast-flowing natural gas transmission pipelines. Ultrasonic techniques (UT) have proven to be effective for inspecting liquids' lines. To operate a traditional UT tool in dry gas lines necessitate either a liquid slug, which requires complex launch and receive equipment, or fluid-filled wheels to couple UT energy to the pipe wall. Electro-magnetic acoustic transducer (EMAT) based UT tools are more robust; however, the analysis and technology is not yet fully proven. Hydro testing a line will reliably ensure that there are no injurious defects in the line; however, the test itself may cause defects to grow and some lines cannot be hydro tested due to line conditions.

Magnetic-flux leakage (MFL) techniques have been used for decades to inspect pipelines for metal-loss defects; however, MFL is not appropriate for the detection of SCC. Self-excited eddy currents (SEEC) builds upon the MFL technique and provides a novel method of SCC ILI specifically for these lines which do not allow liquid couplant or reduction in gas flow velocities. The SEEC technique requires no couplant and operates at speeds up to 5m/s. This paper presents the SEEC phenomenon and details of testing as well as design constraints encountered in building a robust system. Finally some preliminary tool data are presented to demonstrate the SEEC technique in operation.

SCC IS AN EXTREMELY narrow crack, or colony of cracks, in the exterior of the pipe wall, aligned parallel to the main pipeline axis as shown in Fig.1. An MFL-based tool is ill-suited for crack detection due to the limited sensitivity of the technique. An MFL tool works by magnetically saturating the pipe wall: a metal-loss feature will cause magnetic flux to leak out of the pipe and the signal is recorded for later interpretation. Typically, an MFL tool is arranged such that the magnetic field is parallel to the pipe axis. As magnetic flux flows parallel to the crack there is very little cross-sectional area to disturb the flux – hence no leakage and no response. Circumferential MFL tools have been built primarily to locate narrow axial corrosion, but have also had limited success in finding axial cracks. The magnetic flux in a circumferential tool flows around the pipe and across the crack face, which causes some leakage to occur. The problem is that magnetic fields are able to jump the narrow gap of the crack, reducing the associated leakage, and thus may be missed in the interpretation of the signals.

The self-excited eddy current (SEEC) method produces circumferentially oriented bands of eddy currents which interact with crack-like features in the pipe wall. Unlike magnetic fields, eddy currents are not able to jump across the crack and must flow around. The interactions are detected via the associated magnetic-field perturbation using sensors within the SEEC head.

SEEC technology

The SEEC technology extends MFL techniques to provide a new method for interacting with and detecting axially oriented cracks, something that is not possible with traditional MFL.

The SEEC effect is a practical application of Lenz's Law which states the direction of the induced currents derived from Faraday's Law of induction as in Equn 1 in which an induced electric field (*E*) is created via a changing magnetic flux density (δB/δt) with a polarity that opposes the changing magnetic field:

$$\nabla \times \vec{E} = -\frac{\delta \vec{B}}{\delta t} \tag{1}$$

The faster the flux density changes, the greater the induced electric field, and hence the current which will flow to oppose the changing magnetic field.

To illustrate how the SEEC effect is established, consider the cylindrical, right-handed, coordinate system shown in Fig.2. The axial axis is directed down the long pipe axis, the radial direction out of the pipe, and the circumferential direction around the pipe. The relationship between the induced eddy currents and the applied magnetic field is given by Equn 2, where *J* is the induced eddy current density, *v* is the velocity vector, *ó* is the conductivity of the steel, and *B* is the magnetic flux density vector.

$$\bar{J} = \sigma\left(\bar{v} \times \bar{\nabla} \times \bar{A}\right) = \sigma\left(\bar{v} \times \bar{B}\right) \tag{2}$$

The cross product in Equn 2 may be expanded into vector components as shown in Equn 3:

$$\bar{J} = \sigma \cdot \begin{bmatrix} v_R B_C - v_C B_R \\ v_C B_A - v_A B_C \\ v_A B_R - v_R B_A \end{bmatrix} \begin{matrix} \breve{A} \\ \breve{R} \\ \breve{C} \end{matrix} \tag{3}$$

From the geometry of the pipe and the pig, it is possible to simplify Equn 3. A pig moving down pipe only has significant velocity in the axial direction, although there may be a small radial or circumferential component due to roll or the kinematics of the tool; however, these effects are negligible compared to the axial motion of the tool. Setting these terms to zero allows a simpler form of the equation to be written, as in Equn 4.

$$\bar{J} = \left[\sigma \cdot v_A \cdot B_R\right]\hat{c} \tag{4}$$

$$B = \mu \cdot H \tag{5}$$

Substituting Equn 5 into Equn 4, we arrive at the final formulation (Equn 6) for the creation of circumferentially oriented eddy currents caused by the motion of the SEEC tool axially down the pipeline. In Equn 6, ì is the relative magnetic permeability, and the eddy current density is thus related to tool velocity and applied radial field. The faster the tool travels, the larger the rate of change of the magnetic field and the larger will be the generated eddy currents.

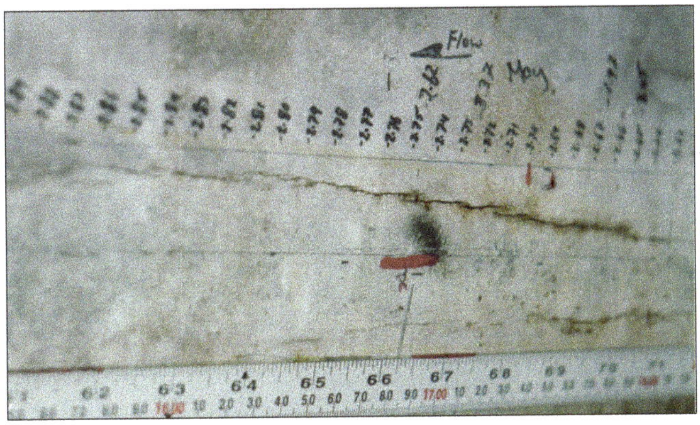

Fig. 1. Stress-corrosion cracking in pipeline steel.

$$\bar{J} = [\sigma \cdot v_A \cdot \mu \cdot H_R]\hat{c} \quad (6)$$

Magnetic modelling

Extensive use of finite-element modelling (FEM) software was used to design and optimize the SEEC head. FEM splits a large problem into smaller pieces, known as elements, which may be solved numerically, allowing for significantly more complex systems to be solved than is possible with a purely analytic solution. Previous work [2] provides a detailed derivation of the equations governing the FEM solutions.

It is a considerable challenge to accurately model the motionally induced eddy currents created by the SEEC tool. A typical MFL tool design does not need to be as concerned about the accuracy of the predicted eddy currents, as the MFL sensors are deliberately placed in a location where the eddy currents generated by the tool magnets will have died out. *Vector Fields* (VF) was chosen to provide the FEM package, as it is a mature system capable of solving motion-induced eddy currents with the solver packages available within the 'Opera' suite. The software provides an advanced parametric modelling system with integrated mesh generation; in the 2D case, automatic mesh refinement is also available. Extremely complex shapes may be modelled with the package using advanced transforms such as lofting and non-uniform surface unions. The VF software handles non-linear and anisotropic magnetization (BH) curves, removing the need for as many approximations in setting up the model. A magnetization or BH curve shows the relationship

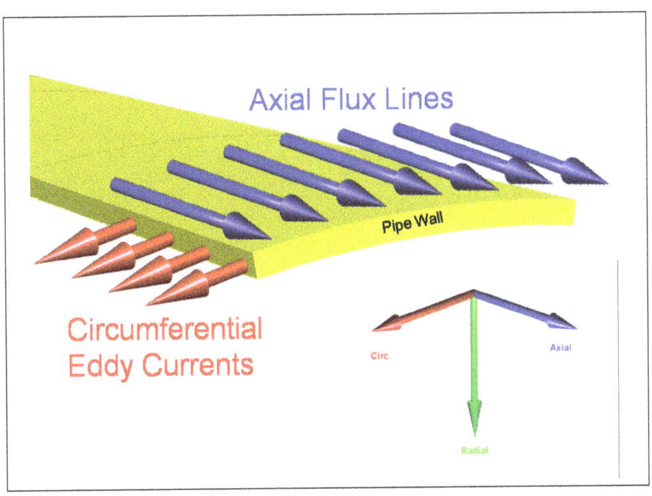

Fig.2. Cylindrical pipeline coordinate system.

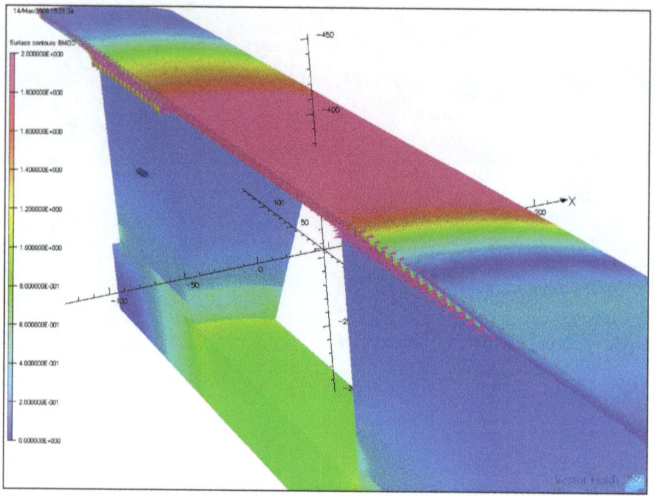

Fig.3. FEM results shown magnetization levels and eddy-current distributions.

between the magnetic induction (B) and magnetizing force (H) for a magnetic material: each component of the system uses a different BH curve to model its magnetic behaviour. Exact magnetic BH curves may be used within the model without the need to force the system to be linear with an arbitrary permeability or saturation magnetization level.

The VF software contains both a 2D and 3D module. The 2D solver was used for initial modelling and parameter testing. The number of elements in the 2D models is relatively low resulting in solutions which could be solved in between minutes and hours. Once a design is found acceptable in 2D, it is extended into 3D for further refinement and analysis. A 3D model may take hours or days to solve, and the complexity of the post-processing also increases dramatically.

By extensive use of the FEM software, development of the SEEC system could be largely performed in model space with limited need for prototyping test heads. The models have made it possible to find optimum sensor densities and locations.

A sample 3D FEM model is displayed in Fig.3. The model contains a moving magnetizer, magnets, brushes, and the pipe wall - only a small section of the model is shown for clarity. The model surface is coloured according to the magnetization levels of the model components: values range from 0 to 2.0 Tesla, transitioning from blue to pink respectively. The motion-induced eddy currents are shown as vector arrows travelling around the pipe circumferentially, shown in more detail in Fig.4.

Physical SEEC system

Physically, the SEEC tool looks very similar to a traditional MFL tool: Fig.5 shows the basic layout. There are bias magnets, brushes, cups, and wheels. However, the SEEC sensors themselves are very different from traditional MFL sensors. The sensors are physically large and arranged in two separate, overlapping, rings to provide full circumferential coverage.

The SEEC tool is launched and received in exactly the same manner as an MFL tool, which allows the use of existing launch and receive equipment and traps. The complete tool train is two bodies long. The tool requires no special line conditions with the exception of speed: as Equn 6 has highlighted, the SEEC tool must move quickly down the pipeline at 3 to 4 m/s in order to generate large eddy-current densities.

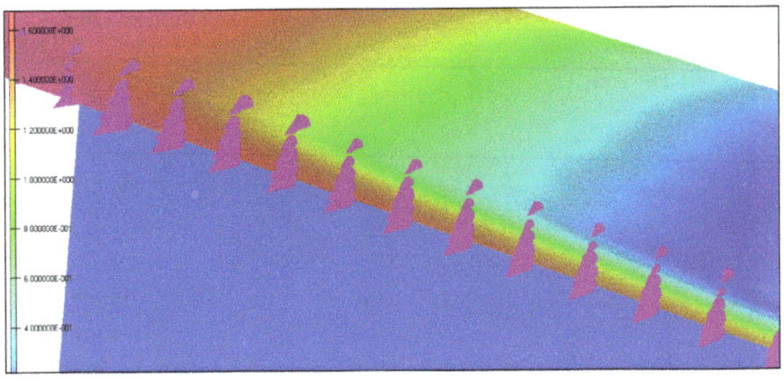

Fig.4. Detail of motion-induced eddy currents.

SEEC sensor system

The SEEC heads contain a unique magnetic system for inducing eddy currents into the pipe wall to perform the actual crack inspection. When designing an eddy-current system, skin depth must be considered: this is a measure of how far a signal can propagate into a conductive material or media before the signal is attenuated to 1/e or 36.79% of its original strength. If the tool-generated eddy currents are not able to penetrate the pipe wall completely, there is a chance of missing a feature or having a feature obscured in the inherent background noise of the system. The skin depth of a 'good' conductor is given by Equn 7, where *f* is frequency, ó is the conductivity, and ì$_r$ is the relative magnetic permeability. Relative permeability is a measure of the degree to which the material has been magnetized: a good conductor [1] is defined as one in which the conductivity is much greater than the product of frequency and permittivity of the material; this condition is satisfied for pipeline steels.

$$\delta = \frac{1}{\sqrt{\pi \cdot f \cdot \mu_r \cdot \sigma}} \qquad (7)$$

As the conductivity is a fixed property of the material, the only way to increase the skin depth is to either lower the frequency or lower the relative magnetic permeability of the material.

The main magnetization circuit of the SEEC tool acts in the same manner as traditional MFL tool to lower the relative permeability of the pipeline steel by conducting large amounts of magnetic flux into the pipe wall via magnets connected to the pipe wall with brushes or bristles. By lowering the relative permeability, the skin depth is increased and the SEEC sensors are able to completely penetrate the pipe wall. The SEEC head itself contains magnets which generate the circumferential eddy currents used for the actual crack detection. Sensors within the SEEC head record data which is later analysed for the presence of SCC type features.

The SEEC tool, as shown in Fig,5, has 34 total sensor heads distributed on two rings offset keyed from each other to provide full circumferential coverage. Axially, the tool records data approximately every 1 mm along the pipe while travelling at 3-4 m/s.

The longevity of the sensor heads is of particular concern. The heads experience significant forces during the course of an inspection and need to be robust enough to handle all pipeline features while maintaining the correct offset from the pipe wall. Extensive testing has been performed on the longevity of the components which contact the pipe wall. The sensor is held at a fixed distance from the pipe wall by wheels built into the head. The wheels, bearings, and axles have to operate reliably for the hundreds of kilometres of a typical inspection. The wear surface comes into direct contact with pipeline when passing over irregularities on the inside surface of the pipe such as

Fig.5. A 36-in SEEC tool.

welds and wall-thickness transitions. In the unlikely event that the SEEC head ride wheels were to completely fail, the wear surface must be able to protect the head and perform while in direct contact with the pipe wall for the remaining duration of an inspection run. In addition to the mechanical constraints the wear surface material also has to be magnetically transparent so not to attenuate the SEEC signal.

Longevity tests were performed on an apparatus called a drum rig. This machine can be adjusted to simulate inspection speeds ranging from 0.25 m/s to 10 m/s. Physical defects may be mechanically installed on the surface of the drum to simulate real effects such as welds, hard surfaces, and pipe-wall transitions. These defects are used to evaluate wear surfaces, reactions to shock and vibration, and overall design durability. The final design of the SEEC heads is capable of enduring thousands of kilometres of simulated inspection runs on the drum rig.

SEEC data

The SEEC tool has been built up as a 36-in tool for initial testing and trials, and testing is being performed at the BJ pull-rig facility in Calgary. The rig can be set up with pipe segments containing a variety of features. Testing has been performed on pipe samples containing metal loss, notches, and real-world SCC removed from in-service pipelines.

Notch samples were created using the electro-discharge machining (EDM) technique, selected as it provides a means of imparting an extremely narrow, sub-millimetre feature with none of the residual machining stresses or material changes typically left by mechanical methods such as grinding or cutting wheels. EDM notches were considered to be the closest approximation to actual cracking that was possible to produce in practice with controlled, known, dimensions. The notch pictured in Fig.6 is 76.2 mm long, 0.7 mm wide, and 80% depth of wall thickness. The red arrows indicate the location of reference holes drilled into the pipe wall which were used in early testing to aid in location and scaling of the recorded SEEC responses.

Figure 7 shows the SEEC response to an 80% EDM notch. The response to a crack-like feature is unique and different that the response from a metal-loss feature. Metal-loss features are recorded as a positive and negative signal at the feature location, which can be seen as a blue positive peak followed by a red negative peak located at the reference features on either side of the EDM feature, as indicated by the red arrows. The signal from the EDM feature is entirely negative or a red

Fig.6. A 76.2-mm long x 0.7-mm wide x 80% deep EDM notch feature in a section of 36in pipe.

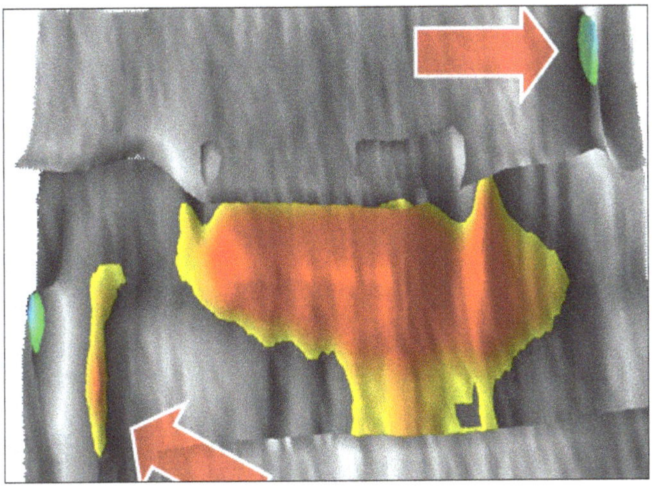

Fig.7. SEEC response from 80% EDM feature: 3D thermal representation.

indication for the length of the feature. The differing responses of the SEEC head to metal-loss and crack-like features makes feature discrimination and identification possible.

A number of EDM-type features were created at various depths ranging from 10% to 80% of wall thickness; all the features were 76.2mm long and axially oriented. The defect amplitudes were compared to the FEM results for similar notch-type features. The plot in Fig.8 shows the non-linear relationship between the SEEC signal amplitude and feature depth. The shape of the curve agrees well with the FEM data for similar defects.

Following-on from the successful EDM notch testing, the SEEC tool was pull-tested past actual SCC samples which had been removed from service. Figure 9 shows the SEEC response to a 20% SCC colony. The red arrows indicate the location of reference holes in the pipe sample; the SCC is located between the reference holes and indicated by the blue oval. The SCC signal is visible as the negative yellow depression in the bottom picture between the reference holes, which show up as positive and negative peaks. The SEEC response is following the orientation of the SCC colony very closely. An amplitude of 60 Gauss was recorded for this feature.

The SEEC response to a deeper 42% SCC colony is presented in Fig.10: the red arrows indicate the location of reference holes and the blue ovals the location of the SCC colonies. The SEEC response is closely following the location and shape of the SCC. The peak SEEC amplitude is 100 Gauss.

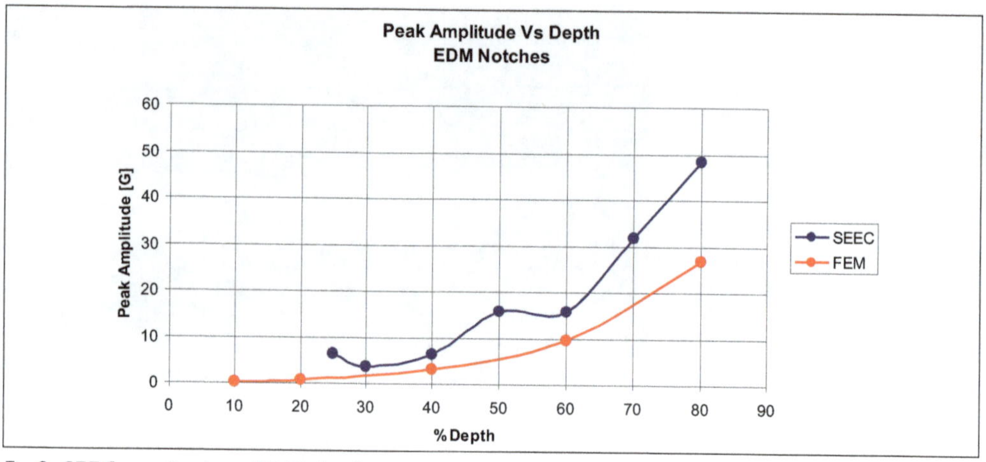

Fig.8. SEEC amplitude vs EDM depth.

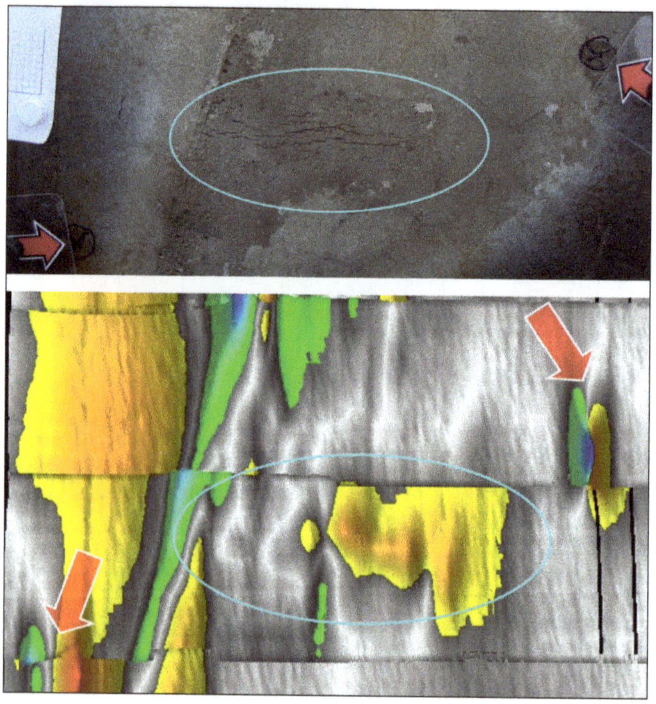

Fig.9. A 20% SCC colony feature (top) and corresponding SEEC data (bottom).

The SEEC technique is capable of distinguishing from metal loss and SCC; furthermore, the SEEC amplitudes scale in a predictable manner, indicating that feature-depth sizing should be possible.

Initial field results

The SEEC tool has been run in two diameter configurations, for two separate pipeline operators, in over 1000 km of pipeline. The initial results of these runs are extremely promising.

Shown in Fig.11 is the SEEC response to a >70% feature located by the SEEC tool in a 36-in diameter natural gas pipeline. The feature depth was estimated to be between 60 to 80% of wall

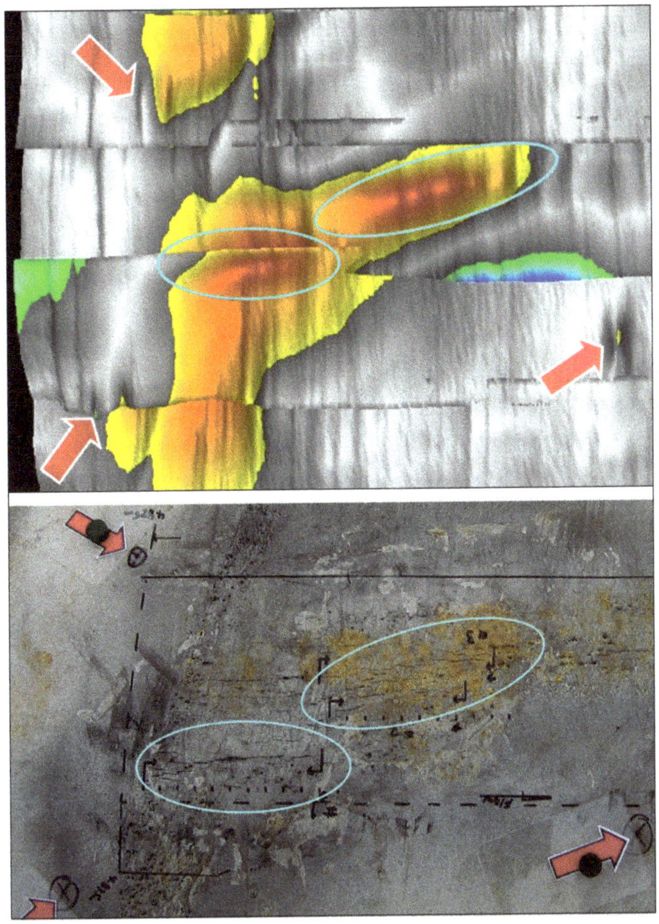

Fig.10. A 42% SCC colony feature (top) and corresponding SEEC data (bottom).

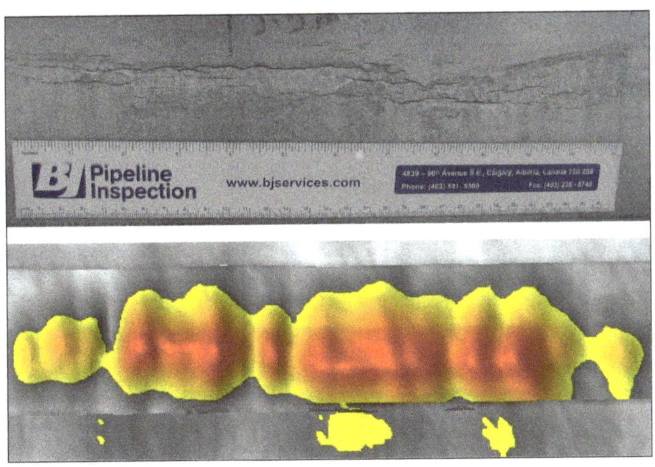

Fig.11. A >70% SCC feature (top) and corresponding SEEC data (bottom).

thickness. In-ditch NDT techniques measured the feature to be over 12 in long with a depth of greater than 70%. The SEEC technique is well suited for this assessment as the recorded amplitudes increase with depth, as discussed previously (see Fig.8). Further verification digs are required to advance the technology and build a knowledge base of known verified features.

Conclusions and further work

SEEC is an exciting, and novel method for crack detection, especially suited to high flow speed gas transmission pipeline systems. SEEC is a new technique which will become an attractive alternative to existing technologies in the crack-detection market.

The system is robust and novel, requiring no special pipeline operating conditions. The tool is physically very similar to a traditional MFL tools in both appearance and field operations.

The SEEC effect has been shown to be effective at locating SCC features in operating pipelines and under pull-through conditions. Moving forward, the SEEC system needs to be run in more pipelines to gain operational experience. Many verification digs will need to be performed to provide feedback into the signal-processing and feature-detection programmes.

References

1. D.J.Griffiths, 1989. Introduction to electrodynamics. 2nd Edn, p371, Prentice Hall, New Jersey.
2. R.C.Ireland and C.R.Torres, 2004. Challenges in circumferential magnetization: an FEA point of view. Proc. Int. Pipeline Conf., Paper IPC2004-0191, Calgary, Canada, October.

A new joint-industry project addressing the integrity management of SCC in gas transmission pipelines

by Dr A David Batte[1], Dr Raymond R Fessler[2], Jim E Marr[3], and Steve C Rapp[4]

1 Macaw Engineering, Newcastle upon Tyne, UK
2 Biztek Consulting, Evanston, IL, USA
3 TransCanada Pipelines, Calgary, AB, Canada
4 Spectra Energy, Houston, TX, USA

IN 2006 a group of natural gas transmission pipeline operating companies in North America collaborated in a joint-industry project (JIP) to address the integrity management of SCC in high-consequence areas. The outcome of the work was a series of reports examining the occurrence of SCC extending over 40 years up to 2005, and developing experience-based guidance for conducting hydrostatic testing and excavations, for assessing the severity of discovered cracks and for establishing the interval before the next assessment. The outcome was published in ASME STP-PT-011 [1] and provided the basis for proposed revisions to ASME B31.8S. It also enabled the closer alignment of ASME B31.8S with the revisions to the CEPA Recommended practice for SCC.

Five years later, a slightly enlarged group of operators has revisited the current status of SCC threat management in North America. The operational experience relating to over 256,000km of gas transmission pipelines during the last five years has been compared with that seen up to 2005. The threat-management procedures and practices, including the application of hydrostatic testing, SCC direct assessment, and the latest-generations of crack-detection in-line inspection (ILI), have been examined, and benchmarks for good practice have been identified. The increasing application of SCC direct assessment and crack-detection ILI has focused attention on the prediction of failure pressures for discovered SCC; a protocol for gathering consistent data during post-ILI excavations has been developed, and the influence of flaw profile on predicted failure pressure has been explored.

This paper presents an overview of the JIP Phase II programme and summarizes some of the early results. It is intended that the outcomes of the individual tasks will be disseminated for the benefit of the wider industry, so that they can provide an informed basis for any proposed modifications and improvements to industry guidance and regulations.

Background

In response to concerns about managing the threat of SCC in high-pressure gas transmission pipelines, and in the light of recently introduced US legislation concerning integrity-management plans focusing on high-consequence areas (HCAs), a group of five major gas transmission companies initiated a JIP to develop technical rationales to support the key processes of SCC integrity management, including hydrostatic testing, ILI, and SCC direct assessment (SCCDA). The JIP commenced in January, 2006, and the overall findings were published in October, 2008, as ASME STP-PT-011 [1].

The overall outcome of the JIP was the development and collation of a significant body of supporting information, made available to pipeline operators and to the pipeline industry, providing the basis for sound decision-making regarding the issues to be addressed when managing the integrity of pipelines that are potentially subject to the threat of SCC. In particular, the JIP delivered the following:

- A review and update of SCC experience in 208,000km of high-pressure gas pipelines, incorporating data extending over more than 50 years and including over 80 in-service ruptures and leaks. This database represented a substantial proportion of the relevant operating experience in North America.

- Validation of the ASME B31.8S criteria for determining segments and HCAs most likely to be susceptible to high-pH SCC, and demonstration that the modified ASME B31.8S criteria are also applicable to near-neutral pH SCC, based on the accumulated service experience.

- Development of guidelines and algorithms for prioritizing pipeline segments and HCAs for SCC assessment, and for selecting excavation sites most likely to show evidence of SCC, using the accumulated service experience and latest research information.

- Development of guidance for conducting SCC hydrostatic tests so as to deliver optimized benefits for SCC integrity management. These test conditions may differ from those for hydrostatic tests conducted for other operational reasons.

- Development of a categorization scheme for determining crack severity and mitigation response, based on predicted failure pressure and estimated remaining life at the operating pressure [2]. The sensitivity of crack severity to input parameters (pipeline attributes, crack growth rate, and assumptions made during calculations) was examined.

- Development of a method for determining the intervals between re-tests when using hydrostatic testing, ILI, or SCC DA to manage SCC [3].

- Provision of guidance for determining how many excavations are necessary during SCC DA.

- Development of a process for utilizing condition monitoring activities for SCC management when little or no SCC is experienced, consistent with the requirements of 'other technology' for integrity management.

- Identification of revisions to improve the existing ASME B31.8S guidance for SCC, and preparation of alternative wording for consideration and balloting by the ASME Committee.

A second phase of the JIP commenced in January, 2011. The aims of this work are to build on the outcome of the first phase in the light of five further years of operational experience in North America. In particular the JIP Phase II tasks focus on:

- Comparing recent experiences of SCC in North American gas transmission pipelines with the trends observed between 1965 and 2005 (JIP Phase I [1]) as further validation of the ASME B31.8S conditions for defining SCC susceptibility.

- Evaluating developments and in-field experience in the application of ILI crack-detection technology, with a view to developing a rationale for demonstrating that ILI crack detection can be used in a manner equivalent to hydrostatic testing for SCC threat management.

- Reviewing the collective experience concerning the application of SCC direct-assessment practices and procedures, and assessment of operators' practices in relation to the requirements of PHMSA's inspection protocols for compliance with *Subpart O: pipeline integrity management.*

- Reviewing recent experience regarding the application of hydrostatic re-testing programmes and their effectiveness in preventing in-service failures in gas transmission pipelines.

- Reviewing the guidance, standards, and legislation concerning SCC threat management in North America, and exploring whether there is scope for any improvements in the light of the above experiences.

This second phase of the JIP is ongoing, and it is intended that the full findings will be disseminated to industry before the end of the year. This paper summarizes the key activities and presents some of the preliminary results.

Update of service experience

The information collected during JIP Phase I covered the period from the first occurrences of in-service failures due to SCC in the mid-1960s up to December, 2005. The Phase II review has collated and reviewed data provided by the participating pipeline operators for the five-year period from January, 2006, to December, 2010. The principal intent of the work has been to discern whether the trends identified up to 2005 have been confirmed during the subsequent five years, focusing on information from in-service and hydrostatic tests.

All the participants in JIP Phase I were operators of substantial systems for the transmission of dry natural gas in various locations in North America. All had some prior experience of SCC in their pipelines, in some instances dating back to the earliest in-service ruptures and breaks in the mid-1960s. The experience spanned both high-pH and near-neutral pH SCC. Several other operators with similar operational experience offered information that was also included in the survey.

Two further operators joined the second Phase of the JIP, one of whom had experienced significant SCC during the 1960s and 1970s in a subsequently-replaced pipeline. Five in-service failures and 50 hydrostatic test failures due to SCC had been experienced. While the SCC mechanism had not been identified during the original investigations, it is now clear[1] that the failures were due to near-neutral pH SCC. These results have been added to the JIP database in order to make correct comparisons and interpretations of trends.

The total amount of data available for analysis, in which SCC was the primary cause of failure, now amounted to 89 in-service failures and 481 hydrostatic test failures. Of these, three in-service failures (all due to near-neutral pH SCC) and 79 hydrostatic test failures had occurred in 2006-

1. Dr Fessler has re-examined his original failure reports in the light of subsequent understanding of near-neutral pH SCC.

Year	65/70	71/75	76/80	81/85	86/90	91/95	96/00	01/05	06/10
High pH SCC	7	12	2	9	8	10	7	4	0
Near-neutral pH SCC	1	2	2	1	1	5	6	5	3

Table 1. Occurrence of in-service failures due to SCC.

2010. The frequency of in-service failures due to both high pH and near-neutral pH (excluding four mixed-mode failures) is shown in Table 1.

The pattern of both in-service and hydrostatic test failures (not presented in this preliminary overview) is generally consistent with the trends reported previously. SCC may occasionally be present at lower operating stresses, or may now occur at greater than 32km downstream from compressor discharges, but these occasional situations are not inconsistent with the ASMS B31.8S guidance, which has previously been shown to address 80-90% of all SCC. The overall situation with regard to the occurrence of in-service failures due to SCC over the last 50 years can be summarized as shown in Table 2.

The pattern of SCC occurrences has not changed significantly during the last five years; hence, the conclusions reached in the JIP Phase I study are still valid, and the guidelines incorporated in ASME B31.8S for managing the threat of SCC are still appropriate.

Review of integrity-management practices and experience

All eight pipeline companies participating in Phase II of the JIP have experienced SCC in their systems, and have addressed the threat of SCC by utilizing hydrostatic testing, excavations, ILI, or a combination of all three. During the course of these activities the companies have amassed a considerable body of expertise and experience on all aspects of SCC threat management.

The review has focused on the experience gained in the last five years or so concerning the application of hydrostatic testing, excavations, and ILI for integrity management. This has highlighted the changes that have occurred, the trends that have been observed, and the issues that warrant further attention by the industry.

All operators have developed SCC threat-management strategies consistent with their other integrity management activities, in response to the requirements of 49 CFR 192 Subpart O [4] and in line with the guidance in ASME B31.8S [5]. Depending on individual pipeline system attributes, operational conditions and prior SCC experiences, the SCC threat-management plans have included hydrostatic testing, ILI, SCC DA, or a combination of all three. The plans have also incorporated the ongoing hydrostatic-testing and excavation activities that had been undertaken over many years prior to the requirement to develop formal integrity-management plans. The range of SCC experiences (1965 to 2010) and SCC management approaches used by different operators is illustrated in Table 3.

By 2005, most of the operators were using hydrostatic testing as the mainstay of their SCC threat-management strategies, combined in most instances with opportunist or targeted excavations. The two operators with the least experience of SCC, and no in-service or hydrostatic test failures, utilized only excavations. Four operators have explored crack-detection ILI, and two operators are

Criterion	High pH SCC	Near-neutral pH SCC
Distance downstream from compressors	90% are within 20 miles	70% are within 20 miles
Operating stress	85% are at >60% SMYS	95% are at >60% SMYS
Pipeline age	No in-service or hydrostatic test failures in pipelines installed after 1981	
Coating type	70% in coal tar lines 25% in tape-wrap lines	40% in asphalt lines 35% in tape-wrap lines 20% in uncoated lines
	No in-service or hydrostatic test failures in FBE-coated lines	

Table 2. Factors linked to the occurrence of high-pH and near-neutral pH SCC.

Operator	BB	DD	FF	JJ	KK
In-service failures and leaks	7 ruptures, 16 leaks	4 ruptures	0	2 ruptures	0
Hydrotest failures	69	24	0	2	1
SCC found by ILI?	Yes	Yes	No	Yes	Yes
SCC found by excavation?	Yes	Yes	One instance, found after MFL	Yes	Yes
Type of SCC	High pH	Mixed	NNpH	NNpH	NNpH
Hydrotest experience	Yes	Yes	No	Yes	Few
ILI crack detection experience?	Yes	Yes	No	Yes	Yes, lots
Opportunistic excavations?	Yes	Yes	Yes	Yes	Yes
Targeted excavations?	Yes	Yes on high-risk lines	No	Yes	Yes
SCC DA?	Yes, low-risk segments	No	Yes, low-risk segments	Yes	No
Current IMP - primary tool	Hydrotest	ILI	Opportunistic excavations	Targeted excavations	ILI
Current IMP - other tools	Opportunistic and targeted excavations, SCC DA	ILI + targeted and opportunistic excavations + hydrotesting	Options for hydrotest, SCC DA	Opportunistic and targeted excavations in low-risk areas, hydrotesting, ILI	Targeted excavations, SCC condition monitoring

Table 3. Illustration of the range of SCC experiences (1965-2010) and SCC management approaches used by different operators.

using ILI combined with excavations (no hydrostatic testing). In total, during the last five years the JIP participants have conducted 80 hydrostatic tests that resulted in removal of near-critical SCC, have completed over 3200km of pipeline inspection using the latest-generation ILI crack-detection technology, and have completed 140 excavations according to NACE SCC DA procedures.

Hydrostatic testing

All the JIP Phase II participants conduct their hydrostatic spike tests at 100-110% SMYS, with the hold times varying from 10 minutes to one hour. The leak tests are conducted at 90-100% SMYS for periods of 2-8 hours. Some operators also use flame ionisation or ground patrols as a further check for leaks on return to service. These procedures are in accordance with the optimum practice described in JIP Phase I, as well as being in line with ASME B31.8S guidance [5].

When the first hydrostatic re-testing programmes were established in the 1970s, the intervals were based on engineering judgement and typically allowed the re-test interval to increase in steps from one year to 7-10 years if no further in-service or hydrostatic test failures occurred. Based on the collective experience over the ensuing 40 years, a new model (the Fessler Model, JIP Phase I, [3]) was developed, re-defining the pattern of re-test intervals for each pipeline. Three of the JIP operators have adopted it for setting hydrostatic re-test intervals, while the other operators have continued with their already-established re-testing schemes.

The review shows that the Fessler Model has been used to good effect during the last five years, and has been of considerable benefit in allowing re-test intervals to be extended. There has, however, been one instance where premature failure occurred due to the coalescence of two adjacent significant flaws; this situation is not addressed by the Fessler Model, and has been the subject of in-depth investigation which has shown that the conditions for such occurrences are very rare.

Excavations and SCC direct assessment

Several of the JIP Phase II participants have used excavations as a means of extending the scope of their SCC threat-management strategies. Several thousand excavations have been completed, either as opportunistic excavations when the pipe has been exposed for other operational reasons, or as targeted excavations supported by soil/attribute/experience models. Most operators continue to use excavations on this basis.

Following the development of the NACE Standard for SCC direct assessment [6] and its incorporation alongside hydrostatic testing and ILI in ASME B31.8S, several JIP operators have incorporated SCC DA in their formalized integrity-management plans. During the last five years or so, SCC DA has been used by three operators, mainly on segments with a low risk of SCC. A total of 150 excavations has now been completed, ten of which have found Category 1 cracking or less.

Crack-detection ILI

At the time of JIP Phase I in 2005, four operators had trialled crack-detection ILI and two operators were using ILI combined with excavations for SCC threat management. However the predominant view was that crack-detection ILI was not sufficiently reliable or accurate for general use as a primary tool for integrity management.

Since 2005 considerable effort has been made by the operators, working with the ILI vendors, to develop and improve ILI crack-detection technology. Four operators have undertaken eight inspection runs totalling around 640km using vehicles in liquid slugs, while three operators have completed 13 inspection runs totalling around 1280km using vehicles with plastic wheel contact (so-called elastic wave). The bulk of the recent experience, over 45 inspection runs totalling around 4800km, has been obtained using EMAT ILI. During the course of the EMAT ILI runs many crack-like features have been detected, and over 100 of the larger features have been confirmed by excavation to be SCC that would probably have failed a hydrostatic test.

EMAT ILI also provides information about the depth and length of detected features. As with feature detection, it is important to quantify the accuracy of depth and length measurements when they are to be used in defect severity assessments. At present both depth and length measurements are difficult to interpret, and length measurements do not take into account the threshold (1-2 mm) below which ILI EMAT does not detect features. These issues are being addressed by both the ILI vendors and the operators, but a standardized approach to the acquisition and interpretation of the data from ILI runs and excavations is needed before sound quantitative information is generated and sufficiently reliable, accurate, EMAT ILI performance can be established; this is being addressed in an ongoing JIP task described below.

Developments in the application of data from crack-detection (EMAT) ILI

The increasing application of crack-detection EMAT ILI has focused attention on the prediction of failure pressures for discovered SCC. In response to this need, the JIP is focusing on three aspects of the issue:

- The development of a protocol for gathering consistent data during post-ILI excavations, especially when the data are being used to confirm the performance of the ILI findings.
- Determining the accuracy of methods for predicting failure pressure, paying particular attention to the influence of flaw profile on the results obtained.
- The equivalence of crack detection ILI and hydrostatic testing.

Protocol for obtaining data from post-ILI excavations

A principal aim of EMAT ILI is to detect and quantify longitudinal surface-breaking cracks and related crack-like features; principally SCC, but also including fatigue, corrosion fatigue and weld toe cracks. To demonstrate that EMAT ILI is sufficiently reliable to be used as an alternative to hydrostatic testing, it is necessary to show that such cracks can be found and sized with a high degree of certainty. For this purpose it is essential to establish a commonly-agreed protocol for excavating features reported by EMAT ILI and acquiring consistent in-the-ditch data describing the cracking that is found; this is then used to determine performance parameters such as probability of detection (PoD) and probability of identification (PoI), in line with the requirements of API 1163 [7] and similar standards.

Based on their recent on-site experiences, the JIP operators have developed a protocol for obtaining consistent information from excavations of longitudinal cracks and related crack-like features identified during EMAT ILI runs. The purpose of the exercise is to obtain quantitative information on three aspects: the location, character, and dimensions (depth and length) of the feature. The steps to be taken in order to gather and evaluate the necessary information are as follows:

- Step 1: Excavate and carry out magnetic-particle inspection (MPI) of 100% of the prepared surface of the pipe joint containing the selected feature.

- Step 2: Carry out ultrasonic examination at the location where the feature was reported by EMAT ILI, and at any other locations where surface-breaking cracks are revealed by MPI.

- Step 3: Record the locations, lengths and depths of the most severe surface-breaking cracks revealed by MPI, and record the locations and dimensions of any sub-surface defects revealed by ultrasonics at the location where the feature was reported by EMAT ILI.

- Step 4: Use the MPI and ultrasonic (or incremental buffing) measurements to determine:
  - the longest interacting surface-breaking crack lengths revealed by MPI, after discounting the portions of any cracks that are less deep than the EMAT ILI crack detection threshold;
  - the maximum depths of the above cracks.

- Step 5: Use the excavation data, the EMAT ILI feature report, and the EMAT ILI performance specification to determine:
  - location: is the feature in the location identified by EMAT ILI?
  - character: has the feature been correctly reported as axially-oriented, surface-breaking, and crack-like?
  - dimensions: are the lengths and maximum depths in agreement with those reported by EMAT ILI?

It is expected that use of this protocol will establish consistent sets of data for use in determining, assessing, and comparing the performance of EMAT ILI tools during pipeline inspections, and for determining the accuracy (tolerance) of crack depth and measurements.

The accuracy of predicted failure pressures

Accurate predictions of the failure pressure of flaws that have been discovered are an important requirement for the management of SCC. ASME B31.8S contains guidance for using predicted failure pressures to categorize the severity of SCC and determine the schedule and nature of mitigation measures.

Over the years several fracture-mechanics'-based calculation methods have been developed for axially-oriented crack-like flaws, and have been validated by comparison with results from burst tests containing artificial and, in some cases in-service, crack-like features. Among the methods in use are API 579 [8], the Ln-secant method [9, 10], and two proprietary methods, *CorLas* [11] and the pipeline axial flaw failure criterion (PAFFC) [12]. Some of these methods have been applied to the assessment of 'real' SCC in pipe samples that failed while in service or were removed from service and subsequently burst tested [13, 14]. The results from these studies indicate that there is greater scatter in the predictions when the methods are applied to real defects, compared to that experienced for artificial flaws or simple-shaped fatigue cracks.

The operators participating in the JIP have assembled information relating to almost 100 in-service failures, hydrostatic-test failures, and pipe burst tests in which failure was due to SCC. Within the database are a wide range of pipe grades and geometries. Failures are due to both high-pH and near-neutral pH SCC, and the flaws that initiated final failure range from simple thumbnails to complex groups of cracks in three-dimensional colonies.

A comprehensive comparative study of the failure pressure predictions obtained using API 579, Ln-secant, *CorLas*, and PAFFC methods, for around 40 of the best-characterized data-sets within the above database, is currently in progress. The sensitivities of the calculations to the input data used and to the manner in which the flaw profile is characterized, are being examined. It is intended that the results will provide useful guidance to all those engaged in predicting failure pressures as part of their SCC threat-management activities.

The equivalence of ILI and hydrostatic testing

Hydrostatic testing has long been used as a tool for managing the threat of SCC, particularly in pipelines that already have a history of SCC, and has proved to be an extremely effective means of removing near-critical defects before they can cause in-service failure. Nevertheless, there are situations where regular hydrostatic testing is difficult or near-impossible to apply, and alternative approaches are sought. Crack-detection ILI has seen substantial improvement during the last decade, and is now used by several operators alongside hydrostatic testing and SCC DA. Both operators and regulators are seeking a basis whereby the outcome from crack-detection ILI can be considered as equivalent to that from hydrostatic testing, when used for SCC threat management.

It is immediately clear that hydrostatic testing and crack-detection ILI provide different information, and that meaningful direct comparisons cannot be made; hence on their own they cannot be shown to be equivalent. A more useful approach is to consider the aims and outcomes of threat management. This leads to the following:

> *Equivalence is achieved when an ILI-based threat-management approach can be shown to prevent in-service failures to the same extent that a hydrostatic-test-based approach does.*

In this context, the threat-management approach, whether ILI-based or hydrostatic-test-based, incorporates regular inspection/testing, assessment of the outcome and establishment of the interval before the next inspection should be undertaken.

A basis for developing an ILI-based approach that is equivalent to a hydrostatic-test-based approach for SCC threat management, is being explored. If the probability of detecting cracks exceeding the 2mm x 50mm size threshold is around 90%, then there is a small probability that some defects exceeding the hydrostatic-test threshold will remain after all those discovered by ILI have been removed. However there is also the opportunity to remove some or all of the discovered defects that exceed the 2mm x 50mm threshold, significantly reducing the total number of defects available to grow to near-critical size during the interval before the next assessment. In some circumstances the aggregate of these two defect groups that would remain after ILI may present a lower overall probability of failure during the interval before the next assessment, compared to removing all the larger defects by conducting a hydrostatic test. The precise trade-off between ILI and hydrostatic testing will be dependent on the size distribution and total number of discovered defects, and on the probability of detection for crack-like defects exceeding the 2mm x 50mm threshold.

The way ahead for integrity management: continuous improvement

While it is important to acknowledge the inherent strength of the current threat-management processes, there is still room for improvement, particularly in the individual tools that are applied.

So far as hydrostatic testing is concerned the procedures are well-established, although it is still necessary to emphasize the need to use 100-110% SMYS for the spike pressure. There is, however, a need to continually review the new results from hydrostatic re-test programmes, particularly as the re-test intervals increase; the recent failure that apparently did not fit the Fessler Model because of unexpected crack coalescence effects is a case in point.

Regarding crack-detection ILI, while the recent experiences point to a significant improvement in EMAT ILI performance in the last five years, the performance still appears to be somewhat variable. In order to achieve the objective of demonstrating that ILI can be used in a manner equivalent to hydrostatic testing for SCC threat management, it is necessary to:

- standardize the procedures for data acquisition and interpretation, and for determining PoD, PoI, and sizing accuracy; and
- determine the best way to calculate predicted failure pressure, especially for complex-shaped and clustered crack-like defects.

The ongoing JIP tasks described above will go some way towards achieving these objectives, but this work in itself may not provide all the answers. Also, it may be necessary to stimulate and support further developments by the ILI vendors to improve the inherent performance of the vehicles, particularly regarding feature discrimination for crack-like and non-crack-like defects.

Regarding SCC DA, the underlying process is well defined but the field experience to date is limited: 140 defects excavated by the JIP participants, of which around 10% revealed SCC. In time, the SCC DA process will benefit considerably from feedback of the information obtained; for example, to improve the weighting of susceptibility factors used to select dig sites and determine the number of digs. To this end it will be important to build-up and share the experience gained, particularly from situations where more than one approach (hydrostatic testing, ILI, SCC DA) has been applied to a segment.

Regarding overall SCC threat management, the experiences of the last five years, concerning the development and application of SCC threat management in accordance with the ASME B31.8S guidance on integrity management, have generally been very positive. The approaches have sought to achieve a workable balance between prescription and guidance, and this has allowed the flexibility for operators to adopt threat-management strategies that are targeted at their particular needs. Hydrostatic testing, ILI, and SCC DA are each used as a primary assessment method by some operators, and most operators use them in combination. Overall, the frequency of in-service failures has been reduced, even though there is a legacy of SCC-susceptible pipeline segments to be managed.

One possible way forward would be to develop an over-arching standard for SCC threat management, based on the integrity-management process defined in ASME B31.8S [5] and incorporating the SCC-specific guidance in NACE RP0204 [6], CEPA SCC Recommended Practice [15] and ASME STP-PT-011 [1]. At present all the JIP operators make extensive use of these documents in their in-house procedures, and many of them are explicitly called up in their

SCC DA procedure documentation. It would not be an insurmountable task to develop a 'best practice' standard based on the already-existing documents. Such an approach would have the benefit of drawing together the practices already in use by the major operators, while incorporating decision-making that allows sufficient flexibility to accommodate the full range of SCC experience seen by operators.

There is at present a natural concentration of attention towards those pipelines that have a legacy of SCC susceptibility but if – as expected – the occurrence of in-service failures remains low, it will become necessary in future to re-focus attention on pipelines that at present have a low likelihood of SCC. The use of monitoring and surveillance techniques such as opportunistic excavations and SCC condition monitoring (looking for changed circumstances that affect the likelihood of SCC) are two important ways of addressing this issue; consideration should be given to development of standardized and formalized approaches for gathering and interpreting such information and reporting the findings. This could be incorporated alongside the new consensus standard on SCC threat management proposed above.

Summary and concluding comments

The experiences of a group of eight major natural gas transmission pipeline operators in North America regarding the implementation and application of SCC integrity-management processes have been reviewed. Preliminary findings from the work are:

- All the operators have implemented integrity-management practices compliant with the latest legislation and guidance, using combinations of hydrostatic testing, ILI, and SCC DA appropriate to their system attributes, and to the perceived risk and/or prior experience of SCC.
- During the five years up to December, 2010, 80 near-critical SCC flaws were removed by hydrostatic testing, over 100 more that would probably failed a hydrostatic test were discovered during 4800km of pipeline inspection using EMAT ILI, and around ten instances of smaller SCC flaws were found during 150 excavations conducted using the recently-established SCC DA procedure.
- During this same period only three in-service failures in which SCC was the primary cause of failure were experienced. This compares with 86 in-service failures experienced prior to December, 2005.
- Hydrostatic testing has proved to be an extremely effective means of minimizing in-service failures, particularly in older pipelines with a legacy of SCC. The Fessler Model establishing re-test intervals, developed during a previous JIP, has been used to good effect during the last five years. Premature failure due to the coalescence of two adjacent significant flaws – a situation not addressed by the Fessler Model – has proved to be a very rare occurrence; further exploration of this issue is an ongoing JIP task.
- SCC DA has been used by several of the operators during the last five years, and has proved effective for ongoing management of segments where the first assessments have shown little or no SCC. SCC DA will benefit from refinement of the assessment algorithms as feedback from new excavations becomes available.

- Most operators have explored the use of EMAT ILI and some are now making regular use of EMAT ILI as part of their integrity-management strategies. EMAT ILI has developed considerably in recent years.

As part of the JIP, a protocol has been developed for obtaining information when excavations are undertaken to investigate ILI-discovered features. Application of this protocol will ensure better consistency in confirming the location and character of discovered defects, and hence in confirming performance parameters such as probability of detection and probability of identification. It will also enable quantification of the tolerances applicable to ILI measurements of defect depth and length.

In another ongoing JIP task, the accuracy of predicted failure pressures is being explored, making use of results from a large number of burst tests, hydrostatic tests, and in-service failures. This work will determine the sensitivity of the calculation methods to input parameters, including the influence of how the flaw profile is characterized.

A further JIP task focuses on the use of the information from the two studies described above to address issues concerning the equivalence of ILI-based and hydrostatic-test-based approaches for SCC threat management. This task is currently at an early stage.

Looking ahead, there is a need to develop integrity-management approaches that are more applicable to segments that have been shown to have little or no SCCv. Most operators are already making opportunistic use of excavations conducted for reasons other than SCC, and are applying various condition-monitoring techniques. Incorporation of this information into a structured and formalized process could provide the basis of an alternative technology, applicable to such segments, to be included in industry guidance alongside hydrostatic testing, ILI, and SCC DA.

Also for future consideration, it may be beneficial for the pipeline industry to formulate an overarching 'SCC threat-management' document utilising the integrity-management framework embodied in ASME B31.8S and incorporating the guidance available from NACE, CEPA, and other ASME documents. A single document would be valuable in achieving consensus among operators and regulators faced with widely differing experiences in different pipeline systems.

Acknowledgements

This Joint Industry Project is sponsored by Centerpoint, El Paso Pipeline Group, Kinder Morgan, NiSource, Panhandle Energy, Spectra Energy, TransCanada Pipelines, and Williams Pipeline. The authors wish to thank their colleagues on the Project Steering Committee for their considerable contributions to the work, and to thank the sponsoring companies for permission to publish this paper.

References

1. R.R.Fessler, A.D.Batte, and M.Hereth, 2008. Integrity management of stress corrosion cracking in high consequence areas. ASME STP-PT-011, ASME, October.
2. A.D.Batte, R.R.Fessler, and S.C.Rapp, 2008. Severity of stress corrosion cracks in pipelines – categories and responses. Paper presented at NACE Corrosion 2008, New Orleans, March.
3. R.R.Fessler and S.C.Rapp, 2006. Method for establishing hydrostatic re-test intervals for pipelines with stress corrosion cracking. Paper presented at International Pipeline Conference, Calgary, September.

4. Code of Federal Regulations 49 CFR Part 192 Subpart O, Pipeline safety management in high consequence areas (gas transmission pipelines); Final Rule (DOT).
5. ASME, 2010. ASME/ANSI B31.8 Gas transmission and piping systems: Managing system integrity of gas pipelines: Supplement ASME B31.8S.
6. NACE, 2008. Standard Recommended Practice SP0204-08, Stress corrosion cracking (SCC) direct assessment methodology.
7. API, 2005. In-line inspection systems. Qualification Standard 1163, 1st Edition, August.
8. API, 2000. Fitness for service, API 597. API Publishing Services, January.
9. J.F.Kiefner, W.A.Maxey, R.J.Eiber, and A.R.Duffy, 1973. Failure stress levels of flaws in pressurised cylinders. Progress in flaw growth and fracture toughness testing, ASTM STP536.
10. J.F.Kiefner, 2008. Modified equation aids integrity management. *Oil & Gas Journal*, October, pp78-82.
11. C.E.Jaske, 2002. Development and evaluation of improved model for engineering critical assessment of pipelines. Paper presented at International Pipeline Conference, Calgary, October.
12. B.N.Leis, F.W.Brust, and P.M.Scott, 1991. Development and validation of a ductile flaw growth analysis for gas transmission line pipe. Pipeline Research Council International Catalogue Number L 51643, June.
13. A.B.Rothwell and R.I.Coote, 2009. A critical review of assessment methods for axial planar surface flaws in pipe. Paper presented at Pipeline Technology Conference, Ostend, October.
14. D.Katz, M.Gao, S.Limon, and R.Krishnamurthy, 2005. Advances in crack assessment for pipeline integrity. Paper presented at International Conference on Fracture.
15. CEPA, 2007. Canadian Energy Pipeline Association Stress corrosion cracking recommended practices, 2nd Edn.

Main subject index

Accuracy, ILI 90
Acoustic-frequency analysis 348
AIS 276
Alliance Pipeline 97
Analysis of dents 199
Andes, pipeline across 225
Anomaly, optimum number
 for excavation 96
Assessment
 of EMAT performance 144
 strain-based 310

Batch-pig facility, 42-in 381
Benchmarking
 history 337
 improving 341
Bi-directional pigging 419
Black powder 1
Black powder
 deposits 3
 cleaning tool 12
 migration 1
 monitoring 7
 movement 2
 other problems 6
 removal 11

Centennial pipeline 317
CEPA 452
Chemical cleaning 19
Chemical gel, for cleaning 31
Chemical-mechanical cleaning 21
Cleaning chemicals 44
Cleaning chemicals, testing 45
Cleaning
 by pigs 8
 chemical 19
 chemical-assisted 43
 chemical-mechanical 21
 field experience 14
 solvents 24
 tool, for black powder 12
Cleanliness, pipeline 4
Coating assessment, by ILI 441
Coating disbondment
 detection 115
 detection 121
Commissioning pigging 364
Compression-wave UT ILI 260
Corrosion growth rate
 determination 59
 determining 108
 local 101
Corrosion methodology,
 statistically-active 102
Corrosion rate
 distribution 221
 effect of sizing error 217
 external 57
 statistics 207
Corrosion science, application 110
Corrosion-scoring
 model 66
 model, calibration 70
Corrosion-verification data 302
Cost reduction, for validation 161
Crack
 assessment, Level 3 256
 detection 115, 121
 detection, refresher 319
 detection, using EMAT 161
 sizing performance 317
Crack-detection
 ILI 502
 studies 281
Cracks, failure model 332

Damage, evaluating 191
Data
 for pipelines 251
 high-resolution NDE 299
 integration, for EMAT 162
 integrity-management 268
 leak 267
 raw 103
 reportable 266
Defect assessment
 by operator 79
 software 87
Defect geometry, effect on sizing 302
Defect size, effect on ILI accuracy 210
Dent assessment, Level 3 262
Dent-gouge failure model 185
Dents, analysis 199

Detection uncertainty 471
Duplex steel pipeline 431

Eddy currents, self-excited (SEEC) 487
Effectiveness, of US IM programme ... 265
EMAT
 data evaluation 119
 data integration 162
 for crack detection 161
 high-resolution 115
 inspection technology 117
 operating principle 162
 technology, current 138
 tool performance vs hydrotesting .. 155
 tool, evaluation 137
 tool, PII 125
 tool performance assessment 144
Ethanol transportation 397
Excavation
 programme 126
 effect of on ILI 93
 of anomaly 96
Exposure, legal 237
Exposure, measuring 243
External interference
 prediction 169, 172
 probability 173

Failure frequency
 prediction 169, 176
 prediction and use 182
Failure model, for cracks 332
Fatigue analysis, real-time 334
Feature depth, effect on ILI accuracy . 212

GE phased-array tool 320
Gel
 chemical, for cleaning 31
 cleaning, preparation 35
Geophone 346

Hydrostatic re-test model 476
Hydrostatic testing 502
Hydrotesting, vs EMAT performance . 155

ILI
 accuracy 90
 accuracy assessment 93
 benchmarking, improving 337
 compression-wave UT 260
 data accuracy, benefits 91
 data, comparisons 103
 data, for integrity assessment 255
 data, for landslide prediction 309
 defects, assessment 79
 effect of defect size on accuracy 210
 for coating assessment 441
 for crack detection 281
 for damage evaluation 191
 for SCC 123
 performance verification 89
 sizing uncertainties 207
 using EMAT 115
Incident data 266
INGAA 270
Inspection, of Duplex steel pipeline ... 431
Integrity assessment 101
Integrity management
 for ethanol 397
 improvement 279
 in the US 240
 OCP pipeline 225
 offshore 275
 programme 265
 services, contracting 246
Integrity
 advanced assessment 255
 legal issues 235
 of seam weld 329
 uncertainty 461
Integrity-management data 268
Interval
 re-assessment 74
 re-assessment for ILI 484
 re-assessment for SCC 475
 re-inspection for ILI 485

Landslide, prediction 309
Launcher
 and launcher systems 408
 batch pig 383
Leak data 267
Legal issues, for pipeline integrity 235
LPG pipeline, commissioning 359

Mapping data, from ILI 309
Methodology, predictive 188
MFL
 inspection 31
 inspection sizing 299
 inspection, for Duplex
  steel pipeline 431

Model
- corrosion-scoring ... 66
- dent-gouge failure ... 185
- for crack ... 332
- for external corrosion rates ... 57
- for landslide ... 311
- hydrostatic re-test ... 476
- pipeline ... 20
- sizing ... 300
- sizing uncertainty ... 208

Modelling, magnetic ... 489
Multi-diameter pipeline, tools ... 371
Multi-diameter pigging ... 419

OCP pipeline ... 225

Performance reporting ... 451
Performance verification, ILI ... 89
Phased-array tool ... 317
Phased-array, refresher ... 319
PHMSA ... 270
Pig tracking, remote ... 348
Pig trap design ... 413
Pig
- design guide ... 372
- for batching ... 381
- multi-diameter ... 371
- stuck ... 359

Piggability study ... 250
Pigging systems, fundamentals ... 405
Pigging
- bi-directional ... 419
- chemical-assisted ... 43
- for black powder removal ... 11
- for cleaning ... 8
- for commissioning ... 364
- for precommissioning ... 419
- multi-diameter ... 419

PII EMAT tool ... 125
Pipeline damage, evaluating ... 191
Pipeline
- data, obtaining ... 251
- efficiency, enhancing ... 19
- how clean? ... 4
- integrity, advanced assessment ... 255
- model, San Martin ... 20

Precommissioning, pigging ... 419
Prediction, of failure frequency ... 169
Predictive methodology ... 188
Predictive model, for corrosion ... 57

Pull test
- for coating assessment ... 447
- for Duplex pipeline ... 436

Re-assessment interval ... 74
Receiver
- and receiver systems ... 410
- batch pig ... 383

Risk-based inspection ... 275
Run data, evaluation ... 14

San Martin pipeline ... 20
SCC DA
- excavations ... 502
- re-inspection interval ... 485

SCC
- detection by SEEC ... 487
- in ethanol pipeline ... 400
- joint-industry project ... 497
- management ... 123
- metallurgical factors ... 402
- mitigation, in ethanol ... 402
- re-assessment intervals ... 475

Seal design ... 424
Seam-weld integrity assessment ... 329
SEEC
- data ... 492
- sensor system ... 491
- technology ... 488

Sensor design ... 447
Sensors, 22-Hz ... 344
Sizing error ... 216
Sizing uncertainty
- from ILI ... 207
- uncertainty ... 464
- uncertainty model ... 208

Sizing, effect of defect geometry ... 302
Solvents, for cleaning ... 24
Strain-based assessment ... 310

Tool performance, evaluation ... 14
Tool, phased-array ... 317
Toughness, quantifying ... 334
Tracking, remote ... 348
TransCanada ... 124
- PII collaboration ... 125
- SCC philosophy ... 126

Trap
- assessments ... 405
- design ... 413

UKOPA 170
Uncertainty
  detection 471
  in integrity 461
  sizing 464
UT ILI data 260

Validation cost reduction 161
Velocity, gas to move solids 2

❖ ❖ ❖